D1249530

**Conference on Research in Psychotherapy.**
　　Research in psychotherapy; proceedings.  ₁1st₁–
1958–
　₁Washington, American Psychological Association₁

　　2 v.  illus., diagrs.  24 cm.

　　Conferences sponsored by the Division of Clinical Psychology, American Psychological Association.


　　1. Psychiatric research—Congresses.　ɪ. American Psychological Association.  Division of Clinical Psychology.　ɪɪ. Title.

　　RC336.C65　　　　　　　132.075　　　　　　59—9192

　　Library of Congress　　　　₁68r63n1₁

# RESEARCH
# IN
# PSYCHOTHERAPY

Proceedings of a Conference,
Chapel Hill, North Carolina, May 17-20, 1961

Hans H. Strupp
Lester Luborsky, *Editors*

This conference, financed by a grant (M-4001) from the National Institute of Mental Health, U. S. Public Health Service, was held under the auspices of the Division of Clinical Psychology, American Psychological Association, with planning and programing by an Ad Hoc Committee of the Division of Clinical Psychology: John M. Butler, Jerome D. Frank, David A. Hamburg, Lester Luborsky, George Saslow, William U. Snyder, and Hans H. Strupp, Chairman.

Reprinted 1969

# Table of Contents

MAY 19, 1961

CONCURRENT PANEL DISCUSSIONS

MAY 20, 1961

SUMMARY REPORTS OF PANEL DISCUSSIONS ON
RESEARCH IN PSYCHOTHERAPY

*David A. Hamburg*, M.D., Moderator

SUMMARIES

# Preface

The content of this volume represents the proceedings of the Second Conference on Research in Psychotherapy held in Chapel Hill, North Carolina, May 17-20, 1961, under the sponsorship of the Division of Clinical Psychology of the American Psychological Association. The conference was financed by a research grant (M-4001) from the National Institute of Mental Health, Public Health Service.

## History

The plan for a second conference had its inception at the first conference held in Washington, D. C., in 1958, which because of its excellent planning and organization was successful beyond expectation. At that time, many participants expressed the hope that it might be possible for research workers to meet again, to exchange ideas, to follow up research projects which were then getting under way, and to encourage critical examination of the major theoretical, methodological, and practical issues facing the investigator in this difficult field. The desirability of another conference was further underscored by the widespread interest in the first volume *Research in Psychotherapy* (1959), representing the proceedings of the first conference, which in a short period of time achieved the status of a standard reference.

Psychotherapy, as a clinical art and as a scientific discipline, has become a major focus of interest for psychiatrists and psychologists over the past decades. It is specified as a major interest by more psychologists than any other single topic in the APA Directory; a large body of literature is tangible evidence of the thirst for systematic knowledge, proven techniques, and new methods for research; at meetings of scientific and professional organizations large segments of time are devoted to symposia and papers; and the problem of training in psychotherapy is a major concern of all the mental health professions, as exemplified by the recent recommendations of the Joint Commission on Mental Illness and Health (1961). However, progress in research has been slow. There are many reasons for this state of affairs, among which might be mentioned the inherent complexity of the subject matter, the relative recency of systematic research, the crudeness of existing research methods, and the difficulties of obtaining adequate data.

Thus, the Executive Committee of the Division of Clinical Psychology received favorably the recommendation of Dr. Eli A. Rubinstein, chairman of the planning committee for the first conference, to plan a second meeting. In the fall of 1958, Dr. Hans H. Strupp was appointed chairman of an Ad Hoc Committee to plan the Second Conference on Research in Psychotherapy. The other members of this committee who shared the responsibility for this task included: Drs. John M. Butler, Jerome D. Frank, David A. Hamburg, Lester Luborsky, George Saslow, and William U. Snyder. Throughout the planning period the Ad Hoc Committee maintained its original composition and conducted its work through formal meetings and informal consultation.

In 1959 a formal proposal for financial support of the conference was approved by the Board of Directors of the American Psychological Association and was submitted to the National Institute of Mental Health, which approved a grant for the holding of the conference and for publication of the proceedings.

In deciding the format, organization, and content of the Second Conference, the

Ad Hoc Committee was guided by the results of a questionnaire survey in which the predecessor committee had solicited the opinions of participants at the first conference. In addition, the members of the Ad Hoc Committee, all of whom had participated in the first conference, drew on their own observations and impressions. The Committee benefited from the counsel of Dr. Eli Rubinstein, who advised on a wide variety of problems which the Ad Hoc Committee encountered in its work.

*Aims*

In contrast to the first conference, which was intended to provide a comprehensive picture of ongoing research in the area of psychotherapy, the Second Conference attempted to deal more intensively with a few selected research issues relevant to individual psychotherapy with adult neurotic patients. In addition, it was designed to facilitate the review and follow-up of several projects which were in formative stages at the time of the first meeting; to consider recent research contributions and assess new research developments; to insure continuity of exchange of information among investigators; to guide and stimulate further research in the area; and, finally, to place research in psychotherapy more squarely within psychological research concerned with understanding interpersonal processes.

In keeping with the objective of striving for thoroughness of exploration of selected key issues rather than comprehensive coverage of the field, the Committee formulated three topics:

1. *Research problems relating to measuring personality change in psychotherapy.* The emphasis here rested on a thorough discussion of relevant variables in patients so as to allow significant assessments of change as a result of therapy; techniques for measuring personality change; selection of patients in terms of predictor variables.

2. *Research problems relating to the psychotherapist's contribution to the treatment process.* Questions to be dealt with under this heading included: ways of evaluating the contribution of the therapist's personality and attitudes upon progress and outcome of therapy; effects of variations in therapist behavior upon the process of therapy.

3. *Research problems relating to the definition, measurement, and analysis of significant variables in psychotherapy, such as transference, resistance, etc.* The purpose here was to bridge the gap between dynamic events observed in the clinical situation and their assessment and measurement by objective means.

*Conference Structure*

In order to insure maximum group participation and to facilitate relatively intensive exploration of each topic, the Committee decided to combine plenary sessions with small group meetings and to dispense with the formal presentation of papers. Thus, it was planned to devote the first day of the Conference to a plenary session, at which time there would be presented formal discussions of invited papers (which had been distributed to the participants in advance) representing the major topic areas, followed by informal group discussion. The second day was to comprise concurrent small group meetings in each topic area. On the third day, designated reporters from each group were to present the results of the small group meetings at another plenary session. Each presentation was to be followed by group discussion. Finally, a closing summary was intended to integrate the discussions. This organization was carried out, and is reflected in the Table of Contents.

The selection of participants at any invitational conference presents multiple problems. In this case, the Committee stipulated that prospective participants should be persons who are either directly engaged in research in psychotherapy relevant to the major topics, or others who might make valuable contributions to the discussion and criticism of research in this field (e.g., persons with strong clinical or theoretical talents). To provide for continuity, it was decided to include a number of investigators who had attended the first conference. To guide the selection, a questionnaire was mailed to a sizable number of potential participants to explore their current research interests, the status of their research, and their interest in participating. The Committee then evaluated the responses and exercised its best judgment in composing the final roster of participants. Clearly, a certain amount of subjectivity, bias, and arbitrariness was unavoidable.

The Conference was held on the campus of the University of North Carolina, which lent a relaxing and contemplative atmosphere for the meeting. On the evening preceding the Conference, at a dinner session, Dr. Jerome D. Frank presented an opening address on "The Role of Cognitions in Illness and Healing."

*Acknowledgments*

As is usually true in projects of this kind, it is difficult to acknowledge fully the contributions of the many persons and organizations whose help was truly indispensable.

First and foremost we are indebted to Dr. Eli A. Rubinstein, who did more than any other single person to translate the idea of a Second Conference into reality. Not only was his expert guidance invaluable, but the organization of the first meeting and the publication of its proceedings in which he had a major share provided a superb model.

The officers of the Division of Clinical Psychology and the Central Office of the American Psychological Association greatly facilitated the planning. Special thanks are due Dr. John G. Darley, Executive Officer of the American Psychological Association, and his predecessor, Dr. Roger W. Russell.

Miss Helen Orr, Managing Editor of APA publications, Dr. Arthur Hoffman, former Managing Editor, and Mrs. Barbara Cummings were most helpful in the planning and publication of this volume.

To the Departments of Psychiatry and Psychology of the University of North Carolina and its respective chairmen, Dr. George C. Ham and Dr. John W. Thibaut; to the University of North Carolina; and to the Carolina Inn goes our appreciation for being such gracious hosts. We wish to thank especially Mr. Anthony Jenzano, Manager of the Morehead Planetarium, for his help in arranging the physical facilities.

We are grateful to Dr. Ronald E. Fox and Mr. Gary Olson for technical assistance, and to Dr. Ronald E. Fox for preparing the Index.

Mrs. Billie Buford's faithful help in handling a large volume of correspondence and coordinating a host of major and minor items is gratefully acknowledged.

Finally, we wish to thank the National Institute of Mental Health for its generous financial support which made the conference possible. Mr. Philip Sapir, Chief of the Research Grants and Fellowships Branch, lent his usual helpful guidance.

HANS H. STRUPP
LESTER LUBORSKY, Editors

# Participants and Guests of the
# Second Conference on Research in Psychotherapy

## CONFERENCE PARTICIPANTS

BARBARA J. BETZ, M.D., Associate Professor of Psychiatry, Johns Hopkins Hospital, Baltimore, Maryland

JACK BLOCK, Ph.D., Associate Professor of Psychology, University of California, Berkeley, California

HEDDA BOLGAR, Ph.D., Chief Psychologist, Psychiatric and Psychosomatic Research Institute, Mount Sinai Hospital, Los Angeles, California

EDWARD S. BORDIN, Ph.D., Professor of Psychology, University of Michigan, Ann Arbor, Michigan

JOHN M. BUTLER, Ph.D., Professor of Psychology, University of Chicago, Chicago, Illinois

MABEL B. COHEN, M.D., Ph.D., Private practice of psychoanalysis; Consultant, National Institute of Mental Health, Chevy Chase, Maryland

KENNETH MARK COLBY, M.D., Associate Professor of Psychology, Stanford University, Stanford, California

JEROME D. FRANK, M.D., Ph.D., Professor of Psychiatry, Johns Hopkins Medical School, Baltimore, Maryland

DONALD D. GLAD, Ph.D., Director of Psychology and Group Therapy, Greater Kansas City Mental Health Foundation, Kansas City, Missouri

ERNEST A. HAGGARD, Ph.D., Professor of Psychology, Department of Psychiatry, University of Illinois College of Medicine, Chicago, Illinois

DAVID A. HAMBURG, M.D., Chairman, Department of Psychiatry, Stanford University, Stanford, California

J. MCV. HUNT, Ph.D., Sc.D., Professor of Psychology, University of Illinois, Urbana, Illinois

LEONARD KRASNER, Ph.D., Assistant Director and Coordinator of Training, Psychology Services, Veterans Administration Hospital, Palo Alto, California; Associate Consulting Professor of Psychology, Stanford University; Director of Research, Consulting Psychologists Associated, Palo Alto, California

HENRY L. LENNARD, Ph.D., Research Associate, Bureau of Applied Social Research, Columbia University; Associate Professor of Sociology, The New School, Graduate Faculty, New York, New York

DANIEL J. LEVINSON, Ph.D., Assistant Professor of Psychology, Department of Psychiatry, Harvard Medical School; Director, Center for Socio-psychological Research, Massachusetts Mental Health Center, Boston, Massachusetts

MAURICE LORR, Ph.D., Chief, Neuropsychiatric Research Laboratory, Veterans Administration; and Catholic University, Washington, District of Columbia

LESTER LUBORSKY, Ph.D., Psychologist, Department of Psychiatry, University of Pennsylvania, Philadelphia, Pennsylvania

GEORGE F. MAHL, Ph.D., Associate Professor of Psychology (Psychiatry), Yale University, New Haven, Connecticut

MORRIS B. PARLOFF, Ph.D., Chief, Section on Personality, National Institute of Mental Health, Bethesda, Maryland

NEVITT SANFORD, Ph.D., Professor of Psychology, University of California, Berkeley, California

GEORGE SASLOW, M.D., Professor of Psychiatry, University of Oregon Medical School, Portland, Oregon

DAVID SHAKOW, Ph.D., Chief, Laboratory of Psychology, National Institute of Mental Health, Bethesda, Maryland

JOHN M. SHLIEN, Ph.D., Associate Professor of . Psychology and Human Development, University of Chicago, Chicago, Illinois; Chairman, Executive Committee, Counseling Center, University of Chicago, Chicago, Illinois

RICHARD S. SIEGAL, Ph.D., Psychologist, The Menninger Foundation, Topeka, Kansas

WILLIAM U. SNYDER, Ph.D., Professor of Psychology, Pennsylvania State University, University Park, Pennsylvania

IAN STEVENSON, M.D., Professor of Psychiatry, University of Virginia School of Medicine, Charlottesville, Virginia

HANS H. STRUPP, Ph.D., Director of Psychological Services, North Carolina Memorial Hospital; Associate Professor of Psychology, University of North Carolina, Chapel Hill, North Carolina

OTTO ALLEN WILL, M.D., Director of Psychotherapy, Chestnut Lodge, Rockville, Maryland

LEON BERNSTEIN, M.D., Clinical Assistant Professor of Psychiatry, University of Illinois, Chicago, Illinois

DONALD A. BLOCH, M.D., Director of Research, Central Research Unit, Jewish Board of Guardians, New York, New York

DONALD R. GORHAM, Ph.D., Chief, Experimental Studies, Central Neuropsychiatric Research Laboratory, Veterans Administration, Perry Point, Maryland

STANLY D. IMBER, Ph.D., Associate Professor of Medical Psychology, Johns Hopkins University School of Medicine, Baltimore, Maryland

MARTIN LAKIN, Ph.D., Assistant Professor of Psychology, Duke University, Durham, North Carolina

MORRIS LIPTON, M.D., Ph.D., Associate Professor of Psychiatry, University of North Carolina, Chapel Hill, North Carolina

IRWIN C. ROSEN, Ph.D., Psychologist, The Menninger Clinic, Topeka, Kansas

MARTIN S. WALLACH, Ph.D., Assistant Professor of Psychology, University of North Carolina, Chapel Hill, North Carolina

## INVITED GUESTS

EWALD W. BUSSE, M.D., Professor of Psychiatry, Duke University, Durham, North Carolina

LOUIS D. COHEN, Ph.D., Professor of Psychology, Duke University, Durham, North Carolina

GEORGE C. HAM, M.D., Professor of Psychiatry, University of North Carolina, Chapel Hill, North Carolina

HALBERT B. ROBINSON, Ph.D., Associate Professor of Psychology, University of North Carolina, Chapel Hill, North Carolina

JOHN W. THIBAUT, Ph.D., Professor of Psychology, University of North Carolina, Chapel Hill, North Carolina

KARL ZENER, Ph.D., Professor of Psychology, Duke University, Durham, North Carolina

# The Role of Cognitions in Illness and Healing

## Jerome D. Frank, M.D.

The task of making sense of psychotherapy is not an easy one, as the participants at this conference well know. The customary research approach is to confine oneself to a particular form of treatment and try either to isolate and manipulate certain of its components, or to encompass all its aspects at once and systematically observe their interplay. Both types of research are well represented here.

All are confined to the same general model of psychotherapy. The conditions it treats are conceived as resulting from the patient's distorted perceptions of himself and others and the resulting maladaptive behavior. The therapist, through offering the patient a nonjudgmental, highly individualized, empathic attitude, and using certain specific methods, tries to create an interpersonal situation that will enable the patient to discover and correct his maladaptive patterns, and so gain more security and satisfaction from life.

Because there are only two participants in the therapeutic interaction and the chief therapeutic instruments are words that can be recorded and studied at leisure, this form of therapy has obvious advantages for research. Viewed from the perspective of the range of psychological ills affecting humanity and the means used to treat them, however, it is obviously a special case. The danger therefore exists that conceptualizations based solely on data obtained from it may contain errors of omission or emphasis.

It therefore occurred to me that I might take this occasion to use a different approach. Instead of the detailed exploration of one type of therapy, I shall consider some cognitive processes involved in all forms of treatment, using the term in a loose sense to include perceptions, concepts, expectations, judgments, and the like.

In embarking on this enterprise one is immediately brought up short with the realization that psychotherapy is treatment for something, and cannot be studied independently from what it attempts to treat. And this requires some consideration of the concept of illness. In accord with conventional medical concepts, a distinction is often made between "organic" and "psychological" illnesses. The former are viewed as the organism's response to tissue damage caused by trauma, infection, or metabolic disorder, the latter as difficulties in living resulting from inability to cope with personal conflicts or other psychological stresses (Szasz, 1960). Empirical evidence suggests that this distinction is probably not valid, but that so-called organic and psychological illnesses are often merely facets of the same maladaptive process. Life history studies of some 3,000 persons, for example, have shown that individuals differed in the amounts of illness they experienced and those with the greater number of bodily illnesses also reported the greater number of disturbances of mood, thought, and behavior. Furthermore, in each person episodes of sickness appeared in clusters when he was trying to adapt to a life situation perceived as stressful by him. That is, the clusters of bodily, mental, and behavioral disturbances occurred at times of conflict with his family, loss of significant social supports, and excessive demands, as he perceived them (Hinkle et al., 1957).

The tendency for persons who are ill to be ill all over, as it were, was also found in a five-year follow-up study of psychiatric outpatients. They were seen four

1

times at intervals of from six months to two years. Their reported illnesses during this period were crudely categorized as primarily psychiatric, primarily medical, and medical complaints with a psychological basis. Of the 30 patients, 27 were checked in more than one category, and 13 in all three. Twenty-seven were checked for chronic illness (lasting throughout one evaluation period) at least once; and 23, or about three-fourths, for both chronic and acute illnesses. As with the persons in the larger study, psychiatric outpatients tended to have a variety of illnesses, some "psychic," some "organic" (Stone et al., 1961).

These findings suggest that all illnesses are failures of adaptation characterized by distress and disability and involving all levels of personal functioning—biological, psychological, and social. Of course, the relative weights of these components differ in different illnesses. At one extreme would be acute bodily disturbances such as pneumonia or acute appendicitis. It is these illnesses which have created the concept of illness as a bodily state "caused" by a pathogen or pathological process and existing inside a patient. If the illness is brief, the psychosocial components can usually be ignored because recovery occurs before they become important. It is well recognized, however, that the disability and distress of the chronically ill is largely unrelated to the extent of their tissue damage, but depends chiefly on how their condition has affected their self-image, expectations for the future, and the attitudes of those about them. The anxiety and despair created by the interplay of these factors may aggravate the pathological processes, heighten the patient's suffering, and reduce his adaptive capacity. The treatment of a patient with chronic heart disease, for example, may have to be directed more to modifications of his attitudes and behavior than adjustment of dosage of digitalis.

Recently a concept of illness has emerged that takes account of the common features of all forms of sickness and methods of treatment. According to this view, the diagnosis of illness is a judgment made by the patient and those about him, which then has certain effects on his attitudes towards himself and his relationships with others (Ausubel, 1961). The judgment is based on three types of data: the person's subjective distress, his disability, and information about his bodily processes. Any one of these may be sufficient to lead to a diagnosis of illness. For example, a depressed patient without identifiable organic damage and who was able to function adequately, would be judged to be ill solely on the basis of his subjective distress. An apathetic chronic schizophrenic would be diagnosed as ill because he could not carry out any of the tasks of life though he appeared to be in no distress and showed no evidence of chronic disease. Organic damage that affects neither the patient's subjective state nor his performance is considered to indicate illness when it forecasts future distress and disability. For example, a man may be perfectly well until a routine X ray reveals that he has asymptomatic cancer of the lung. This information immediately makes him ill, with full-scale psychosocial consequences.

Not only the state of illness or health, but the specific nature of the illness is based on a judgment determined to a large extent by the setting in which it occurs, how it is regarded by the patient and others, and the way it is treated. This has been clarified by studies of patients with delayed convalescence from infectious diseases. In the Philippines during the last war I was asked to examine a number of hospitalized soldiers suffering from persistent weakness, shakiness, and headache. These symptoms were viewed by them and their physicians as evidences of continuing infestation with a liver parasite. The doctors had begun to wonder about this; hence, asked for an examination. Interviews with these soldiers clearly showed that their symptoms were actually manifestations of resentment, fear, and depression created by conflicts and uncertainties produced by the hospital milieu (Frank, 1946).

Recently this phenomenon has been pinpointed by two careful investigations. The first, a retrospective study, found that patients who failed to recover from brucellosis were more depressed, on various measures, than those who made a prompt recovery. Analysis of the data indicated quite convincingly that the depression was not merely secondary to the stress of illness but was more critically related to the pre-illness personality structure and the concurrent life situation (Trever et al., 1959; Cluff et al., 1959; Imboden et al., 1959). To clinch the matter, the investigators then did a prospective study. The psychological tests were given to a large number of government personnel just prior to an expected influenza epidemic. Of those who became ill, patients who retained symptoms for more than three weeks had scored significantly higher on pre-illness measures of depression than those who recovered within two weeks, though the initial severity of the illness was the same in both groups (Imboden, Canter, & Cluff, 1961).

These studies demonstrate that the previous experience of certain patients, combined with a special treatment environment, led them and their physicians to interpret symptoms of depression as evidence of failure to recover from a specific infectious disease. Before the psychological findings were known, they "had" the disease and were treated accordingly; the introduction of this new bit of information changed them from sick to "depressed."

The role of situational cues in the definition of disease can also be readily demonstrated in psychiatric patients. Various groups of patients were interviewed at a veterans hospital to determine whether they regarded their illness as psychological or organic. Seventy-one percent of a group of male schizophrenics described their illnesses as psychological immediately after admission to the hospital. After four weeks of receiving nothing but drug therapy, the percentage dropped to 38 percent. Another group who were interviewed after having received an average of seven months of psychotherapy with drugs unanimously described their illnesses in psychological terms (Whitman & Duffey, 1961).

Recently, a student nurse arrived as a patient at Phipps after many months on surgical and dental services at another hospital where she was being treated for persistent, severe spasm of the jaw that prevented her from closing her mouth. The symptom started after a dislocation of the jaw while undergoing dentistry. She had been subjected to drastic procedures, including surgical destruction of the temporo-mandibular joint, cutting of certain nerves bilaterally—or rather attempted cutting which fortunately was largely unsuccessful—and finally her jaws were wired together. To this point she, her physicians, and members of her social environment had defined her illness as physical and had a rationale for this judgment—namely, that the spasm was caused by a so-called circular reflex instigated by the original dislocation. She was a patient with a surgical illness treated by surgeons. When they reached the end of their tether, they called a psychiatrist. His perception of her illness was that the spasm was related to severe conflicts about her choice of career. Conversations along these lines were followed by disappearance of the spasm, and she was transferred to a psychiatric service. The jaw symptom has not recurred, but she is involved in intense emotional turmoil over whether or not to continue in nurses' training. Now, even though her jaw joint is permanently damaged, in the eyes of herself, her colleagues, and her physicians, she has a mental illness. No surgeon or dentist has come near her and no one has laid a knife or needle upon her. Treatment consists in talks with a psychiatrist, sometimes under hypnosis. It is unnecessary to labor the point that the diagnosis of this patient's illness as organic or psychological has depended largely on the settings in which she became ill, the persons with whom she interacted, and the treatment methods used.

Implicit in the above examples is that distress, disability, or organic damage do not in themselves constitute illness. To warrant this designation they must, in addition, be regarded as undesirable, as uncorrectable by the person's own unaided efforts, and as curable by a culturally defined healer. Once a person is judged to be ill, he is relieved of his usual social responsibilities, in return for which he is expected to cooperate with his therapist (Parsons, 1951).

Some examples may clarify these generalizations. Disturbances of thought or behavior are considered to be signs of illness only if they are regarded as undesirable. The visions of a religious mystic would be evidences of illness if reported by a patient in a state hospital. To the mystic and those who accept the validity of his experiences, they are evidences of saintliness, and any implication that they are signs of disease would be rejected.

The questions as to whether or not a person can cure himself, and the extent to which he is to be absolved from his usual responsibilities are crucial with certain conditions whose status as illness thereby becomes a matter of controversy. Alcoholism is a good example. As long as a person's drinking stays within socially acceptable bounds, no one would think him ill. After his drinking has become clearly undesirable to himself and others, as long as the alcoholic thinks he can "take it or leave it alone" he is not ill in his own eyes.

Even after he realizes that he cannot control his craving unaided, and so considers himself to be ill, others may refuse to consider him so because they believe he can stop by act of will.

The alcoholic also illustrates the fact that the third ingredient, the culturally defined healer, is an integral part of the definition of illness. Many who realize that their condition is undesirable and that they are powerless to control it, go for help to AA instead of to a medical or psychiatric resource, and this keeps them out of the category of the sick.

Before leaving this subject, it must be stressed that the issue of moral responsibility may arise with any illness, and therefore does not afford a sound basis for distinguishing neuroses from organic disease. Examples of the difficulty of drawing such distinctions would be the diabetic whose condition is aggravated by voluntary overeating, or the cardiac who accepts a life of chronic dependency as opposed to one with equal organic damage who continues to support himself.

In short, the definition of all illness involves a consensus of the patient and his social unit based on his distress, his apparent disability, and information as to their presumed cause. If this information leads to the judgment that the person's state is undesirable, that he cannot correct it unaided, and that a socially designated healer can help him, he is ill. The distinction between so-called organic and psychic illness is one of degree, not kind, depending on such factors as the relative importance of identifiable bodily disorders, and the extent to which the person is believed to be responsible for his condition and its rectification.

Health, like illness, is a complex judgment based on evaluation of all aspects of a person's functioning. If a person says he feels well, performs well, and is regarded as well by his family, colleagues, and friends, then, in the absence of information indicating that this condition cannot be maintained (as, for example, an X-ray diagnosis of lung cancer), I would maintain that he *is* well. Until diagnostic tools are developed that reliably predict future distress or disability in an apparently healthy person, the first three criteria must be regarded as offering an adequate determination of health. This state of affairs still obtains at the psychological end of the illness continuum, though one may hope that progressive improvement of diagnostic methods at both psychological and physiological levels may alter it.

Insofar as illness and health involve social judgments, treatment methods can be viewed in part as efforts to influence the patient's concept of himself and of the therapeutic procedure in a favorable direction. Psychotherapeutic procedures rely essentially on personal influence to do this. Any ill person may, under some circumstances, benefit from psychotherapy. Persuading the preoperative patient to sign a release and the chronic cardiac to resume activities commensurate with his cardiac reserve are forms of psychotherapy.

This must not be taken to imply that psychotherapy may not have special features, nor that only physicians should conduct this form of treatment. Though acute appendicitis and work inhibition share certain characteristics as illnesses, and methods of treating them have common features, this does not imply that surgeons should do psychotherapy or psychotherapists remove appendices.

I should now like to consider three aspects of psychotherapy as a means of influencing a patient's judgments about himself in the direction of health: the therapist as a socially designated healer, the patient's and therapist's expectations about treatment, and some effects of the therapist's interpretations on the patient's emotions.

The therapist's social role has two

therapeutic aspects: it enhances the patient's expectation of help and conveys to him acceptance by his group. The power of the former factor, though well known, is greater than one likes to admit. For example, the prestigeful role of the physician in Western society until recently was essentially the only source of his healing power, since the pharmacopoeia contained almost nothing but noxious or harmless substances. Yet through his ability to arouse the patient's expectation of cure by diagnosing his illness and prescribing a "remedy" he was able to heal patients often enough (with the tendency to spontaneous recovery also working in his favor) to maintain his reputation through the ages (Shapiro, 1960).

In group methods of treatment, the therapist's function as intermediary between the patient and the group is obvious. But even in dyadic treatments some of his efficacy lies in the fact that his attitudes by implication reflect the attitudes of the culture or, in societies as diversified as ours, perhaps only a subculture, which is important to the patient because he belongs to it or aspires to do so. Insofar as illness involves a sense of alienation from others—and this is particularly true of mental illness—the therapist's acceptance of the patient may serve as a powerful symbol of the concern of the group for his welfare, with markedly beneficial effects on his morale.

Thus it is not surprising that the healing role itself may be therapeutic, regardless of who fills it. Many healing rituals, especially in religious settings, are mediated by persons, to be sure, but do not depend for their effectiveness on any particular individual. Priests at Lourdes are interchangeable as, within limits, are medicine men in primitive societies and physicians and psychotherapists in Western ones. In a study of placebo responsivity with outpatients we assigned patients serially to two members of the Phipps resident staff who represented the available extremes in personality. One was forceful, lively, and vigorous, the other quiet and shy. Their differences were sufficiently clear-cut to show up on several personality tests. Yet their patients showed precisely the same degree of symptom relief from placebo. Perhaps they did not differ sufficiently in personality—they had, after all, both been accepted as members of the Phipps residency staff, and one does not know how much selectivity is exercised in this choice. A more plausible assumption is that placebo reactivity depends primarily on the patient's ability to accept the doctor in his role as healer, and the fact that both these physicians were identified as Hopkins doctors and gave the medication in the Hopkins Hospital overshadowed the possible effects of any personality differences.

In emphasizing the healing potential of the physician's role and setting, I do not wish to minimize the importance of his personal qualities. Some physicians have more healing power than others of equal technical competence. Accounts in the anthropological literature suggest that this may also be true of medicine men (Lévi-Strauss, 1958). Finally, we must not avert our gaze from certain religious figures and nonreligious healers who seem to exude some sort of healing force. This personal attribute has not been adequately conceptualized or studied, forcing one to take refuge in such unsatisfactory descriptive terms as personal magnetism or charisma.

The importance of personal qualities of treatment personnel was recently illustrated in an unusually specific fashion by a patient who had come out of a catatonic-like condition in which she was mute and had to be tube-fed. She described vividly how for some days after emerging she would at times begin to feel frightened, things would become unreal, and she would feel herself sliding back into her catatonic state. She singled out two attendants on the ward, one male, one

female, who could dissolve this feeling by speaking with her, while others frightened her or had no effect one way or the other.

After assigning some healing power to the therapist's social role and some to general qualities of his personality, is anything left for his capacity to form a highly individualized, empathic relationship with a particular patient? I believe that this may be crucial for patients who have difficulty perceiving the therapist as potentially helpful. The largest category of these patients is the schizophrenics, whose massive and generalized distrust precludes their acceptance of a therapist as helpful simply on the basis of his socially defined role or personal magnetism. Their trust can often only be won by a highly perceptive and skillful therapist over a long period of time.

These considerations suggest that the ability of patient and therapist to meet each other's expectations is an important component of healing. There is some experimental evidence that a patient's failure to remain in treatment, or to improve, may be related to failure to establish this mutuality of expectation.

With respect to remaining in treatment, this hypothesis accounts for the well-known tendency of lower-class patients to drop out—or be rejected by the therapist—more often than those of higher classes. The latter come to therapy knowing how to present their difficulties in terms which permit them and the therapist to perceive them as amenable to psychotherapy. Lower-class patients, lacking this prior knowledge, tend to cast the psychotherapist in the traditional medical role with which they are familiar, and present their complaints accordingly. This impedes the therapist from playing his accustomed role, and the relationship, lacking a basis of shared expectations, collapses.

Pertinent in this connection is a study of formerly hospitalized schizophrenics which showed that remaining in treatment was not directly related to the therapist's warmth, but to whether this attitude was congruent with the patient's view of his illness. The psychiatrists were rated on a "relationship index" determined by the extent to which their notes described the patient's interpersonal behavior and his subjective feelings; the patients, in terms of whether they denied or accepted their illnesses. The deniers were much more likely to drop out of treatment if faced with a doctor who scored high on the relationship index than with one who scored low. The acceptors showed the reverse tendency. It seems as if the deniers were trying to communicate that they did not wish the physician to poke around in their personal affairs. If he did not do so, they came back; if he persisted in trying to be "therapeutic," they left (Freedman et al., 1958).

Failure to establish mutuality of expectation seems related not only to termination of therapy but to failure to improve. When the patients in the Phipps outpatient study were dichotomized into most and least improved on the basis of combined change in discomfort and ineffectiveness at the end of five years, it was found that the latter did much more shopping around than the former. All five patients who reported trying every type of treatment resource were among the least improved. This appeared related to their perception of their illness. Most and least improved were checked with equal frequency for illnesses in the follow-up period which were unequivocally psychiatric or unequivocally medical in the eyes of the raters. However, the least improved were scored half again as often for illness which they saw as medical but the raters believed was primarily psychological, and 11 times as often for illnesses which the raters were unable to categorize because they were so inadequately described. The least improved either conceptualized their complaints in a way which brought them

to the wrong treatment resource—they went to medical practitioners for psychologically based disorders—or were unable to define them clearly at all.

If the patient's failure to form an expectation of improvement is related to his failure to improve, the converse should also hold. That is, expectation of improvement should be correlated with actual improvement. Several experimental studies offer tenuous support for this hypothesis. In a preliminary study at Phipps, outpatients were given a symptom check list immediately after they registered. They were first asked to score themselves as they felt at the moment, and then how they expected to feel in six months. After the initial diagnostic interview by a medical student, they were asked to score themselves again as to how they felt. Confirming similar results found by others (Goldstein & Shipman, 1961), a positive correlation was obtained between the amount of symptom reduction they anticipated at six months and the amount they reported at the end of the initial interview (Friedman, 1961). A related finding obtained by others was that placebo responsiveness was a remarkably good prognosticator of whether previously hospitalized schizophrenic patients would stay out of the hospital. Of those who had to be rehospitalized within thirty days, not one responded favorably to placebo, while four-fifths of those who remained well enough to stay out of the hospital had shown a favorable response. Apparently placebo responsiveness was an indicator of their ability to accept the doctor as a source of help—perhaps even an indirect measure of their capacity to trust their fellow man—and this was related to their ability to cope with life outside a hospital (Hankoff et al., 1958).

From the therapist's side, there is a bit of evidence that his expectation of being able to help the patient may also be related to therapeutic benefit. In one study, medical student therapists were asked to rate how much improvement they expected to see in their patients, at the start of therapy. After 15 sessions, patients were dichotomized into those who perceived their problems as improving and those who felt their problems had intensified. Therapists of those patients who reported improvement had expected significantly more improvement than therapists of patients who felt they got worse (Goldstein, 1960). Another study found that experienced therapists expected their patients to improve more than inexperienced ones, and brought about more positive change (Chance, 1959). The results of both these studies might be accounted for in several different ways. The first may simply reflect accuracy of prognosis, the second the beneficial effects of experience. Nevertheless, in conjunction with other data, they may be tentatively regarded as confirmatory evidence that the therapist's expectations may affect his results and are related to his perception of the patient. How the therapist's expectations are transmuted into therapeutic efficacy remains to be determined. One possibility is that therapists, being human, are more inclined to like patients they think they can help, and this must affect the amount of effort they put out (Strupp, 1960).

Implicit in much of what has been said so far is that the patient's emotional state is related to his responsiveness to psychotherapy. One property of the patient related to capacity to improve is his emotional reactivity. The despair of the psychotherapist is the apathetic patient or the one who manages to prevent emotional arousal by intellectualizing. Certain patterns of responsiveness of blood pressure to injections of adrenalin and mecholyl seem to be related to capacity to respond not only to electroshock therapy, for which this was originally proposed as a prognostic test (Funkenstein, Greenblatt, & Solomon, 1948), but to psychotherapy as well (Brothers & Bennett, 1954). Pursuit of this lead, however, soon

reveals that the capacity for response depends not only on the properties of the patient's nervous system, but on how he perceives his environment. One series of chronically psychiatrically ill men, whose condition was characterized by "dull dejection and bland hopelessness," and who therefore might be thought to be unresponsive, showed marked behavioral signs of affect and changes in heart rate and blood corticoids in response to certain highly specific stresses that threatened their dependent status. The investigators concluded that the patients' apparent unresponsiveness, which undoubtedly was related to the chronicity of their condition, was a reflection of their ability to shut out or evade stressful stimuli (Oken et al., 1960). Common stimuli for sick people are other persons, including therapists. In our follow-up studies of psychiatric outpatients we were impressed with the amount of help they sought from physicians, psychologists, ministers, and others designated as sources of help by our society. All went at least once to such a person during the four-and-one-half-year follow-up period, and two-thirds went to more than one type of socially defined help-giver. Thus from the patient's standpoint, his capacity for improvement may lie in part in this ability to be emotionally aroused in certain ways by the treatments he receives.

Many of the emotional states stirred up by psychotherapy would be expected to have therapeutic effects. These include hope, friendship, love, and so on. Psychotherapeutic methods, however, characteristically also elicit emotions which appear to be therapeutically irrelevant or actually damaging. A pilgrimage to Lourdes, for example, may entail an arduous journey and exhausting participation in the activities at the shrine, culminating in immersion in an icy spring. In directive psychotherapy the patient may be pressured to go into situations or attempt activities which make him anxious. Evocative treatment may mobilize feelings of guilt, anxiety, rage, or frustration. Therapy groups may stir intense antagonisms as patients clash with others of different backgrounds or outlook, or contend for the therapist's attention, or become involved in multiple mirror and transference reactions.

This leads to the question, why do the same emotions which are neutral or destructive in a nontherapeutic context, such as suffering, guilt, or anxiety, contribute to the healing power of therapy? The reason is, I believe—and this brings me to the final consideration—that all psychotherapeutic activities have a cognitive component which restructures the patient's perceptions so that the same feelings which formerly indicated despair or anxiety now convey a message of hope.

A hint as to the mechanism by which this occurs is given by an experiment which demonstrates with considerable probability that if a person has a feeling which he cannot evaluate he interprets it in terms of cognitions offered by his environment. The basic experiment consisted of injecting naive subjects with adrenalin. In one experimental condition they were told exactly what sensations they would feel; that is, that they would experience mild heart palpitations, sweating of the palms, and trembling. In others they were either told nothing or misinformed, so that they had no adequate explanation for the sensation of internal unrest produced by the injection. A stooge entered the room while they were experiencing the effects of the drug and behaved either in an amusing or an anger-producing fashion, and the subject's behavior was rated by a concealed observer. After this, subjects' self-ratings were obtained on scales of happiness and anger. Those who had been given an adequate explanation for their feelings reported no emotion and showed none in the test situations. Those who had no such explanation acted happy in the amusing situation and

angry in the anger-producing one, and the former reported much more subjective happiness than the latter. They interpreted the internal sensations produced by the adrenalin in terms of cognitions provided by the situation (Schachter & Singer, 1961).

These findings may be relevant to the ability of psychotherapeutic situations to transmute destructive emotions into helpful ones through providing a certain general context of healing. They also suggest a source for the therapeutic power of the therapist's interpretations. One may surmise that most patients have no adequate explanation of their distressing feelings, or have an explanation which is obviously wrong, or which aggravates the feelings. A patient with diffuse anxiety would represent the first category; a phobic patient who knows his fears cannot really be caused by the objects to which they are attached, might represent the second. The third would be the patient who interprets his anxiety or depression as a sign of impending insanity. The therapist supplies an explanation for the feelings which the patient can accept as valid and this becomes the way he actually feels. For example, he may discover that diffuse anxiety is really repressed rage at his mother, or the phobia an expression of fear of his own destructive impulses. The therapist may convey the explanation directly or, through subtle cues, bring the patient to the point of verbalizing it for himself. The new cognition is usually part of a self-consistent conceptual scheme, which further helps the patient to organize his feelings. These cognitions also suggest certain lines of behavior which tend to lead to improved relationships with others. This further diminishes the feelings, and so the patient gets better.

There is no independent, objective criterion for the truth of any interpretation in psychotherapy. As is well known, therapists of different schools, or even of the same school, may vigorously defend widely differing interpretations of the same material, and each is unable to convince the others that his is the correct one. The patient's acceptance of the therapist's interpretations, therefore, is probably largely determined by their plausibility in the light of the material and the prestige of the influencer (Kelman, 1958). In this sense the observation may be justified that the therapeutic effect of an interpretation depends not on its truth, but on whether both therapist and patient believe it to be true (Reid & Finesinger, 1952).

Recently a patient after a single interview experienced one of those rare miracle cures which are so puzzling and gratifying. As it seemed as if something of the sort I have just outlined accounts for the successful outcome, I should like to conclude by presenting the case for your consideration. She is the wife of a struggling young lawyer, who came to see me reluctantly following a particularly stormy bout of depression and anger, at the insistence of her husband, in whose eyes, incidentally, I have high prestige. She had had episodes of depression and preoccupation at one- or two-week intervals since shortly before her marriage, which was of some five years' duration. Following the birth of a daughter a few months before coming for treatment, she was determined to be a perfect mother, and developed extreme irritability, often culminating in violent outbreaks connected with fears that she was not handling the child exactly right. She feared she would fail the child as her mother had failed her. The intensity of her feelings played into her fear of impending insanity.

A review of her past history revealed that her mother was away much of the time in her infancy and vanished for good and all when she was about three. Her few memories of her mother were scenes of tender care. The father soon remarried and shortly thereafter went overseas in the armed forces for a year and a half. During this period the patient described herself as a crybaby. After the

father's return she became apparently happy and carefree until at the age of 14 she discovered some of her mother's letters and a newspaper clipping in the attic which seemed to imply that she had been mentally ill and had suicided. This precipitated a new period of brooding and irritability. She was afraid to tell her father of her discovery lest she hurt his feelings. She angrily withdrew from him, and began to fantasy about whether her mother had committed suicide, whether her father was somehow responsible through his insensitivity, and whether she too would suicide. Again these feelings lifted apparently spontaneously after a year or so, and she became her former self until late in her courtship. As she was Jewish and her fiancé Protestant, both families opposed the marriage and this led to tension between the engaged couple, which seemed to have something to do with the recurrence of her depression. A final bit of information was that in the interview she showed obvious conflict about whether to confide in me.

Before indicating the interpretation I offered, let me remind you that this material has been selected out of the patient's total productions because it supports it. Another therapist might conceivably select equally convincing supportive material for another interpretation. That is to say, the plausibility of what follows may be somewhat spurious. I suggested to the patient that, having been twice abandoned by people on whom she felt dependent, her mother and her father, she was afraid to put her trust in anyone, including her husband, and that she was showing this attitude in the interview itself. The earlier periods of depression I attributed to the original desertions by her mother and father and their reactivation by discovery of the letter.

As she said later, this interpretation went off like a gong. She confirmed her acceptance of it in the next interview by spontaneously attributing the recurrence of her depression and irritability during the courtship to her fiancé's periodic threats to terminate the engagement because of the family opposition, which had reactivated the feelings of desertion by her mother and father. In the three months since the initial interview, during which she was seen only twice, she has continued essentially symptom-free. For the first time she has fully accepted the fact that her mother suicided. Previously she had always toyed with possible alternative explanations. She feels more friendly to her father, and he seems to act less reserved towards her. She no longer tries to be a perfect housewife and mother. For example, she has been able to admit to her husband sometimes that she is too tired to cook. Above all, she confides her feelings to him and has realized, to her astonishment, that in her brooding periods she thought she was speaking her feelings aloud but was actually reciting them to herself.

A plausible explanation of what happened might be the following. The patient's feelings were inexplicable to her. Insofar as she had an explanation for them, namely, that she was going crazy like her mother, this aggravated them. She could not share these feelings with anyone, which isolated her. An additional source of stress was her perfectionism, which could be viewed as an effort to reassure herself that she was not incompetent like her mother and did not have to depend on anyone.

On the basis of the information she supplied, plus her behavior in the interview, I offered an explanation of her feelings which was plausible and which was the more acceptable because of my high prestige in her eyes. My interpretation enabled her to relabel her feelings as fears of again being abandoned by someone on whom she depended—her husband. The obvious implication was that the best way to overcome this fear was not to prove to herself that she didn't need him but to

take him into her confidence. Fortunately he was able to respond by offering support and encouragement, dissolving the barrier between them and reinforcing the new behavior.

This case, then, illustrates how a new cognition offered by the therapist can directly produce a change of feeling which instigates behavior re-establishing the patient's solidarity with a person who matters to her.

To sum up, this review suggests that the patient's potentiality for improvement depends in part on his emotional arousal in the context of his perception of the therapist and his therapeutic method as potentially beneficial. This perception depends largely on the therapist's social role enhanced sometimes by indefinable personal qualities. From the standpoint of arousing expectation of help, the therapist's warm, nonjudgmental attitude and his sensitive awareness of the patient's problems may be important only with profoundly mistrustful patients who are not prepared to accept him at face value as a healer.

The healing potential of any form of treatment depends in part on congruence of expectations of patient and therapist. Their failure to reach a consensus about what each expects of the other seems to be a major obstacle to a successful outcome. The importance of consensus is often overlooked because it can be taken for granted with the clientele of many psychotherapists.

Finally, cognitive insights can influence behavior not only through the familiar processes of learning, but through capitalizing on the powerful drive to evaluate one's own emotional state in terms of environmental clues. This seems related to the therapeutic effect of apparently destructive emotions when aroused in a healing context, and to the ability of the therapist's formulations to directly modify the patient's feelings.

REFERENCES

Ausubel, D. P. Personality disorder is disease. *Amer. Psychologist*, 1961, **16**, 69-74.

Brothers, Anita U., & Bennett, A. E. The Funkenstein test as a guide to treatment in the neuroses and psychoses. *Dis. nerv. System*, 1954, **15**, 335-339.

Chance, Erika. *Families in treatment*. New York: Basic Books, 1959.

Cluff, L. E., Trever, R. W., Imboden, J. B., & Canter, A. Brucellosis: II. Medical aspects of delayed convalescence. *AMA Arch. int. Med.*, 1959, **103**, 398-405.

Frank, J. D. Emotional reactions of American soldiers to an unfamiliar disease. *Amer. J. Psychiat.*, 1946, **102**, 631-640.

Freedman, N., Engelhardt, D. M., Hankoff, L. D., Glick, B. S., Kaye, H., Buchwald, J., & Stark, P. Drop-out from outpatient psychiatric treatment. *AMA Arch. Neurol. & Phychiat.*, 1958, **80**, 657-666.

Friedman, H. Patient-expectancy and the reduction of symptom intensity. *Arch. gen. Psychiat.*, in press.

Funkenstein, D. H., Greenblatt, M., & Solomon, H. C. Autonomic nervous system changes following electric shock treatment. *J. nerv. ment. Dis.*, 1948, **108**, 409-422.

Goldstein, A. P. Therapist and client expectation of personality change in psychotherapy. *J. counsel. Psychol.*, 1960, **7**, 180-184.

Goldstein, A. P., & Shipman, W. G. Patient expectancies, symptom reduction and aspects of the initial psychotherapeutic interview. *J. clin. Psychol.*, 1961, **17**, 129-133.

Hankoff, L. D., Freedman, N., & Engelhardt, D. M. The prognostic value of placebo response. *Amer. J. Psychiat.*, 1958, **115**, 549-550.

Hinkle, L. E., Plummer, N., Metraux, Rhoda, Richter, P., Gittinger, J. W., Thetford, W. N., Ostfeld, A. M., Kane, F. D., Goldberger, L., Mitchell, W. E., Leichter, Hope, Pinsky, Ruth, Goebel, D., Bross, I. D., & Wolff, H. G. Studies in human ecology. *Amer. J. Psychiat.*, 1957, **114**, 212-220.

Imboden, J. B., Canter, A., & Cluff, L. E. Convalescence from influenza: A study of the psychological and clinical determinants. *AMA Arch. intern. Med.*, 1961, **108**, 393-399.

Imboden, J. B., Canter, A., Cluff, L. E., & Trever, R. W. Brucellosis: III. Psychologic aspects of delayed convalescence. *AMA Arch. intern. Med.*, 1959, **103**, 406-414.

Kelman, H. C. Compliance, identification, and internalization: Three processes of attitude change. *J. conflict Resolution*, 1958, **2**, 51-60.

Lévi-Strauss, C. *Anthropologie structurale*. Paris: Librairie Plon, 1958.

Oken, D., Grinker, R. R., Heath, Helen A., Sabshin, M., & Schwartz, Neena. Stress response in a group of chronic psychiatric patients. *Arch. gen. Psychiat.*, 1960, **3**, 451-466.

Parsons, T. *The social system*. Glencoe: Free Press, 1951.

Reid, J. R., & Finesinger, J. E. The role of insight in psychotherapy. *Amer. J. Psychiat.*, 1952, **108**, 726-734.

Schachter, S., & Singer, J. E. Cognitive, social and physiological determinants of emotional state. Unpublished manuscript, 1961.

Shapiro, A. K. A contribution to a history of the placebo effect. *Behav. Sci.*, 1960, **5**, 109-135.

Stone, A. R., Frank, J. D., Nash, E. H., & Imber, S. D. An intensive five-year follow-up study of treated psychiatric outpatients. *J. nerv. ment. Dis.*, 1961, **133**, 410-422.

Strupp, H. H. *Psychotherapists in action*. New York: Grune & Stratton, 1960.

Szasz, T. S. The myth of mental illness. *Amer. Psychologist*, 1960, **15**, 113-118.

Trever, R. W., Cluff, L. E., Peeler, R. N., & Bennett, I. L. Brucellosis: I. Laboratory-acquired acute infection. *AMA Arch. intern. Med.*, 1959, **103**, 381-397.

Whitman, J. R., & Duffey, R. F. The relationship between type of therapy received and a patient's perception of his illness. *J. nerv. ment. Dis.*, 1961, **133**, 288-292.

# The Psychotherapist's Contribution to the Patient's Treatment Career

DANIEL J. LEVINSON, PH.D.

The official title of this section of our conference is "Research Problems Relating to the Psychotherapist's Contribution to the Treatment Process." I am not sure how much consensus there is concerning the meaning of the term "treatment process." To me, this term refers to the concrete goings-on between therapist and patient: the evolving course of their negotiations, exchanges, and relationship during their work together. The treatment process, in this sense, is but one aspect of the total phenomenon of "treatment." Another aspect is outcome—that is to say, the degree and kind of change in the patient's personality and life adjustment. There are other aspects as well. I assume that it is legitimate and of general interest here to consider the therapist's contribution to various aspects of treatment.

If the above reasoning is correct, then we need a broader and analytically more useful title for our present universe of discourse. To my mind, the term that embraces most adequately the range of phenomena and the kinds of analysis with which we are concerned is "the patient's treatment career." This approach has most recently been elaborated by Goffman (1959). My own concern, at any rate, is

with various stages and aspects of this career, and with the therapist's influence therein.

Conceiving of the problem in this way has two specific advantages. First, it connects our work on treatment with a broader theory and investigation concerning careers and social roles of various kinds; for example, the career of student in a college, or that of criminal in a prison. Of particular relevance here are various "educational" and "correctional" systems within which a trained professional staff attempts to induce psychological change in successive generations of students or other "inmates." Studies of careers in these several settings may be expected to be mutually illuminating (Cohen, 1961; Stern, Stein, & Bloom, 1956; Holt & Luborsky, 1958).

A second advantage of the notion of career is that it points to a number of areas of analysis which might otherwise be overlooked. It brings to bear sociological and sociopsychological perspectives in addition to a purely clinical one. The notion of career serves to emphasize that treatment usually takes place within an organized social setting such as a clinic or hospital; that becoming a "patient" is

13

not a simple act but represents a personal and social achievement by a mentally ill person; that treatment involves not only an intimate personal relationship between therapist and patient, but also a complex set of formal and informal contractual arrangements; and so on (Pine & Levinson, 1961). A broad view of the treatment career also leads, as I hope to indicate below, to a more complex view of the forms of influence exerted by the therapist and others.

My aims here are as follows: (*a*) to delineate briefly the major issues or theoretical domains within this total area of inquiry; (*b*) to indicate the range and types of research problems, including some which have until now been neglected; and (*c*) to give a brief account of relevant research in which my colleagues and I have been engaged. Let us turn now to the first of these.

MAJOR ISSUES OR ANALYTIC DOMAINS

The recent proliferation of research on psychotherapy has been characterized above all by its variousness. Investigators have focused on diverse aspects of psychotherapy. They have dealt with a number of dependent variables and have explored the possible effects of a number of determinants. They have used a variety of experimental, observational, rating, and "testing" methodologies. They have been guided by a variety of theoretical approaches—Rogerian, Freudian, Skinnerian, Parsonian, transactional, and many more. This abundance is in keeping with the times, and I imagine that few of us would want things otherwise. It is well represented in our conference, which will be enriched, if also made more complicated, by the widely representative character of its membership.

However, if we are to forego theoretical unity, we must at least have a common framework on which to hang our differences. I should like to offer an outline of

such a framework. It is stated in "theoretically neutral" terms, to use Koch's apt phrase. "Theoretically neutral" does *not* mean "atheoretical." Rather, the framework is theoretically encompassing in the sense that it deals with issues which are relevant to various theoretical approaches. To the extent that it does in fact take into account the events and variables dealt with in the diverse studies, it may serve to sharpen our view of the ways in which these studies overlap, converge, complement each other, and stand in direct opposition.

I shall propose seven major domains or classes of variables and events. Our various theories and empirical investigations deal with single domains or, more commonly, with relationships between two or three domains. For present purposes, it must suffice merely to name and briefly identify each domain.

### 1. Relatively Stable Personal-Social Characteristics of the Therapist

I refer here to characteristics that the therapist brings with him, within himself, to the therapeutic situation, and that are "therapeutically relevant" in the sense that they operate as significant determinants of his dealings with the patient, and of his therapeutic effectiveness. All sorts of variables are of potential interest. For example:

(*a*) At the most general level, the "school" of personality theory and of therapeutic technique to which he nominally subscribes.

(*b*) At a more individualized level, the therapist's conception of the patient, of treatment, and of his own role as therapist. What kind of "therapeutic contract" does he prefer to establish? What is his conception of the "good" and the "bad" patient? What is his conception of the "mentally well" person, and what kinds of treatment goals does he set? What are his preferred modes of participation in the therapeutic relationship?

(c) The therapist's character traits, values, and affective qualities. Of interest here are such variables as emotional warmth, capacity for empathic relationship, obsessiveness, impulsiveness, authoritarianism, tolerance for various kinds of value-violating behavior, values relating to achievement, creativity, sensuality, work, honor, and the like. An example is the work of Betz and Whitehorn (1956) on "A" vs. "B" personality types among therapists, in relation to therapeutic success with schizophrenic patients.

(d) The therapist's psychosocial characteristics: class origin and mobility, ethnicity and ethnic identity, marginality, religion, age, sex, political outlook, and the like. Recent evidence (e.g., Hollingshead & Redlich, 1958; Imber et al., 1956; Kahn, Pollack, & Fink, 1959; Gallagher, Levinson, & Erlich, 1957) on the treatment relevance of these characteristics in patients adds to our interest in exploring their relevance in therapists.

## 2. Relatively Stable Personal-Social Characteristics of the Patient

It seems reasonable to suppose that the above characteristics of the therapist will be activated differentially, and will have differential therapeutic effects, as a function of the characteristics of the individual patient. In assessing the influence of the therapist on the course and outcome of psychotherapy, we must therefore take into account the kinds of patients involved. Indeed, a large part of the total effort in every clinic and hospital goes into the selection of patients for psychotherapy. Since the supply of psychotherapists is so small as compared to the number of persons needing help, it becomes especially important to allocate it wisely—to make it available to those most likely to profit from it. Establishing the patient's prognosis for response to psychotherapy is at least as important as diagnosing his psychopathology, and is considerably more difficult. Numerous suggestions have been made concerning the characteristics that make for favorable treatment outcome, but the research evidence thus far is meager (Knapp et al., 1960; for a comprehensive review, see Fulkerson & Barry, 1961).

From a purely clinical point of view, this is a problem in treatment prognosis. However, the problem can be formulated in more general theoretical terms. In this perspective, the patient's personal-social make-up just prior to the onset of his treatment career is seen as providing one set of determinants of the course and outcome of this career. His career development is also influenced by the nature of the treatment situation, which presents multiform demands and opportunities for work, learning, and personal growth, and by other determinants (see below).

What characteristics of the patient are most likely to influence the course and outcome of his treatment career? Perhaps the greatest attention has been given thus far to diagnostic features, that is, to the nature and severity of his illness. It is often suggested, for example, that hysterics do better in psychotherapy than obsessives. The research evidence to date, however, indicates that the relevance of diagnostic categories has been overrated in this as in many other types of prediction.

In any case, numerous other characteristics must be considered in addition to those relating to pathology. In particular, the kinds of "therapist" variables noted in the first domain above may be of strategic importance in the patient. We need to know more about the patient's conception of mental illness, of his own difficulties, of treatment and his own role within it. The person who finds psychotherapy threatening or, worse, meaningless, is not likely to seek it out, to accept it, or, should he take part, to confront the tasks it presents with serious commitment (Gallagher, 1958; Levinson, 1960). Character traits, values, and affective qualities not ordinarily included in the formulation of the patient's psychopathology may crucially affect his participation in treatment. Finally, psychosocial characteristics relating to social class, ethnicity, age, religion, and the like are coming to be recognized as therapeutically relevant.

### 3. Characteristics of the Patient-Therapist Pair

The foregoing Domains 1 and 2 refer to characteristics of the therapist and of the patient taken singly. For many purposes (such as the prediction of outcome), however, it may be more useful to consider the *match* between therapist and patient, that is, the ways in which they are similar and dissimilar in enduring personal-social features of the kind previously discussed. Similarities of certain kinds may facilitate the formation of a therapeutic relationship and the carrying through of therapeutic work. Other similarities may become sources of impasse, as when the patient presents problems that the therapist has not resolved within his own personality. Similarly, treatment may be helped or hindered by differences in pathology, in character traits, in values and life goals, in age, intelligence, and social origins.

A number of interesting questions are just beginning to be studied. To what extent is there mutual selection by similarity? It would appear that many patients in psychotherapy and analysis strongly resemble their therapists in education, values, professional interests, treatment ideology, and the like. (Less is known about the clientele of more somatically oriented therapists.) Psychotherapists tend to prefer patients who are, like themselves, "psychological-minded" (Sharaf & Levinson, 1957). At the same time, such patients often use their self-probing skills in the service of defense, and it may well be that patients who initially find the therapist more of an alien figure can bene-

fit more once they come to identify with him and gain a new perspective on their lives (Rosenthal, 1955). I shall later return to this and related questions.

### 4. Stages in the Treatment Career

We have been considering, in the first three domains, relatively enduring characteristics that patient and therapist bring to the treatment situation. We turn now to the treatment career proper, to the arrangements, conditions, negotiations, and evolving relationships of which it is comprised.

It is useful first to distinguish several stages in treatment, especially since studies differ in their focus on one or another stage or on the long-term sequence. The division of a total "flow" into successive stages is in large part arbitrary and will vary according to the nature of the therapy and the purposes of the research. For present purposes, it is probably sufficient to distinguish the following stages.

(a) The *candidacy stage*. This is the period in which the ill person negotiates with a therapist (and, often, with other staff members at a clinic or hospital) over the possibility of becoming a patient in psychotherapy. Since this period occurs prior to the instigation of treatment, it is usually not considered to be an intrinsic part of the therapeutic enterprise. I would suggest, however, that it is in fact the first step in the patient's treatment career and that our analysis of psychotherapy ought properly to begin with it. For the candidate who "passes" the admission requirements and continues to the next stage, the events of the candidacy period may well be decisive in shaping the initial character of the therapeutic relationship. Moreover, an adequate understanding of psychotherapy, and of the therapist's contribution to it, must take into account the selection process, and the differences between the successful and the unsuccessful candidates. One of the major functions of the therapist is to decide which candidates *not* to accept, and the problems involved here are of as great importance as those of the subsequent stages.

In this stage, as in the others, we may focus variously on process, structure, or outcome. By *process* I refer to analyses of the stream of events: the temporal sequence of negotiations, emotional exchanges, transactions involving the patient, the therapist, and, in a treatment facility, other staff members. The *structural* features of a stage have to do with the more or less stable arrangements, "working conditions," and behavioral characteristics of the persons involved. Structural features of the candidacy period in a public clinic, for example, would ordinarily include the following: the requirement that the patients must demonstrate financial need; the condition of scarcity—the supply of therapists is not equal to the demand for treatment, so that there is a long waiting list and needy candidates must be rejected; the use of certain diagnostic techniques; the fact that the staff hold certain conceptions of the "good" and the "bad" patient; and so on.

The *outcome* of a stage refers to the ways in which its problematic features—the initial aims and the issues worked on—have been resolved or left unchanged. In the case of the candidacy stage, the most dramatic consequence is of course whether the applicant has been accepted or rejected for the next stage, psychotherapy proper. More refined outcome variables may also be investigated. For example, in many clinics the psychotherapists are grouped according to degree of experience and professional background (e.g., psychiatrists, psychologists, social workers). Successful candidates are often allocated among the several staff groupings according to a rationale that reflects assorted implicit assumptions and value judgments concerning the attributes of a good therapist. "Type of therapist received" may be a significant outcome variable in this stage (Schaffer & Myer,

1954). The actual efficacy of a given system of allocation is usually not scrutinized by the clinic staff. A more subtle aspect of outcome concerns the effect of the candidacy period on the patient's feelings toward therapy and toward his own illness. In some cases, the selection process works in such a way as to facilitate the candidate's transition into patienthood. In other cases it serves to increase anxiety and defensiveness, hindering or preventing the instigation of treatment. Therapists are inclined to attribute the candidate's affective response primarily to his inner proclivities; in doing so, they may overlook some of the noxious or anxiety-arousing features of the selection situation.

So much for the candidacy stage. Within the course of psychotherapy, the following stages may be roughly distinguished.

(*b*) *The initial stage:* forming a therapeutic contract and a therapist-patient relationship.

(*c*) The *main stage* of productive work on the patient's problems.

(*d*) The *pretermination stage:* ending the relationship and preparing for next steps in the patient's life.

Consideration of stages *b, c,* and *d* would take us far beyond the scope of the present brief review. There are of course wide variations in the structure, process, and outcome of each stage. A given therapist may function well in one stage and poorly in another. Many patients leave or are ejected from the treatment at various points along the way. The determinants of variation are not well understood. Indeed, we have very little in the way of data describing the kinds of variation that occur. We need more substantial descriptive evidence on the nature and outcome of each stage before we can embark upon meaningful studies of the therapist's contribution to it.

*5. Over-all Treatment Outcome: In What Ways Has the Patient Changed?*

This is, clearly, the pay-off question in

psychotherapy. Despite all the controversy about the relative merits of psychotherapy (or various brands thereof), comparative research on the outcome of various forms of treatment is notable by its scarcity.

In assessing treatment outcome, different investigators have been concerned with numerous forms of change in the patient. The variables have included symptom-reduction, improved social adjustment, general "comfort" in living, increased self-esteem, and a host of more subtle but highly valued changes subsumed under such rubrics as "emotional growth," "self-realization," and "ego strength." Data have been obtained from various sources—the patient himself, the therapist, independent clinical observers and testers, family members, employers— and by various techniques ranging from behavior observations to $Q$ sorts to global clinical judgments. However, single studies have for the most part utilized only a small portion of the total spectrum of variables and measuring techniques. It is to be hoped that more attention will in future be given to the systematic analysis of outcome and that more comprehensive assessment procedures will be used.

### 6. The Institutional Setting of Treatment in Clinic or Hospital

Psychotherapy is usually conceived of as a dyadic relationship located within the boundaries of the therapist's office. The "private practice" situation is thus taken as the prototype of treatment. The fact is, however, that most of the psychotherapy in this country is done in the clinic or in the hospital. The therapeutic work thus takes place within an institutional context that exerts manifold influences upon it. In the hospital, for example, the therapist is not merely an "auxiliary ego" or a "reinforcing agent"; he is also an authoritative figure who plays an important part in determining the patient's movement through the hospital. In addition, other aspects of hospital life may crucially facili-

tate or hinder the course of psychotherapy. Even in the clinic, the therapist-patient relationship is influenced by the therapy supervisor, by other staff members, and by clinic requirements and policies. Except for a few studies (such as the pioneering work of Ekstein and Wallerstein, 1958), the impact of institutional influences upon psychotherapy has been virtually ignored.

### 7. The Social Context of the Patient's Life

I refer in particular to influences stemming from the patient's family, friends, work situation, and other sectors of the community that loom large in his life space. The importance of these influences has long been recognized in clinical work —as witness the efforts of social workers, rehabilitation programs, and the like— but it has by and large been overlooked in psychotherapy research. The patient's response within various stages of treatment, as well as the nature and stability of over-all treatment outcome, may be due as much to the stresses, supports, and resources in his social environment as to the psychotherapy itself. This is especially true in the treatment of children, and of adults with psychoses, borderline states, and character disorders.

### Summary

My thesis, then, is that a truly comprehensive theoretical analysis of psychotherapy must encompass the seven domains noted above. How to conceptualize these domains, and how to investigate systematically the interrelationships within and among them are, I believe, the fundamental issues confronting us.

By way of final summary, Figure 1 is a diagrammatic representation of the proposed model of the patient's treatment career.

### SOME RESEARCH PROBLEMS

We turn now from the analytic domains to a consideration of various types

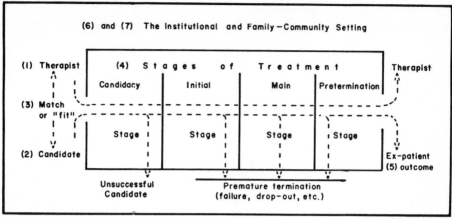

Figure 1. Diagrammatic representation of a proposed model of the patient's treatment career.

of research problems, with emphasis upon the relevance of the therapist.

One set of problems involves the derivation of significant events and variables. An example is the demonstration that the patient's social class position (Domain 2) is a widely significant variable in the sense that it is related to type of illness, treatment preference, place of hospitalization, treatment received, and the like. Findings of this kind indicate that class should be taken into account in further studies of all sorts. Similarly, evidence that the therapist often acts within the treatment process, so as to reinforce certain behaviors of the patient, leads us to further investigation of the influence of type and frequency of reinforcement on the course and outcome of psychotherapy (see Krasner's paper). Dynamically oriented research approaches would be greatly benefited by the derivation of theoretically relevant "therapist" variables (Domain 1) having demonstrable significance in predicting the patient's treatment fate. Our need is equally great with regard to meaningful "outcome" variables.

There is a second line of work that may seem trivial in itself and yet is needed to provide a base for more complex analyses. I refer to simple, descriptive data on the relative frequency of various characteristics in various populations; e.g., on the personal and social characteristics of patients in various treatment settings. Data recently gathered on the occupational and educational characteristics of patients in psychoanalysis offer useful leads for research on the possibilities and limitations of psychoanalytic treatment. Equally interesting leads for studying the role of the therapist in various types of psychotherapy might be found in data on the personal and social characteristics of therapists having various professional backgrounds and theoretical persuasions (Sharaf & Levinson, 1957; Klerman et al., 1960).

Another important type of research problem is the determination of relationships between variables in different analytic domains. A central problem of this kind involves the correlates (predictors, determinants) of treatment outcome. If we represent the domains by the numbers used above, the paradigm here is: $5 = f$ (1, 2, 3, 4, 6, 7). That is to say, variables in each of the other domains are possible predictors or determinants of final outcome.

In this connection, we may point out various routes for study of the therapist's contribution to outcome. The route

through Domain 1 seeks to relate enduring characteristics of the therapist to his
general efficacy in producing favorable
treatment results. A second route, through
Domain 3, is based on this question: Do
certain kinds of initial "fit" (patterns of
similarity and dissimilarity) between
therapist and patient tend to increase the
probability of treatment success? Again,
we may work through Domain 4, asking:
How is treatment outcome influenced by
the therapist's modes of dealing (intellectually, emotionally, conatively) with various issues that arise in each stage of the
patient's treatment career? I have in mind
here such features of the therapist's functioning as the kinds of clarifications and
interpretations he offers, the ways in
which he balances neutrality and involvement, his firmness in setting limits, his
sensitivity to the immediate emotional
interchange between himself and the patient, the treatment goals he sets, and so
on. Finally, there are routes through Domains 6 and 7: The therapist may contribute to treatment outcome in part by
the ways in which he intervenes, or fails
to intervene, in the patient's institutional
and community situation. To the extent
that the therapist has the opportunity
directly to exert control or indirectly to
induce others to behave in certain ways
toward the patient, the use he makes of
this opportunity is an intrinsic aspect of
his therapeutic role.

The therapist contributes in equally
multiple ways to the course and outcome
of each stage within the treatment enterprise. Ultimately, if we are to understand
the therapist's contribution to treatment,
we must follow all of the above routes and
deal with the questions they raise. Viewed
in this broad perspective, the present state
of research seems primitive indeed. On
this sobering note, I turn to a brief account of our work in one sector of the
terrain outlined above.

## ANALYSIS OF THE NATURE AND OUT-
## COME OF THE "CANDIDACY" STAGE

It seems only natural, if we want to
understand psychotherapy, to focus our
investigations upon the psychotherapeutic
process or upon the treatment careers of
those ill persons who become patients. To
do this, however, is to neglect some fundamental problems, since a large proportion
of the persons who seek treatment do not
receive it. We need to know much more
about the character of the candidacy
period. What about the unsuccessful
candidates — those who seek to become
patients but who, for various reasons, do
not make the grade? How do they differ
from those who succeed? What are the
admission policies and selection procedures by which candidates are evaluated?
What part does the therapist play in this
initial stage of the would-be patient's
career?

I shall consider the candidacy period
chiefly as it occurs in the mental hospital
and psychiatric clinic. It is most amenable
to study here, and my own work has been
carried out in these settings.

There is increasing evidence that, in
most clinics, only a small percentage of
the applicants are actually taken into
psychotherapy. Within the "successful"
group, moreover, a sizable attrition occurs
during the first several weeks. I would
venture the estimate that, on the average,
not more than 20-30% of clinic applicants embark on a psychotherapy career
of more than a few interviews. The
paucity of even the most simple descriptive data bearing on this question is truly
remarkable. The situation is more extreme
in mental hospitals where, except for a
very few in which virtually all patients
receive psychotherapy, only small numbers of patients receive more than routine
care and drugs.

One of our major research concerns is

with the determinants of outcome of the candidacy stage. On what bases are candidates evaluated and accepted or rejected? Two contrasting conceptions of the selection process may be noted.

1. One view, held by many psychotherapists, is that the therapist selects patients largely on rational grounds, by an informed assessment of their ability to profit from this form of treatment. The candidate's fate is, from this point of view, essentially a matter of his own personality; treatment is something he *earns* through his own capacity and effort. Whether a candidate is selected for psychotherapy, and how well he does in it, depend upon his (dynamically based) readiness to do the work involved. Therapist and clinic are regarded as resources available to those who can genuinely make use of them. Two types of patient characteristics are given the greatest explicit attention in the selection process: first, diagnostic criteria relating to the nature and severity of psychopathology (e.g., hysterics may be considered better treatment bets than character disorders); and second, those relating to the patient's "motivation for therapy"—his desire for inner change, his readiness to be a responsible agent in treatment, his capacity for introspection and self-examination, and the like (Lichtenberg et al., 1960).

Thus, in the above view, patients are selected by means of a relatively dispassionate, rational assessment of diagnostic and prognostic indications. This highly rationalistic conception is, of course, a part of the heritage that dynamic psychiatry and clinical psychology have accepted from traditional medicine. Unfortunately, we have as yet only the most meager basis for prognostic judgment, and selection is often as much a matter of the therapist's personality as of the patient's. All sorts of nonrational and irrational factors may influence the selection of patients. We need to know much more, not only with regard to valid prognostic indicators, but also with regard to the total process of candidate selection.

2. A second approach, more commonly held by social scientists, regards psychotherapy primarily as a commodity that the therapist or agency selectively *allocates*. The focus here is more on the staff than on the patient. Treatment is something the staff gives rather than something the patient earns. In exploring the criteria for allocation, social scientists have shifted the emphasis from the patient's psychodynamics to the social characteristics (notably class, ethnicity, mobility) of patient and therapist. And, indeed, various studies have shown that psychotherapy is allocated in part along class and sociocultural lines (e.g., Hollingshead & Redlich, 1958). Some proponents of this view are inclined to blame the therapist, to imply that he is showing prejudice toward candidates whose class origin or religio-ethnic identity differs greatly from his own. This may well be true at times, but an approach that focuses narrowly on social characteristics is, in our opinion, as self-limiting as one dealing exclusively with psychodynamics.

In the approach taken here, the two conceptions noted above are seen as complementary rather than as antithetical. The acceptance or rejection of a candidate is an outcome of complex negotiations in which the candidate himself, the therapist, other clinic or hospital staff, the institutional setting, and influences from the patient's social world play important parts. We may limit ourselves to one or another of these in particular studies, but our theoretical conception must be enlarged to encompass them all. With regard to the therapist's contribution to candidate selection, I would suggest that his decision to accept or reject the candidate is influenced to varying degrees by at least the following: rational diagnostic and prognostic considerations, personal values, feelings toward the particular candidates as these develop over the course of their negotiations, stereotypes regarding "good" versus "poor" patients, ethnicity- and class-linked preferences and antipathies, and the like.

We have carried out two large-scale studies of the inpatient population at the Massachusetts Mental Health Center (MMHC). The first was reported by Gallagher, Levinson, and Erlich (1957). The second has been described in part by Gallagher (1958) and by Levinson (1960); a more extensive manuscript is now in preparation. The MMHC is a short-term, active-treatment hospital. At the time of these studies, it housed 150 patients, of whom approximately half received psychotherapy. Our research question: what are the differences, if any, between the patients who receive psychotherapy and those who do not?

We found the following major correlates of psychotherapy receipt: (a) As in several other investigations, *social class* was shown to be a relevant factor. We used the Hollingshead Two-factor Index based on education and occupation. The higher the social class (especially education), the greater the probability of receiving psychotherapy. (b) The patient's *age* is likewise a significant correlate: as age increases (especially as it exceeds 40), the chances for psychotherapy decrease. (c) Degree of *authoritarianism*, as measured by the F Scale, also plays a part. The higher the F score, the lower the incidence of psychotherapy. (d) Finally, there is the influence of the *patient's orientation* toward the hospital, toward various treatments, and toward himself as a patient. Patients who do not receive psychotherapy are more likely than the others to prefer a custodial, benignly autocratic hospital setting; they prefer somatic treatments; they make a sharp distinction between having a nervous breakdown and being really

crazy, and place themselves in the former category; they regard themselves as passive objects of treatment rather than as active participants in treatment. The foregoing orientation variables were measured by the CMI Scale (Gilbert & Levinson, 1956) and by several newly developed scales dealing with patients' role-conceptions. (For a more intensive exploration of these and other variables in a small sample of MMHC patients, see Ditmore, 1960.)

Taken alone, each of the measures in (a), (b), (c) and (d) above yielded modest correlations of .30 to .40 with psychotherapy receipt. Combining several measures, we achieved a multiple correlation of about .70. It may also be of interest to note that the F Scale gave correlations in the range of .40 to .70 with the ideology and role-conception scales in (d). We thus have a basis for conceptualizing a broad syndrome comprising an autocratic, antipsychotherapeutic orientation to patienthood within an authoritarian personality structure. This syndrome is somewhat more common among lower-class than among upper-class patients, to the extent of a correlation of .30 to .40. (All of these correlations are highly significant in the samples of 150 and 100 patients, used in the two studies.)

It would appear, then, that psychotherapy receipt is related in a complex rather than a simple way to the patient's class, age, personality, and view of patienthood. Our findings suggest that class is relevant but by no means overriding influence. Within each class level there are wide individual differences in personality and treatment orientation. While acknowledging the fact and the importance of class differences, let us be careful not to exaggerate these differences nor to develop overly homogenized images of "the" lower class (or other class) patient. The conjoint investigation of class (and other group membership), psychodynamics and relatively conscious orientations regarding treatment will be more fruitful than the study of any of these domains by itself.

To what extent do the above findings reflect social and psychological characteristics of the therapists (resident psychiatrists) at the MMHC? Although we have not pursued this question intensively, one bit of striking evidence may be noted: with regard to the characteristics that differentiate successful from unsuccessful candidates for psychotherapy, the residents typically resemble the former group. That is to say, the residents are largely of middle- or upper-class position, younger age, lower authoritarianism, and strongly oriented toward a "psychotherapeutic" conception of patienthood (Sharaf & Levinson, 1957). We thus propose a "homophilic" hypothesis; in selecting patients for psychotherapy, the therapist tends to prefer candidates who resemble him in social background, outlook, and personality. He tends to reject candidates who differ markedly in most of these respects.

The homophilic hypothesis is obviously in need of further refinement and empirical testing. With this and other purposes in mind, we are engaged in a more intensive exploration of the candidacy stage, this time in our outpatient clinic. Presentation of our work on this and other related studies is beyond the scope of the present paper.

REFERENCES

Betz, Barbara J., & Whitehorn, J. C. The relationship of the therapist to the outcome of therapy in schizophrenia. *Psychiat. res. Rep.*, 1956, 5, 89-105.

Cohen, Y. A. *Social structure and personality.* New York: Holt, Rinehart, & Winston, 1961.

Ditmore, M. Catherine. The patient's view of illness. Unpublished doctoral dissertation, Radcliffe College, 1960.

Ekstein, R., & Wallerstein, R. S. *The teaching and learning of psychotherapy.* New York: Basic Books, 1958.

Fulkerson, S. C., & Barry, J. R. Methodology and research on the prognostic use of psychological tests. *Psychol. Bull.*, 1961, 58, 177-204.

Gallagher, E. B. A sociopsychological study of patienthood in the mental hospital. Unpublished doctoral dissertation, Harvard University, 1958.

Gallagher, E. B., Levinson, D. J., & Erlich, Iza. Some sociopsychological characteristics of patients and their relevance for psychiatric treatment. In M. Greenblatt, D. J. Levinson, & R. H. Williams (Eds.), *The patient and the mental hospital.* Glencoe, Ill.: Free Press, 1957.

Gilbert, Doris C., & Levinson, D. J. Ideology, personality, and institutional policy in the mental hospital. *J. abnorm. soc. Psychol.*, 1956, 53, 263-271.

Goffman, E. The moral career of the mental patient. *Psychiatry*, 1959, 22, 123-142.

Hollingshead, A. B., & Redlich, F. C. *Social class and mental illness.* New York: Wiley, 1958.

Holt, R. R., & Luborsky, L. *Personality patterns of psychiatrists.* New York: Basic Books, 1958.

Imber, S. D., Frank, J. D., Gliedman, L. H., Nash, E. H., & Stone, A. R. Suggestibility, social class, and the acceptance of psychotherapy. *J. clin. Psychol.*, 1956, 12, 341-344.

Kahn, R. L., Pollack, M., & Fink, M. Sociopsychologic aspects of psychiatric treatment. *AMA Arch. gen. Psychiat.*, 1959, 1, 565-574.

Klerman, G. L., Sharaf, M., Holzman, Mathilda, & Levinson, D. J. Sociopsychological characteristics of resident psychiatrists and their use of drug therapy. *Amer. J. Psychiat.*, 1960, 117, 111-117.

Knapp, P. H., Levin, S., McCarter, R. H., Wermer, H., & Zetzel, Elizabeth. Suitability for psychoanalysis: A review of 100 supervised analytic cases. *Psychoanal. Quart.*, 1960, 29, 459-477.

Levinson, D. J. Role, personality, and social structure: The case of the mental hospital patient. Presented at meetings of the American Psychological Association, 1960.

Lichtenberg, P., Kohrman, R., & MacGregor, Helen. *Motivation for child psychiatry treatment.* New York: Russell & Russell, 1960.

Pine, F., & Levinson, D. J. A sociopsychological conception of patienthood. *Int. J. soc. Psychiat.,* 1961, **7**, 106-123.

Rosenthal, D. Changes in some moral values following psychotherapy. *J. consult. Psychol.,* 1955, **19**, 431-436.

Schaffer, L., & Myers, J. K. Psychotherapy and social stratification: An empirical study of practice in a psychiatric outpatient clinic. *Psychiatry,* 1954, **17**, 83-93.

Sharaf, M. R., & Levinson, D. J. Patterns of ideology and role-definition among psychiatric residents. In M. Greenblatt, D. J. Levinson, & R. H. Williams (Eds.), *The patient and the mental hospital.* New York: Free Press, 1957.

Stern, G. G., Stein, M. I., & Bloom, B. S. *Methods of personality assessment.* Glencoe, Ill.: Free Press, 1956.

---

Note:—This paper is an outgrowth of research sponsored in part by Grants M-687 and M-1000 from the National Institutes of Health, and by a grant from the Foundations Fund for Research in Psychiatry. The author wishes also to express his indebtedness to his colleagues at the Center for Sociopsychological Research, who contributed significantly to the approach developed here.

# The Therapist's Contribution to the Treatment Process: Beginnings and Vagaries of a Research Program[1]

### HANS H. STRUPP, PH.D.

It cannot be said that psychotherapists have generally welcomed the researcher-scientist with open arms. In fact, only the last decade has seen beginning changes which must be credited to the growing recognition that psychotherapy is not a congeries of magic operations, but an applied art—perhaps even a scientific discipline—and, as such, susceptible to study by the usual methods of science. This tolerance, however, was more likely to extend to research concerned with changes occurring in the patient as a result of psychotherapy rather than to research focused on the person of the therapist or on therapeutic techniques. The reluctance to subject psychotherapy to scientific scrutiny embodied reasonable as well as unreasonable elements. In particular, the issue of invading the privacy of the therapeutic setting should not be lightly dismissed (for an eloquent statement of this view, see Szasz, 1959). Research concerned with the therapist's personality and his therapeutic operations is of even more recent origin; indeed, we have scarcely done more than broken the ground for what in future years must become a major research effort.

Because of the complex difficulties involved in studying the naturally occurring events in psychotherapy—the First Conference on Research in Psychotherapy (Rubinstein & Parloff, 1959) has done

[1] This research was supported by Research Grant M-2171 (C2) of the National Institute of Mental Health, Public Health Service. Members of the project staff are Joan W. Jenkins, Ph.D., Martin S. Wallach, Ph.D., and the author.

much to highlight the problems—investigators often have had recourse to experimental or quasi-experimental procedures which, hopefully, permit isolation of the process or processes one is interested in elucidating. Such procedures present problems of their own, perhaps chiefly those of relevance or validity. I am referring to the question upon which I hope to elaborate later, namely: To what extent do findings generated by experimental procedures contribute to and advance knowledge about psychotherapy and the psychotherapeutic process? Needless to say, a technique or method may give the semblance of being relevant to psychotherapy, i.e., it may be face-valid, without possessing any intrinsic validity.

In this paper I wish to discuss: (a) the evolution of a research method, together with a brief summary of the major results to which it has given rise; (b) a few considerations pertaining to the validity of the method, together with a critical appraisal of its potential promise; (c) some selected problems of research strategy and methodology, which have become clearer as the investigative work progressed; and (d) a brief description of current work by means of which we hope to further the objectives of our over-all program.

## DEVELOPMENT OF AN EXPERIMENTAL METHOD

The experimental method, whose evolution I will describe in the following pages, had its origin in a doctoral dissertation proposal (which, like many such ventures, was overly ambitious). My interest, stimu-

25

lated by my teachers, Dr. E. Lakin Phillips and Dr. Leon Salzman, involved the problem of trying to make explicit the therapist's mental processes in formulating a communication (interpretation, question, etc.) addressed to a patient in psychotherapy. Another source of inspiration was Glover's (1955, Pt. II) questionnaire survey of British psychoanalysts (conducted in the late 1930's), which perhaps was the first approximation to studying the actual operations of psychotherapists, as opposed to the prevalent practice of reporting, through clinical case descriptions or theoretical expositions, what transpired between therapist and patient. While Glover's survey was restricted to questions relating to practices *in general,* the data amply supported his original hunch, that the practices of even a relatively homogeneous group of psychotherapists, all of whom had been trained in a single method (orthodox psychoanalysis), diverged considerably. In subsequent publications Glover continued to draw attention to individual differences among psychotherapists, advocating increasing "standardization" of the therapeutic instrument, including the therapist. It was obvious to him, and it has since been increasingly recognized by others, that the person of the therapist, in conjunction with the techniques he uses, is an important source of variance, which may be a crucial factor in determining the course and outcome of psychotherapy. Thus, whether one is interested in the problem of therapeutic results, or in more process-oriented problems, it is important to focus on what the therapist actually does in psychotherapy. Parenthetically, it might be mentioned that the therapist's activities may be perceived and experienced very differently by himself, the patient, and by external observers. Because of the traditional bias against introspection, far too little attention has been paid to the patient's subjective experience in psychotherapy, at least as far as "objective" research is concerned.

One approach to this research problem is to devise an experimental situation, resembling the therapeutic setting, to keep the stimulus invariant, and to study the responses of a group of therapists under these conditions. Whatever differences are observed must necessarily then be attributable to the therapist variable. Using such a technique, one might succeed in establishing systematic relationships between the therapist's responses and such variables as: level of experience, theoretical orientation, professional affiliation, attitudes, and the like.

A procedure somewhat resembling the above paradigm was used in a study by Phillips and Agnew (1953) to study the degree to which reflection-of-feeling responses were preferred to other kinds of therapeutic communications. Therapists were presented with a series of patient statements, each of which was followed by a set of five hypothetical therapist responses from which a preferred comment was to be selected. Among the shortcomings of this method were the lack of a meaningful context for patient statements, restrictions imposed upon the respondent to choose from a limited number of response alternatives, the assumption that the response alternatives were equally attractive in all respects save the reflection-of-feeling dimension, etc. In reflecting upon possible improvements, it seemed that a marked increase in realism could be achieved by letting the therapist formulate his own response.

The modified method (Strupp, 1955a, 1955b, 1955c) consisted of a series of 27 short paragraphs of patient statements culled from published therapeutic interviews, and typed on individual cards. A minimum of background information about the patient preceded each statement. Included in the series, thought to represent a fair cross section of verbalizations heard from neurotic patients in early interviews, were a variety of complaints, statements by a borderline patient, suicide threats, and communications illustrating blocking, requests for direct advice, hostility, and negativism.

The procedure consisted in presenting therapists individually with the card series, asking them to assume that the patient statement occurred early in therapy, that the problem had come up for the first time, and that none of the patients were hospitalized. Respondents were free to formulate a comment to the patient in their own words; "silent" responses were also considered acceptable.

What kinds of data does an experimental situation of this kind generate, and what can be said about the relevance of such responses to the verbal behavior of the psychotherapist in a real therapeutic interview? Minimally, one may assert that responses collected from, say, 50 psychotherapists represent the verbal behavior of a particular group of persons with certain specialized training vis-à-vis a more or less arbitrary collection of verbal stimuli attributed to a variety of patients alleged to be in the beginning phase of psychotherapy. Whether and to what extent these responses correspond to what these therapists, individually or collectively, do in actual therapy remains an open question, but the assumption of congruence is implicit in the experimental procedure and represents its raison d'être. Plainly, the purpose is to generalize, and the card series fulfills the function of a psychological test—to sample a psychological process under standardized conditions.

At this point it may be apposite to point out some of the major difficulties obstructing the researcher's effort to study the behavior of a group of psychotherapists under "natural" conditions. Logically and practically, it is patently impossible to hold constant the patient's behavior, and even one interviewer cannot perfectly replicate an interview with the same patient. If, as is done in psychiatric board examinations, the same patient is inter-

viewed successively by different candidates, one needs to make the assumption that the slate is wiped clean, as it were, before each interview. Strictly speaking, such an assumption is not warranted. If we use different patients for interview purposes we are only compounding the lack of comparability.[2] It becomes evident that, strictly speaking, it is impossible to study the interview behavior of two or more therapists under identical conditions, or of one therapist on two occasions. If, despite this state of affairs, one persists in the aim to obtain *strictly* comparable data on the performance of psychotherapists, he is forced to accept compromises. Obviously, the closer the compromise situation remains to the criterion situation, the better. In addition to the desideratum of the highest possible validity, however, one also strives to achieve research economy. It can be readily agreed that a card series, such as the one used in the above experiment, is highly economical; its validity remains a question yet to be answered. The difficulty of specifying an "ultimate" criterion is that of deciding upon a truly representative measure of the therapist's interview behavior under standard conditions. Nevertheless, samples of the therapist's behavior in different interview situations might come reasonably close, and in any case it should be kept in mind that the validity of the "model" is a strictly empirical question.

It may be anticipated that the model is probably neither completely valid nor completely invalid. Validity is always relative. A more important question appears to be: How relevant (valid) is the experimental situation to actual therapy, and can it be considered a fruitful device for generating hypotheses about the

2 In passing only I wish to allude to the fallacies inherent in the frequent use of samples of "neurotic" or "schizophrenic" patients in many clinical investigations. Such labels all too often suggest information about the characteristics of a population, when in fact very little is known.

therapist's contribution to the treatment process? This question, it seems to me, is of the utmost importance for psychotherapy research in general, because it highlights a crucial issue of research strategy: Shall we invest our energies in studying the naturally occurring events in psychotherapy? Or, alternatively, are advances in research more likely to come from experimental (and often seemingly unrelated or only superficially related) analogies? Is it desirable and/or feasible to introduce experimentation into the therapeutic situation proper? Or, is laboratory experimentation to be preferred? With reference to the experimental procedure used in a number of investigations, I shall enumerate some evidence which, I believe, has a bearing on its validity. Before doing so, however, it will be appropriate to describe certain refinements in the procedure which have evolved over the last five years. Parenthetically, it may be noted that these modifications are not entirely uncorrelated with the project's increasing affluence through grant support.

It is easy to see that the method of the card series was highly static, lacking in context, and, that it represented a greatly impoverished stimulus situation. In search for a better technique, the medium of the sound film suggested itself.[3] Lacking funds to produce a motion picture specifically designed for experimental purposes, adaptations were made in an existing film, which had originally been produced by the Veterans Administration for training purposes. Designed to illustrate phobic mechanisms, it depicted an unrehearsed interview between a middle-aged neurotic man and a young resident in psychiatry. Essentially, the interviewer lets the patient tell his own story, frequently repeating a word or phrase, but otherwise focusing very little. At times, he seeks to elicit further information, which seems, how-

ever, to have the effect of diverting the patient from an emotionally charged topic.

To prepare the film for experimental purposes, the interview sequence was interrupted at a number of predetermined points, thus giving the prospective audience of psychotherapists an opportunity to indicate what they would have done had they been the interviewer. Uniform titles ("What would you do?") were inserted at 28 points in the 30-minute sequence, usually immediately preceding a comment by the film therapist. Through the use of this procedure, data were collected from over 200 therapists at several centers. (For a detailed description of the method, see Strupp, 1960a.)

Since that time, in order to diversify the stimulus material and in order to cross check results obtained by means of the initial film, six motion picture sequences, each lasting approximately 15 minutes have been produced through motion picture and television facilities at the University of North Carolina. These films show different patients and therapists. All roles are portrayed by actors. The scripts, however, were derived from actual psychiatric interviews. In all films the focus is almost exclusively on the patient, with the interviewer contributing only minimally. The intent is to avoid "competition" with the film therapist and thereby to facilitate "participation" by a vicarious interviewer, and to make the situation as realistic as possible.[4]

The most recent version of the experimental procedure consists in showing a film to a psychotherapist in a private setting, without other persons being present. The titles "What would you do?", each

---

[3] To the best of my recollection, credit for this idea belongs to Leon Yochelson, M.D.

[4] Dr. John Williams Jenkins has played an important part in this, as well as subsequent phases of the work. Grateful acknowledgment is made also to Mr. Ross Scroggs and Mr. John E. Young, of the Department of Radio, Television, and Motion Pictures, for their generous assistance and advice.

lasting about 30 seconds, have been retained, and occur 6-8 times in each sequence. Each time the viewer responds by speaking into a microphone connected with a tape recorder. If he wishes to give no response he either remains silent or says "no response." Previously, the earlier (and much longer) film was shown to groups of therapists who recorded their responses in writing.

Among the advantages of the sound film technique, the following are apparent: It provides the therapist-respondent with a fairly realistic sample of a person's behavior without depriving him of the visual and auditory cues usually present in an interview situation;[5] since each sequence is presented as an initial interview, no prior knowledge of the patient need be assumed; the patient's verbal communications occur in a context, and while the respondent may feel that the sample of the patient's behavior is too small to form a good impression, the same may be said about any interview or series of interviews: the interviewer's knowledge is never "complete," since for diagnostic as well as therapeutic purposes he must always make inferences on the basis of limited information.

On the debit side, the criticism of artificiality is still cogent. There is no "true" interaction between respondent and patient, and despite instructions to the contrary, the viewer is reduced to a more or less passive bystander who is prevented from influencing the course of the interview which is immutably fixed on celluloid. Moreover, to some extent at least, any interviewer must "compete" with the film therapist. By the same token, the respondent is deprived of the opportunity to assess the patient's reaction to him as a person—a tremendously important source of information to the sensitive clinician—

nor can he evaluate the impact of his own communications on the patient. There is then the legitimate criticism that, in a real sense, the respondent is never "in the picture." The foregoing objections do not exhaust possible criticisms, but the stricture that the film situation bears only a superficial resemblance to the essence of the therapeutic situation—a living experience between two participants—is undoubtedly the most serious one. Let it be noted that one or more of these comments were heard at one time or another from therapists, who for the most part however cooperated very willingly, even if they had reservations about the fruitfulness of the procedure.

IS THE "TEST" VALID?

Such terms as "artificiality," "superficial resemblance," and the like are value judgments which proceed from the implied assumption that an experimental situation must bear a one-to-one relation to the "real" (therapeutic) situation. Clearly this extreme position is not defensible, nor has such a claim been made. Rather the issue resolves itself to the question raised earlier: What is the *degree* of validity? In other words, is there *sufficient* resemblance between the therapist's behavior in the experimental and the real situation to consider the former a reasonable analogue of the latter? If the answer is essentially in the negative, we may be playing a fairly interesting game with therapists as participants, which may teach us something about their psychological make-up and performance in this particular situation. The game may be relevant to or have a counterpart in the lives of these respondents, but their behavior vis-à-vis patients would not be one of them. If there is *some* validity in the procedure —we know from test theory that even tests whose correlation with some external criterion is low can be exceedingly useful —we have an intrisically interesting (face-valid) and appealing instrument, repeat-

_____

[5] The manner and extent to which therapists utilize auditory and visual cues is another problem deserving much further study.

able without variation, economical to
administer, and—most important—capable of generating and testing further
hypotheses about the psychotherapist and
his contribution to the therapeutic process.
As already indicated, our interest is not
only in the communications addressed by
the therapist to the patient but also (and
equally importantly) in such questions
as: How is the patient perceived? How
does the therapist react to him? What
diagnostic impressions does he form?
How are clinical impressions translated
into plans and goals of therapy, etc.?

As stated earlier, a criterion is difficult
to define. What can be taken as a representative measure of the therapist's style
or typical behavior in interaction with a
patient? Undoubtedly there are variations
in the therapist's behavior with Patient A,
as compared with Patient B; or with Patient A, in the first hour and in the tenth
hour. There will be variations depending
on the patient's attitudes, character structure, and approach to the therapist, etc.,
etc. Despite such variations there are
probably regularities or invariants in the
therapist's behavior, determined by his
training, level of experience, theoretical
orientation, personality, etc. which more
or less delimit and characterize his performance or "style." It is precisely these
more stable elements which we have been
interested in exploring, on the assumption
that they typically play a vital part in the
therapist's relationships with his patients,
and that, for better or for worse, they influence the therapist's interaction. The
goal, then, is to isolate from the multitude
of idiosyncratic facets of the therapist-
patient interaction—variations introduced
by the individual patient, the situation,
the stage of therapy, and so on—those
variables which characterize most crucially
a particular therapist's modus operandi,
and to form a clearer picture of the nature of the therapeutic influence he exerts.
If this formulation and its implied one-
sided emphasis on what the therapist

"does" sounds odious, the matter may be
stated from the patient's point of view:
Which particular aspects of the therapist's
behavior (attitude, communications, etc.)
make it possible for the patient to use the
therapeutic relationship to the end of
modifying his own behavior, attitude, and
psychic experience in ways which are
more constructive and more adaptive, less
conflictual and less conducive to the formation of mental and somatic symptoms,
and more in keeping with adult standards
of human behavior?

Granted that the evidence for the
validity of the experimental model is not
well established, certain congruencies between therapists' performance under the
stated conditions and (admittedly impres-
sionistic) information about characteristics of expert therapists, available from
other sources, lends a measure of credence
to the assertion. If the experimental procedure is regarded as a psychological
"test," the following correlates are analogous to trait validity coefficients (Campbell, 1960). The principal sources of support include the following:

1. As part of the experimental procedure in one major study (Strupp, 1958a),
therapists were asked to formulate a brief
statement of the psychodynamics of the
patient portrayed in the film. A global
rating of "dynamic quality" was made by
independent raters taking into account the
degree of complexity, degree of inference,
precision, and operational aspects of the
formulation. Low, but statistically significant, correlations were found between
these ratings and therapists' experience,
the more experienced therapists contributing a larger proportion of formulations
whose dynamic quality was rated high.
This finding was obtained separately for
fairly sizable groups of psychiatrists and
psychologists.

2. Similarly, qualitative ratings derived
from therapists' formulations about the
course of the transference showed that

the more experienced therapists tended to give statements in terms of interpersonal dynamics rather than statically descriptive ones. (This finding applied to the psychiatrist sample but not to the psychologist sample.)

3. Each therapist's responses to the first sound film were rated on an over-all basis by independent judges for the presence or absence of empathy.[6] (It will be recalled that there were 28 stopping points in the film, hence 28 opportunities to respond.) While exceedingly gross, this over-all rating may be regarded as an index of the therapist's skill in establishing a professional relationship with the patient, keeping in mind the limitations and exigencies of the experimental situation. There was a slight tendency (reliable at the .12 level) for the more experienced therapists to obtain a positive empathy rating—a finding which might have escaped notice had it not been for additional explorations in which the variable of personal analysis was taken into account. Using two samples matched for experience, some interesting relationships emerged from comparisons between psychiatrists whose training had included a personal analysis and those whose training had not. Specifically, it was found that at the lower levels of experience (0-3 years), a psychiatrist with personal analysis was as likely to obtain a positive empathy rating as an unanalyzed colleague. At higher levels of experience, however, a sharp differentiation was observed: analyzed therapists received a much larger proportion of positive empathy ratings than unanalyzed psychiatrists, irrespective of whether the respond-

ent described his personal reaction to the patient as positive or negative. The practical significance of this result seems to lie in the differential influence of the therapist's personal attitude toward the patient upon the degree of empathy communicated to him, such that personal analysis, combined with experience, enables the respondent to be more empathic irrespective of his like or dislike for the patient. Stated otherwise, personal analysis seems to permit the therapist to separate his emotional reactions to the patient from his therapeutic activities (assuming that empathy, as defined in this study, is considered a desirable quality). Since a primary aim of personal analysis is to decrease the therapist's subjectivity, the foregoing result accords with a prediction most experts would make from the psychoanalytic theory of psychotherapy.

4. There appear to be distinct qualitative differences, consonant with skills in empathizing with and responding to patient communications, between the protocols of highly experienced and inexperienced therapists. These differences are not easily specified objectively, but sophisticated judges have no difficulty in assigning a protocol to the appropriate group. Differentiating characteristics appear to be: a certain respectful warmth, incisiveness in phrasing a comment, responsiveness to the patient's feelings rather than the manifest content of his verbalizations, a quality of humaneness, ability to adopt the patient's frame of reference without "taking sides," etc.

5. Clear-cut differentiations were observed between therapists subscribing to diametrically opposed theoretical positions, such as client-centered and analytically oriented therapists. These differences encompassed both communications as well as diagnostic, prognostic, and other clinical evaluations.

While these indices, singly or collectively, cannot be considered as demon-

[6] The criteria which were used to judge the degree of empathy of therapists' responses are spelled out in Strupp (1958a, p. 62). Major elements included responsiveness to the patient's problem, a willingness to extend help via a psychotherapeutic relationship, respect for the patient's suffering regardless of his hostility, anger, demandingness, and seemingly antisocial attitudes.

strating unequivocally the validity of the experimental model, they are congruent with clinical data and general knowledge about the performance of psychotherapists. In addition, the studies in which the procedure has been used (Strupp, 1958a; Strupp, 1958b; Strupp, 1958c) have yielded a number of new findings (for example, interrelationships between therapist's attitude toward the patient, clinical evaluations, and certain aspects of therapists' communications). Furthermore, confirmation of these results was obtained by separately analyzing the data for samples of psychiatrists and psychologists, replication of major findings on a new sample (Rieger, 1960), and through the results of related studies using somewhat different methodologies (Strupp & Williams, 1960; Fey, 1958).

## SOME PROBLEMS OF RESEARCH STRATEGY AND METHODOLOGY

Let it be conceded then—if only for purposes of the argument—that there is a certain congruency between a psychotherapist's performance in the experimental situation and his behavior in actual therapy. Perhaps this congruency is narrowly circumscribed, and will hold only for patients roughly resembling in personality structure the patient portrayed in a particular film; perhaps wider generalizations are justified. Whatever the answer may turn out to be, the question is of some importance, since it touches upon the therapist's flexibility, adaptability, or versatility. Rather than pursuing it further, I should like to address myself to a series of interrelated questions, which I hope this conference might help to illuminate:

To what extent does an experimental analogue touch *crucial* aspects of the therapist's contribution? If analogues currently available fail to do so, is there a reasonable hope for realizing this goal in the future? If both answers are in the

negative, what are the alternatives? In phrasing the question this way, I invite renewed analysis of the old issue relative to the study of the naturally occurring events in psychotherapy vs. experimental approaches.

These questions are essentially questions of research strategy, and ultimately of research philosophy. At the same time, they appear to be realistic ones. As researchers, we are continually faced with the problem of deploying our resources, of investing our research energies and dollars to the end of obtaining the greatest possible returns. Each research project we undertake—whether a methodological study or substantive research, a doctoral dissertation we sponsor, or a five-year program we outline to a granting agency—each project demands a decision with far-reaching consequences for the professional life and career of the researcher. For the most part, such decisions involve highly personal factors, which belong to the realm of autobiography rather than to science. Our predilections for theories, for research techniques, and for research topics are, as we know, determined to a greater degree by personal needs than by objective criteria, no matter how eloquently we may defend the rationale of a procedure or approach which had been decided long before by considerations which, in some instances, we might prefer to remain ignorant about. It is likewise significant that whenever such questions are raised for debate, the discussion soon becomes emotionally tinged, and the participants tend less to defend their respective positions than they become defensive about them. Yet, there should be other considerations determining the decisions under discussion.

With respect to the therapist's contribution to the treatment process, the following observations appear germane:

1. Although the importance of the therapist variable has long been recog-

nized—Freud introduced the concept of countertransference in 1910—virtually no objective research efforts have been devoted to the problem until about ten years ago. Major reasons for this lag are probably (*a*) notable reluctance on the part of therapists to participate in research and to expose their therapeutic operations to the scrutiny of outsiders (this problem has in some measure been overcome in recent years as evidenced, for example, by the widespread use of electronic sound recordings of therapeutic interviews for purposes of training, supervision, research, etc.); (*b*) the relative absence of truly sensitive research techniques for measuring differences in therapeutic technique, therapist's personality, attitudes, character of the emotional relationship between patient and therapist, and the like; and (*c*) various difficulties in carrying out research projects over extended periods of time (methodological, financial, etc.).

2. In recent years, much research effort has been invested by different researchers in laboratory-type, quasi-therapeutic investigations. In this way it has been possible to subject part-processes or segments to closer scrutiny by controlled research, but, as exemplified by the discussion relating to the research technique used in our studies, the question of validity, i.e., the degree to which we are dealing with processes which play a *significant* part in psychotherapy, remains unsolved.

3. There has been a declining interest in naturalistic observation of the psychotherapeutic process, the method by which Freud and others made most of the lasting contributions (see Luborsky, 1959, p. 337).

4. The major issue has been whether the therapist's contribution is primarily *personal* or primarily *technical*. In part, this issue is a philosophical one, with strong emotional commitments on both sides. In recent years it has become accentuated through the impact of existentialist

teachings in this country (see, for example, May et al., 1958). Partly, however, the problem is amenable to research, insofar as it is possible to define and measure relevant treatment variables and to agree on measurable criteria of therapeutic outcomes. Greater progress, relatively speaking, has been made in research dealing with the *technical* aspects of the therapist's contribution (example: methods of content-analysis; manipulation of various techniques for therapeutic purposes, such as variations of interviewing techniques, operant conditioning, and the like), and greater investment of research effort has been made in this area than in investigations dealing with the therapist's personality. As I have attempted to point out elsewhere (Strupp, 1959, 1960b), I believe the deficiencies in research dealing with the therapist's personality have largely to do with problems of defining and measuring significant but highly elusive variables, such as: therapist's attitudes as communicated directly or (more importantly) indirectly through his communications which ostensibly have a technical objective; his dedication, faith, commitment, emotional investment in therapy with a given patient—all of which may have differential effects on his ability to empathize with, and respond to (interpret), the metaphoric aspects of the patient's communications. None of the currently available psychological techniques (tests, *Q* sorts, or whatever) seem to be even remotely sensitive to the detection and reliable measurement of these variables. The conclusion appears inescapable that we have as yet little precise knowledge about the *psychological impact of the person of the therapist on the person of the patient as well as about the relative permanence of changes taking place in the patient's psychic structure.*

Restating the problem in somewhat different terms, it might be said that a large part of the difficulty arises from the fact that (*a*) linguistic symbols are inadequate to deal with the phenomena to be described, defined, and measured; and (b) psychotherapy as a technique relies heavily on verbal symbols to bring about changes in the affective processes of another person. There is nothing unique about Problem (a), which is a common problem in science, and which can often be successfully overcome. Problem (b), on the other hand, is truly a stumbling block. I should like to point up the researcher's problem by means of a common example.

Patient X, let us say, comes to the psychotherapist and complains about marital difficulties. On the basis of various assessments the diagnosis is made that the difficulty cannot be "explained" by the "reality" of the situation. That is to say, the hypothesis is advanced that the problem lies in the way X structures the situation and responds affectively to this structure (of which he is not aware) in such a way that the state of affairs is mirrored in consciousness as "anxiety," "inhibition," or "unhappiness." The verbal symbols which X uses to communicate to the therapist his consciously experienced distress are in some manner related to an underlying structure (wish-defense), but neither participant at the beginning knows what "conflicts" in the underlying process give rise to the particular verbalizations. X wants to "solve" his problem, that is, he wants to change himself, the other person, or the situation in such a way that his affective processes signal greater "happiness" or less "conflict." Typically, he wants a cognitive solution to a noncognitive problem.

Now the therapist realizes that affective processes are not readily influenced in this manner, and he proceeds to approach the situation in different terms. He proceeds to do psychotherapy, that is, he helps the patient—the means need not concern us here for the moment—to restructure his wish-defense system. It is merely restating a commonplace to say that the structure of X's wish-defense system (psychic apparatus) is not directly observable, but must be inferred from his relationship to the therapist (transference). To an important degree—but by no means exclusively—this relationship is mediated by verbal communications. At some points, feelings toward the therapist are expressed directly (anger, crying, etc.), but for the most part, X's affects are bound (defended against). It is the current state of X's wish-defense system that the therapist is interested in, and he learns about it through clues from the patient's verbal and nonverbal communications. The clues may derive from a large variety of sources (gestures, inflection, associative trends, attitudes, bodily tensions, silences, etc.), but the inferential process is the therapist's. It is he who on the basis of training, experience, clinical acumen, etc. sifts, arranges, and structures the data to form a hypothesis about the current state of affairs of the patient's emotional dynamics. His verbal communications are designed to alter the dynamics in ways which he judges to be therapeutic (permitting freer and more direct expression of feelings through enfeeblement of the defenses).

The grave difficulty, from the researcher's point of view, results from the lack of invariance between the verbal symbols (their syntactic meaning) and the underlying emotional process to which they (in part) refer. Put otherwise, it is the difference between secondary and primary process. If we are interested in analyzing the content of the patient's communications, how can one identify and define measurable units? What metric can one use? Similarly, how can the therapist's communications be dealt with quantitatively? To call a communication an "interpretation" is of some value, but this is merely a beginning. To measure "depth" or "degree of inference" presently involves one in a host of difficulties. Even if such a judgment is made—the experience of several investigators shows that it can be done with a fair degree of reliability— only a relatively superficial characteristic has been measured. Similar problems confront a group of external observers who may be called upon to describe and conceptualize the events in a given hour of therapy (see, for example, the work of Bellak & Smith, 1958, and the more recent work of the group associated with Franz Alexander [Levy, 1960]).

In some exploratory work of my own, I devised a rating sheet which the therapist completes at the end of each hour. It calls for simple (5-point) ratings of such variables as anxiety, defensiveness, resistance, etc. Correspondingly, the therapist rates the relative frequency of his interventions, interpretations, the nature of his attitudes toward the patient, and so on. It is too early to evaluate the kinds of data generated by such a device. Since ratings must be made over an extended period of time, the statistical problems are quite complex. I suspect we shall find that the value of such ratings is fairly narrowly circumscribed, because they are at best only an epiphenomenon of the interplay of forces, which themselves undergo continual shifts during a single therapeutic hour. What moment of the hour do the ratings represent? Often there may be several discernible shifts in a single hour. If this is so, how do we demarcate the units? The ratings may to some degree measure important aspects of the patient-therapist interaction, but their sensitivity is probably not very great. This is not to preclude the possibility that they may illuminate some aspects of the interaction (such as relationships between therapist's attitude toward the patient, intensity of the patient's resistance and depth of interpretations, etc.). They may also help to sharpen the therapist's powers of observation because the rating procedure forces attention to a systematic assessment of important variables.

Theories of psychotherapy attempt to account for the changes occurring in the patient in terms of the therapeutic relationship, or, more accurately, in terms of the patient-therapist interaction in the therapeutic relationship. Even in the psychoanalytic theory of psychotherapy, as I have tried to elaborate elsewhere (Strupp, 1960c), opinion is by no means undivided concerning the precise nature of the therapeutic action. Clearly, a rearrangement of psychic forces does take place, and it is attendant upon a more or less intense emotional experience by the patient. There is strong reason to believe that (at least in intensive psychotherapy) the favorable therapeutic change is due to something more than the therapist's respectful, benevolent, tolerant, empathic, etc. attitude toward the patient. This "something" is usually (and undoubtedly correctly) subsumed under the heading of the therapist's technical operations (interpretations, analysis of resistances, etc.). The crucial question, however, remains as to the *precise* manner in which the communication of verbal symbols impinges upon, affects, and modifies the patient's psychic economy. Whatever changes take place, their effects can only be measured *indirectly,* as in changed attitudes of the patient toward himself and others, diminution of symptoms, greater subjective comfort, greater productivity, etc.

Psychological measures of many kinds, to be sure, are indirect, and no less valuable on that account. As I have tried to indicate in the foregoing, the problem becomes acute in content-analysis studies of psychotherapy, when in quantitative indices derived from verbal symbols a kind of isomorphism is assumed between the verbal symbols and the underlying psychic process. The training of the psychotherapist is largely aimed at sensitizing him to the metaphor in linguistic symbols, that is, it fosters the ability to read "between the lines," an ability possessed to some degree by everyone. This clinical sensitivity, unfortunately, cannot be built into measurement instruments available today, nor can it be programed for electronic computers.

For the reasons mentioned, efforts to improve and refine naturalistic observation, i.e., sharpening of the incomparably more sensitive human observation instrument, may be more productive in expanding the frontiers of knowledge than experimental or quasi-experimental approaches. The method of naturalistic observation, as we know, has its own difficulties. However, such efforts at controlled observation as carried out by the research group of Franz Alexander may in the long run be highly productive, provided it is possible to bring to bear a variety of theoretical frames of reference on the observations made by trained judges.

## BRIEF REVIEW OF OUR PROGRAM

In the remaining space I shall present a brief sketch of our program—where it started, where we hope it is going, and the kinds of problems it has attempted to tackle.

*Therapists' perceptions, clinical evaluations, communications, attitudes towards patients, and interrelationships of these variables.* A series of quasi-experimental studies (Strupp, 1958a, 1958b, 1958c) has shed some light on differences in therapists' reactions to an identical stimulus situation (a simulated interview) and has attempted to account for observed variations in perceptions, evaluations, and communications directed to a patient in terms of the therapist's theoretical orientation, level of experience, attitude toward the patient, and the like. The experimental procedures by which these investigations were mediated have been examined in the course of this essay; since the substantive results of this work have been reported in the cited references, they need not be repeated here. I believe we have had some success in elucidating the influence of therapist variables upon clinical evaluations and therapeutic operations. The find-

ings have also served as a stimulus to inquire further into the nature of the therapist's contribution (Strupp, 1959; Strupp, 1960c) to refine the experimental method (see the earlier discussion in this paper), to take a critical look at the potentialities of experimental research in this area in general (Strupp, 1960b), and to stimulate alternate research approaches. With respect to the last point, it was possible to confirm the high degree of positive association among therapists' judgments of the patient's capacity for insight, lack of defensiveness, motivation for therapy, favorableness of prognosis, and the therapist's liking for the patient (Strupp & Williams, 1960). The confirmatory strength of this study lies in the fact that the ratings were made by two therapists following independently conducted interviews with some 20 patients. Thus, contrary to the earlier experimental studies, the statistical association refers to a sampling of patients rather than of therapists. Wallach and Strupp (1960) experimentally varied the variable "motivation for therapy" in presenting written case histories to a group of therapists, and were able to adduce evidence in favor of the hypothesis that, within limits set by the patient's degree of disturbance, more highly motivated patients are given more favorable prognostic ratings and tend to be better liked by therapists. W. S. Jones, in a study recently completed, showed that college students, having no familiarity with psychotherapy as patients, therapists, or students tend to vary in their reactions to patients presented to them via sound films, depending on their own authoritarian attitudes, as measured by the well-known F Scale. He found that high authoritarians tend to be more rejecting of a hostile, demanding patient, and more directive and moralizing in their communications to him, than students obtaining low F Scale scores. While these findings cannot be directly translated to the therapeutic situation, they may throw some light on the attitudes of therapists who evinced rejecting attitudes toward the same film patient in an earlier study. Jones contributed a number of additional results having a bearing on this problem.

*Toward the comparative study of therapists' operations.* An interest in developing techniques for quantifying the therapist's communications led to the development of a multidimensional system of analysis (Strupp, 1957a) which attempted to assess each communication in terms of five dimensions: type of therapeutic activity, depth-directedness, dynamic focus, initiative, and therapeutic climate. The system was used in quantifying therapist's communications in the experimental investigations reported earlier, as well as in several analyses of actual therapy interviews. Thus a series of interviews reported by Wolberg (1954, pp. 688-780) was analyzed (Strupp, 1957b); subsequently, a comparison between therapist's activity in the Wolberg series was compared with Dr. Carl Rogers in a somewhat comparable case history (Strupp, 1957c). These studies can be considered only a beginning; however, it is clear that in the future more adequate methods must be found to carry out comparisons between therapists subscribing to different theoretical systems. A continuing need exists for abstracting and measuring dimensions in therapists' communications which cut across theoretical frameworks.

A few limitations of content-analysis systems have been discussed in earlier pages. With respect to the system developed in the course of our program, considerable overlap among the several dimensions was found, resulting in a recent modification by Strupp, Williams, and Wallach. This modification reduces the various dimensions to a single series of categories ("types" of therapeutic activity), with provision for scaling the interpretive "depth" of communications. While this revision appears to retain most

of the measures previously obtained by the system, it fails to do justice to the attitudinal component. That is to say, the quantitative indices give some information about the "kinds" of communications the therapist uses (for example, questions, interpretations, etc.) as well as their degree of inference ("depth"); however, the system has nothing to say about the degree to which the therapist empathizes with the patient, the warmth, gentleness, etc. of his comments, or any other connotative qualities. This omission is no reflection on the importance of these aspects—on the contrary, it should be apparent that I consider them crucial—rather it demonstrates our inability to devise objective and reliable measures.

*Studies in progress.* In conclusion, I wish to list briefly the studies currently being carried out by members of our group or by graduate students working under our direction:

1. A series of six motion pictures has been produced over the past several years, each approximately 15 minutes in length and depicting an interview with patients manifesting fairly typical but contrasting neurotic problems. These films are being used in the manner described earlier to collect data from groups of psychotherapists. Currently, data from some 60 therapists who responded to two films are being analyzed statistically. In a subproject we are evaluating differences in therapists' responses when the subject writes his "communications" to the patient as opposed to speaking into a microphone. Preliminary results indicate that the "spoken" method is generally preferred by therapists as more natural, face-valid, and convenient, and that it results in longer communications (roughly twice the number of words). In addition, the method of recording permits—at least potentially—the analysis of nonverbal (attitudinal) elements in therapists' communications.

2. In an effort to learn more about patients' perceptions of the therapeutic relationship, retrospective data from former psychotherapy patients have been collected by means of a fairly extensive questionnaire. The analysis of these data will focus on the quality of the therapeutic relationship and personality aspects of the therapist, as perceived retrospectively by these patients. While the number of cases thus far available is small (about 40), the data refer to four or five patients of each collaborating therapist. Thus it is hoped that it will be possible to (a) study differences in the perceptions of different patients who have been seen by the same therapist, and (b) relate the data obtained from patients to comparable ratings and evaluations by their former therapists.

3. Another study in progress is designed (a) to replicate previous findings relative to the interrelationships between therapist's attitudes towards a patient, clinical impressions, and treatment recommendations, and (b) to arrive at a clearer understanding of the kinds of information, impressions, attitudinal components, etc. affecting estimates of the patient's motivation for therapy. The investigation requires that over a period of one year every patient seen in the Psychiatric Outpatient Clinic of N. C. Memorial Hospital for a diagnostic work-up be rated on a number of rating scales by the medical student or resident conducting the diagnostic interview. In addition, immediately upon termination of the interview, the interviewer completes some open-ended questions. In contrast to earlier work, the present study utilizes ratings based on actual interviews with a large number of patients. Furthermore, it will provide data on the performance of two groups of relatively well defined respondents (medical students and psychiatric residents). The results of this investigation may have direct application to the psychiatric setting from which they derive.

4. Closely related to, and partly overlapping, the foregoing investigation is another study focused upon the isolation of variables which might be prognostic of a patient's entering and remaining in psychiatric treatment. Such variables may be divided into two groups: (a) those which may be said to reside in the patient, such as age, sex, degree and kind of illness, motivation for therapy, etc., and (b) those which are more directly attributable to the interviewer or therapist, such as his level of experience and his liking for the patient. Pertinent data have been collected on all persons coming to the outpatient clinic for a diagnostic evaluation during the first five months of 1960. Additionally, information is available on final diagnosis, recommendations for treatment, duration of therapy, experience level of the therapist, as well as the data described in the preceding paragraph. Finally, questionnaires sent to patients subsequently provide data on the patient's feelings about the diagnostic and/or therapeutic experience and his current well-being.

These additional data are potentially valuable for several reasons. Many of the patients who are seen for diagnostic evaluation in the clinic are not seeking psychotherapy nor is it recommended for them. Of the others, however, a large proportion are seen less than five additional times. It will be important to determine whether short-term cases can be predicted, either on the basis of the patient's characteristics or on the basis of the characteristics of the interviewer or therapist. Conversely, it would be encouraging if one were better able to match the "good patient" with the "good therapist."

5. Longitudinal ratings of a series of therapeutic variables (see above) are being collected from two therapists seeing several patients in psychotherapy. It will be recalled that the therapist completes a rating sheet on a number of patient and therapist variables following each therapy

hour. (This project is carried out in collaboration with Drs. John A. Ewing and J. B. Chassan.) The objective is to (a) develop an instrument which would aid in making systematic observations of the therapeutic process, and (b) study objectively patient changes in selected variables over an extended period of time, in relation to self-rated therapist attitudes. Supplementary process notes are also being collected.

6. Following a study recently reported by Knupfer, Jackson, and Krieger (1959), a project by Mr. Ron E. Fox is intended to compare personality characteristics of psychotherapists (psychiatric residents) receiving high or low ratings on several dimensions of competence. The earlier study was carried out on subjects treating primarily schizophrenic patients. The present study focuses on therapists treating principally neurotic patients. In addition, therapists' personality characteristics are being studied in relation to typical neurotic personality patterns displayed by patients applying for therapy to an outpatient clinic.

7. Stimulated by an interesting study published by Colby (1960), we are in the process of designing several studies attempting to explore some basic dimensions relating to the process of free association. Considering the widespread use of the technique of free association in psychotherapy, it is amazing how little systematic research has been conducted on the conditions determining content, resistances, and the like. Colby was concerned with the effects of the presence of an observer (quasi-therapist) on the content of free associations (significant persons in the subjects' lives). The proposed research (to be carried out by Mr. Gary Olson) is expected to make a contribution to a rather neglected area.

As may be noted from the foregoing developments, we are directing our attention increasingly to research concerned with (a) greater systematization of observations of the naturally occurring events in psychotherapy, (b) basic processes in psychotherapy, and (c) patients' perception of psychotherapy and the therapist's personality. We are continuing research, albeit with somewhat less emphasis, on the personality of the psychotherapist.

REFERENCES

Bellak, L., & Smith, B. M. An experimental exploration of the psychoanalytic process. Psychoanal. Quart., 1956, 25, 385-414.
Campbell, D. A. Recommendations for APA test standards regarding construct, trait, or discriminant validity. Amer. Psychologist, 1960, 15, 546-553.
Colby, K. M. Experiment on the effects of an observer's presence on the imago system during psychoanalytic free-association. Behav. Sci., 1960, 5, 216-232.
Fey, W. F. Doctrine and experience: Their influence upon the psychotherapist. J. consult. Psychol., 1958, 22, 403-409.
Glover, E. The technique of psycho-analysis. New York: Int. Universities Press, 1955.
Knupfer, Genevieve, Jackson, D. D., & Krieger, G. Personality differences between more or less competent psychotherapists as a function of criteria of competence. J. nerv. ment. Dis., 1959, 129, 375-384.
Levy, N. A. An investigation into the nature of psychotherapeutic process: A preliminary report. In J. H. Masserman (Ed.), Psychoanalysis and social process. New York: Grune & Stratton, 1961. Pp. 125-140.
Luborsky, L. Psychotherapy. In P. R. Farnsworth & Q. McNemar (Eds.), Annual review of psychology. Vol. 10. Palo Alto, Calif.: Annual Reviews, 1959. Pp. 317-344.
May, R., Angel, E., & Ellenberger, H. F. Existence: A new dimension in psychiatry and psychology. New York: Basic Books, 1958.
Phillips, E. L., & Agnew, J. W. A study of Rogers' "reflection" hypothesis. J. clin. Psychol., 1953, 9, 281-284.
Rieger, Rebecca E. Unpublished doctoral dissertation, Catholic University of America, 1960.
Rubinstein, E. A., & Parloff, M. B. (Eds.) Research in psychotherapy. Washington, D. C.: American Psychological Association, 1959.

Strupp, H. H. An objective comparison of Rogerian and psychoanalytic techniques. *J. consult. Phychol.*, 1955, **19**, 1-7. (a)

Strupp, H. H. Psychotherapeutic technique, professional affiliation, and experience level. *J. consult. Psychol.*, 1955, **19**, 97-102. (b)

Strupp, H. H. The effect of the psychotherapist's personal analysis upon his techniques. *J. consult. Psychol.*, 1955, **19**, 197-204. (c)

Strupp, H. H. A multidimensional system for analyzing psychotherapeutic techniques. *Psychiatry*, 1957, **20**, 293-306. (a)

Strupp, H. H. A multidimensional analysis of techniques in brief psychotherapy. *Psychiatry*, 1957, **20**, 387-397. (b)

Strupp, H. H. A multidimensional comparison of therapist activity in analytic and client-centered therapy. *J. consult. Psychol.*, 1957, **21**, 301-308. (c)

Strupp, H. H. The psychotherapist's contribution to the treatment process. *Behav. Sci.*, 1958, **3**, 34-67. (a)

Strupp, H. H. The performance of psychiatrists and psychologists in a therapeutic interview. *J. clin. Psychol.*, 1958, **14**, 219-226. (b)

Strupp, H. H. The performance of psychoanalytic and client-centered therapists in an initial interview. *J consult. Psychol.*, 1958, **22**, 265-274. (c)

Strupp, H. H. Toward an analysis of the therapist's contribution to the treatment process. *Psychiatry*, 1959, **22**, 349-362.

Strupp, H. H. *Psychotherapists in action.* New York: Grune & Stratton, 1960. (a)

Strupp, H. H. Some comments on the future of research in psychotherapy. *Behav. Sci.*, 1960, **5**, 60-71. (b)

Strupp, H. H. Nature of psychotherapist's contribution to treatment process. *Arch. gen. Psychiat.*, 1960, **3**, 219-231. (c)

Strupp, H. H., & Williams, Joan V. Some determinants of clinical evaluations of different psychiatrists. *Arch. gen. Psychiat.*, 1960, **2**, 434-440.

Szasz, T. S. Recollections of a psychoanalytic psychotherapy: The case of "Prisoner K." In A. Burton (Ed.), *Case studies in counseling and psychotherapy.* Englewood Cliffs, N. J.: Prentice-Hall, 1959. Pp. 75-110.

Wallach, M. S., & Strupp, H. H. Psychotherapists' clinical judgments and attitudes towards patients. *J. consult. Psychol.*, 1960, **24**, 316-323.

Wolberg, L. R. *The technique of psychotherapy.* New York: Grune & Stratton, 1954.

# Experiences in Research in Psychotherapy with Schizophrenic Patients[1]

## BARBARA J. BETZ, M.D.

For this Second Conference on Research in Psychotherapy, I have been asked to prepare a paper on the topic of the psychotherapist's contribution to the treatment process as it affects the progress and outcome of therapy. This invitation surely reflects interest in studies which Dr. John Whitehorn and I have been carrying out at the Henry Phipps Psychiatric Clinic of the Johns Hopkins Hospital during the past several years. Therefore, I shall give an account of some of these studies and their substantive results. I shall then present a discussion of modes of research in psychotherapy, in an effort to consider, in basic terms, procedures and methods relevant to some of the realities of the clinical phenomena involved. I hope that the data and experiences to be reported, and the lines of thought into which they have led, will stimulate not only critique—although that is welcome —but also imaginative appraisal as to their implications for further clarification of the psychotherapeutic process.

The studies which I shall describe have not been concerned with the nature of "psychotherapy" in an abstract or general sense. Their *aim has been to establish with definite reliability what makes a difference in the treatment of schizophrenic patients*. The research focus has been on the schizophrenic patient in actual therapeutic contact with his doctor. This focus,

we felt, would provide a simultaneous source of data for illuminating the nature of the clinical problem and the nature of its solution. The directions taken by these studies have been guided by two basic questions: (1) What are the underlying conditions in the patient which give rise to and sustain the schizophrenic reaction, to the exclusion of more effective behavior? (2) What are the conditions in the treatment situation which facilitate or hinder the reduction of the schizophrenic mode of reaction and its replacement by more satisfactory personal and social capacities? The first question is clearly a search for diagnostic specificity, the second for therapeutic specificity. In the tradition in which clinical medicine has raised its scientific status, the two questions are interlocking.

The broad lines along which these studies have been conducted might be designated an operational approach. Clinical situations were not contrived in order to investigate them by a priori methods and design. Actual clinical operations, ongoing whether investigative interest was brought to bear on them or not, were utilized as a continuing source of grass roots data. The approach has been to attempt to capture, by systematic attention, what is authentic and vital in these clinical operations.

## PART I. RESEARCH STUDIES AND RESULTS

### Phase I. 1943-1950: Method of Participant-Observation

Studies of individual schizophrenic patients were carried out over a number of

[1] From the Henry Phipps Psychiatric Clinic of the Johns Hopkins Hospital. This work has been supported in part by funds from the Scottish Rite Committee on Research in Dementia Praecox of the Supreme Council, Thirty-Third Degree Masons, Northern Jurisdiction, administered by the National Association for Mental Health.

41

years in which the investigator was the patient's therapist and functioned as a participant-observer. This mode of study was effective in shedding light on some of the meanings and motivations in the schizophrenic patient's behavior, and also in demonstrating his latent potentialities for more normal and satisfying behavior. It also produced indications that the conditions in the treatment situation which affected the clinical course favorably lay in the actual, present relationship between the patient as a person and the doctor as a person.

Subsequently, as I shall describe below, methods were developed for exploring the importance of the psychotherapist's personal qualities in determining his effectiveness in working as a therapeutic partner with the schizophrenic patient. These later studies yielded independent data which warrant the statement, as a general principle, that *the doctor is the important, even crucial, factor in determining the outcome of treatment with schizophrenic patients.*

Although this conference is not focused on the schizophrenic illness, some understanding of this psychotic reaction is essential to understand the progress of the studies Dr. Whitehorn and I have been making. As is well known, the schizophrenic illness is the most serious of mental disorders. It tends to run a chronic course unless interrupted by effective therapeutic intervention. Cases that are episodic or self-curing are the exception rather than the rule. A favorable turn in the clinical course is not readily achieved even with therapeutic effort, and the prognosis for the individual patient, in terms of statistical probability of favorable outcome, remains grave.[2] Various physical therapies (insulin, electric shock, tranquilizing drugs) have affected sympto-

matic improvement in numbers of these patients, and reduced the doctor's feelings of therapeutic helplessness. However, such symptomatic improvement has tended to be transient unless deeper, human problems underlying the symptoms could also be resolved.

Because the nature of these deeper, human problems remained quite obscure 20 years ago, our studies, then, were concerned with searching them out and illuminating them, as a requirement for developing a body of knowledge about means to their therapeutic solution.

From the participant-observer mode of study, the meaning of the schizophrenic patient's characteristic social distance became increasingly intelligible as a sensitive, interpersonal pattern of separateness, motivated by fearful and hateful distrust of himself and others. A common theme was noted to underlie the many varieties of clinical manifestation, centering about the issue of "authority." Much of the psychotic symptomatology and behavior became meaningful as an expression of a special orientation toward "authority" as external and imposed—its source in others, not in the self. The patient's classical inward experience of feeling "controlled" or "influenced" by outside forces both expresses, and is an indicator of, his dominant concern with imposed authority. This theme was apparent in the patient's image of himself and of others in his life, including the doctor.

In the participant-observer mode of study it was possible to see this special problem of authority resolve itself, as ( a ) the patient developed a trusting, confidential relationship with the doctor, and ( b ) as he began to locate and rely on his own inner resources as reliable guides for personal and social behavior. These two changes in attitudinal orientation were accompanied by the simultaneous attenuation or disappearance of clinical "schizophrenia."

[2] Twenty-five percent of all the hospital beds in the United States are occupied by schizophrenic patients.

The establishment of such a confidential relationship with the schizophrenic patient, once thought not to be possible, is not readily accomplished. In these early studies, it was observed that modes of approach by the therapist which exemplified personal steadiness and firmness coupled with a sense for mutual free, and fair, play were effective in evoking the patient's trust and spontaneity. This was shown first in the relationship with the doctor, later in broadened social participation with others.

Why is this confidential kind of relationship so difficult to achieve with the schizophrenic patient? Do some doctors achieve it more readily and frequently than others? If so, why and how? Questions such as these sharpened interest in focusing more intensively on the personality of the doctor as an important factor in the treatment of the schizophrenic patient. In particular, it seemed desirable to investigate possible variations in the approach of *different* doctors.

In order to accomplish this it became necessary to find a mode of investigative procedure which would enlarge the possibilities of observation beyond what a single therapist working as a participant-observer could do. In the method of participant-observations, the individual psychiatrist can apply himself to the task of individual therapy in patient after patient, can observe whether the patients seem to gain increasing benefits, and can attempt to analyze the interpersonal transactions to ascertain if possible what has been helpful and what has not. But this experimental method has serious limitations. The total sample which can be accumulated is necessarily limited. To a certain extent it is possible, in a planned way, to vary somewhat one's style and method of attempted psychotherapy. But it is difficult for one physician to plan and maintain crucially different approaches and attitudes, for the sake of planned experimen-

tation, because some of the significant variables appear to be manifestations of his own personal characteristics, not readily changed by planned effort. For the same reason, it is difficult, if possible at all, to "coach" another person in a certain experimentally designed "role" in which he is expected to participate with a patient for research purposes.

*Phase II. 1950-1955: Studies of Differences in Clinical Style*

Because of these difficulties and because of the possibility that subtleties in the doctor's personality made a difference in the schizophrenic patient's response, another methodological approach for carrying out systematic studies in this technically difficult field was devised. In this new approach, the investigator is not a therapeutic participant with the patient, but studies the therapeutic transactions and events which take place between other doctors and their schizophrenic patients. This method brings a much larger sample of doctors and patients under study. Similarities and contrasts between different physicians—in their styles of clinical transactions with schizophrenic patients, and in their personal characteristics—can now be looked for and systematic comparisons made, designed to reveal any differential effects on the patient's progress and outcome.

Fortunately it was not only desirable to make such a shift in the mode of investigative procedure, but also possible, in the working situation at the Phipps Clinic. The resident psychiatrists and their schizophrenic patients now became the focus of study. In pursuing the aims of looking for contrasting personal characteristics in the doctor, relevant to different patient outcome, two methods of study have been successfully utilized. The first was a study of data recorded in the individual case records by the doctors and by nurses during the time when treatment was in progress. This method yielded characterizations of the doctors in terms of differences in their clinical "styles" in therapeutic transactions with their schizophrenic patients.

The second method was to study the personal interest patterns of the doctors by the use of an independent instrument, the Strong Vocational Interest Inventory. By the use of this second method, as will be described in detail below, it has been possible *to predict successfully, in advance of therapeutic performance, that doctors with one kind of personal interest patterns will have a high proportion of their schizophrenic patients improve, and that doctors with an opposite kind of personal interest patterns will have a lower proportion improve.*

First, however, it was necessary to see *whether* doctors differ in the improvement rates achieved with schizophrenic patients. That doctors do differ, only some consistently getting high improvement rates,[3] was demonstrated in the following way. A list of doctors was assembled, each of whom had treated a minimum of four schizophrenic, four depressed, and four neurotic patients (to control for the variable of range of clinical experience). The improvement rate with schizophrenic patients achieved by each of the doctors was then calculated by dividing the number of patients discharged "improved" by the number treated. The physicians were then listed in order of descending rank. This procedure was carried out on two independent samples of doctors. For convenience, doctors achieving 68% or better improvement rates with their schizophrenic patients were designated as A physicians, those achieving 67% or lower improvement rates as B physicians. In an initial series of 14 doctors, the A physicians averaged an improvement rate of 75% with their 48 schizophrenic patients, while the B doctors averaged an improve-

---

[3] Criteria of improvement are discussed in detail in a later section.

ment rate of only 27% with their 52 schizophrenic patients. In a second series of 18 doctors, the A physicians averaged an improvement rate of 82% with their schizophrenic patients and the B doctors only 34%.

Why did the schizophrenic patients of the A doctors improve almost three times as frequently as the schizophrenic patients of the B doctors?

The possibility that the patients of the A doctors were clinically "easier" cases than those of the B physicians was ruled out by a detailed comparison of the two patient groups in respect of certain personal and clinical characteristics which revealed that both patient groups were initially clinically comparable. The possibility that the A doctors were "better therapists" than the B doctors, with greater general therapeutic aptitude was ruled out by demonstrating that both physician groups did equally well with other types of patients than schizophrenic.

The possibility that the A doctors carried out their therapeutic transactions in a different style than did the B doctors, and that these differences were related to differences in therapeutic outcome, remained to be explored. When this was done, by a detailed analysis of the individual case records, differences in clinical "style" between the A and the B doctor groups were demonstrated at high levels of statistical significance by the chi square test. (Details of the findings and the methods have been reported elsewhere (Whitehorn & Betz, 1954, 1956, 1957). The empirical findings may be summarized briefly for the present purpose. The A doctors, more frequently than the B doctors, it was found, grasped the personal meaning and motivation of the patient's behavior, going beyond mere clinical description and narrative biography. Likewise, the A doctors, more frequently than the B doctors, selected personality-oriented rather than psychopathology-oriented goals in the treatment of a particular patient, i.e., aimed at assisting the patient in definite modification of adjustment patterns and more constructive use of assets rather than mere decrease of symptoms or correction of faulty "mechanisms." Finally, while the B doctors tended to be passively permissive or to point out to a patient his mistakes and misunderstandings and to interpret his behavior in an instructional style, the A doctors did little of this. Rather they expressed attitudes more freely on problems being talked about, and set limits on the kind and degree of obnoxious behavior. The patients of the A doctors were those with whom trustful communication was most frequently established. They were also the patients who reached the highest levels of excellence of improvement.

The chi square test was used to establish that the differences between the two doctor groups had statistical significance. The level of significance was .001.

These findings were established in an initial series of 14 doctors and 100 schizophrenic patients, and were cross-validated on an independent sample of 18 doctors and 109 schizophrenic patients.

In a follow-up study on these 209 schizophrenic patients five or more years after discharge, 70% were rated as still improved.

In summary, these studies provided data to support the conclusion that differences between doctors exist, manifest in differences in their clinical "styles" with schizophrenic patients and highly associated with differences in patient outcome. Alternative explanations for the differences in patient outcome were controlled by establishing that both groups of doctors were comparable in clinical experience, in their therapeutic effectiveness with patients other than schizophrenic, and in the kind of schizophrenic patients treated.

*Phase III. 1956-1960: Studies of Doctor's Personal Values Based on the Strong Vocational Interest Inventory*

An independent method for discriminating between A and B doctors was next sought. Means for doing this were developed from a series of empirical studies utilizing the Strong Vocational Interest Inventory for characterizing the doctors in terms of personal interest patterns. By the use of this inventory it has been possible to identify differences in personal interest patterns and attitudes between the A and B doctors, and to explore the relevance of these differences to differences in the outcome of treatment of schizophrenic patients.

The Strong Inventory is a well standardized research tool, not psychopathologically oriented but focused on human interests. It selects out from a fairly wide range interests highly shared by an individual with some groups of his fellow beings, and interests only slightly shared with other groups of persons. In all, the Inventory matches the interest patterns of any given individual with known interest patterns of individuals in 45 vocations, by a scoring scale ranging from high to low matching. (All tests in these series were machine scored by the Testscor Service in Minneapolis.)

A brief account of these studies will now be presented (Betz, 1958; Whitehorn & Betz, 1960; Whitehorn, 1960).

At the present time, the research material consists of 72 physicians whose therapeutic results with schizophrenic patients are known, and on whom Strong Vocational Interest Test scores are available. Twenty-six of these physicians are among those on whom our original studies of styles of clinical transactions with schizophrenic patients were based (15 A and 11 B). The remaining 46 physicians (28 A and 18 B) represent a separate group accumulated subsequently whose therapeutic performance with their schizophrenic patients during their residency training became known.

As an initial step in analyzing this material, a comparison was made of the Strong Test scores of the 15 A and 11 B physicians on whom our earlier clinical studies have been based. From this comparison some interesting findings emerged. Both physician groups scored high in three vocations: Physician, Psychologist, and Public Administrator. In 38 other vocations differences in the scores of the two physician groups were not found.

By the scores on 4 vocations, however, it was possible to detect definite differences in the interest patterns of the A and B physicians. These differences are at levels of statistical significance between .10 and .02 by the chi square test. The actual findings are shown in Table 1. These four vocations are: Lawyer and Certified Public Accountant (A's high, B's low); Printer and Mathematics Physical Science Teacher (A's low, B's high). These empirical findings are independent data constituting a source of possible clues to some distinguishing personal characteristics of each physician group, relevant to their different therapeutic results and their different styles of clinical transaction with schizophrenic patients.

*Development of First Predictive Screen*

We next considered how these observations on interest patterns might serve as a predictive device to indicate which

physicians would have high improvement rates with schizophrenic patients and which would not.

We had no particular interest in any direct application of such a predictive device in the assignment of physicians to patients. In fact, we wished to avoid any such maneuver, intentional or unintentional, because it could bias our investigation. Rather we thought that a predictive study, if successful, would serve as a rigorous check on the validity of the differences observed in the first study.

Furthermore, the level of predictive accuracy might serve as an indicator whether the crucial determinants of successful interaction lay in the doctor or in the patient. We had been keeping in mind the possibility that the A doctors might have owed their A rating to the good luck of getting schizophrenic patients who, for some reason, unknown to us, had the knack of establishing confidential relationships, etc., etc. Such an hypothesis had not seemed to us probable, but it did seem possible. *If, however, success in therapy with schizophrenic patients could be predicted in advance, with reasonably high reliability, from indicators of the doctors' characteristics, such a result would support the idea that the crucial determinants of success lay in the doctors.*

A five-point screening device was developed from the four vocational scores discussed above. The highest point (4)

TABLE 1

DISTRIBUTION OF HIGH STRONG TEST SCORES OF 26 A AND B PHYSICIANS
USED AS BASIS FOR CONSTRUCTING A PREDICTIVE SCREEN

|  | No. | Lawyer | | CPA | | Printer | | Math. Phys. Sci. Teach. | |
|---|---|---|---|---|---|---|---|---|---|
|  |  | Score A or B+ | | A, B+ or B | | A or B+ | | A or B+ | |
|  |  | No. | % | No. | % | No. | % | No. | % |
| A physicians | 15 | 8 | 53% | 9 | 60% | 1 | 7% | 5 | 33% |
| B physicians | 11 | 2 | 18% | 1 | 9% | 6 | 54% | 8 | 73% |

on this screen indicates a full four-point matching of an individual's interest patterns with the constellation of vocations characteristic of the A physicians (high for Lawyer and CPA, low for Printer and Mathematics Physical Science Teacher); the intermediate points (3, 2, and 1) indicate matching this constellation in 3, 2, or 1 of these categories. And the lowest point (0) indicates matching in none of these categories. Points 4 and 3 on the screen (matching weighted toward the characteristic A physician constellation) would be expected to predict A physicians. Points 1 and 0 on the screen (matching weighted toward the characteristic B physician constellation) would be expected to predict B physicians. Point 2 on the screen (weighted equally between characteristic A and B patterns) would not be predictive (see Table 2).

As indicated, this screen was originally developed from the Strong Test scores on 26 physicians on whom our original studies of styles of clinical transaction were based. To check the predictive accuracy of this screen, another group of physicians, 46 in number, was used. Strong Test scores were available on each of these physicians. Predictions were made on each of them, using the screening device, whether they would achieve improvement rates of 68% or more with

their schizophrenic patients, or not. When these predictions were then compared with the actual improvement rates achieved with schizophrenic patients, the A predictions turned out to be 80% correct and the B predictions 67% correct. More concretely, out of 25 physicians predicted to meet the A criterion, only 5 failed to do so; out of 12 physicians predicted to fall below this criterion, 8 did so.

These results thus constitute a check supporting the validity of the differences between the interest patterns of A and B physicians observed in the first study. They also support the idea that crucial determinants of success in the treatment of schizophrenic patients lie in the physicians. The cluster of interest patterns represented by high scores for Lawyer and CPA and the low scores for Printer and Mathematics Physical Science Teacher presumably contain clues pointing to special qualities in the physician's personality more likely to evoke favorable clinical response from schizophrenic patients. And the inverse constellation of interest patterns presumably point to special personal qualities less likely to evoke acceptance as an effective working partner.

One possibility to be explored is that individuals represented at the extreme points of the scale comprising this screening device operate from an idiosyncratic

TABLE 2

ACTUAL PREDICTIVE CHECK ON PREDICTIVE VALUE OF SPECIAL STRONG
VOCATIONAL INTEREST SCREEN ON NEW GROUP OF 46 PHYSICIANS

| Predictive Screen (High score Lawyer, CPA; Low score Printer, MPST) | | Actual number of physicians qualifying as: | | Accuracy of prediction (upper zone vs. lower zone) |
|---|---|---|---|---|
| Scale | Predicts | A | B | |
| 4 | A | 10 | 2 | |
| 3 | A | 10 | 3 | 20/25 = 80% |
| 2 | A or B | 4 | 5 | |
| 1 | B | 3 | 5 | |
| 0 | B | 1 | 3 | 8/12 = 67% |

stance in their attitudes and values and temperamental disposition in dealing as a person with their fellows; and that each stance is different from the other in some significant way which can be characterized, and brought into relevance to the schizophrenic patient's attitudes and expectations. For instance, the possibility that there may be a difference in orientation toward the issue of "authority" between the lawyer and the printer suggests itself.

*Development of A Second Predictive Screen*

To explore these possibilities further, a more detailed characterization of the personal qualities of A and B doctors was attempted. This was done by examining their responses to each of the 400 items composing the Strong Inventory. As an initial step, a comparison was made between the actual responses (like, indifferent, dislike) of the original 15 A and 11 B doctors to each item. By this procedure 23 items were found out of the 400, to which A and B doctors have contrasting responses at levels of statistical significance of between .02 and .05 by the chi square test.

Responses characterizing the A doctors (but not the B's) and those characterizing the B doctors (but not the A's) are listed in Table 3. On the basis of these findings a screening device was then developed embodying the ten starred items in the table. The highest point of this screen indicates a matching with characteristic A responses on all 10 items. The lowest point indicates a matching with none of the A responses (i.e., a matching with characteristic B responses on all 10 items). The middle point on the screen indicates an equal number of A and B matchings. And points above the middle (upper zone) indicate the net weighting toward A responses; while points below the middle (lower zone) indicate a net weighting toward B responses.

TABLE 3

CHARACTERISTIC RESPONSES TO INDIVIDUAL STRONG VOCATIONAL INTEREST TEST ITEMS WHICH DIFFERENTIATE 15 KNOWN A PHYSICIANS FROM 11 KNOWN B PHYSICIANS; DIFFERENCES ARE AT LEVELS OF STATISTICAL SIGNIFICANCE OF BETWEEN .02 AND .05 BY THE CHI SQUARE TEST

(The * indicates items used in constructing the predictive screen whose performance is shown in the next Table)

Responses characterizing the A doctors (but not the B doctors):

| "Like" | *311 | President of a society or club |
| | *356a | Many women friends |
| "Yes" | 367 | Accept just criticism without getting sore |
| | 375 | Can correct others without giving offense |
| "Dislike" | 59 | Marine engineer |
| | *60 | Mechanical engineer |
| | *68 | Photoengraver |
| | *90 | Specialty salesman |
| | 94 | Toolmaker |
| | *185 | Making a radio set |
| "No" | *368 | Have mechanical ingenuity |

Responses characterizing the B doctors (but not the A doctors):

| "Like" | 17 | Building contractor |
| | *19 | Carpenter |
| | *87 | Ship officer |
| | 121 | Manual training |
| | 122 | Mechanical training |
| | 187 | Adjusting a carburetor |
| | 189 | Cabinet making |
| | 216 | Entertaining others |
| | 218 | Looking at shop windows |
| "Dislike" | 151 | Drilling in a company |
| | 290 | Interest public in a new machine through public addresses |
| | *381 | Follow up subordinates effectively |

Used as a predictive device, the upper zone would be expected to predict A doctors; the lower zone would predict B doctors; and the middle point would not be predictive.

To check the predictive accuracy of this screen, the second series of 46 physicians was again used. As shown in Table 4 the upper zone of the screen performed with 77% accuracy in predicting A doctors. Specifically, out of 26 doctors predicted to meet the A criterion only 6 failed to do so. The lower zone of this screen performed with 83% accuracy in predicting B doctors. Specifically, out of 12 doctors predicted to fall below this criterion 10 did so.

It is thus apparent that this second screen, based on only 10 out of the 400 items on the Strong Inventory, performs as a predictive device with accuracy comparable to the first screen based on the final scores in the four vocational categories.

These specific items, identified in one series of known A and B doctors, and cross-validated in a second series, provide another set of leads for characterizing personal qualities distinguishing A and B doctors, to whom schizophrenic patients make such a different clinical response.

## Another Validation Study

These findings point to the presence of two opposite sets of qualities in the personalities of the A and the B doctors, presumably relevant to the marked differences in their therapeutic results with schizophrenic patients. At this stage in the studies, the following important questions arose: Are these results particular in some way to the psychiatric milieu and working points of view prevalent in the Phipps Clinic? Or do they have a more general validity—i.e., would doctors with the same differential personal characteristics working in any clinical setting with schizophrenic patients have the same kind and degree of differential therapeutic results?

An obvious method for clarifying these questions is to make a study, comparable to that on the Phipps doctors, on a sample of doctors trained elsewhere and working with schizophrenic patients in a different hospital setting. If the same personal characteristics of the doctors were found to be highly associated with favorable or

TABLE 4

ACTUAL PREDICTIVE CHECK ON PREDICTIVE VALUE OF SECOND SPECIAL STRONG
VOCATIONAL INTEREST SCREEN ON NEW GROUP OF 46 PHYSICIANS

| Predictive Screen[a] | | Actual number of physicians qualifying as: | | Accuracy of prediction (upper zone vs. lower zone) |
|---|---|---|---|---|
| Scale | Predicts | A | B | |
| +5 | A | | | |
| +4 | A | 4 | | |
| +3 | A | 7 | 1 | 20/26 = 77% |
| +2 | A | 7 | 1 | |
| +1 | A | 2 | 4 | |
| 0 | A or B | 6 | 2 | |
| −1 | B | | 5 | |
| −2 | B | | 2 | |
| −3 | B | 1 | 2 | 10/12 = 83% |
| −4 | B | 1 | 1 | |
| −5 | B | | | |

[a] Net excess of A or B matchings: Number of A minus number of B matchings divided by 2.

unfavorable therapeutic results as has been demonstrated with the Phipps doctors, the general validity of these particular variables as significant influences in the outcome of treatment would be supported.

One such study on a small scale has been made on data provided by a neighboring psychiatric hospital.[4] This hospital is a completely separate institution from the Phipps Clinic, with its own residency training program, which is psychoanalytically oriented, and with a traditional interest in the treatment of schizophrenic patients. Information on the improvement rates achieved by the individual doctors treating patients in this hospital was available. Eleven doctors were selected for study: 5 who had met the A criterion of improvement rate (68% or better) and 6 who had not met this criterion. Strong Vocational Interest Inventory scores were obtained on each of these 11 doctors. On the basis of each doctor's responses, and scores, on this test, his position on the two predictive screens was ascertained.

The results of this procedure, using the first screen, are shown in Table 5. It will be noted that 5 of the 11 doctors fell in

[4] We wish to thank Dr. Joseph D. Lichtenberg (1958) of the Sheppard and Enoch Pratt Hospital for his kindness in obtaining responses on the Strong Vocational Interest Inventory, and for cooperation in our studies.

the middle, borderland group (two A's and three B's) which is equally weighted between characteristic A and B scores, and so is a nonpredicting zone. However, 6 doctors were located in either the upper or lower zones where an accurate predictive effect is expected. It will be seen that the direction of prediction was accurate in four of the six instances, or 67%. That is, of 3 doctors predicted to meet the A criterion, 2 did so; and of 3 doctors predicted not to meet this criterion, 2 failed to do so.

A more striking separation of the A and B doctors is found by the use of the second screen (Table 6). With this screening device the separation in the predicted directions is clear-cut. On this screen, only two doctors fall in the middle zone (one A and one B). Of the 5 doctors whose screen position is in the upper zone, and who would be expected to meet the A criterion in actual therapeutic results, 4 did so—an 80% level of predictive accuracy. And of 4 doctors who fall in the lower zone, and who would be expected not to meet the A criterion in actual therapeutic results, none did so— a 100% level of predictive accuracy.

These results constitute supportive evidence of some general validity of the thesis that the crucial determinants of therapeutic outcome of schizophrenic pa-

TABLE 5

ACTUAL PREDICTIVE PERFORMANCE OF FIVE-POINT SCREEN OF 11 PHYSICIANS
WORKING IN ANOTHER PSYCHIATRIC HOSPITAL

| Predictive screen (High score Lawyer, CPA; Low score Printer, MPST) | | Actual number of physicians qualifying as: | | Accuracy of prediction (upper zone vs. lower zone) |
|---|---|---|---|---|
| Scale | Predicts | A | B | |
| 4 | A | | | |
| 3 | A | 2 | 1 | 2/3 or 67% |
| 2 | A or B | 2 | 3 | |
| 1 | B | 1 | 1 | |
| 0 | B | 1 | 1 | 2/3 or 67% |

tients lie in certain personal qualities in the physician.

It would be useful to seek further corroboration of the general validity of these findings, by studies of other samples of doctors working in several other hospitals. It is hoped that in time such studies can be carried out.

*Interpretation*

Certain inferences as to the meanings of these findings may next be considered. One line of thought is that the A's with interests resembling lawyers[5] have a problem-solving, not a purely regulative or coercive, approach. By reason of a basic self-distrust, the schizophrenic patient does not live interdependently by give and take in personal leadership and in cultural expectations, but avoids involvement with others. In the A physician he would find the values of responsible self-determination more honored and exemplified than those of obedience and con-

[5] And CPAs whose interests correlate more highly with lawyers in our society than with teachers or printers as Strong has shown.

formity—an emphasis providing an avenue of progress out of his own entanglements in mutinous commitments toward authoritative influences seen as imposed from external sources. The A physicians, in their clinical styles of transaction with schizophrenic patients, reveal a capacity to be perceptive of the individualistic inner experiences of the patient, while themselves functioning in responsibly individualistic roles. This is acceptable to the resentful, boxed-in patient likely to respond to restrictive pressures by more withdrawal, and to mere permissiveness by inertia. With the A doctors, solutions to the patient's problems are worked out through collaborative exploration of possibilities, rather than in the model of authoritative instruction.

The B doctors, with attitudes resembling printers, or mathematics physical science teachers—black or white, right or wrong—are likely to view the patient as a wayward mind needing correction, an approach likely to alienate him further rather than intrigue him into hopeful effort. In the B physician the patient

TABLE 6

ACTUAL PREDICTIVE PERFORMANCE OF ELEVEN-POINT SCREEN ON 11 PHYSICIANS
WORKING IN ANOTHER PSYCHIATRIC HOSPITAL

| Predictive screen[a] | | Actual number of physicians qualifying as: | | Accuracy of prediction (upper zone vs. lower zone) |
|---|---|---|---|---|
| Scale | Predicts | A | B | |
| +5 | A | | | |
| +4 | A | 1 | | |
| +3 | A | | 1 | 4/5 or 80% |
| +2 | A | 1 | | |
| +1 | A | 2 | | |
| 0 | A or B | 1 | 1 | |
| −1 | B | | 3 | |
| −2 | B | | 1 | |
| −3 | B | | | 4/4 or 100% |
| −4 | B | | | |
| −5 | B | | | |

[a] Net excess of A or B matchings: Number of A minus number of B matchings divided by 2.

would find an emphasis on value systems weighted more heavily toward deference and conformity to the way things are. The particular rigidity of attitude implied by their mechanically inclined interests and orientation toward precision and a rule of thumb approach probably constitutes an actual hindrance to the development of self-trust and social spontaneity in the schizophrenic patient.

Physicians whose attitudes tend to expect and respect spontaneity tend to evoke self-respectful social participation more effectively than those whose attitudes tend to restrict spontaneity by preference for conventionalized expectations. This appears to be the basic difference in attitude between A and B physicians.

Although the emphasis in this discussion has been on contrasts between A and B physicians, it is evident from our data that there is a borderland group suggesting that some physicians might move from a B position to an A position in their therapeutic performance, if appropriately informed and motivated, and that guidance along the lines of interpretation which have been presented can improve therapeutic effectiveness with schizophrenic patients.

PART II. MODES OF RESEARCH IN
PSYCHOTHERAPY

The challenge in bringing scientific appraisal to bear on the psychotherapeutic process is to develop working viewpoints and procedures appropriate to the nature of the phenomena involved. The significant data in the field of clinical psychiatry are often inferential in character. Underlying human themes and issues giving rise to certain symptoms and patterns of behavior must be sought and identified through clues provided by such phenomena as attitudes, values, and expectations in the patient and in other significant persons in his life. Scientific efforts to shape this "human material" into work-

able data are relatively recent. Human problems and motivations were depicted successfully and eloquently in literary productions (novels and plays) long before they attracted the serious attention of psychologists and physicians. The scientific investigator has the task of dealing with this human material with a perceptiveness equal to that of his literary colleagues, and of transmuting it into communicable form which lends itself to scientific manipulation.

This is probably still best done by a *qualitative scientific approach* in which the investigator uses his own human perceptiveness and imagination, channeled by his intelligence, as the surest means for localizing and differentiating that which is trivial and that which is truly basic and central. The first task, certainly, is to seek to understand where the important phenomena lie and to attempt to characterize some of them in workable form. *Quantitative methods* are probably more useful in developing than in originating understanding and hypotheses. Quantitative methods are indispensable aids at the right time—sorting, counting, testing for the significance of differences, and in cross-validation and prediction studies. They supplement, but do not substitute for, the curiosity and imagination of the investigator who, himself, is a major instrument in his research.

Although the ultimate "productions" of scientific efforts have general and objective validity, the process through which they arise, and the means devised and selected to bring them to independent existence, take place within the mind and personality of the individual scientist. He is the source of *new* angles, new problems and possibilities, and new solutions. The subjectivity of the investigator as a scientific asset, and not just a liability, is sometimes not fully appreciated. Subjective involvement, necessarily strong in studies of one's fellow beings, may lead into objective errors. But these are likely to be temporary, for they are subject to correction from several sources: the investigator's own intellectual integrity and self-critique; the consensus of his colleagues; and success or failure in replication of his findings by others.

The general problem of "objectivity" in scientific research is clarified, if not simplified, in the *principle of relativity* which calls to attention the mutual relationship between the observer and the events which he is observing. It is possible, for instance, to view schizophrenic phenomena from points of view other than the therapeutic, e.g., etiologic, psychologic, ontogenic, psychoanalytic, existential, organic, etc. Inquiries carried out from these diverse points of view would presumably produce a series of different formulations of schizophrenic phenomena, each relevant to the angle from which it is observed. Similarly, different investigators, working from the *same* angle of focus, may see and report things differently because of variations in their own inner talent and perceptiveness. In psychotherapy, particularly where the investigator is working as a participant observer with the patient, variations in observation may also reflect actual differences in the behavior of patients who may respond in one way in relation to one partner, and in quite a different way to another. This is relevant to the different ways that A and B doctors approach the treatment of the schizophrenic patient.

In research in psychotherapy, the points of view of investigators, even *about* psychotherapy, may introduce variations in what is looked for and what is excluded. Similarly, points of view about *what* constitutes favorable or unfavorable patient outcome may vary, so that in one case certain criteria are accepted or rejected which are not similarly accepted or rejected by others.

Differences between formulations of

different investigators are therefore not necessarily to be explained, as sometimes happens, on the basis that only one is correct and the other is in error. Rather, in the absence of error, these differences reflect differences in the angle of focus of the observers or differences in their subjective modes of processing what they see, rather than in the phenomena observed. "Objective" (invariant) formulations of the events observed can be approximated only by taking these modifying transformations into account.

Such differences are inevitable and perhaps even desirable. But it seems essential for each investigator to state as clearly as he can the angle from which he is working, and the concepts and criteria which he is employing. He can then adhere to his own individual approach, and at the same time appraise his colleagues' findings in the context in which they were made. Different observations, made from different points of view, with scientific appreciation of the variations in the viewpoints, may contribute richly to the development of an accurate body of knowledge about the general problems with which all are concerned.

*Minimum Requirements for Research in Psychotherapy*

The concept of "psychotherapy," if kept too abstract, can lead to needless pitfalls or ambiguity. Ambiguity can be reduced by focusing on the following specific considerations: "Psychotherapy of whom?" "By whom?" "To what end?" Although the *goals in studying* psychotherapy may vary in a wide range, the *goal of psychotherapy* itself seems simply stated: *to assist a patient with a psychiatric disability to a state of improved well-being.* That is, the purpose of psychotherapy is favorable patient outcome. Success in efforts to achieve this purpose, the procedures taken toward it, even concepts of what "it" is may vary. But it is the presence of this purpose that determines that a "psychotherapeutic situation" exists. The nature of a two-person professional relationship is intrinsically distinguishable as one that is "psychotherapeutic" or one that is "nonpsychotherapeutic" by whether this purpose is present or absent.

Minimum requirements for research in psychotherapy, therefore, include a focus on three basic variables: (a) the patient, (b) the therapist (as the focal point of the therapeutic situation), and (c) patient outcome. Each of these variables will now be discussed in some detail.

a. The Patient. "Psychotherapy," like "surgery" or "medical treatment" etc., may be discussed in very general terms in respect of its common denominators for any patients regardless of the specific nature of this patient's disability. It is sometimes even discussed in such general terms as "a psychiatrist functioning," as though there were "a" mode or method of behaving or a "technic" which constitutes "psychotherapy." However, in a consideration of the actual functioning of the doctor the nature of the clinical problem is an essential concern. It is the specific nature of the problem which determines what the doctor does, how he does it, and why.

In studying psychotherapy from a research point of view, it is of the greatest importance to take the patient variable into clear account. Studies of psychotherapy focused on varying conditions in the treatment situation and on the doctor's behavior, with patient outcome used as the criterion for comparing and contrasting the effectiveness of therapeutic conditions, will be meaningful only if the patients being treated are controlled for homogeneity. The most technically careful studies of the treatment situation and of patient outcome, if the patients being treated represent a variety of clinical and personal problems, will have low scientific validity as a study of "psychotherapy." In this line of reasoning, the finding, as in our studies that certain conditions in the treatment situation facilitate favorable

outcome for the schizophrenic patient, does not provide any basis for generalizing that these same conditions will have any significant effect in determining outcome in other kinds of clinical problems, for example, in depressed or neurotic patients.

Even among patients selected for homogeneity along broad diagnostic lines, a fairly wide variation will be found. However, this variation is likely to be around a common theme, rather than in number and kind of themes. This kind of variation can be controlled by insuring randomization between any two groups who are being compared. This was done early in our studies by showing that the one group of doctors did not have "easier cases," but that the range of clinical variation in the patients treated by the A and by the B doctors was comparable.

It will be recalled that, whereas the A doctors were almost three times as effective as the B doctors in treating schizophrenic patients, both doctor groups achieved comparable results with depressed and neurotic patients. These findings underscore the importance of a careful designation of who is being treated in research studies in psychotherapy.

b. The Therapist. The therapist is the next important variable to be considered in connection with research in psychotherapy. The effective treatment of a psychiatric patient is a complex professional responsibility. The psychiatrist undertakes it with a background of training designed to equip him to appraise the ramifying expression of emotional and mental disturbance at somatic as well as behavioral levels; and to draw from the broad range of therapeutic armamentarium measures of treatment which can supplement and facilitate the psychotherapeutic task. For the purpose of the present discussion, other modes of treatment of psychiatric patients than psychotherapy will be excluded from the discussion, although they are many. At the Phipps Clinic they are drawn on as seems clinically indicated, but regarded as adjunctive to the psychotherapeutic task.

In this discussion I shall not include a review of the range of concepts which have developed about the role of the psychotherapist and about psychotherapeutic techniques. For present purposes, I shall limit myself to that aspect of the therapist variable which is the particular topic of attention here. This is the possibility, supported by the Phipps studies on the treatment of the schizophrenic patient, that the *personality of the therapist may be an important therapeutic factor*. Scientific interest in studying whether and how this is so seems to be growing. Methodological problems for carrying out studies, using actual doctors treating actual patients whose clinical outcome could be evaluated, have been found difficult to solve. This undoubtedly accounts for the absence of other studies comparable to those which Dr. Whitehorn and I have been carrying out at the Phipps Clinic where facilities for overcoming many of the obstacles have been relatively favorable. However, "meanwhile" studies of psychiatrist's personalities have been attempted by ingenious methods, such as supervisor's ratings of residents, self-descriptive $Q$ sorts, and demonstrations of differences in response among psychiatrists exposed to the same interviewing or clinical situations.[6] Studies of this sort have demonstrated that psychiatrists vary in their personal characteristics and modes of clinical functioning. It has apparently not yet been possible to evaluate these differences for their possible relevance to therapeutic effectiveness with actual patients.

*c. Patient Outcome.* The purpose of

psychotherapy is favorable patient outcome. Since the broad aim of research in psychotherapy is to clarify what conditions in the treatment situation facilitate favorable patient outcome for specific patients, *actual outcome is the essential, logical criterion for evaluating what conditions are or are not effective in psychotherapeutic effort.* In reference to this methodological point, it is of interest to note that the studies from the Phipps Clinic are the only ones in the literature in which patient outcome is used as the criterion of what conditions are effective or ineffective in the psychotherapy of schizophrenic patients.[7] This criterion needs to be used more extensively and can be used when research studies are carried out on actual psychiatric patients in a hospital setting. Because of the importance of this variable for sound research in psychotherapy, I should like to consider it in some detail.

In order to use the criterion of patient outcome, two conditions are necessary. One is that a sufficient number of patients, at the termination of treatment, must be represented in each of the two outcome groups: "improved" and "unimproved" to make comparisons and contrasts possible. Most neurotic patients tend to improve, at least symptomatically, in a variety of treatment situations. The improved group, with these patients, is therefore likely to be embarrassingly high for research purposes. Schizophrenic patients, in contrast, are notoriously not self-curing. Since few schizophrenic patients improve without therapeutic intervention, and sometimes not readily then, the improved group here may be embarrassingly low for research purposes. However, when improvement does occur the presumption

<hr/>

[6] Studies by Holt and Luborsky (1958), Knupfer, Jackson, and Krieger (1959), Raines and Rohrer (1955), Strupp (1958), and Uhlenhuth, Canter, and Neustadt (1959) are examples.

[7] Frank and his associates have used this criterion in studies of psychotherapy carried out in the Phipps Outpatient Department (Imber et al., 1957; Gliedman et al., 1957; Frank et al., 1957; Gliedman et al., 1958; Frank et al., 1959).

is that treatment has had something to do with the favorable outcome. Conversely, when improvement does not occur, the presumption is that conditions facilitating good therapeutic outcome have been lacking, or that the conditions present had a hindering effect, or no effect at all on good therapeutic response.

The situation at the Phipps Clinic has been relatively favorable for scientific purposes in respect of this condition, as is shown in Table 7. An expectation of about 50% favorable response was realistically justified by the actual results during the early years of the studies. In more recent years this expectation has risen to about 75%. Actually, at present, the numbers of unimproved patients are reaching somewhat unfavorable proportions for research purposes. In connection with this table, it is interesting to note that the improvement rate for schizophrenic patients during the first eight years listed was 48%, while the improvement rate during the last eight years was 73%. The level of statistical significance of this difference, by the chi square test, is well beyond the .001 level. In this connection it may be interesting to know that during the second eight-year period there were twice as many doctors as during the first eight-year period whose Strong Test scores matched with the characteristic constellation of interests of A doctors (see Table 8).

A second condition in using patient outcome as a criterion is that of having acceptable means for judging that patients are, in fact, improved and of demonstrating in what way they are improved. Although universally accepted "objective" criteria of what constitutes "improvement" do not yet exist, this does not mean that valid judgments cannot be made. This is particularly the case with psychotic patients in whom changes for the better are often dramatic and clear-cut, both to the patients themselves and to objective observers. In most patients there is little practical difficulty in making a distinction between "improved" and "unimproved" when actual favorable changes are taking place. Considerable attention has been given in our studies to establishing the validity of the judgment that a patient is "improved." The appraisal of the patient's condition at discharge is made not only by the physician who treated him, but also by the senior resident psychiatrist and by the psychiatrist-in-chief. Any personal bias of the individual physician is thus, presumably, subject to correction by the clinical judgment of more objective observers. Further evidence, still more objective in nature, was sought from the following sources: (a) the disposition of the patient at the time of discharge—

TABLE 7

NUMBER OF SCHIZOPHRENIC PATIENTS DISCHARGED, NUMBER IMPROVED, AND PERCENT IMPROVED EACH YEAR FROM 1944 THROUGH 1959

(The difference in improvement rates between the first 8-year period and the second 8-year period is significant, by the chi square test, well below the .001 level)

| Year | No. of Patients | Improved No. | Percent |
|------|------|------|------|
| 1944 | 47 | 24 | 51% |
| 1945 | 49 | 21 | 43% |
| 1946 | 55 | 27 | 49% |
| 1947 | 44 | 24 | 54% |
| 1948 | 55 | 20 | 37% |
| 1949 | 51 | 20 | 39% |
| 1950 | 61 | 31 | 51% |
| 1951 | 59 | 34 | 57% |
| Total | 421 | 201 | 48% |
| 1952 | 79 | 52 | 62% |
| 1953 | 60 | 37 | 62% |
| 1954 | 42 | 30 | 71% |
| 1955 | 47 | 36 | 77% |
| 1956 | 38 | 31 | 82% |
| 1957 | 37 | 30 | 81% |
| 1958 | 72 | 57 | 79% |
| 1959 | 57 | 41 | 72% |
| Total | 432 | 314 | 73% |

whether to the community or to another hospital; (b) evidence of increased participation in social relationships with other patients, as recorded in daily notes kept by the nurses; (c) increased participation in the clinic activity programs, as recorded in nursing and occupational therapy reports, and (d) changes in behavior chart markings. The Behavior Chart is a graphic chart for demonstrating change in a patient's behavior which merits respect as a scientific instrument in research in psychotherapy. The nurses' daily observations of the patient are recorded on this chart, supplemented by descriptive notes of the patient's behavior. These charts have been kept in the Phipps Clinic since 1914, and have proved sensitive indicators of the changes in the patient's behavior, both in favorable and unfavorable directions. Since they are kept by the nurses, they provide another record of observation of the patient during his hospitalization, independent of the physi-

cian's judgment. Items marked on the chart are organized in four zones according to whether they characterize normal, overactive, underactive, or "odd" behavior (hallucinations, delusions, mannerisms, etc.). We have used the Behavior Chart quantitatively by counting the number of markings in each of the four behavior zones during the first ten days after admission and the last ten days before discharge and noting the direction of the shift. These data disclosed differences between the "improved" and "unimproved" patients in a direction favorable to the "improved" patients at levels of significance, by the chi square test, ranging between .02 and .001. The reliability of the clinical appraisals of the patient's progress is thus supported.

Q sorts and other psychological tests have been avoided in the studies of the schizophrenic patients, since they require patient cooperation which is often quite unreliable in the early psychotic stages of

TABLE 8

DISTRIBUTION ON FIRST SPECIAL STRONG VOCATIONAL INTEREST SCREEN OF DOCTORS TREATING SCHIZOPHRENIC PATIENTS FROM 1944 THROUGH 1959, BY EIGHT-YEAR PERIODS
(The differences in percent of doctors with interest patterns like known A doctors in the two eight-year periods is at the .01 level of significance by the chi square test.) [a]

| Predictive screen (High score Lawyer, CPA; Low score Printer, MPST) | | 1944-1951 | | 1952-1959 | |
|---|---|---|---|---|---|
| | | No. | Percent | No. | Percent |
| Scale | Predicts | | | | |
| 4 | A | | | | |
| 3 | A | 12 | 29% | 34 | 60% |
| 2 | A or B | 10 | 25% | 10 | 17% |
| 1 | B | | | | |
| 0 | B | 19 | 46% | 13 | 23% |
| | Total | 41 | | 57 | |

[a] In the 1944-1951 period, scores are not available on 20 doctors who were residents before the Test was used systematically for research purposes; in the 1952-1959 period scores are available on all but 2 doctors. (The possibility of some reason for a bias in the selection of doctors for testing in the 1944-1951 period, so that A doctors would be unduly represented in those for whom Strong Tests were available, was considered. Such a bias could not be located. Even if all 20 untested doctors were A doctors, which seems unlikely, the percentage would be less than in the 1952-1959 period—50% vs. 60%.)

treatment. It is possible, however, that appropriate techniques for the special situation presented by the study of psychotic patients can be developed.

In addition to establishing that improvement had occurred, and the frequency of improvement, it is also possible to characterize the *quality* of improvement made by schizophrenic patients. In the Phipps studies, *quality of improvement* has been evaluated under three general headings or *grades of improvement:* Grade I—symptom decrease only; Grade II—symptom decrease and increase in personal effectiveness; and Grade III—symptom decrease, increase in personal effectiveness, and progress in personal problem solving.

These three grades of improvement seem to correspond with three consecutive phases of progress made by the schizophrenic patient during the course of treatment. Each phase represents a step toward the ultimate resolution of the personal problem generating the patient's psychotic reaction. These three phases of treatment were noted a number of years ago (Betz, 1947) and designated in the following way: Phase I—timid rigidity, Phase II—spontaneity in mutual interaction, and Phase III—broadened social participation.

Some patients take only the first step, during their psychotherapeutic experience, and may be said to have reached a Grade I level of qualitative improvement. Some patients progress further and accomplish the second step—a Grade II improvement. Other patients (mostly those treated by A doctors) progress still further, achieving a radical reorientation of their attitudes toward themselves and others—what we have called personal problem solving or a Grade III improvement.

This step-wise course does not seem to follow a random path, but moves along the central axis of the "authority" issue which seems to constitute a basic personal

problem in the schizophrenic patient. As already described, the prevalent (but hated) schizophrenic assumption is that authority and power lie in others, not in the self. The more this issue is dominant, the more marked is the patient's state of passivity, lack of initiative, fearful distrust of the self and others, withdrawal, and delusional and hallucinatory sense of being controlled by outside forces, and the more relationships with others tend to be reduced to watchful waiting in an attitude of fatalistic resignation. The first problem to be solved through the treatment experience—and this is done in Phase I if at all—is the achievement of a mutually confidential relationship between patient and doctor, and the replacement of mistrustful psychotic aloofness by trustful dependence. This step is not readily accomplished with schizophrenic patients, particularly by the B doctors. It represents a decrease in alienation and is accompanied by a decrease in psychotic symptoms, but not immediately by increased social activity.

The next problem to be solved—and this is done in Phase II if at all—is that of where "authority" is to lie—in others, even the doctor who is now trusted—or in one's self. This step is not readily accomplished either, particularly by the B doctors who are likely to fall into the role of benign authority figures. Given sufficient leeway and support to do so, many schizophrenic patients take this step toward the solution of their problems, and accept the responsibility for self-determined action. This step constitutes a growth in self-respect and confidence, and is accompanied by an increase in social effectiveness and participation, readily observed.

The final problem to be worked out—accomplished in Phase III of treatment—is that of getting personally involved in real life situations, with choices and actions based on self-determined planning and implemented through consultative help from others. It is accompanied by broadened social participation, and by a decreased need for consultation and support from the doctor.

This brief perspective on phases of treatment and grades of improvement of schizophrenic patients has been derived from a study of the clinical progress of actual patients. It provides a schematization which can serve two functions. It represents a progress continuum for locating the point at which a patient is functioning at a given period of time in his treatment, in terms of clinical manifestations, of social participation, and of his attitudes on the problem of "authority" as displayed in his interactions with the doctor. It also provides criteria for estimating the relative degree and quality of improvement which has reached when treatment is terminated, for whatever reason. This schematization does not pretend to be a complete or final map of what "really" takes place in the psychotherapeutic changes which occur in schizophrenic patients. It is an example of an attempt to rough in and bring together in an orderly sequence some of the phenomena which have been repeatedly observed. It is a tentative schematization subject to revision and supplementation. It is a kind of effort, however, which may prove useful in studying the issues involved and the sequence of events in the psychotherapy of patients other than schizophrenic.

Thus, psychotherapeutic change is conceived as the solution of specific personal problems and the activation of latent inner potentialities for more healthy functioning, brought about through meaningful human experience provided along specific lines through the relationship with the therapist. For the schizophrenic patient this is a profound, personal experience, superseding that with any previous interpersonal partners. It is customarily an absorbing professional experience for the doctor. It is the goal of research in

psychotherapy to contribute to a body of knowledge about how these profound changes can be brought about so that they can be produced by more doctors for more patients with a high probability of success.

## BIBLIOGRAPHY

Betz, Barbara J. Experiences in the psychotherapy of the obsessive-schizophrenic personality. *Sth. Med. J.*, 1946, **39**, 249-257.

Betz, Barbara J. A study of tactics for resolving the autistic barrier in the psychotherapy of the schizophrenic personality. *Amer. J. Psychiat.*, 1947, **104**, 267-273.

Betz, Barbara J. Strategic conditions in the psychotherapy of persons with schizophrenia. *Amer. J. Psychiat.*, 1950, **107**, 203-215.

Betz, Barbara J. How do personal attitudes interests influence psychotherapeutic effectiveness? *Proc. VI Am. Psychiat. Inst., Princeton, New Jersey*, 1958, 14-28.

Betz, Barbara J., & Whitehorn, J. C. The relationship of the therapist to the outcome of therapy in schizophrenia. *Psychiat. res. Reports*, 1956, **5**, 89-105.

Frank, J. D., Gliedman, L. H., Imber, S. D., Nash, E. H., & Stone, A. R. Why patients leave psychotherapy. *AMA Arch. Neurol. & Psychiat.*, 1957, **77**, 283-299.

Frank, J. D., Gliedman, L. H., Imber, S. D., Stone, A. R., & Nash, E. H. Patients' expectancies and relearning as factors determining improvement in psychotherapy. *Amer. J. Psychiat.*, 1959, **115**, 961-968.

Gliedman, L. H., Nash, E. H., Imber, S. D., Stone, A. R., & Frank, J. D. Reduction of symptoms by pharmacologically inert substances and by short-term psychotherapy. *AMA Arch. Neurol. & Psychiat.*, 1959, **79**, 345-351.

Gliedman, L. H., Stone, A. R., Frank, J. D., Nash, E. H., & Imber, S. D. Incentives for treatment related to remaining or improving in psychotherapy. *Amer. J. Psychother.*, 1957, **11**, 589-598.

Holt, R. R., & Luborsky, L. *Personality patterns of psychiatrists*. New York: Basic Books, 1958. Pp. 386.

Imber, S. D., Frank, J. D., Nash, E. H., Stone, A. R., & Gliedman, L. H. Improvement and amount of therapeutic contact: An alternative to the use of no-treatment controls in psychotherapy. *J. consult. Phychol.*, 1957, **21**, 309-315.

Knupfer, Genevieve, Jackson, D. D., & Krieger, G. Personality differences between more and less competent psychotherapists as a function of criteria of competence. *J. nerv. ment. Dis.,* 1959, **129**, 375-384.

Lichtenberg, J. D. A statistical analysis of patient care at the Sheppard and Enoch Pratt Hospital. *Psychiat. Quart.,* 1958, **32**, 13-28.

Raines, G. N., & Rohrer, J. H. The operational matrix of psychiatric practice: I. Consistency and variability in interview impressions of different psychiatrists. *Amer. J. Psychiat.,* 1955, **111**, 721.

Strupp, H. H. The psychotherapist's contribution to the treatment process. *Behav. Sci.,* 1958, **3**, 34-37.

Uhlenhuth, E. H., Canter, A., Neustadt, J. O., & Payson, H. E. The symptomatic relief of anxiety with meprobamate, phenobarbital and placebo. *Amer. J. Psychiat.,* 1959, **115**, 905-910.

Whitehorn, J. C. Studies of the doctor as a crucial factor for the prognosis of schizophrenic patients. *Int. J. soc. Psychiat.,* 1960, **6**, 71-77.

Whitehorn, J. C., & Betz, Barbara J. A study of psychotherapeutic relationships between physicians and schizophrenic patients. *Amer. J. Psychiat.,* 1954, **111**, 321-331.

Whitehorn, J. C., & Betz, Barbara J. A comparison of psychotherapeutic relationships between physicians and schizophrenic patients when insulin is combined with psychotherapy and when psychotherapy is used alone. *Amer. J. Psychiat.,* 1957, **113**, 901-910.

Whitehorn, J. C., & Betz, Barbara J. Further studies of the doctor as a crucial variable in the outcome of treatment with schizophrenic patients. *Amer. J. Psychiat.,* 1960, **117**, 215-223.

# The Therapist as a Social Reinforcement Machine[1]

## LEONARD KRASNER, PH.D

In recent years the therapist has emerged, reluctantly, from the shadow of the patient to a fuller recognition of the influence of his behavior in the psychotherapy process. Certain assumptions are implicit in the selection of the type of research studies used to illustrate the major issues in research on the therapist variable in the psychotherapy process. These assumptions may be stated as follows: (*a*) Psychotherapy is a lawful, predictable, and directive process which can be investigated most parsimonously within the framework of a reinforcement theory of learning. (*b*) The variables which affect the therapy process are the same as those in other interpersonal situations which involve the reinforcement, control, manipulation, influencing, or redirection of human behavior.

If these general assumptions about psychotherapy are accepted, a number of deductions follow which can guide research programs: (*a*) The therapist, as the central variable in the therapeutic situation, is a social "reinforcement machine," programed by prior training and experience. The therapist has been trained to use his behavior as a decisive factor in interpersonal situations with individuals who come to him for assistance. His goal

is to influence his patient's behavior in the therapy situation so that certain changes may occur in the patient's total life situation. (*b*) The therapist has available to him a series of reinforcement techniques to influence the probability of selected behavior change in the patient. (*c*) The effectiveness of the reinforcement process can be maximized by appropriate interactions of the therapist, situational, and patient variables.

It is difficult to find an area of human endeavor whose effectiveness is as strongly defended with as little concrete evidence as "psychotherapy" (Eysenck, 1952). It is increasingly difficult for research in this field to break out of the confines of the narrow boundaries of the framework of *traditional* psychotherapeutic interaction. Research in psychotherapy will not be as productive as it could be until the therapist can accept his role as an influencer of behavior and thus permit investigation of the variables of behavior control. Within this concept, new approaches and new techniques can develop. Further, we will be able to develop predictive devices for evaluating the changes in behavior which may result from such techniques.

To put into proper perspective the variables of the therapy process, we must investigate relevant research in a number of related fields, in addition to traditional psychotherapy research. This should include other "influencing" processes such as: "brainwashing," hypnosis, "placebos," role-taking, sensory deprivation, attitude influence, verbal operant conditioning, motor operant conditioning, and subliminal perception. The process of psychotherapy is an integral part of a broader

[1] From the Behavioral Research Laboratory, VA Hospital, Palo Alto. The preparation of this paper was facilitated by support, in part, from Research Grant M-2458 from the National Institute of Mental Health, Public Health Service, through Stanford University. The author wishes to express his appreciation to his colleagues Leonard Ullmann, Robert Weiss, and Paul Ekman for their valuable assistance in the conception, design, and analysis of data of the various studies in this project.

61

psychology of behavior control (Frank, 1961; McConnell[2]; Meerloo, 1956; Rotter, 1960; Sargant, 1957).

In recent years, this point of view has become increasingly prominent in a wide range of both theoretical and research papers. A series of earlier papers and books had placed psychotherapy within the framework of learning or social reinforcement theory (Dollard & Miller, 1950; Mowrer, 1953; Schaffer & Lazarus, 1952; Shaw, 1948; Shoben, 1949). However, learning theory approaches usually limit themselves to the reinterpretation or translation of the ongoing therapy process into learning theory terminology, and as such, offer little in the way of relevant new research techniques into the process. More recent works (Bachrach, in press; Bandura, 1961; Frank, 1958, 1959a, 1961; Kanfer, 1961; Krasner, 1955; Lunden, 1961; Marmor, 1961; Salzinger, in press; Shaw, 1961) have moved sharply in the direction of interpreting the therapist as one who manipulates and controls the therapy situation by his knowledge and use of learning techniques in a social reinforcement situation. This approach to psychotherapy research is implicit in verbal operant conditioning studies (Krasner, 1958a; Salzinger, 1959) which have been strongly influenced by the work of Skinner (1953a, 1953b, 1957, 1958), and Keller and Schoenfeld (1950). These studies have features in common that distinguish them as a unique body of research. In verbal operant conditioning, $S$ is required to emit verbal behavior as part of a given task, and $E$ reinforces a preselected class of $S$'s verbal behavior by carefully controlled verbal and/or nonverbal behavioral cues. The conditioning of verbal behavior is developing as a major technique for systematically exploring variables of interpersonal situations. Relevant studies will be cited as they illuminate the psychology of behavior control.

[2] McConnell, J. V. Persuasion and behavioral change. Unpublished manuscript, 1960.

Historically, in the conceptualization of therapy, major emphasis was placed on the role and attributes of the patient, with relatively little regard for the therapist's characteristics, except that he be a well-trained person who was warm and "accepting." If anything, the therapist variable was to be controlled by removing the therapist's personality from the therapy situation by his own analysis, which would clear him of any involvement or "illegal" influence on the patient. Even the seating arrangements, with the therapist located *behind* the patient on the couch, was calculated to take the therapist "out" of the situation. Then, later writers began to push the therapist back into the therapy situation by emphasis on the "relationship," or the therapist role as a "participant observer" (Sullivan, 1947). The current reinforcement viewpoint de-emphasizes the uniqueness of the role of the patient, while pushing to the fore the role of the therapist and his interaction with the patient.

In the literature, there is a growing acceptance of the therapist as being in a controlling role. For example, Rogers (Rogers & Skinner, 1956) is willing to concede, perhaps reluctantly, that "in client-centered therapy, we are deeply engaged in the prediction and influencing of behavior, or even the control of behavior. As therapists, we institute certain attitudinal conditions, and the client has relatively little voice in the establishment of these conditions. We predict that if these conditions are instituted, certain behavioral consequences will ensue in the client." Haley (1959) interprets psychoanalytical psychotherapy as being a "controlling type of therapy." He suggests that "the therapist must take control of what happens in his relationship with the patient," and "to control a relationship a person must be in a position to establish the rules for what is to happen between himself and another person." Haley cites the works of Lindner, Rosen, and Erikson as examples of what he calls "New Style Directive Therapy."

Thus, from two "schools" which might be expected to refuse to acknowledge that all psychotherapy is directive in nature, the "nondirective" and the "psychoanalytical," there is tacit recognition from at least some writers of the controlling aspects of the therapist's behavior (Marmor, 1961). Rogers, however, in his symposium discussion with Skinner (1956), contends that the therapist's goal is to establish a self-directing or self-controlling patient. Skinner, on the other hand, feels that this is unrealistic, and that the controlling forces on the patient will continue to come from the patient's environment.

Gill and Brenman (1948) point out that the "raw data in psychotherapeutic research is inevitably influenced by the therapist's views . . . the subtleties of showing interest in certain kinds of material, often not consciously detected either by therapist or patient, are manifold. This may include a questioning glance, a shifting of visual focus, a well-timed 'mm-hmm,' a scarcely perceptible nod, or even a clearing of the throat. The therapist's conception of what his interpersonal relationship with a patient should be will also seriously influence the kind of material he obtains. If one therapist believes he should be 'friendly' and another that he should be 'distant,' the raw data obtained by each will obviously differ."

Therapists have usually recognized that they are dealing primarily with "talk," "word." Shaffer and Lazarus (1952) point out that "the techniques of getting the patient to talk and to continue to talk must be the real core of the treatment." Verbal behavior can be approached systematically in research with the advent of verbal conditioning techniques and other techniques of analyzing of verbal behavior, such as content analysis (Murray, 1954; Auld & Murray, 1955; Auld & White, 1959); grammatical characterizations (Goldman-Eisler, 1952, 1954; Lorenz & Cobb, 1953); word-counting and verbal input-output procedures (Mowrer, 1953a; Lennard, Calogeras, & Hendin, 1957); interaction chronographs (Saslow & Matarazzo, 1959); and others (Bales, 1950; Dibner, 1956; Dittmann, 1952; Glad, 1959; Grossman, 1952; Leary, 1957; Mahl, 1956, 1959; Palmore, Lennard, & Hendin, 1959; Starkweather, 1956a, 1956b; Whitehorn & Betz, 1954). Further, Skinner's (1957) definition of verbal behavior as "behavior reinforced through the mediation of other persons," points up the social learning involved in verbal behavior and places it squarely within the bounds of a reinforcement approach to psychotherapy research (Bachrach, in press; Kanfer, 1960; Krasner, 1955; Salzinger, in press).

If we are to conceive of psychotherapy as a process involving reinforcement procedures, then the major research task is to investigate the conditions under which the reinforcement procedure is most effective. These variables involved can be considered under three categories: (a) variables related directly to therapist characteristics, (b) situational variables, (c) therapist-patient interaction variables.

The "therapist characteristics" variables include: (a) the personal characteristics of the therapist, such as sex, personality, prestige, and socioeconomic status, (b) the specific influences on the therapist's concept of his role, such as his value and ethical system, and his formal and informal training, (c) the special techniques used by the therapist. The situational variables include the environmental setting and "atmosphere" in which the reinforcement process is taking place. The interaction variables are the result of the interaction of the therapist behavior with various characteristics of the patient population, such as diagnostic category, personality, response class, and awareness.

## THERAPIST CHARACTERISTICS

*Personal*

The effectiveness of the interpersonal influencing process is related directly to the personal characteristics of the "influencer." These characteristics include: age, sex, personality, appearance, voice quality, prestige, and socioeconomic status. These are all characteristics that can be varied, and can be interrelated with variables of the situation and of the "influencee" to determine most effective reinforcement combinations.

*Personality.* The literature is replete with literally hundreds of adjectives descriptive of the personality of the ideal therapist. However, the number of research studies investigating the influence of therapist personality upon patient behavior is relatively small. The usual approach involves investigation by content analysis of correlational relationships between: (*a*) therapist personality characteristics, such as "warmth," "conflict," or "anxiety level," and (*b*) aspects of patient behavior, such as "staying in therapy" or "expressions of hostility" (Aronson, 1953; Bandura, 1956; Cutler, 1958; Fiedler, 1953; Ford, 1959; Hiler, 1958; Parloff, 1956).

Another research approach to the investigation of the interpersonal influencing process has been that of verbal operant conditioning. This approach is potentially more productive than content analysis approaches because of the ability to manipulate experimental variables, and to break out of the confines of the circularity of reasoning inherent in the more traditional "protocol" bound investigations.

For example, verbal conditioning studies have been used to explore the differences in E characteristics as they differentially affect S behavior. Binder, McConnell, and Sjoholm (1957) found differences in the effectiveness of two Es who differed sharply in physical, sexual, and personality

characteristics. An attractive appearing, petite, female was significantly more effective in conditioning hostile words than a husky, ex-Marine male, although both were able to achieve conditioning. Ferguson and Buss (1960) follow up the study by Binder by using a male and female E reinforcing hostile words. These Es varied their behavior to the Ss and found that it was the aggressiveness, not the sex, of E that led to significant differences in S's responsivity. In both studies the differences in effectiveness were hypothesized to be related to specific differences in physical characteristics of E. In contrast, Matarazzo, Saslow, and Pareis (1960) found that two Es differing in age, professional background, and attitude toward verbal conditioning obtained the same verbal conditioning effects.

Kanfer (1958) approaches this same problem in a slightly different manner. He found that in addition to status and physical characteristics, another source of variability was the *ability* of E to delineate a verbal class and to identify its class members. Since reinforcing operations usually must immediately follow the emitted response, quick decisions by E are required in classifying verbal material. Learning in such situations would thus be more variable than learning of easily discriminable responses which are not subject to interpretation by E. Kanfer suggests that E's role as a reinforcing agent in clinical situations such as therapy interviews, might vary as a function of his *perception* of the client's attitudes as inferred from the client's verbal behavior.

Krasner, Ullmann, Weiss, and Collins (1961) extended these studies by testing two hypotheses: (*a*) that different Es can obtain the same verbal conditioning effects, and (*b*) that different Es can obtain similar correlations between S's conditionability and S's response to a personality inventory. Two of the Es used were male Ph.D.s and the third E was a female A.B. The results indicated that all three $Es$ obtained an increase in the use of emotional words from operant to reinforced trials, but this increase was significant only for the two male Ph.D. examiners. Correlations between $S$'s responsivity to verbal conditioning and $S$'s scores on personality measures were obtained for each of the three individual $Es$. The three $Es$ did not differ significantly in the correlations they obtained, thus pointing up the stability on this type of measure of responsivity to verbal conditioning. A technique is thus being developed which can be used to investigate the effects of $E$'s personality as it interacts both with $S$ responsivity and with $S$ personality measures. Although in this particular study (Krasner et al., 1961) $E$'s attributes of prestige, sex, or personality were not separated, the technique can readily be adapted to exploring the effects of differences in these kinds of $E$ personal attributes.

An important study in this direction is Sapolsky's (1960) use of verbal conditioning to explore systematically the effects of the therapist variable in a factorial design. Sapolsky used the Schutz FIRO-B Scale of interpersonal "needs" to determine the relative "compatibility" of two given individuals. He hypothesized that the influence process in verbal conditioning would be most effective when $S$'s and $E$'s "needs" were compatible with each other. In one study, he assigned students as $Ss$ and as $Es$, on a basis of compatibility of personality "needs" for one group, and incompatibility of "needs" for another. Results were that during the acquisition period the compatible group conditioned, whereas incompatible $Ss$–$Es$ did not. During the extinction period ($E$ out of room), compatible $Ss$ did not extinguish in their use of reinforced pronouns, whereas incompatible $Ss$ increased their use of the pronouns to the level obtained by the compatible $Ss$. A second study, similarly designed, instead of com-

patibility, used an experimental "set" of high personal "attraction" on the part of the $Ss$. The resulting curves in this study were almost identical with those in the first study. The implications of these studies for the influencing process are: ($a$) the influencing process is most effective when the personality of the $S$ and the $E$ are "compatible," ($b$) the influencing process is most effective when the $S$ expects or has the "set" that he will like the $E$, ($c$) the influencing process, even with an incompatible $E$, is effective when he is physically removed, and ($d$) the relationship between $S$ and $E$ can be experimentally manipulated.

In a design also investigating the interaction of examiner-subject personality, Sarason[3] found a significant interaction between hostile $Es$, hostile responses, and hostile $Ss$. Campbell (1960) also investigated this interaction by using nurses who had previously been exposed to verbal conditioning as examiners with patients as subjects in a verbal conditioning task.

Strupp (1960) expresses the viewpoint that the therapist personality is almost inextricably interwoven with his technique and that it is extremely difficult, if not impossible, to determine the particular antecedent of a given therapeutic result. The kind of conditioning research being described, however, would hold constant the two variables, personality and technique, and enable us to determine antecedents of specific results.

These verbal conditioning studies emphasize earlier findings of the importance of the $E$ variables, and offer techniques for investigating in detailed analysis these variables in interpersonal situations. Implicit in these types of studies is the assumption that various gross therapist variables, such as sex, appearance, and status, can be reduced to a few dimensions of $E$'s influence on $S$ and can be investi-

[3] Sarason, I. G. Individual difference and situational variables in verbal conditioning. Unpublished manuscript, 1961.

gated independently or in various combinations. Further, implicit is the belief that there is no aspect of the reinforcement "machine" which cannot be taken apart to see what makes it tick.

*"Placebo" effects.* Essential to the most meaningful application of reinforcement theory to psychotherapy is the inclusion of the implications of a phenomenon usually termed the "placebo" effect. Reports on the effects of placebos have culminated in the excellent review by Shapiro (1960) of the history of the placebo effects, and the important studies by Frank (1959a, 1959b), Gliedman, Nash, Imber, Stone, and Frank (1958), and Whitehorn (1958).

Shapiro's (1960) review starts with a definition of the "placebo" effect as the "psychological, physiological, or psychophysiological effect of any medication or procedure given with therapeutic intent, which is independent of or minimally related to the pharmacological effect of the medication or to the specific effects of the procedure, and which operates through a psychological mechanism." He points out that until recently the majority of the cures effected by physicians were due to this "placebo" effect. He contends that the physician actually helped his patient not through the ritual and drug which he may have given, but rather by something "inherent in the doctor-patient relationship." "The great lesson, then, of medical history is that the placebo has always been the norm of medical practice, and it was only occasionally and at great intervals that anything really serviceable, such as the cure of scurvy by fresh fruits, was introduced into medical practice." In discussing the implications of this "placebo" effect for psychotherapy and psychiatry, Shapiro cites the well known fact that a large variety of different methods have been reported as being successful in bringing about therapeutic behavior changes. This would certainly imply some communality in behavior cutting across all techniques.

Shapiro quotes Janet's views on the factors in the patient, physician, and situation, which underlie therapeutic success: "in the patient—enthusiasm, faith, belief, feelings in general, power of the imagination, expectant attention, faith in authority, the importance to the patient of being the object of investigation; in the physician—undoubting enthusiasm, faith, and belief, the unconscious personality of the healer; in the situation—the ritual, mystery, and strangeness of the proceedings and the situation, changed environment, repetitive education, and suggestibility factors." These variables are similar to those under discussion, but under less specifiable terminology. Shapiro concludes with a suggestion which is of importance in attempting to determine experimentally the influence of the "placebo" effects in a research setting: "the principles underlying the effect of this variable can be extended to non-therapeutic experimental situations which involve an interpersonal relationship with an investigator, or even some symbolic representative of the latter."

Frank (1958, 1959a), Frank, Gliedman, Imber, Stone, and Nash (1959), Rosenthal and Frank (1956), and Whitehorn (1958) stress the role of faith, expectancy, and confidence both in achieving effective results and as basic ingredients for the "placebo" effect. Frank (1959a) says that in seeking communality in the therapy process the "common feature is the patient's reliance on the therapist to relieve his distress." He terms the expectancy of relief to be strong enough to justify the term "faith." He points out that there are two attitudes of the therapist which foster the patient's confidence in him: (*a*) his faith in the patient's capacity to benefit from treatment, and (*b*) his confidence in his theory and method of treatment. For example, the replies of psychotherapists to a questionnaire by Wolff (1956) indicated that 70% believe their particular form of therapy to be the best. Frank goes on to conclude that there is a good possibility that the emotional state of trust or "faith," in itself, can sometimes produce far-reaching and permanent changes in attitude or body states, although he points out that this phenomenon cannot be predicted or controlled, and cites as evidence religious conversions and miracle cures. Finally, Frank is careful to state that he does not believe that all, or even most, of the process of psychotherapy can be explained on the basis of trust or faith: "there are obviously many important determinants of the processes and outcomes of treatment besides the direct influence of the therapist based on faith and trust in him." Frank contends that the therapist's influence over the patient arises from this strong faith and favorable expectations strengthened by cultural factors, aspects of the referral or intake process, cues in the therapy situation, and the therapist's confidence in his ability to help. Cartwright and Cartwright (1958) take issue with Frank's emphasis on the role of patient's expectancies as a major determinant of the therapist's influence and his concern for the "placebo" effect. They feel that the terms "faith" and "belief" are too nebulous to specify objectively.

The reinforcement approach offers the techniques for translating the concepts of faith, expectancy, and other unknown factors involved in the "placebo" effect into terms which would allow for systematic investigation. The same may also be said for the kinds of therapist personality characteristics discussed by Strupp (1960) as essential in the therapeutic situation—integrity, honesty, and dedication—these are analyzable in terms of behaviors associated with effective reinforcement.

The obvious point generally missed in discussing the "placebo" effect is that one person's behavior is serving as a source of reinforcement for another's behavior. In analyzing the behavior of the therapist, Krasner (1955) has called attention to the one common factor in *all* psychotherapy, the presence of another person listening, paying attention, showing some interest. The therapist focuses more attention on those aspects of the patient's verbal behavior which his particular orientation calls for, but in any case, he displays a generalized form of behavior cues which may be called "attention." In speculating why these behavioral cues should serve as a means of reinforcing behavior, Skinner's (1953a) classification of attention as a generalized reinforcer is appropriate. The attention of other people is reinforcing because it is a necessary condition for receiving other more specific reinforcements from them. Only people who are "attending" reinforce behavior. It is reinforcement of an intermittent nature, not dependent on the momentary condition of the organism and continually being used to shape the behavior of others.

Ferster (1961) develops Skinner's notion about the use of generalized reinforcers in an analysis of the effects of positive reinforcement on autistic children. Ferster points out that parental responses, such as smiling, "good," and "right," can have little effect on the child if there is not a history by which, on these occasions, many different forms of the child's performance have produced various reinforcers. Without the parental generalized reinforcement, educational processes and positive parental control are all but impossible. This control is normally carried out by the use of praise, parental attention, coupled with a mild form of threat of discontinuing the reinforcers.

The therapist or influencer is a "reinforcement machine," which by its very presence is supplying generalized reinforcement at all times in the therapy situation, irrespective of the particular technique or personality involved. In psychotherapy, there is a subtle manipulation of the patient's behavior by the therapist's reinforcing behavior, often without awareness of either person of what is taking place. This is the basic ingredient in the so-called "placebo" effect. There is no need to postulate a mysterious interactional effect, but rather what is taking place are the kinds of behavior control which are being cited throughout this paper. Thus, the "placebo" effect (generalized reinforcement) *is* the common element in all influencing processes. There is reluctance by most researchers to take the final plunge and eliminate the last drop of faith, hope, and warmth, from psychotherapy—that last element of a mysterious unknown, and probably unknowable. But, until the therapist recognizes the full implications and potentialities of a psychology of behavior control, then the aura of mysticism which still clings to psychotherapy will remain.

*Role-taking.* Further conditions affecting reinforcement effectiveness include attitudinal variables such as those of the therapist's and patient's role conceptualizations of themselves and their role expectancies of each other (Krasner, 1959). Psychotherapy studies frequently cite the self-confidence and assurance of the therapist as having an important effect on the patient. The elements that go into producing the therapist "self-assured role," such as personality, physical characteristics, prestige, training techniques, and socioeconomic status, are involved in the building of a particular "reinforcement machine" and determine its effectiveness and the kinds of behavior it will select to reinforce. On the patient's part, Sarbin's (1950) hypothesis about the variables associated with learning of the patient role are relevant. Sarbin feels that this would include favorable motivation, ability to perceive roles, and ability to

take roles, all of which are also associated with learning the role of the hypnotic subject. "Role-taking" ability is an important aspect both of patient and therapist personality and, as such, is measurable and manipulatable (Krasner, 1959; Krasner, Weiss, & Ullmann, 1961).

*Prestige.* The prestige or status variable readily lends itself to behavioral analysis by conditioning techniques. This can be done by the role expectancies created by instructional set under which E (or therapist) is presented to S (or patient). One difficulty is separating role attributes from other E characteristics, and this can be done by the same E being presented in differing roles, without E knowing what role expectancies S has of him.

As an example of this approach, Ekman and Friesen (1960) investigated the effects of *status* of the E, holding personality constant, as an influence on verbal conditioning effectiveness. They performed a series of studies in which an officer and enlisted man served as Es, both in their own role, and switching roles. They were unable to obtain consistent differences in either conditioning or extinction attributed to either the status or personality of the Es, although both obtained significant conditioning. They concluded that in the particular army setting in which they worked, everyone giving "tests" to recruits had "status" even if he was an enlisted man. This points up the relevance of S's expectancies toward E and E's role. Examiner "status" or lack of it is also considered in the interpretation of the results of other verbal conditioning studies (Daily, 1953; Marion, 1956; Krasner, Ullmann, Weiss, & Collins, 1961).

### Influences on Therapist Role

*Values and ethics.* Most therapists are uncomfortable in a role labeled as a "controller" or "manipulator" of behavior. The evidence, however, is that this is an accurate description of what the therapist role actually is. For example: Sheehan

(1953) and Graham (1960) both report studies in which key Rorschach categories of successful patients changed significantly in the direction of those of the therapist. Rosenthal (1955) found that "improved" patients changed their "moral" values in the direction of the therapist. Palmore, Lennard, and Hendin (1959) report increasing similarity in verbal behavior between patients and therapists as therapy proceeds. Stekel (1951) points out that patients' dreams always confirm the theoretical formulations of their therapist. Heine (1953) reports a study of three different approaches to therapy in which the patients' subjective report of the changes which took place within themselves did not differ, while there were sharp differences along "school" lines as to the theoretical explanation of these changes by the patients. Whitehorn (1959) points out that successful psychotherapy involves leadership "toward preferred values, toward the therapist's conception of what constitutes value in life." The evidence is strong that the therapist by virtue of his role has the power to influence and control the behavior and values of other human beings. For the therapist not to accept this situation and to be continually unaware of influencing effects of his behavior on his patients would in itself be "unethical."

Skinner's comments (Rogers & Skinner, 1956) on the general problem of the therapist as a controller are relevant to consideration of the ethical problems involved. Frequently, an important reinforcement for the therapist himself is his success in manipulating human behavior. He may be involved in proving the value of a particular theory of behavior or of psychotherapy. There is always the possibility that the therapist control will be misused. The counter-control which discourages the misuse of power is represented by the ethical standards and practices of the organized profession of psychotherapy. Skinner feels that it is this

danger of misuse which explains the popularity of theories of psychotherapy which deny that human behavior can be controlled and refuse to accept responsibility of control. However, to refuse to accept control is merely to leave control in other hands. Skinner does not agree with Rogers that the individual always holds within himself the solution to his problems. If the individual were the product of training and education which have effectively supplied the inner kinds of solutions which Rogers advocates, then it would be unlikely that the individual would be a therapy candidate. But, as is more likely, if the individual were the product of excessive or damaging kinds of control or extreme deprivation, it is unlikely that an acceptable solution was available within himself, but must come from environmental contacts. Kanfer (1961) also comments on the motivation of the therapist, pointing up the long-range source of reinforcement as lying in the "professional role" and all of its attractions for the therapist. Krasner (1961a) has pointed out that the investigation of "values" of behavior controllers such as psychotherapists as they are related to other variables such as "effectiveness" can, and should be, investigated by experimental techniques.

*Socioeconomic status.* Only brief mention will be made of the by now accepted fact that there are important socioeconomic influences on the social role of the therapist. The New Haven studies (Hollingshead & Redlich, 1958) have pointed out the different social and economic class attitudes toward the importance of psychotherapy and the differential assignment of patients to psychotherapy according to social class. This further emphasizes the cultural conditioning of therapy role expectancies, both in the patient as well as in the therapist. Auld's (1952) study of the influence of social class on personality test responses is also quite relevant to viewing psychotherapy within the context of social role expectancies. This is a variable which is often acknowledged, but to which very little research has been directed.

The reinforcement paradigm enables us to determine how the socioeconomic status of the therapist influences his patient interactions. It may be surmised, for example, that the particular response class reinforced or punished will be determined by the therapist's class morality background. Further, the reinforcing value of therapist "prestige" does not exist for all potential patient groups. A group such as delinquents may consider a therapist to be a "square," thus decreasing the likelihood of reinforcement from such a source being effective.

*Training and experience.* A major variable which must enter into evaluating the therapist role is that of his background and specific training. This may be put in terms of investigating the information that has been programed into the "reinforcement machine." It is this information which will determine the probability of the influencer responding to one kind of behavior, rather than another, and the contingencies related to his effectiveness. Training represents the conscious efforts of a profession to "program" future therapists. There has been recent investigation of the effect of training variables as they have influenced the psychotherapist's behavior (Ashby, Ford, Guerney, & Guerney, 1957; Fey, 1958; Fiedler, 1950, 1951; Holt & Luborsky, 1958; Lakin & Lebovitz, 1958; Strupp, 1955a, 1957a). The particular "school" of training, the professional discipline, the presence or absence of personal analysis, and the therapist's experience, have been found to be related to the types of verbal behavior and techniques used by the therapist and his effectiveness in changing patient behavior (Strupp, 1955a, 1955b, 1955c, 1957a, 1957b, 1958a, 1958b, 1960).

Studies on the effects of training highlight the kinds of information that is

programed into the therapist-reinforcer. They also, however, point out that this particular "machine" is self-correcting and continually modifying its own behavior, based on the kinds of feedback or reinforcement received from patients, other therapists, and living experiences.

The verbal conditioning technique offers considerable promise for investigating the influence of training on therapist techniques. Krasner (1958b) reports a technique of selecting a given response class in a storytelling situation and manipulating it with selected cue reinforcement by E. He reported that changes in a preselected class of verbal behavior vary as a function of the systematic applications of behavior cues by E. Using this technique, Dinoff, Rickard, Salzberg, and Sipprelle (1960) developed an experimental design in which categories of verbal behavior comparable to different therapeutic approaches could be observed, reinforced, and measured to determine the effects of the reinforcement. Dinoff et al. demonstrated that varying theoretical positions may direct the verbalizations of Ss into areas in keeping with E's own "theoretical biases." They found that the frequency of responding was significantly increased as predicted, in the three response categories — "Environment," "Patient," and "Therapist." Further, the authors suggest that their technique is an objective, reliable, and essentially content-free way of manipulating and scoring therapeutic verbal responses. These studies point the way to future research in which therapist behavior can be deliberately programed and manipulated by the kinds of information and role-sets to which the therapist (E) is exposed (Krasner, 1961b).

Winokur (1955) points out the similarity between extracting "confessions," as done in "brainwashing," and certain professional situations such as psychotherapy. He goes further in this direction by interpreting the supervisor-student relationship in psychotherapy as an example of "brainwashing." To reduce anxiety, "prisoners change their thinking to conform with that of their 'captors.'" He feels that the training situation (applicable to psychiatrists, psychologists, and social workers) is a forced modification of both behavior and thinking to conform to that of the teacher-supervisor. The evidence he cites is anecdotal, rather than experimental, but it is quite provocative.

*Therapist Techniques*

The therapist has a broad spectrum of behavioral techniques available to him, limited only by his ingenuity in varying his behavior and the setting. The traditional way of classifying therapist techniques is by the "schools of therapy" approach. One way of investigating these differences would be to develop a classification of techniques which describe the characteristics of reinforcement.

*Type of reinforcement.* (*a*) Positive: These are cues controlled by the therapist so as to *reward* specific responses of the patient. These may range from generalized reinforcers, such as head nodding or "mm-hmm," to more specific reinforcement such as tokens (Buss & Gerjuoy, 1958; Buss, Gerjuoy, & Zusman, 1958; Ferguson & Buss, 1960), or candy (Peters & Jenkins, 1954), or cigarettes (Lindsley, 1956, 1960). They may also include specific interpretive statements which expressly verbalize the contingencies in a patient's behavior. Such reinforcements may be difficult to classify as to whether they are rewarding or punishing. (*b*) Negative (punishing): These may range from verbal admonishments, such as "you are wrong" (Kanfer & Karas, 1959), through subtler head shaking and "huh-huh" (Greenspoon, 1955; Hartman, 1955; Mock, 1957), to actual physical pain-evoking stimuli, such as shock. (*c*) Negative (withdrawing of positive reinforcement [Ferster, 1957]): Illustrations of this would include techniques which vary "silences" (Saslow & Matarazzo, 1959), and techniques which use extinction

(withdrawal of reinforcement) as a deliberate controlling device (Weiss, Krasner, & Ullmann, 1960).

It should be emphasized that the same stimulus is not necessarily reinforcing under all conditions; for example, "good" would appear to be an excellent illustration of a positive verbal reinforcer. However, there is evidence (Cohen & Cohen, 1960) that "good" is not necessarily reinforcing for schizophrenics. The reinforcement history of the schizophrenic is such that "good" may have taken on aversive properties (Atkinson, 1957; Robinson, 1957). "Mm-hmm" is probably a more effective reinforcer with schizophrenics because it does not have the social connotations of "approval" that "good" has acquired for the schizophrenic (Krasner & Ullmann, 1958). On the other hand, Hildum and Brown (1956) found that with a college population, "good" was an effective reinforcer, whereas "mm-hmm" was not. Mandler and Kaplan (1956) found that the effectiveness of a reinforcer such as "mm-hmm" was related to $S$'s subjective interpretation of the stimuli as being either "positive" or "negative."

If generalized reinforcers are effective because of the "need" for them by the patient, then this can be controlled by deprivation procedures (Gewirtz & Baer, 1957, 1958a, 1958b; Peters & Jenkins, 1954; Walters & Karal, 1960). Various "brainwashing" reports (Lifton, 1956, 1957a, 1957b) also illustrate the method of depriving $S$s of particular needs so that they may be more amenable to being influenced by techniques designed to meet the artificially created need.

*Medium of expression.* (*a*) Verbal: This is the most frequent in therapy and would include the range of cues from "mm-hmm" through "good," "right," "fine," "paraphrasing" (Verplanck, 1955), "repetition" (Fahmy, 1953), to interpretative statements of behavior contingencies. (*b*) Gestural: These cues include head nodding (Mock, 1957), head shaking (Hartman, 1955), smiling (Verplanck, 1955), and forward movement of body (Ekman, 1958). (c) Mechanical: These may include light flashes (Ball, 1952; Greenspoon, 1954; Nuthmann, 1957), a buzzer (Ball, 1952; Greenspoon, 1954), a bell tone (McNair, 1957), or mechanical gadgets delivering objects such as candy (Lindsley, 1956). In some instances, e.g., McNair, the mechanical device was labeled as signifying approval. (d) Symbolic: These include poker chips or tokens to be turned in for cigarettes or candy (Buss, Gerjuoy, & Ferguson, 1958). Various combinations of these mediums of expressing the reinforcement may be explored to determine the most effective combinations.

*Schedules of reinforcement.* In the therapy situation, timing of therapist behavior vis-à-vis patient verbalizations is of major importance. The therapist must make a quick decision whether a response of the patient belongs to the class to be reinforced. If so, is this the time to reinforce it? A failure to do so may extinguish the response, at least for the moment. Thus in an analysis of the effectiveness of the cueing of E, scheduling of this cueing is a major factor. The effectiveness of various intermittent reinforcement schedules has been demonstrated with laboratory animals. Ferster and Skinner (1957) have provided a detailed description of such schedules. There have been successful applications of various schedules to reinforcing of verbal behavior (Bachrach, Candland, & Gibson, 1959; Grossberg, 1956; Kanfer, 1954, 1958; McNair, 1957; O'Donnell, 1959).

Kanfer (1958) compared three types of reinforcement schedules in a verbal conditioning situation and concluded that reinforcing behavior of a therapist, such as agreement, reassurance, or approval, might be regulated to occur on a ratio schedule, if it is desirable that a client continue to make similar responses. On the other hand, he points out, if flexibility in topics were desired, characterized by a high rate of talk about a given topic only when the therapist supplies a cue for its relevance, then an interval schedule would be more effective in controlling the desired behavior pattern.

O'Donnell (1959) obtained significant results in conditioning mildly hostile verbs using "good" as a reinforcement, with a reinforcement ratio of $66\frac{2}{3}\%$. Bachrach et al. (1960) applied "pseudo-fixed interval schedules" in a verbal conditioning situation. The Ss were reinforced only during the last 30 seconds of each successive 1-minute period. Although their results were somewhat equivocal, they concluded that social behavior may be examined as a function of the schedule of reinforcement, but that a mechanical reinforcer may be necessary to assure accurate programing.

In his review of verbal conditioning studies, Krasner (1958a) divided the response class into four types of tasks demanded of the S: saying words or numbers, storytelling and interviews, completing sentences, and test-like situations. In three of these tasks the responses may be considered to be discrete, whereas in the storytelling and interview type of situation (Dinoff et al. 1960; Krasner, 1958b; Mock, 1957; Pisoni & Salzinger, 1960; Salzinger & Pisoni, 1958, 1960; Salzinger, Pisoni, & Feldman, 1960; Verplanck, 1955; and others), there is a continuous flow of conversation. E must be alert to make a discriminative response and must quickly make a number of decisions as to his own behavior. In such situations, the rate of reinforcement is rarely continuous. This is virtually impossible, and not necessarily desirable. In a storytelling situation, Krasner (1958b) found that approximately 80% of reinforceable responses were actually reinforced. Tobias (1960), using the same type of situation, found that only 76%

of the animal responses which he was reinforcing were actually followed by reinforcing stimuli. What is taking place in situations requiring continuous verbalization, as in psychotherapy, is an intermittent reinforcement schedule, which is more effective, and more realistic, than a continuous reinforcement schedule.

Both the amount and patterning of the reinforcement are also important aspects of the mediating contingencies. Salzinger (in press) reports conditioning with both normal and schizophrenic Ss who receive a *large* amount of reinforcement in contrast to failure to condition in Ss receiving a *small* amount of reinforcement. Patterning of reinforcement can also be used as a controlling technique in itself (Weiss, Krasner, & Ullmann, 1960).

SITUATIONAL VARIABLES

The situation variables are manipulatable environmental and interpersonal *conditions* under which the therapist influences the patient. They include: the "atmosphere" in which therapy takes place; the "set" which is created for the patient; antecedent contacts between therapist and patient; sensory input permitted the patient; and "ambiguity." All are controlled by the therapist, often without awareness of their effect.

*Atmosphere*

An important element of the situation in which the influencing process occurs may be labeled "atmosphere." This refers to the class of variables dealing with the S's attitude toward the E and/or toward the influencing session itself. These are important in the "rapport" which is so frequently mentioned as a necessary element of psychotherapy. Several studies have attempted to manipulate experimentally the emotional atmosphere of the conditioning session. Kanfer and Karas (1959) provide a success and a failure condition on a preconditioning task. Sub-

sequent conditioning scores were not significantly affected by the success and failure manipulations, even though Ss in the failure condition reported that E had annoyed them and had made them feel tense. They note that their failure condition had the effect of increasing S's motivation to try harder and thus Ss may have been more responsive to the E's directions during the conditioning session. The Sapolsky (1960) study previously described can be seen as manipulating "atmospheres" by instructional set to affect the influencing process.

Weiss, Krasner, and Ullmann (1960) investigated the effects on responsivity of manipulating the atmosphere under which conditioning took place. College students told TAT-like stories during which E verbally reinforced the use of emotional words (Ullmann & McFarland, 1957). Following this, hostile and neutral emotional atmospheres were experimentally induced, after which the verbal conditioning was repeated. The induced hostile atmosphere resulted in a decrease in responsiveness. This study indicated that by using a validated response class and a validated procedure for inducing hostility, atmospheres can have a demonstrable effect on conditioning. Thus "atmosphere" as an important variable in the influencing situation can be manipulated and experimentally investigated.

*Antecedent Contacts*

Gewirtz and Baer (1957, 1958a, 1958b) report a series of studies with children, investigating the relationship between antecedent social contacts between Es and Ss, and subsequent effectiveness of social reinforcement. Walters and Karal (1960) and Kanfer and Karas (1959) extend this approach with adults. Kanfer and Karas (1959) found that Ss with prior experience with E, irrespective of the type of experience, were more effectively conditioned than Ss having no prior experience with E. The authors suggest that if additional contacts increase the effectiveness of the conditioning process, this may be one source of the increased control by the therapist as the treatment process continues. Solley and Long (1958) also report obtaining significant verbal conditioning effects with "mm-hmm" only when E carries out "chit-chat," or informal "rapport"—getting conversation with S prior to the conditioning sessions. They conclude that conditioning results only when antecedent contacts have been made.

Walters and Karal (1960) report a series of studies investigating the hypotheses of Gewirtz and Baer that social deprivation is a motivating condition and, consequently, social reinforcement cues would be more effective following social deprivation than following social satiation. The results of Walters and Karal are somewhat equivocal, but generally do *not* provide support for the concept of a motivational state resulting from social deprivation. They suggest that social deprivation may be a special case of sensory deprivation in which Ss are deprived of social contact. They point out the possibility that some effects of sensory deprivation studies attributed now primarily to the lack of visual, auditory, and tactual stimulation can actually be attributed to the absence of social contacts, and consequent anxiety. Walters and his colleagues (Walters & Ray, 1960; Walters & Quinn, 1960; Walters, Marshall, & Shooter, 1960) also report a series of other studies relating social isolation, anxiety, and susceptibility to social influence. One conclusion they reach is that social isolation has, in itself, no effect upon susceptibility to social influence, but that under the anxiety-arousing conditions, sometimes produced by social isolation, Ss can be more readily influenced than when anxiety is not present. The implicit relationship between social deprivation studies and sensory deprivation studies is relevant also to the discussion in the next section on sensory deprivation.

## Sensory Input

*Sensory deprivation.* The sensory input variable refers to the amount, variety, and kind of physical stimuli permitted the patient or "influencee." On one extreme, we have the conditions of DDD—debility, dependency, and dread, described by Farber, Harlow, and West (1957), as being a basic ingredient of the thought-reform process used by the Chinese Communists both on prisoners of war and on their own people. Farber et al. point out that the conditions of DDD lead to increasing susceptibility to conditioning. The Chinese used the DDD on an intermittent reinforcement schedule to condition prisoner expectancies. Lifton (1956, 1957a, 1957b) also describes what he terms "milieu control" in the Chinese thought-reform process. This is the control and manipulation of all communication and sensory stimulation directed to the "reformee." Lifton compares the effects of the "milieu control" on a prisoner to the effects on the sensory deprived Ss of Lilly (1956). In both processes the S is unable to check on what is reality. Having no other source of verification or information, the S has no alternative but to accept the communications which come to him. In one instance, this is the propaganda of the Chinese Communists; in the other, it is the internal push which manufactures the hallucinations which fill out his environment. The works of Hebb (1958), Heron, Doane, and Scott (1956), Azima and Cramer-Azima (1956b, 1957) and the symposium edited by Solomon (1961) further amplify these points. Hebb (1958) analyzes the effects of perceptual deprivation on human motivation. Since the adult is dependent on his sensory environment, the first approach to him in "brainwashing" is by isolation (others being sleep, fatigue, and hunger). The effects of isolation are hallucinations, disturbances of self perception, impaired intelligence test score, changes in EEG records, and visual disturbances. Such effects Hebb found to be reversible, disappearing in a few days after the isolation ends. However, after telling Ss "ridiculous" things during their state of isolation, he found that such "propaganda effects" were longer lasting. Thus, it would appear that an individual is more responsive to influence from his environment while under sensory deprivation, and less likely to extinguish behavior learned while under such conditions.

Studies by Adams, Carrera, Cooper, Gibby, and Tobey (1960) and Azima and Cramer-Azima (1956a) also use sensory deprivation procedures as such, to enhance therapeutic change in patients. Azima and Cramer-Azima (1956a) used sensory isolation as a therapeutic technique in modifying behavior of psychotic patients with problems of depersonalization. They put a variety of patients in a situation of partial sensory and expressive isolation for an average period of four days. Some of the patients appeared to have been helped by this process, others possibly worsened.

The kinds of physical stimuli conditions which the therapist controls may include: couch or easy chairs (face to face); room illumination; sound proofing; mood music; heavy carpets; bland clothing. These types of stimuli can be manipulated to make behavior control more effective. It would seem reasonable that cutting down external stimuli would enable the patient to focus on and pay more attention to therapist originated stimuli, making them more effective.

*Sensory enhancement.* On the opposite side of the sensory input continuum, there are several studies which approach psychotherapy by sensory enhancement. McReynolds, Acker, and Daily (1959) reason that if certain symptoms of schizophrenia, such as hallucinations, feelings of depersonalization, and difficulties in concentration, are the result of functional sensory deprivation, then it would be expected that "perceptual enhancement" in

schizophrenics would bring about alleviation of the symptoms indicated. In preliminary work on six patients, each participating in a number of activities designed to enhance rate of perceptual input and assimilation, the evidence points in the direction of their hypothesis. In a verbal conditioning study, Chan (1958) found that the effect of enhancing visual sensory input in the form of geometric forms, colors, algebraic signs, and Chinese characters increased the probability of susceptibility to verbal conditioning.

*Subliminal stimulation.* Under the heading of sensory input variable should also be included the studies on subliminal stimulation. These studies are relevant for the study of behavior control in at least three ways: they are essentially techniques of behavior control; they are related to learning without awareness; and they raise ethical problems. The excellent reviews by McConnell, Cutler, and McNeil (1958) and Goldiamond (1958) bring the field together in such a way that subliminal stimulation can be incorporated into the more general field of behavioral control.

*Set and Ambiguity*

A person in an influencing situation is continually seeking cues as to what is expected of him. It does not follow, however, that these cues should be clear cut for maximum effectiveness, as evidenced by studies of the importance of ambiguity in the influencing process. Frank (1959) points out that "it is in the ambiguity of the therapeutic situation, however, that its greatest potentiality for influence probably lies. Like the interrogators in thought reform, some psychotherapists convey to the patient that they know what is wrong with him, but that he must find it out for himself in order to be helped. This is one means of enlisting his participation, but it also gives the patient an ambiguous task." Bordin (1955) also sees ambiguity as part of the stimulus value of the therapist. Dibner (1958) found evidence to confirm the deduction that anxiety is positively related to ambiguity in an interpersonal relationship.

Ambiguity is closely related to the variable of "set" which can be expressed in terms of $S$'s expectancies of what is to occur during a particular influencing session. Asch (1948) reports that in his studies $S$ changes his set from "what differences can I observe between these materials" to "which of these am I expected to like and dislike." Hall (1958) found significant verbal conditioning only in $S$s who had become "ego-involved" by the instructional set. In a study by Krasner, Weiss, and Ullmann (1961) the very questioning about awareness influenced $S$'s performance. One effect of the reported awareness interview itself was to change $S$'s definition of the experimental task; that is, $E$ signaled $S$ that the latter's knowledge of what is going on was a part of the experimental situation. Thus, conditioning trials occurring after an awareness interview can be viewed as problem solving trials. This served to decrease the ambiguity for $S$, and in this study (Krasner et al., 1961) the result was a decrease in responsivity. In his investigation of the psychology of affiliation, Schacter (1959) concludes that ambiguous situations lead to a desire to be with others as a socially evaluating event which helps determine the appropriate and proper reaction. These findings are consistent in interpreting ambiguity as enhancing the reinforcing value of the therapist. The studies of Ekman, Krasner, and Ullmann[4] and Sarason and Ganzer[5] investigated the relationship between instructional set, operant level, and responsivity to reinforcement. In both studies, responsivity was manipulated by the instructional set.

[4] Ekman, P., Krasner, L., & Ullmann, L. P. The interaction of set and awareness as determinants of response to verbal conditioning. Unpublished manuscript, 1961.

[5] Sarason, I. G., & Ganzer, V. J. Anxiety, reinforcement, and experimental instructions. Unpublished manuscript, 1961.

*Group Setting*

One final note about the situation variable: the influencing process need not be limited to a one-to-one relationship (Asch, 1948; Bachrach, 1960; Cieutat, 1959; Dinoff, Horner, Kurpiewski, & Timmons, 1960; Sidowski, 1959). Asch (1948, 1956) and those using his influencing techniques have investigated the process under simulated group conditions. Bachrach et al. (1960) defined a group setting as using two $E$s working as a team of "human programers" reinforcing the third person in the group, the naive $S$. Dinoff et al. (1960) investigated the effectiveness of verbal conditioning in a group therapy situation with a schizophrenic population.

THERAPIST-PATIENT INTERACTION
VARIABLES

The "therapist variables" cannot be investigated except insofar as they interact with patient characteristics. For maximal effectiveness of the reinforcement process the following manipulable patient characteristics should be considered in the context of therapist and situational variables: type of population; personal characteristics such as age, sex, intelligence, education, personality; and socioeconomic class.

*Type of Populations*

One of the trends in verbal conditioning studies has been the extension of these techniques to adult populations other than college students and schizophrenics. This has included extension along diagnostic lines: delinquents (Cairns, 1960); mental defectives (Barnett, Pryer, & Ellis, 1959); "neurotics" (Leventhal, 1959; and Johns & Quay[6]); and along education lines: medical students (Kras-

[6] Johns, J. H., & Quay, H. C. The effect of social reward on verbal conditioning in psychopathic and neurotic military offenders. Unpublished manuscript, 1959.

ner, Ullmann, Weiss, & Collins, 1961); high school educated military trainees (Ekman & Friesen, 1960a, 1960b; Friesen & Ekman, 1960). Johns and Quay[6] report failure in conditioning a psychopathic group which was interpreted as evidence of psychopathic resistance to social reward. Systematic attempts at comparing diagnostic group responsivity are necessary as preliminary to predicting reaction to psychotherapy, and some studies have moved in this direction (Campbell, 1960; Franks, 1956; Hagen, 1959; Hartman, 1955; Johns & Quay[6]; Leventhal, 1959; O'Connor & Rawnsley, 1959; Salzinger, in press).

Although verbal conditioning techniques have been effective with this wide variety of people, there are questions as to the susceptibility of schizophrenics to conditioning procedures (Cohen & Cohen, 1960). However, both Dinoff et al. (1960) and Salzinger and Pisoni (1958) found that they could condition schizophrenics, but the effect is short-lived and extinction is rapid. Dinoff et al. suggest the use of partial reinforcement during conditioning to extend the period of extinction in schizophrenics. The authors suggest that negative findings with schizophrenics (Cohen & Cohen, 1960) may have resulted because the effect was hidden due to its brevity. Others reporting successful conditioning of schizophrenic patients include: Krasner (1958b); Krasner and Ullmann (1958); Mock (1957); Weiss, Krasner, and Ullmann (1961). Specification of type of schizophrenia and severity of illness are essential in these studies as in all research with schizophrenics.

*Patient Characteristics*

*Personality.* The relationship between S personality and S susceptibility to conditioning techniques has been investigated under a variety of conditioning procedures (Anderson, 1959; Babladelis, 1960;

Buss & Gerjuoy, 1958; Cairns, 1960; Campbell, 1960; Cushing, 1957; Daily, 1953; Ekman, 1958; Franks, 1956, 1957; Kirman, 1958; Gelfand & Winder, 1961; Matarazzo et al., 1960; McKee, 1960; Medini, 1958; O'Donnell, 1960; Sarason, 1958; Sarason & Campbell, in press; Taffel, 1955). Some studies hypothesize differentiations in responsivity along personality dimensions, such as anxiety, whereas others are nosologically oriented. Since the focus of this paper is on the therapist variable as such, we will not go further into the patient personality variables, other than to point to two types of studies which can be used to investigate the effects of the patient variable on the reinforcement process. First, there is manipulation by instruction of the therapist personality-patient personality interaction (Sapolsky, 1960). The second is a manipulation of the patient personality variable by inducing an experimental atmosphere (Weiss, Krasner, & Ullmann, 1960).

In a broader view of a psychology of behavior influence there are other important approaches to investigating the relationship between personality characteristics and susceptibility to the influencing process (Asch, 1948, 1956; Berkowitz & Lundy, 1957; Helson, Blake, Mouton, & Olmstead, 1956; Kelman, 1956; Janis, 1954). All are relevant to a psychology of behavior control and consequently to the psychotherapy process.

*Socioeconomic status.* The factors discussed above affecting the behavior of the therapist as a function of his class identification also hold for the patient, and interaction effects become crucial. Although much lip service is given to the importance of this variable, few research data are available. Imber, Frank, Gliedman, Nash, and Stone (1956) and Imber, Nash, and Stone (1959) investigated the relationship between suggestibility, social class, the acceptance, and duration of psychotherapy. Imber et al. (1956) found that suggestible patients, as measured by the Sway Test, tend to remain in psychotherapy. It was postulated that suggestible patients were influenced by the authority of the doctor in his role as expert advisor and the general prestige of the medical setting. No differences in suggestibility were found between middle- and lower-class patients, but middle-class patients who were "suggestible" were most responsive to psychotherapy in terms of rate of "staying in."

*Response class.* The specific point of interaction in the therapist-patient relationship is between the patient response class and the therapist reinforcing cue behavior. That such interaction is lawful and predictable in the therapy situation has been demonstrated in studies such as Murray (1954), Bandura, Lipsher, and Miller (1960), and others. The response class is usually the most important aspect of patient behavior which the therapist influences. Response classes that are influenceable are limited only by E's ingenuity in labeling them. In the verbal conditioning studies alone a whole variety of response classes directly relevant to psychotherapy have been shown to be influenceable under certain specified reinforcement conditions. These are: affect statements (Anderson, 1959; Buss & Durkee, 1958; Cushing, 1957; Doering, 1959; Krasner, Ullmann, Weiss, & Collins, 1961; Pisoni & Salzinger, 1960; Salzinger & Pisoni, 1958, 1960; Salzinger, Pisoni, & Feldman, 1960; Weiss, Ullmann, & Krasner, 1960); self-reference statements (Adams & Hoffman, 1960; Babladelis, 1960; Rogers, 1960); "hallucinations" (Dobie, 1959); "negative words" (Zedek, 1959); "neurotic" verbalizations (Everstine & Bendig, 1960); "early childhood memories" (Quay, 1959); references to "mother" (Krasner, 1958b; Mock, 1957); opinions and attitudes (Verplanck, 1955; Ekman, 1958); "complex" sentences (Barik & Lambert, 1960); "acceptance of self"

(Nuthmann, 1957); and "confiding responses" (Cairns, 1960).

Berg (1958) and Bachrach (in press) report work currently in progress by Greenspoon that is even more directly related to psychotherapy. This is being done within the context of a therapy interview with patients. When the patient verbalizes bizarre material, the therapist swivels his chair around, turning his back on the patient, opens his mail, or makes a telephone call. When the patient talks realistically, the therapist reinforces this rational content by leaning forward and nodding or saying "mm-hmm." Irrational material begins to drop out and material such as realistic discussion of illness increases. Greenspoon also reports observations, systematically gathered during regular counseling sessions of the therapist reinforcing patient verbalizations about a response class such as sex by looking interested and leaning forward. The number of sex references then markedly increase during the course of the interview. Rickard, Dignam, and Horner (1960) report the manipulation of verbal behavior in an actual therapeutic treatment case. Rational verbalizations in a 60-year old delusional patient were positively reinforced, while delusional material was "punished" by the therapist "looking away." A high level of rational speech was obtained, but extinction also was rapid.

Krasner and Ullmann (1958) demonstrated that E could switch from reinforcing one response class to another with a significant increment of the second class. In this study, using storytelling procedures, the response class reinforced was switched from "mother" to "father" references with the same patients, and the new reinforced response class increased significantly as a function of E's behavior.

Studies have also appeared in other areas which have demonstrated the effects of the influencing process on verbal response classes, especially those which may be termed as indicating "attitudes" or "opinions" (Asch, 1948; Back, 1951; Bergin, 1960; Helson, Blake, Mouton, & Olmstead, 1956; Hovland, Janis, & Kelley, 1953; Janis & King, 1954; Kelman, 1950, 1956, 1958; Schacter, 1959; Scott, 1957; Staats, 1959; Staats & Staats, 1958; Staats, Staats, & Heard, 1959). All of these approaches have in common the use of influencing techniques to change verbal behavior. Blake and Mouton (1957), based on their studies of the dynamics of influence and coercion, conclude that the most significant dimensions operating in the exertion of influence under face-to-face conditions are: (a) the properties of the direct influence induction, and (b) the properties of the social background. Their major emphasis is on training in various phases of social science so that the therapist may become aware of the forces within the social situation which must be shifted in order to effect behavior changes.

*Awareness.* The variable of awareness is crucial to the influencing process. The problem of whether learning without awareness does, or does not, occur has been repeatedly explored under many different guises in laboratories and experimental settings (Adams, 1957; Dulany, 1961; Eriksen, 1961; Kanfer & McBrearty, 1961; Levin, 1960; Sidowski, 1954; Tatz, 1956). In psychotherapy the question is whether you can have behavioral changes in a patient without his verbalizing insight into the relationship between his present behavior and (a) a set of events which have occurred in his past life, and/or (b) the therapist's behavior. As is true of other aspects of psychotherapy, the process of awareness has been difficult to measure. Verbal conditioning studies are faced with the difficulty of an extremely unreliable measure of awareness, namely that of the S's self report. The issue is the same as that found in psychotherapy—self reports are unreliable and also subject to the influencing

process. Krasner, Weiss, and Ullmann (1961) investigated relationships between awareness and behavior change in a verbal conditioning situation with college students using "mm-hmm" to reinforce "emotional words." The authors' position was that awareness is not a single phenomenon but refers to a complex of different cognitive events. Therefore, awareness was first investigated as a dependent variable by the technique of reported awareness typical in other verbal conditioning studies. Reported awareness at this point of the study was *not* significantly related to (a) increased responsivity on reinforced trials as compared to operant trials, (b) previously induced emotional atmospheres, either hostile or neutral (Weiss et al., 1960), or (c) previous pattern of reinforced trials. Thus, a typical measure of S's awareness, his self report, was not associated with either responsivity to verbal conditioning or with two experimental manipulations (atmospheres and patterns of reinforcement) which in themselves had significantly decreased responsiveness to verbal conditioning. Awareness was then treated as an independent variable and was manipulated by means of two different sets of instructions. Half the Ss were given cues designed to focus attention on the phenomenon of verbal conditioning. It was found that induced-awareness cues decreased responsiveness on *subsequent* reinforcement trials. The second experimental manipulation of awareness followed one of two sets of instruction: Ss were explicitly informed of the reinforcing contingency and were told that either (a) they had been controlling E, or (b) E had been controlling them. Two reinforcement trials followed these instructions. These resulted in significant heterogeneity of variance. Whether S would respond by increasing or decreasing his "emotional words" was predictable based on the previous experimental conditions to which he had been exposed.

The following conclusions were drawn:
(a) Conflicting reports on the relationship between reported awareness and conditioning reflect conceptual confusion with regard to the role of reported awareness in performance. (b) Ss' awareness of the reinforcing contingency will affect performance in verbal conditioning experiments when awareness is made an integral part of Ss' task. (c) The specific effect that awareness will have on performance depends on subject-determined variables, e.g., Ss' emotional attitude toward E.

In another study in which "awareness" was experimentally manipulated (Ekman, Krasner, & Ullmann, see Footnote 4) the storytelling task was introduced to half the Ss as a measure of empathy (amount of warmth and feeling towards other people) and was introduced to the other half as a measure of personal problems (difficulties in getting along with other people). Half the Ss in each group were told that "after the first few stories I [E] will let you know that you are revealing your own personal problems (or that you are showing warmth) by going 'mm-hmm' whenever you do this." In this factorial design, there were no differences among the four groups in number of emotional words used during operant trials. However, the groups differed significantly in increase of number of emotional words used during reinforced trials. The groups for whom the task had been structured as a measure of empathy showed significantly greater increase of emotional words during reinforced trials than the group for whom the task had been structured as revealing personal problems. The greatest increase was in the "empathy" group who had been given "awareness" instructions. In short, both the structure given the examiner's reinforcing behavior and the subject's awareness of said behavior were germane to the direction of his verbal behavior. The "personal problem" group who had been given "awareness" instruc-

tions decreased slightly under reinforcement. Thus, verbal conditioning allows for the manipulation of "awareness" itself in such a way as to permit the measurement of its influence on S's subsequent behavior. Taken by itself, in terms of verbal report, "awareness" is a concept of dubious validity in verbal conditioning studies.

GENERALIZATION AND PREDICTION

Two major problems facing the therapist, as well as E in other influence situations, are those of generalization and prediction: (a) What is the relationship between S's verbalizations in the influencing situation and S's behavior outside of that situation? (b) What are the techniques of predicting those who will be most susceptible to the influencing process?

*Prediction*

Implicit, of course, in all verbal conditioning studies is the element of determining the most effective influencing conditions for predictive purposes. This is especially so for studies hypothesizing relationships between S personality variables and conditionability, previously discussed. I. G. Sarason (1958) carries this closer to psychotherapy by investigating responsivity to verbal conditioning as it is related to rated behavior in the psychotherapy situation itself. One finding, for example, was that patients compliant in psychotherapy were significantly more conditionable than noncompliant patients. A major assumption still to be demonstrated is that the S who is susceptible to influence in one situation, such as hypnosis or brainwashing, would also be susceptible to influence in other situations, such as verbal conditioning or Asch type procedures.

Weiss, Ullmann, and Krasner (1960) found in a group of college students a positive relationship between responsivity to verbal operant conditioning and an indirect measure of susceptibility to hyp-

nosis—a scale of likelihood of hypnotizability adopted from hypnosis research of
Hilgard and Weitzenhoffer. In a later
study by Krasner, Ullmann, Weiss, and
Collins (1961), this scale was expanded
into a more general "Resistance to Conditioning Scale" which includes items
from the CPI and MMPI. This scale correlated significantly with responsivity to
verbal conditioning (of emotional words)
in a group of medical students. Further
refinements on this prediction scale are
now in progress (Ullmann, Weiss, &
Krasner, 1961).

Along similar lines, Crowne and Strickland (1961) found positive and significant relationships between responsivity to
verbal conditioning and scores on a social
desirability scale. This scale correlated
significantly with a tendency to conform
as measured by the Barron Scale and performance in a standard Asch conformity
situation. Crowne and Strickland found
that those Ss (college students) scoring
high on this social desirability or need for
approval scale were conditionable in the
verbal conditioning situation, whereas
those scoring low on this scale were not.

*Generalization*

No other issue is of more concern to
the therapist than that of the generalization of behavior change from office to
"life outside." Verbal conditioning studies
have offered a clear-cut approach to this
problem (B. R. Sarason, 1957), although
generalization effects have been difficult
to demonstrate (Dinoff, Horner, Kurpiewski, Rickard, & Timmons, 1960; Ekman & Friesen, 1960a; Moos, 1961;
Rogers, 1960; Sandler, Gersten, & Greenspoon[7]; Tobias, 1960; Weide, 1960;
Williams, 1958).

Ullmann, Krasner, and Collins (1961)
approached the problem of generalization

[7] Sandler, J. S., Gersten, C. O., & Greenspoon, J. The effects of behavioral cues on test
performance in a clinical setting. Unpublished
manuscript, 1960.

by first isolating the behaviors of the
therapist and patient which are characteristic of the psychotherapy situation. Then
they systematically manipulated these behaviors to test hypotheses about the psychotherapeutic process. These hypotheses
were: (a) a person can influence the
behavior of another in a predictable direction, (b) this behavior change has a
desirable effect on behavior in a second
criterion situation, and (c) the changed
behavior in the criterion situation is associated with a specific aspect of the already
circumscribed behavior of the therapist.

Neuropsychiatric patients who were receiving group therapy participated in
storytelling sessions during which emotional words were reinforced in one of
three ways: a positive-personal manner
("mm-hmm" and head nodding); an im-
personal-unstructured manner (the click
of an electric counter); and no reinforcement at all. Ratings (Finney, 1954) made
by the group therapist before and after
the experimental storytelling sessions indicated a significant gain in adequacy of
interpersonal relationships manifested in
group therapy for the group receiving
positive-personal reinforcement (t=1.83).
There was no significant gain for the
other two groups on this criterion measure (t=0.34 and t=0.15). The results
supported the hypothesis that one person
can influence another in a positive way
and that this change is measurable by an
independent criterion situation. Further,
this change in an S's behavior was demonstrated to be associated with specific behavior on the part of the experimenter.
The authors point out that the hypothesis
of the positive correlation between change
in use of verbal class during experimental
sessions and change in the criterion may
be oversimplified. Using a different E,
new Ss, and introducing nonreinforced
operant trials, Ullmann, Krasner, and Ekman (1961) found that patients in a
positive-personal reinforcement group increased significantly in group therapy

scores ($t$=2.25), while the change of a "no-contact" comparison group approached but did not reach significance ($t$=1.69). More importantly, when only $S$s were used whose admission had occurred at least three months prior to the start of the experiment, it was found that the positive-personal reinforcement group gained an average of 9.00 points on Finney's Group Therapy Scale, while no-contact comparison subjects gained only 1.15 points on the average. The difference between the means of the two groups was statistically significant ($t$=1.95). In this study, the relationship between increased group therapy scores and increased use of emotional words during the first two reinforced trials was insignificant. Thus, it is unlikely that the improvement in rated behavior was due to an increase in the use of emotional words, per se. Rather, we would hypothesize that the major element underlying these results was a form of role retraining in terms of learning the appropriateness of spontaneous expression in an interpersonal situation.

It should be pointed out that Rogers (1960) and Williams (1958) both failed to obtain generalization effects after having obtained significant effects of conditioning. It is speculated that the difference in results lies in the different relationship between the response class conditioned and the criterion behavior.

A significant generalization effect (favorable effect on a clinical criterion associated with verbal conditioning) was also obtained in another study with psychiatric patients (Ullmann, Weiss, & Krasner, 1961). A perceptual defense task consisting of matched threatening and neutral words on successive carbons was administered to one group *prior* to verbal conditioning of emotional words and to another group *after* verbal conditioning of emotional words. The latter group had lower defensive scores than the former. Further analysis of the data indicated that the "inhibitors" (repressors) as measured

by the MMPI (Ullmann, 1962) showed significant generalization, while "facilitators" (externalizers) showed no significant effect of prior verbal conditioning of emotional words.

PSYCHOTHERAPY RESEARCH—
PRESENT AND FUTURE

In his review chapter on "psychotherapy," Rotter (1960) summarizes several current research trends which have been emphasized in this paper: a greater flexibility in techniques; greater appreciation of patient-therapist interaction; greater willingness to challenge old taboos and beliefs in regard to psychotherapy, such as the importance of personal analysis and the "passive, constrained, and nonjudgmental role of the therapist"; more concern with psychotherapeutic procedure and less with outcome; concentration on the therapist and his verbal and nonverbal responses; and the increasing importance of "values" in psychotherapy. Further, Rotter suggests that more attention be paid to conceiving of psychotherapy as "a social interaction which follows the same laws and principles as other social interactions, and in which many different effects can be obtained by a variety of different conditions." He also feels that there is a relative lack of appreciation of the potential for using laboratory analogues in which the principles underlying psychotherapy can be investigated under relatively controlled conditions.

In fully assessing the implications of verbal conditioning studies for investigating psychotherapy, it should be pointed out that a certain percentage of these studies report negative results. In his review of 31 verbal conditioning studies, Krasner (1958a) found that approximately 25% of these studies report some aspects of negative results—the "reinforced" behavior either did not increase significantly or its increase was no more than in a control group. A recent study of Sullivan and Calvin (1959) also reports failure to condition "opinions" in a student group. These studies point to the need for investigation of the conditions under which the influencing process is *not* effective. Azrin, Holz, Ulrich, and Goldiamond (1961) report difficulties in replicating Verplanck's (1955) earlier work, and discuss some of the problems involved in adequate measurement of verbal operants and in training examiners. Barik and Fillenbaum (1961) also discuss "failures" to condition as they are related to the use of control groups.

A brief summary of the current trends in verbal operant conditioning studies would point up the directions that this approach to research on interpersonal processes has been headed, as well as offer a guide for future research: (*a*) an increasing complexity of design which places greater emphasis on the interaction of variables; (*b*) wider range of types of people being reinforced; (*c*) wider range of response class being reinforced with more emphasis on using continuous verbal behavior, rather than discrete verbal behavior; (*d*) explicit use of verbal conditioning as a therapeutic technique; (*e*) the study of issues which have evolved out of other learning studies, such as scheduling of reinforcement, learning without awareness, and instructional set; (*f*) the employment of operant conditioning techniques to lead to mechanical *instrumentation* for more effective behavior change; (*g*) the use of verbal conditioning techniques as stable measures of responsivity as the dependent variable in evaluating personality changes; (*h*) extension of verbal conditioning techniques to group situations; (*i*) the construction of predictive personality scales of responsivity to verbal conditioning and other influencing situations; (*j*) verbal conditioning responsivity as a predictor of success in psychotherapy; (*k*) verbal conditioning procedures as an experimental "control" on other treatment techniques. Finally, it should be emphasized that this technique of investigation offers oppor-

tunities to bring the process of psychotherapy within the framework of a scientific learning theory. Further, these techniques of investigation can fit in with a broader psychology of behavior control by incorporating into their design such techniques as hypnosis, sensory deprivation, isolation, drugs, physiological measurements, and nonverbal behavior. Future research can also use these techniques to investigate the counter-controls exerted by the patient on the therapist. The ideal "reinforcement machine" will have these effects programed in, just as the experienced therapist is able to recognize and use patient "controlling" behavior.

One of the criticisms leveled against extrapolating the results of "laboratory" studies, such as verbal conditioning, into the "living process" of psychotherapy is that these studies miss many of the subleties and complexities involved in the psychotherapy process and tend to oversimplify the process. Rather than being defensive in interpreting laboratory studies of the influencing process, there is now enough evidence that these techniques can be used not only for research, but as actual therapeutic techniques. The studies by Ullmann, Krasner, and Collins (1961) and by Rickard et al. (1960) were used in psychotherapeutic context to change patient behavior in a desired direction. Other studies (Salzinger & Pisoni, 1958, 1960) take place within the context of ordinary clinical interactions, or were labeled as "psychotherapy" (Williams, 1958). Greenspoon[8] is in the process of developing a modified tape recorder which can be utilized as a mechanical reinforcer in a psychotherapy situation.

As part of an ongoing study by Ullmann, Krasner, and Gelfand,[9] each instance of the reinforced verbal class, emo-

[8] Greenspoon, J. Personal communication, 1960.
[9] Ullmann, L. P., Krasner, L., & Gelfand, Donna M. Fantasy hostility associated with the attenuation of aggression. Research in progress, 1961.

tional words, was scored on a scale of "Pleasantness-Unpleasantness." To eliminate individual differences in *number* of emotional words used, the *average* rating of emotional words determined each $S$'s score. The correlations between pairs of raters for 25 cases were .96, .93, and .93. Comparing these scores for emotional words used during operant and reinforced trials for 80 college $S$s (Weiss, Krasner, & Ullmann, 1960), the emotional words used during reinforcement were significantly pleasanter than the emotional words used during operant trials, the critical ratio being 5.27. Similarly, for another group of 48 college students (Ekman, Krasner, & Ullmann, see Footnote 4) emotional words used during reinforced trials were significantly pleasanter than the emotional words used during operant trials, the critical ratio being 4.84. Aside from the similarity of this score to the Discomfort-Relief Quotient (DRQ) (Mowrer, 1953a), work in progress indicates that "Pleasantness-Unpleasantness" scores are associated with tension measures such as Barron Ego-strength (1953) and McReynolds Incongruency Technique (1958).

Krasner and Winder have used role-taking techniques for training schizophrenic patients to take the $E$ role in a verbal conditioning situation with college students as $S$s. Preliminary work indicates that this type of training is feasible, and the plan is to gradually extend the kind and complexities of verbal behavior which the schizophrenic patient is trained to reinforce, as well as to increase the complexities of the cues which the schizophrenic patient will use as reinforcers.

The motor operant conditioning studies (Bullock, 1960; Bullock & Brunt, 1959; Driskell & Tremaine, 1960; King, Merrell, Lovinger, & Denny, 1957; Lindsley, 1956, 1960; Lindsley & Skinner, 1954; Peters & Jenkins, 1954; Tilton, 1957; Verplanck, 1956) use as dependent variables changes in behavior which may be termed "thera-

peutic." An illustration of this is the work of Ferster (1958) and Ferster and De Myer (1961) with autistic children in which the conditioning of motor operants is used to shape up and bring into contact with his environment the behavior of the autistic child. A series of investigations with children as $S$s further illustrate the use of motor and verbal operant conditioning techniques in behavioral analysis and in "therapeutic manipulation" of behavior (Azrin & Lindsley, 1956; Baer, 1960, 1961; Bijou, 1955, 1957; Bijou & Baer, 1961; Bijou & Orlando, 1961; Lovaas, 1961; Patterson, 1959; Patterson, Helper, & Wilcott, 1960; Warren & Brown, 1943). Other recent developments have included the application of operant conditioning techniques to: the "reinstatement" of verbal behavior in psychotics (Isaacs, Thomas, & Goldiamond, 1960); the control of stuttering (Flanagan, Goldiamond, & Azrin, 1958, 1959); and working with "unreachable cases" (Slack, 1960); and the shaping of a wide range of behaviors in schizophrenics by appropriate "behavioral engineering" techniques (Ayllon, 1960; Ayllon & Michael, 1959).

Viewing research in psychotherapy as part of a broader psychology of behavior control has other implications which must be faced. Many therapists will object to having their sacred healing process identified with concepts such as "brainwashing," sensory deprivation, or "placebos." They will refuse to acknowledge that a therapist can be "programed" to maximize efficiency in the influencing process. They may contend that this is too mechanical an approach and as such belongs to the science fiction world of Orwell and Huxley (Skinner, 1948; Vandenberg, 1956) but not to the psychotherapy world of Freud. However, the research approaches cited in this paper are investigating a process that occurs every day in the therapist's office. They demonstrate that this process is lawful and amenable to systematic approach as part of the interpersonal influencing process. It is conceivable that future research will find that this process is most effective under certain conditions which may utilize: sensory deprivation; hypnosis; conditioning techniques; subliminal stimuli; manipulation of antecedent contacts, set, awareness, and ambiguity; and "programed" therapists. With our goal as therapists to better the lives of our patients, to make them more comfortable with themselves, and to better their interpersonal relationships, then we cannot avoid recognition of our use of these techniques, if this is the way people's behavior is influenced. Intrinsically, there is nothing evil or unethical in such techniques. The task for the research investigator is now to determine the most effective techniques of behavior control. He must also give serious consideration to helping develop societal *safeguards* so that these techniques will not be misused or exploited for "nontherapeutic" purposes (Krasner, 1961a). This is a far more difficult task than any discussed in this paper and is worth a "conference" in its own right.

## REFERENCES

Aronson, M. A study of the relationships between certain counselor and client characteristics in client-centered therapy. In W. U. Snyder (Ed.), *Group report of a program of research in psychotherapy.* State College, Pa.: Pennsylvania State Univer., 1953. Pp. 39-54.

Adams, H. B., Carrera, R. N., Cooper, G. D., Gibby, R. G., & Tobey, H. R. Personality and intellectual changes in psychiatric patients following brief partial sensory deprivation. *Amer. Psychologist,* 1960, **15**, 448. (Abstract)

Adams, J. K. Laboratory studies of behavior without awareness. *Psychol. Bull.,* 1957, **54**, 383-405.

Adams, J. S., & Hoffman, B. The frequency of self-reference statements as a function of generalized reinforcement. *J. abnorm. soc. Psychol.,* 1960, **60**, 384-389.

Anderson, D. E. Personality variables and

verbal conditioning. *Dissertation Abstr.,* 1959, **19**, 1811.

Asch, S. E. The doctrine of suggestion, prestige, and imitation in social psychology. *Psychol. Rev.,* 1948, **55**, 250-277.

Asch, S. E. Studies of independence and conformity: I. A minority of one against a unanimous majority. *Psychol. Monogr.,* 1956, **70** (9, Whole No. 416).

Ashby, J. D., Ford, D. H., Guerney, B. G., Jr., & Guerney, Louise F. Effects on clients of a reflective and a leading type of psychotherapy. *Psychol. Monogr.,* 1957, **71** (24, Whole No. 453).

Atkinson, Rita L. Paired-associate learning by schizophrenic and normal subjects under conditions of verbal reward and verbal punishment. Unpublished doctoral dissertation, Indiana University, 1957.

Auld, F., Jr. Influence of social class on personality test responses. *Psychol. Bull.,* 1952, **49**, 318-332.

Auld, F., Jr., & Murray, E. J. Content-analysis studies of psychotherapy. *Psychol. Bull.,* 1955, **52**, 377-395.

Auld, F., Jr., & White, Alice. Sequential dependencies in psychotherapy. *J. abnorm. soc. Psychol.,* 1959, **58**, 100-104.

Ayllon, T. Some behavioral problems associated with eating in chronic schizophrenic patients. Paper presented to American Psychological Association, Chicago, September, 1960.

Ayllon, T., & Michael, J. The psychiatric nurse as a behavioral engineer. *J. exp. Anal. Behav.,* 1959, **2**, 323-334.

Azima, H., & Cramer, Fern J. Effects of partial perceptual isolation in mentally disturbed individuals. *Dis. nerv. Syst.,* 1956, **17**, 117-122. (a)

Azima, H., & Cramer-Azima, Fern J. Effects of the decrease in sensory variability on body scheme. *Canad. Psychiatric Ass. J.,* 1956, **1**, 59-72. (b)

Azima, H., & Cramer-Azima, Fern J. Studies on perceptual isolation. *Dis. nerv. Syst., Monogr. Suppl.,* 1957, **18**, No. 8.

Azrin, N. H., Holz, W., Ulrich, R., & Goldiamond, I. The control of the content of conversation through reinforcement. *J. exp. Anal. Behav.,* 1961, **4**, 25-30.

Azrin, N. H., & Lindsley O. R. The reinforcement of cooperation between children. *J. abnorm. soc. Psychol.,* 1956, **52**, 100-102.

Babladelis, Georgia. A study of the effects of a personality variable in verbal conditioning. Unpublished doctoral dissertation, University of Colorado, 1960.

Bachrach, A. J. Notes on the experimental analysis of behavior. In H. Lief, N. Lief, & V. Lief (Eds.), *The psychological basis of medical practice*. New York: Hoeber, in press.

Bachrach, A. J., Candland, D. K., & Gibson, Janice T. Experiments in verbal behavior: I. Group reinforcement of individual response. *Tech. Rep.*, 1960, Contract Nonr. 474 (8).

Back, K. W. Influence through social communication. *J. abnorm. soc. Psychol.*, 1951, 46, 9-23.

Baer, D. M. Control of thumbsucking in a young child by withdrawal and representation of positive reinforcement. *Amer. Psychologist*, 1960, 15, 475. (Abstract)

Baer, D. M. Effect of withdrawal of positive reinforcement on an extinguishing response in young children. *Child Develpm.*, 1961, 32, 67-74.

Bales, R. F. *Interaction process analysis*. Cambridge, Mass.: Addison-Wesley, 1950.

Ball, R. S. Reinforcement conditioning of verbal behavior by verbal and non-verbal stimuli in a situation resembling a clinical interview. Unpublished doctoral dissertation, Indiana University, 1952.

Bandura, A. Psychotherapist's anxiety level, self-insight, and psychotherapeutic competence. *J. abnorm. soc. Psychol.*, 1956, 52, 333-337.

Bandura, A. Psychotherapy as a learning process. *Psychol. Bull.*, 1961, 58, 143-159.

Bandura, A., Lipsher, D. H., & Miller, Paula E. Psychotherapists' approach-avoidance reactions to patients' expressions of hostility. *J. consult. Psychol.*, 1960, 24, 1-8.

Barik, H. C., & Fillenbaum, S. Negative reinforcement of two grammatical response classes. *Canad. J. Psychol.*, 1961, 15, 107-115.

Barik, H. C., & Lambert, W. E. Conditioning of complex verbal sequences. *Canad. J. Psychol.*, 1960, 14, 87-95.

Barnett, C. D., Pryer, Margaret, W., & Ellis, N. R. Experimental manipulation of verbal behavior in defectives. *Psychol. Rep.*, 1959, 5, 593-596.

Barron, F. An ego-strength scale which predicts response to psychotherapy. *J. consult. Psychol.*, 1953, 17, 327-333.

Berg, I. A. Comments on current books and the passing scene. *J. counsel. Psychol.*, 1958, 5, 316-317.

Bergin, A. Personality interpretation as persuasive communication. Unpublished doctoral dissertation, Stanford University, 1960.

Berkowitz, L., & Lundy, R. M. Personality characteristics related to susceptibility to influence by peers or authority figures. *J. Pers.*, 1957, 25, 306-316.

Bextion, W. H., Heron, W., & Scott, T. H. Effects of decreased variation in the sensory environment. *Canad. J. Psychol.*, 1954, 8, 70-76.

Bijou, S. W. A systematic approach to an experimental analysis of young children. *Child Develpm.*, 1955, 26, 161-168.

Bijou, S. W. Patterns of reinforcement and resistance to extinction in young children. *Child Develpm.*, 1957, 28, 47-54.

Bijou, S. W., & Baer, D. M. *Child development: A systematic and empirical theory.* Vol. 1. New York: Appleton-Century-Crofts, 1961.

Bijou, S. W., & Orlando, R. Rapid development of multiple-schedule performances with retarded children. *J. exp. Anal. Behav.*, 1961, 4, 7-16.

Binder, A., McConnell, D., & Sjoholm, Nancy A. Verbal conditioning as a function of experimenter characteristics. *J. abnorm. soc. Psychol.*, 1957, 55, 309-314.

Blake, R. R., & Mouton, Jane S. The dynamics of influence and coercion. *Int. J. soc. Psychiat.*, 1957, 2, 263-274.

Bordin, E. S. Ambiguity as a therapeutic variable. *J. consult. Psychol.*, 1955, 19, 9-15.

Bullock, D. H. Some aspects of human operant behavior. *Psychol. Rec.*, 1960, 10, 241-258.

Bullock, D. H., & Brunt, M. Y., Jr. The testability of psychiatric patients in an operant conditioning situation. *Psychol. Rec.*, 1959, 9, 165-170.

Buss, A. H., & Durkee, Ann. Conditioning of hostile verbalizations in a situation resembling a clinical interview. *J. consult. Psychol.*, 1958, 6, 415-418.

Buss, A. H., & Gerjuoy, Irma R. Verbal conditioning and anxiety. *J. abnorm. soc. Psychol.*, 1958, 57, 249-250.

Buss, A. H., Gerjuoy, Irma R., & Zusman, J. Verbal conditioning and extinction with verbal and nonverbal reinforcers. *J. exp. Psychol.*, 1958, 56, 139-145.

Cairns, R. B. The influence of dependency-anxiety on the effectiveness of social reinforcers. Unpublished doctoral dissertation, Stanford University, 1960.

Campbell, J. M. Verbal conditioning as a function of the personality characteristics of experimenters and subjects. Unpublished doctoral dissertation, University of Washington, 1960.

Cartwright, D. S., & Cartwright, Rosalind D. Faith and improvement in psychotherapy. *J. counsel. Psychol.*, 1958, 5, 174-177.

Chan, Kathleen Swat Hoon. The effect of enhanced visual sensory input on the probability of verbal response. *Dissertation Abstr.*, 1958, 18, 283-284.

Cieutat, V. J. Surreptitious modification of verbal behavior during class discussion. *Psychol. Rep.*, 1959, 5, 648.

Cohen, E., & Cohen B. D. Verbal reinforcement in schizophrenia. *J. abnorm. soc. Psychol.*, 1960, 60, 443-446.

Crowne, D. P., & Strickland, Bonnie R. The conditioning of verbal behavior as a function of the need for social approval. *J. abnorm. soc. Psychol.*, 1961, 63, 395-401.

Cushing, M. C. Affective components of the response class as a factor in verbal conditioning. *Dissertation Abstr.*, 1957, 17, 2313.

Cutler, R. L. Countertransference effects in psychotherapy. *J. consult. Psychol.*, 1958, 22, 349-356.

Daily, J. M. Verbal conditioning without awareness. *Dissertation Abstr.*, 1953, 13, 1247-1248.

Dibner, A. S. Cue-counting: A measure of anxiety in interviews. *J. consult. Psychol.*, 1956, 20, 475-478.

Dibner, A. S. Ambiguity and anxiety. *J. abnorm. soc. Psychol.*, 1958, 56, 165-174.

Dinoff, M., Horner, R. F., Kurpiewski, B. S., Rickard, H. C., & Timmons, E. O. Conditioning verbal behavior of a psychiatric population in a group therapy-like situation. *J. clin., Psychol.*, 1960, 16, 371-372.

Dinoff, M., Horner, R. F., Kurpiewski, B. S., & Timmons, E. O. Conditioning verbal behavior of schizophrenics in a group therapy-like situation. *J. clin. Psychol.*, 1960, 16, 367-370.

Dinoff, M., Rickard, H. C., Salzberg, H., & Sipprelle, C. N. An experimental analogue of three psychotherapeutic approaches. *J. clin. Psychol.*, 1960, 16, 70-73.

Dittmann, A. T. The interpersonal process in psychotherapy: Development of a research method. *J. abnorm. soc. Psychol.*, 1952, 17, 236-244.

Dobie, Shirley I. Operant conditioning of verbal and hallucinatory responses with nonverbal reinforcement. Paper read at Midwestern Psychological Association, Chicago, May, 1959.

Doering, M. F. A test of a training procedure designed to increase the intensity of angry verbalizations. *Dissertation Abstr.*, 1959, 19, 2144.

Dollard, J., & Miller, N. E. *Personality and psychotherapy.* New York: McGraw-Hill, 1950.

Driskell, Joyce C., & Tremaine, D. L. Operant conditioning of human motor behavior without subjects' awareness. *Amer. Psychologist*, 1960, 7, 430. (Abstract)

Dulany, D. E., Jr. Hypotheses and habits in verbal "operant conditioning." *J. abnorm. soc. Psychol.*, 1961, 63, 251-263.

Ekman, P. A comparison of verbal and nonverbal behavior as reinforcing stimuli of opinion responses. Unpublished doctoral dissertation, Adelphi College, 1958.

Ekman, P., & Friesen, W. V. The conditioning of hostile responses to photographs of peers: Three measures of generalization. Paper read at Eastern Psychological Association, New York, April, 1960. (a)

Ekman, P., & Friesen, W. V. Status and personality of the experimenter as a determinant of verbal conditioning. *Amer. Psychologist*, 1960, 15, 430. (Abstract) (b)

Eriksen, C. W. Discrimination and learning without awareness: A methodological survey and evaluation. *Psychol. Rev.*, 1960, 67, 279-300.

Everstine, L., & Bendig, A. W. Conditioning neurotic verbalizations. *Amer. Psychologist*, 1960, 15, 430. (Abstract)

Eysenck, H. J. The effects of psychotherapy: An evaluation. *J. consult. Psychol.*, 1952, 16, 319-324.

Fahmy, Sumaya A. Conditioning and extinction of a referential verbal response class in a situation resembling a clinical diagnostic interview. *Dissertation Abstr.*, 1953, 13, 873-874.

Farber, I. E., Harlow, H. F., & West, L. J. Brainwashing, conditioning, and DDD (debility, dependency, and dread). *Sociometry*, 1957, 20, 271-285.

Ferguson, D. C., & Buss, A. H. Operant conditioning of hostile verbs in relation to experimenter and subject characteristics. *J. consult. Psychol.*, 1960, **24**, 324-327.

Ferster, C. B. Withdrawal of positive reinforcement as punishment. *Science*, 1957, **126**, 509.

Ferster, C. B. Development of normal behavioral processes in autistic children. *Res. relat. Children*, 1958, **9**, 30.

Ferster, C. B. Positive reinforcement and behavioral deficits of autistic children. *Child Develpm.*, 1961, **32**, 437-456.

Ferster, C. B., & De Myer, Marian K. The development of performances in autistic children in an automatically controlled environment. *J. chronic Dis.*, 1961, **13**, 312-345.

Ferster, C. B., & Skinner, B. F. *Schedules of reinforcement*. New York: Appleton-Century-Crofts, 1957.

Fey, W. F. Doctrine and experience: Their influence upon the psychotherapist. *J. consult. Psychol.*, 1958, **22**, 403-409.

Fiedler, F. E. A comparison of therapeutic relationships in psychoanalytic, non-directive, and Adlerian therapy. *J. consult. Psychol.*, 1950, **14**, 436-445.

Fiedler, F. E. Factor analyses of psychoanalytic, non-directive, and Adlerian therapeutic relationships. *J. consult. Psychol.*, 1951, **15**, 32-38.

Fiedler, F. E. Quantitative studies on the role of therapists' feelings toward their patients. In O. H. Mowrer (Ed.), *Psychotherapy: Theory and research*. New York: Ronald, 1953.

Finney, B. C. A scale to measure interpersonal relationships in group therapy. *Group Psychother.*, 1954, **7**, 52-66.

Flanagan, B., Goldiamond, I., & Azrin, N. Operant stuttering: The control of stuttering through response-contingent consequences. *J. exp. Anal. Behav.*, 1958, **1**, 173-177.

Flanagan, B., Goldiamond, I., & Azrin, N. H. Instatement of stuttering in normally fluent individuals through operant procedures. *Science*, 1959, **130**, 979-981.

Ford, D. H. Research approaches to psychotherapy. *J. counsel. Psychol.*, 1959, **6**, 55-60.

Frank, J. D. Some effects of expectancy and influence in psychotherapy. In J. H. Masserman & J. L. Moreno (Eds.), *Progress in psychotherapy*. Vol. III. New York: Grune & Stratton, 1958.

Frank, J. D. The dynamics of the psychotherapeutic relationship: Determinants and effects of the therapist's influence. *Psychiatry*, 1959, **22**, 17-39. (a)

Frank, J. D. Problems of controls in psychotherapy as exemplified by the psychotherapy research project of the Phipps Psychiatric Clinic. In E. A. Rubinstein & M. B. Parloff (Eds.), *Research in psychotherapy*. Washington, D. C.: American Psychological Association, 1959. (b)

Frank, J. D. *Persuasion and healing: A comparative study of psychotherapy*. Baltimore: Johns Hopkins Press, 1961.

Frank, J. D., Gliedman, L. H., Imber, S. D., Stone, A. R., & Nash, E. H. Patients' expectancies and relearning as factors determining improvement in psychotherapy. *Amer. J. Psychiat.*, 1959, **115**, 961-968.

Franks, C. M. Conditioning and personality: A study of normal and neurotic subjects. *J. abnorm. soc. Psychol.*, 1956, **52**, 143-150.

Franks, C. M. Personality factors and the rate of conditioning. *Brit. J. Psychol.*, 1957, **48**, 119-126.

Friesen, W. V., & Ekman, P. Conditioning of hostile and friendly responses to peer photographs. *Amer. Psychologist*, 1960, **15**, 430. (Abstract)

Gelfand, Donna M., & Winder, C. L. Operant conditioning of verbal behavior in dysthymics and hysterics. *J. abnorm. soc. Psychol.*, 1961, **62**, 688-689.

Gewirtz, J. L., & Baer, D. M. The effects of deprivation and satiation on behaviors for a social reinforcer. *Amer. Psychologist*, 1957, **12**, 401. (Abstract)

Gewirtz, J. L., & Baer, D. M. Deprivation and satiation of social reinforcers as drive conditions. *J. abnorm. soc. Psychol.*, 1958, **57**, 165-172. (a)

Gewirtz, J. L., & Baer, D. M. The effect of brief social deprivation on behaviors for a social reinforcer. *J. abnorm. soc. Psychol.*, 1958, **56**, 49-56. (b)

Gill, M. G., & Brenman, Margaret. Research in psychotherapy. *Amer. J. Orthopsychiat.*, 1948, **18**, 100-110.

Glad, D. D. *Operational values in psychotherapy*. New York: Oxford University Press, 1959.

Gliedman, L. H., Nash, E. H., Imber, S. D., Stone, A. R., & Frank, J. D. Reduction of symptoms by pharmacologically inert substances and by short-term psychotherapy. *AMA Arch. Neurol. Psychiat.*, 1958, **79**, 345-351.

Goldiamond, I. Indicators of perception: I. Subliminal perception, subception, unconscious perception: An analysis in terms of psycho-physical indicator methodology. *Psychol. Bull.*, 1958, 55, 373-411.

Goldman-Eisler, Frieda. Individual differences between interviewers and their effect on interviewees' conversational behavior. *J. ment. Sci.*, 1952, 98, 660-671.

Goldman-Eisler, Frieda. On the variability of the speed of talking and its relation to the length of utterances in conversations. *Brit. J. Psychol.*, 1954, 45, 94-107.

Graham, S. R. The influence of therapist character structure upon Rorschach changes in the course of psychotherapy. *Amer. Psychologist*, 1960, 15, 415. (Abstract)

Greenspoon, J. The effect of two nonverbal stimuli on the frequency of members of two verbal response classes. *Amer. Psychologist*, 1954, 9, 384. (Abstract)

Greenspoon, J. The reinforcing effect of two spoken sounds on the frequency of two responses. *Amer. J. Psychol.*, 1955, 68, 409-416.

Grossberg, J. M. The effect of reinforcement schedule and response class on verbal conditioning. *Dissertation Abstr.*, 1956, 16, 2211.

Grossman, D. An experimental investigation of a psychotherapeutic technique. *J. consult. Psychol.*, 1952, 16, 325-331.

Hagen, J. The conditioning of verbal affect responses in two hospitalized schizophrenic diagnostic groups during the clinical interview. Unpublished doctoral dissertation, Washington State University, 1959.

Haley, J. Control in psychoanalytic psychotherapy. In J. H. Masserman & J. L. Moreno (Eds.), *Progress in psychotherapy*. Vol. IV. New York: Grune & Stratton, 1959.

Hall, W. E. The effects of set and reinforcement in verbal conditioning. *Dissertation Abstr.*, 1958, 19, 1115-1116.

Hartman, C. H. Verbal behavior of schizophrenic and normal subjects as a function of types of social reinforcement. *Dissertation Abstr.*, 1955, 15, 1652-1653.

Hebb, D. O. The motivating effects of exteroceptive stimulation. *Amer. Psychologist*, 1958, 13, 109-113.

Heine, R. W. A comparison of patients' reports on psychotherapeutic experience with psychoanalytic, nondirective, and Adlerian therapists. *Amer. J. Psychother.*, 1953, 7, 16-23.

Helson, H., Blake, R. R., Mouton, Jane S., & Olmstead, J. A. Attitudes as adjustments to stimulus, background, and residual factors. *J. abnorm. soc. Psychol.*, 1956, 52, 314-322.

Heron, W., Bexton, W. H., & Hebb, D. O. Cognitive effects of a decreased variation in the sensory environment. *Amer. Psychologist*, 1953, 8, 366. (Abstract)

Heron, W., Doane, B. K., & Scott, T. H. Visual disturbances after prolonged perceptual isolation. *Canad. J. Psychol.*, 1956, 10, 13-18.

Hildum, D. C., & Brown, R. W. Verbal reinforcement and interviewer bias. *J. abnorm. soc. Psychol.*, 1956, 53, 108-111.

Hiler, E. W. An analysis of patient-therapist compatibility. *J. consult. Psychol.*, 1958, 22, 341-347.

Hollingshead, A. R., & Redlich, F. C. *Social class and mental illness: A community study.* New York: Wiley, 1958.

Holt, R. R., & Luborsky, L. *Personality patterns of psychiatrists.* New York: Basic Books, 1958.

Hovland, C. I., Janis, I. L., & Kelley, H. H. *Communication and persuasion: Psychological studies of opinion change.* New Haven: Yale Univer. Press, 1953.

Imber, S. D., Frank, J. D., Gliedman, L. H., Nash, E. H., Jr., & Stone A. R. Suggestibility, social class, and the acceptance of psychotherapy. *J. clin. Psychol.*, 1956, 12, 341-344.

Imber, S. D., Nash, E. H., & Stone, A. R. Social class and duration of psychotherapy. *J. clin. Psychol.*, 1955, 11, 281-284.

Isaacs, W., Thomas, J., & Goldiamond, I. Application of operant conditioning to reinstate verbal behavior in psychotics. *J. speech hear. Dis.*, 1960, 25, 8-12.

Janis, I. L. Personality correlates of susceptibility to persuasion. *J. Pers.*, 1954, 22, 504-518.

Janis, I. L., & King, B. T. The influence of role playing on opinion change. *J. abnorm. soc. Psychol.*, 1954, 49, 211-218.

Kanfer, F. H. The effect of partial reinforcement on acquisition and extinction of a class of verbal responses. *J. exp. Psychol.*, 1954, 48, 424-432.

Kanfer, F. H. Verbal conditioning: Reinforcement schedules and experimenter influence. *Psychol. Rep.*, 1958, 4, 443-452.

Kanfer, F. H. Incentive value of generalized reinforcers. *Psychol. Rep.*, 1960, 7, 531-538.

Kanfer, F. H. Comments on learning in psychotherapy. *Psychol. Rep.,* 1961, **9**, 681-699.

Kanfer, F. H., & Karas, Shirley C. Prior experimenter-subject interaction and verbal conditioning. *Psychol. Rep.,* 1959, **5**, 345-353.

Kanfer, F. H., & McBrearty, J. F. Verbal conditioning: Discrimination and awareness. *J. Psychol.,* 1961, **52**, 115-124.

Keller, F. S., & Schoenfeld, W. N. *Principles of psychology.* New York: Appleton-Century-Crofts, 1950.

Kelman, H. C. Three processes of acceptance of social influence: Compliance, identification, and internalization. *Amer. Psychologist,* 1956, **11**, 361 (Abstract)

King, G. F., Merrell, D. W., Lovinger, E., & Denny, M. R. Operant motor behavior in acute schizophrenics. *J. Pers.,* 1957, **25**, 317-326.

Kirman, W. J. The relationship of learning, with and without awareness, to personality needs. *Dissertation Abstr.,* 1958, **19**, 362-363.

Krasner, L. The use of generalized reinforcers in psychotherapy research. *Psychol. Rep.,* 1955, **1**, 19-25.

Krasner, L. Studies of the conditioning of verbal behavior. *Psychol. Bull.,* 1958, **55**, 148-170. (a)

Krasner, L. A technique of investigating the relationships between behavior cues of examiner and verbal behavior of patient. *J. consult. Psychol.,* 1958, **22**, 364-366. (b)

Krasner, L. Role taking research and psychotherapy. *VA Res. Rept., Palo Alto,* Nov., 1959, No. 5.

Krasner, L. Behavior control and social responsibility. Paper presented at Western Psychological Association, Seattle, June, 1961. (a)

Krasner, L. Behavior control, values and training. In Symposium on predoctoral Training, Western Psychological Association, Seattle, June, 1961. (b)

Krasner, L., & Ullmann, L. P. Variables in the verbal conditioning of schizophrenic subjects. *Amer. Psychologist,* 1958, **13**, 358. (Abstract)

Krasner, L., Ullmann, L. P., & Weiss, R. L. Distribution and validation of modal perceptual responses of normal and psychiatric subjects. Paper presented at American Psychological Association, New York, September, 1961.

Krasner, L., Ullmann, L. P., Weiss, R. L., & Collins, Beverly J. Responsivity to verbal conditioning as a function of three different examiners. *J. clin. Psychol.,* 1961, **17**, 411-415.

Krasner, L., Weiss, R. L., & Ullmann, L. P. Responsivity to verbal conditioning as a function of "awareness." *Psychol. Rep.,* 1961, **8**, 523-538.

Lakin, M., & Lebovits, B. Bias in psychotherapists of different orientations. *Amer. J. Psychother.,* 1958, **12**, 79-86.

Leary, T. F. *Interpersonal diagnosis of personality.* New York: Ronald, 1957.

Lennard, H. L., Calogeras, R., & Hendin, Helen. Some relationships between verbal behavior of therapist and patient in psychotherapy. *J. Psychol.,* 1957, **43**, 181-186.

Leventhal, A. M. The effects of diagnostic category and reinforcer on learning without awareness. *J. abnorm. soc. Psychol.,* 1959, **59**, 162-166.

Levin, S. M. The effects of awareness on verbal conditioning. *J. exp. Psychol.,* 1961, **61**, 67-75.

Lifton, R. J. "Thought reform" of western civilians in Chinese communist prisons. *Psychiatry,* 1956, **19**, 173-195.

Lifton, R. J. Chinese communist thought reform. In *Group processes: Transactions of the third Conference.* New York: Josiah Macy, Jr. Foundation, 1957. Pp. 219-311. (a)

Lifton, R. J. Thought reform of Chinese intellectuals: A psychiatric evaluation. *J. soc. Issues,* 1957, **13**, (3) 5-20. (b)

Lilly, J. C. Mental effects of reduction of ordinary levels of physical stimuli on intact, healthy persons. *Psychiat. res. Rep.,* 1956, **5**, 1-9.

Lindsley, O. R. Operant conditioning methods applied to research in chronic schizophrenia. *Psychiat. res. Rep.,* 1956, **5**, 118-139.

Lindsley, O. R. Characteristics of the behavior of chronic psychotics as revealed by free-operant conditioning methods. *Dis. nerv. Syst.,* 1960, **21**, 66-78.

Lindsley, O. R., & Skinner, B. F. A method for the experimental analysis of the behavior of psychotic patients. *Amer. Psychologist,* 1954, **9**, 419-420. (Abstract)

Lorenz, Maria, & Cobb, S. Language behavior in psychoneurotic patients. *AMA Arch. Neurol. Psychiat.,* 1953, **69**, 684-694.

Lovaas, O. I. The control of operant responding by rate and content of verbal operants. Paper presented at Western Psychological Association, Seattle, June, 1961.

Luchins, A. S., & Luchins, Edith H. On conformity with true and false communications. *J. soc. Psychol.*, 1955, **42**, 283-303.

Lundin, R. W. *Personality: An experimental approach.* New York: Macmillan, 1961.

Mahl, G. F. Disturbances and silences in the patient's speech in psychotherapy. *J. abnorm. soc. Psychol.*, 1956, **53**, 1-15.

Mahl, G. F. Measuring the patient's anxiety during interviews from "expressive" aspects of his speech. *Trans. New York Acad. Sci.*, 1959, **21**, 249-257.

Mandler, G., & Kaplan, W. K. Subjective evaluation and reinforcing effect of a verbal stimulus. *Science,* 1956, **124**, 582-583.

Marion, A. J. The influence of experimenter status upon verbal conditioning. Unpublished doctoral dissertation, University of California, Los Angeles, 1956.

Marmor, J. Psychoanalytic therapy as an educational process: Common denominators in the therapeutic approaches of different psychoanalytic "schools." Paper presented at Academy of Psychoanalysis, Chicago, May, 1961.

Matarazzo, J. D., Saslow, G., & Pareis, E. N. Verbal conditioning of two response classes: Some methodological considerations. *J. abnorm. soc. Psychol.,* 1960, **61**, 190-206.

McConnell, J. V., Cutler, R. L., & McNeil, E. B. Subliminal stimulation: An overview. *Amer. Psychologist,* 1958, **13**, 229-242.

McKee, M. G. Examiner-subject relationship in verbal conditioning. Unpublished doctoral dissertation, University of California, 1960.

McNair, D. M. Reinforcement of verbal behavior. *J. exp. Psychol.,* 1957, **53**, 40-46.

McReynolds, P. Anxiety as related to incongruencies between values and feelings. *Psychol. Rec.,* 1958, **8**, 57-66.

McReynolds, P., Acker, M., & Daily, J. On the effects of perceptual enhancement on certain schizophrenic symptoms. *VA Res. Rept.* Palo Alto, 1959, No. 1.

Medini, G. J. Learning without awareness and its relationship to insight and the hysteric-obsessive dimension. *Dissertation Abstr.,* 1958, **18**, 666.

Meerloo, J. A. M. *The rape of the mind: The psychology of thought control, menticide and brain-washing.* New York: World Publishing, 1956.

Mock, J. F. The influence of verbal and behavioral cues of a listener on the verbal productions of the speaker. Unpublished doctoral dissertation, University of Kentucky, 1957.

Moos, R. H. The retention and generalization of operant conditioning effects in a free interview situation. Paper presented at Western Psychological Association, Seattle, June, 1961.

Mowrer, O. H. Changes in verbal behavior during psychotherapy. In O. H. Mowrer (Ed.), *Pyschotherapy: Theory and research.* New York: Ronald, 1953. (a)

Mowrer, O. H. (Ed.) *Psychotherapy: Theory and research.* New York: Ronald, 1953. (b).

Mowrer, O. H., Hunt, J. McV., & Kogan, L. S. Further studies utilizing the Discomfort-Relief Quotient. In O. H. Mowrer (Ed.), *Psychotherapy: Theory and research.* New York: Ronald, 1953.

Murray, E. J. A case study in a behavioral analysis of psychotherapy. *J. abnorm. soc. Psychol.,* 1954, **49**, 305-310.

Murray, E. J. A content-analysis method for studying psychotherapy. *Psychol. Monogr.,* 1956, **70**(13, Whole No. 420).

Nuthmann, Anne M. Conditioning of a response class on a personality test. *J. abnorm. soc. Psychol.,* 1957, **54**, 19-23.

O'Connor, N., & Rawnsley, K. Two types of conditioning in psychotics and normals. *J. abnorm. soc. Psychol.,* 1959, **58**, 157-161.

O'Donnell, W. F., Jr. The effects of individual differences and hostility arousal on the expression of hostility in a verbal conditioning situation. Unpublished doctoral dissertation, University of Washington, 1959.

Palmore, E., Lennard, H. L., & Hendin, Helen. Similarities of therapist and patient verbal behavior in psychotherapy. *Sociometry,* 1959, **22**, 12-22.

Parloff, M. B. Some factors affecting the quality of therapeutic relationships. *J. abnorm. soc. Psychol.,* 1956, **52**, 5-10.

Patterson, G. R. Fathers as reinforcing agents. Paper read at Western Psychological Association, San Diego, April, 1959.

Patterson, G. R., Helper, M. E., & Wilcott, R. C. Anxiety and verbal conditioning in Children. *Child Develpm.,* 1960, **31**, 101-108.

Peters, H. N., & Jenkins, R. L. Improvement of chronic schizophrenic patients with guided problem-solving motivated by hunger. *Psychiat. quart. Suppl.,* 1954, **28**, 84-101.

Pisoni, Stephanie, & Salzinger, K. The unidimensionality of verbal affect and its distinctiveness from verbal nonaffect. *Amer. Psychologist,* 1960, **15**, 431. (Abstract)

Quay, H. C. The effect of verbal reinforcement on the recall of early memories. *J. abnorm. soc. Psychol.,* 1959, **59**, 254-257.

Rickard, H. C., Dignam, P. J., & Horner, R. F. Verbal manipulation in a psychotherapeutic relationship. *J. clin. Psychol.,* 1960, **16**, 364-367.

Robinson, Nancy M. Paired-associate learning by schizophrenic subjects under conditions of personal and impersonal reward and punishment. Unpublished doctoral dissertation, Stanford University, 1957.

Rogers, C. R., & Skinner, B. F. Some issues concerning the control of human behavior: A symposium. *Science,* 1956, **124**, 1057-1066.

Rogers, J. M. Operant conditioning in a quasi-therapy setting. *J. abnorm. soc. Psychol.,* 1960, **60**, 247-252.

Rosenthal, D. Changes in some moral values following psychotherapy. *J. consult. Psychol.,* 1955, **19**, 431-436.

Rosenthal, D., & Frank, J. D. Psychotherapy and the placebo effect. *Psychol. Bull.,* 1956, **53**, 294-302.

Rotter, J. B. *Social learning and clinical psychology.* New York: Prentice-Hall, 1954.

Rotter, J. B. Psychotherapy. In P. R. Farnsworth (Ed.), *Annual review of psychology.* Vol. 11, Palo Alto: Annual Reviews, 1960, Pp. 381-414.

Salzinger, K. Experimental manipulation of verbal behavior: A review. *J. gen. Psychol.,* 1959, **61**, 65-94.

Salzinger, K. The experimental analysis of the interview. In J. Zubin (Ed.), *Experimental abnormal psychology,* in press.

Salzinger, K., & Pisoni, Stephanie. Reinforcement of affect responses of schizophrenics during the clinical interview. *J. abnorm. soc. Psychol.,* 1958, **57**, 84-90.

Salzinger, K., & Pisoni, Stephanie. Reinforcement of verbal affect responses of normal subjects during the interview. *J. abnorm. soc. Psychol.,* 1960, **60**, 127-130.

Salzinger, K., Pisoni, Stephanie, & Feldman, R. S. The experimental manipulation of continuous speech in schizophrenic patients. *Amer. Psychologist,* 1960, **15**, 430. (Abstract)

Sapolsky, A. Effect of interpersonal relationships upon verbal conditioning. *J. abnorm. soc. Psychol.,* 1960, **60**, 241-246.

Sarason, Barbara R. The effects of verbally conditioned response classes on post-conditioning tasks. *Dissertation Abstr.,* 1957, **17**, 679.

Sarason, I. G. Interrelationships among individual difference variables, behavior in psychotherapy, and verbal conditioning. *J. abnorm. soc. Psychol.,* 1958, **56**, 339-344.

Sarason, I. G., & Campbell, J. M. Anxiety and the verbal conditioning of mildly hostile verbs. *J. consult. Psychol.,* 1962, **26**, 213-216.

Sarbin, T. R. Contributions to role taking theory: I. Hypnotic behavior. *Psychol. Rev.,* 1950, **57**, 255-270.

Sargant, W. *Battle for the mind.* Garden City, N. Y.: Doubleday, 1957.

Saslow, G., & Matarazzo, J. D. A technique for studying changes in interview behavior. In E. A. Rubinstein & M. B. Parloff (Eds.), *Research in psychotherapy.* Washington: American Psychological Association, 1959.

Schacter, S. *The psychology of affiliation.* Stanford: Stanford Univer. Press, 1959.

Scott, W. A. Attitude change through reward of verbal behavior. *J. abnorm. soc. Psychol.,* 1957, **55**, 72-75.

Shaffer, G. W., & Lazarus, R. S. *Fundamental concepts in clinical psychology.* New York: McGraw-Hill, 1952.

Shapiro, A. K. A contribution to a history of the placebo effect. *Behav. Sci.,* 1960, **5**, 109-135.

Shaw, F. J. Some postulates concerning psychotherapy. *J. consult. Psychol.,* 1948, **12**, 426-431.

Shaw, F. J. (Ed.) Behavioristic approaches to counseling and psychotherapy. *Univer. of Alabama Studies No. 13,* 1961, Southeastern Psychological Association Symposium.

Sheehan, J. G. Rorschach changes during psychotherapy in relation to personality of the therapist. *Amer. Psychologist,* 1953, **8**, 434. (Abstract)

Shoben, E. J., Jr. Psychotherapy as a problem in learning theory. *Psychol. Bull.,* 1949, **46**, 366-392.

Sidowski, J. B. Influence of awareness of reinforcement on verbal conditioning. *J. exp. Psychol.,* 1954, **48**, 355-360.

Sidowski, J. Reinforcement in social situations. Paper read at Western Psychological Association, San Diego, April, 1959.

Skinner, B. F. *Walden two.* New York: Macmillan, 1948.

Skinner, B. F. *Science and human behavior.* New York: Macmillan, 1953. (a)

Skinner, B. F. Some contributions of an experimental analysis of behavior to psychology as a whole. *Amer. Psychologist,* 1953, **8**, 69-78. (b)

Skinner, B. F. *Verbal behavior.* New York: Appleton-Century-Crofts, 1957.

Skinner, B. F. Reinforcement today. *Amer. Psychologist,* 1958, **13**, 94-99.

Slack, C. W. Experimenter-subject psychotherapy: A new method of introducing intensive office treatment for unreachable cases. *Ment. Hyg. N Y,* 1960, **44**, 238-256.

Solley, C. M., & Long, J. When is "uh-huh" reinforcing? *Percept. mot. Skills,* 1958, **8**, 277.

Solomon, P. (Ed.) *Sensory deprivation.* Cambridge: Harvard Univer. Press, 1961.

Staats, A. W. Verbal habit-families, concepts and the operant conditioning of word classes. *Tech. Rep. No. 10,* 1959 (Aug.), Contract Nonr. 2794(02).

Staats, A. W., & Staats, Carolyn K. Attitudes established by classical conditioning. *J. abnorm. soc. Psychol.,* 1958, **57**, 37-40.

Staats, Carolyn K., Staats, A. W., & Heard, W. G. Attitude development and ratio of reinforcement. *Tech. Rep. No. 9,* 1959 (June), Contract Nonr. 2305 (00).

Starkweather, J. A. The communication-value of content-free speech. *Amer. J. Psychol.,* 1956, **69**, 121-123. (a)

Starkweather, J. A. Content-free speech as a source of information about the speaker. *J. abnorm. soc. Psychol.,* 1956, **52**, 394-402. (b)

Stekel, W. *How to understand your dreams.* New York: Eton, 1951.

Strupp, H. H. The effect of the psychotherapists's personal analysis upon his techniques. *J. consult. Psychol.,* 1955, **19**, 197-204. (a)

Strupp, H. H. An objective comparison of Rogerian and psychoanalytic techniques. *J. consult. Psychol.,* 1955, **19**, 1-7. (b)

Strupp, H. H. Psychotherapeutic technique, professional affiliation, and experience level. *J. consult. Psychol.,* 1955, **19**, 97-102. (c)

Strupp, H. H. A multidimensional comparison of therapist activity in analytic and client-centered therapy. *J. consult. Psychol.,* 1957, **21**, 301-308. (a)

Strupp, H. H. A multidimensional system for analyzing psychotherapeutic techniques. *Psychiatry,* 1957, **20**, 293-306. (b)

Strupp, H. H. The performance of psychiatrists and psychologists in a therapeutic interview. *J. clin. Psychol.,* 1958, **14**, 219-226. (a)

Strupp, H. H. The psychotherapist's contribution to the treatment process. *Behav. Sci.,* 1958, **3**, 34-37. (b)

Strupp, H. H. The nature of the psychotherapist's contribution to the treatment process: Some research results and speculations. Lasker Memorial Lecture, Michael Reese Hospital, April, 1960.

Sullivan, H. S. *Conceptions of modern psychiatry.* Washington: William Alanson White Psychiatric Foundation, 1947.

Sullivan, M. W., & Calvin, A. D. Further investigation of verbal conditioning. *Psychol. Rep.,* 1959, **5**, 79-82.

Taffel, C. Anxiety and the conditioning of verbal behavior. *J. abnorm. soc. Psychol.,* 1955, **51**, 496-501.

Tatz, S. J. Symbolic mediation in "learning without awareness." Paper read at Eastern Psychological Association, Atlantic City, March, 1956.

Tilton, J. R. The use of instrumental motor and verbal learning techniques in the treatment of chronic schizophrenics. Unpublished doctoral dissertation, Michigan State University, 1957.

Tobias, S. Effects of verbal reinforcement on response changes in a nonreinforced situation. *Amer. Psychologist,* 1960, **15**, 390. (Abstract)

Ullmann, L. P. An empirically derived MMPI scale which measures facilitation-inhibition of recognition of threatening stimuli. *J. clin. Psychol.,* 1962, **18**, 127-132.

Ullmann, L. P., Krasner, L., & Collins, Beverly J. Modification of behavior through verbal conditioning. *J. abnorm. soc. Psychol.,* 1961, **62**, 128-132.

Ullmann, L. P., Krasner, L., & Ekman, P. Verbal conditioning of emotional words: Effects on behavior in group therapy. *VA Res. Repts., Palo Alto,* 1961, No. 15.

Ullmann, L. P., Weiss, R. L., & Krasner, L. Verbal conditioning of emotional words: Effects of recognition of threatening stimuli. Paper presented at American Psychological Association, New York, September, 1961.

Ullmann, L. P., & McFarland, R. L. Productivity as a variable in TAT protocols: A methodological study. *J. proj. Tech.*, 1957, **21**, 80-87.

Vandenberg, S. G. Great expectations or the future of psychology (as seen in science fiction). *Amer. Psychologist*, 1956, **11**, 339-342.

Verplanck, W. S. The control of the content of conversation: Reinforcement of statements of opinion. *J. abnorm. soc. Psychol.*, 1955, **51**, 668-676.

Verplanck, W. S. The operant conditioning of human motor behavior. *Psychol. Bull.*, 1956, **53**, 70-83.

Walters, R. H., & Karal, Pearl. Social deprivation and verbal behavior. *J. Pers.*, 1960, **28**, 89-107.

Walters, R. H., Marshall, W. E., & Shooter, J. R. Anxiety, isolation and susceptibility to social influence. *J. Pers.*, 1960, **28**, 518-529.

Walters, R. H., & Quinn, M. J. The effects of sensory and social deprivation on autokinetic judgments. *J. Pers.*, 1960, **28**, 210-220.

Walters, R. H., & Ray, E. Anxiety, isolation and reinforcer effectiveness. *J. Pers.*, 1960, **28**, 358-367.

Warren, A. B., & Brown, R. H. Conditioned operant response phenomenon in children. *J. gen. Psychol.*, 1943, **28**, 181-207.

Weide, T. N. Conditioning and generalization of the use of affect-relevant words. Unpublished doctoral dissertation, Stanford University, 1960.

Weiss, R. L., Krasner, L., & Ullmann, L. P. Responsivity to verbal conditioning as a function of emotional atmosphere and pattern of reinforcement. *Psychol. Rep.*, 1960, **6**, 415-426.

Weiss, R. L., Krasner, L., & Ullmann, L. P. Responsivity of psychiatric patients to verbal conditioning: "Success" and "failure" conditions and pattern of reinforced trials. Paper presented at American Psychological Association, New York, September, 1961.

Weiss, R. L., Ullmann, L. P., & Krasner, L. On the relationship between hypnotizability and response to verbal operant conditioning. *Psychol. Rep.*, 1960, **6**, 59-60.

Whitehorn, J. C. Psychiatric implications of the "placebo effect." *Amer. J. Psychiat.*, 1958, **114**, 662-664.

Whitehorn, J. C. Goals of psychotherapy. In E. A. Rubinstein & M. B. Parloff (Eds.), *Research in psychotherapy*, Washington: American Psychological Association, 1959.

Williams, R. I. Verbal conditioning in psychotherapy. *Amer. Psychologist*, 1958, **14**, 388. (Abstract)

Winokur, G. "Brainwashing": A social phenomenon of our time. *Hum. Organization*, 1955, **13**, 16-18.

Wolff, W. *Contemporary psychotherapists examine themselves.* Springfield, Ill.: Charles C Thomas, 1956.

Zedek, Meira E. The conditioning of verbal behavior with negative cultural connotations. *J. Pers.*, 1959, **27**, 477-486.

# Discussion of Papers on Therapist's Contribution

KENNETH MARK COLBY, M.D.

The trouble with my task lies not in its size or complexity or indefiniteness. The trouble lies in suggesting our next worthwhile research steps.

I think we would all agree today that the therapist *is* important. (Indeed, I cannot recapture in my imagination a climate of opinion which asserted he was not). The therapist, as a person and as an expert, is certainly pivotal and crucial in the process of phychotherapy. But after accepting this proposition, what should we do next? In deciding what might be worthwhile doing, we enter areas of individual opinion based on unspecified experience rather than on tested knowledge. The opinions I would like to offer are grounded in what one might call a historic-epistemologic image of what we are trying to do in psychotherapy research and what is happening to us in this attempt.

Psychotherapy is one of the practical arts. It is not a science, it is not even an applied science. It is a practical art, a craft like agriculture or medicine or wine-making in which an artisan relies on an incomplete, fragmentary body of knowledge and empirically established rules traditionally passed on from master to apprentice. The artisan lacks a systematic, thoroughly tested or even well-defined set of explanatory principles. His scraps of knowledge are not simply applied to an individual case but *interpreted for* each individual case in accordance with the artisan's judgment and intuition. He looks to science for help, not to make him an applied scientist—which cannot be done anyway—but *to elucidate acute difficulties*

*in the art*. He wants help with failures, with troubles, with lapses from the expected. When called upon for help, a scientist in turn realizes *he* cannot (since life is short and art is long) develop a tested explanatory theory accounting for every event in a practical art, nor is it even necessary. His repertoire of scientific procedures is highly limited relative to the number of questions which can be asked about any subject matter. If a scientist is to contribute to a problem, he must be able to formulate a *decidable* question about it. By "decidable" I mean a question which is worded in such a way that there are only two possible and incompatible answers, yes and no. Guided by the artisan, a scientist must select a certain crucial problem in the art and judge whether the problem is ready for and accessible to a systematic inquiry using currently available procedures. A scientist hopes to reduce the degree of empiricism in the art by finding that some acute problem in it can be solved through understanding an underlying explanatory principle. Other problems in the art will continue to be managed by the artisan using judgment, intuition, and personal skills.

A historical illustration of this relation between science and practical art involved Pasteur and wine-making. Wine-makers came to him for scientific help with the problem of souring, turning, and deterioration of wines. Pasteur discovered these undesirable alterations in wine were due to the presence of living organisms mingled with yeast cells. The next step consisted of killing these microorganisms by heat sterilization of the wine. Out of

95

this attempt to elucidate a crucial difficulty in a practical art developed the science of bacteriology, the germ theory of infections, and ultimately great mastery over certain infectious diseases. If Pasteur could not have seen the organisms under the microscope nor demonstrated that they oxidized alcohol to acetic acid, the art of wine-making at that time could not have been improved in this way by a scientific study. Today wine-making remains a practical art, and wine still turns occasionally in spite of our understanding of the process. Empiricism has only been reduced, not eradicated, by the discovery of explanatory principles.

I realize one can appeal to the history of science to support almost any position, and one can use history as a guide to almost any future. But I would like to take the position at this time that in our research efforts in psychotherapy we should attempt to elucidate specific crucial difficulties in the art. Charts for the terrain of these difficulties must be provided the scientist by the artisan. To construct itineraries for fruitful relations between sicence and practical art we must first try to identify those crucial points at which current science, with its limited stock of conceptual and manipulative procedures, has a good chance at an attainable answer rather than attempting, in the Greek tradition, to swarm all over the whole subject matter searching randomly for an all-encompassing explanatory principle in a futile effort to make scientific that which is neither ready nor amenable to become so. Dr. Strupp, in his paper, has emphasized that we are faced with problems of strategy, or research philosophy, of deploying our resources. I would like to echo his feelings that every research project we undertake involves a commitment of part of our time, our energies, our lives. Just because we now have lots of dollars to spend in research does not mean we can squander our energies and our productive scientific years.

Since I am only one-half clinician and two-thirds behavioral scientist, I well know that such general preachings and imperatives can become dreary to researchers who go their own way and do mainly what they want to do anyway. So now I shall try to articulate my particular viewpoint as specifically as I can in terms of the papers by Dr. Betz, Dr. Strupp and Dr. Krasner on the therapist in the treatment process.

If this artisan represents an essential factor we are interested in, what are difficulties in him we might want scientific help in elucidating? Can we first identify a difficulty, clarify it through thought and discussion, and then fromulate a decidable yes or no question about it?

It appears an important difficulty has been clearly and adeptly identified by Dr. Betz in her study of doctors working with schizophrenic patients. As you have read, A doctors do much better with schizophrenic patients than B doctors. In searching for an explanation of this difference, Dr. Betz has found that A doctors show the interests of a lawyer and a CPA, while B doctors show interests of a printer and a mathematics-physical science teacher. Dr. Betz in her paper welcomes critique and also asks for an "imaginative appraisal" of implications of her work. I have a slight criticism and a slender implication in mind. Neither of them, however, is particularly imaginative.

My criticism is that the category designated "schizophrenic illness" is not controlled for homogeneity among psychiatrists. Now that the stigmas of poor prognosis and untreatability have been lessened, more and more patient-states are classified as schizophrenia, and a class which has never been well-defined has been recently expanding its boundaries to include less ill people. There is no agreed-on rule in psychiatry to tell us whether a patient belongs in the class "schizophrenia" or not. There is no consensus as to what limits are to be put on the inclusiveness of the term "schizophrenia." There is great variability among psychiatrists, among clinics, among different parts of the country, and among different countries.

The expanding inclusiveness of diagnostic criteria might account for the Table 7 in Dr. Betz's paper which indicates a great rise in improvements rates during the second 8-year period from 1952-1959. I mention this as a possibility, but I do not think it is very likely. Her explanation that in this second 8-year period there were twice as many A doctors at the hospital seems much more plausible to me.

In spite of my doubts about the precision or even usefulness of the category "schizophrenia" I do *not* doubt Dr. Betz's finding that some doctors do better than others with severely ill patients. A doctors are described as expecting and respecting spontaneity, while B doctors restrict spontaneity. This is a cogent description of the trouble with certain therapists. It matches my own experience in consulting with residents and young psychiatrists. It suggests an implication which could be put in the form of a hypothesis, namely, that B doctors are more frightened by those patients who tend to lose control, to become violent, to express bizarre thoughts, to communicate in deranged nonsequiturs. A commonly understood motive in becoming a psychiatrist is the need to master counter-phobically an anxiety which arises from being in the presence of a person out of control. Such a mastery can be achieved in small repeated doses in situations regulated by one's own control as is found in therapeutic work with mentally ill patients. A and B doctors do equally well with less threatening illnesses. But with patients who have actually gone out of control or who are thought to have a propensity for doing so, B doctors become more scared and defend against this anxiety by attempting to exert external control. They curb spontaneity in sicker patients since they see spontaneity as a dangerous step towards the materialization of a dreaded out-of-control figure.

Such a hypothesis, while plausible, leaves us with $n$ minus 1 other plausible hypotheses. How might one proceed to test such notions? Ideally in science we would like to test hypotheses by experiment, but Dr. Strupp has raised some well-posed questions regarding the limitations of experimental methods in our field. Experiment has in the past been a powerful collateral aid to many practical arts. In consulting the textbooks of course one finds only a record of the *success* of experiments. Some problems have turned out to be too hard for experimental methods, while others, to begin with, cannot be reduced to a necessarily simplified and precisely specified experimental situation.

The best critic of his own work is a man who has thoroughly thought it out, and Dr. Strupp's paper exemplifies this. His extensive experience with an impressive research program has led him to a balanced criticism of himself and others.

He points out, in paragraph numbered 3 of his paper under the section "Some Problems of Research Strategy and Methodology," that there has been a declining interest in naturalistic observation of the psychotherapeutic process, although this was the initial source of most of the useful hypotheses we have today. Here again, it seems to me, we have in focus those functional relations which can hold between scientific approaches and a practical art. If we consider a therapist to be an artisan and, as Dr. Betz has indicated, some artisans perform significantly better than others, why don't we methodically study the on-going mental operations of that artisan, his flow of associations, *while performing his task?* This, in my opinion, represents a glaring gap in our knowledge which could be filled in by naturalistic and experimental observation. The design would involve a therapist describing out loud the moment-to-moment sequences of his mental states as he listens to the sequential descriptions of a patient's self-observation. It should be an intensive design running through stretches of time long enough to capture the stochastic properties of both therapist and patient state-sequences. In this manner we can study not only the interactional but transactional nature of psychotherapy in which a patient has a reciprocal influence on a therapist, even affecting his personality in a time-enduring way. I am referring here in passing to those small partial identifications which therapists make with certain patients and which every honest therapist can detect in himself, long after the termination of therapy, in the form of minute but unmistakable residues of his occupational experience.

As a groping experimentalist I share some of Dr. Strupp's discontent with our results thus far. We are discontented, perhaps, but not disgruntled. We should really blame ourselves rather than inherent limitations of experiment or an unwieldy subject matter. It seems to take long years of patient, primarily qualitative experimental work before a discipline can sort out and make inroads at those points where experiment will have its greatest yield. We are still moving, striving, inching along, trying out, and abandoning various experimental directions. Hilbert's advice for mathematical discovery was to make a lot of beginnings. I believe we are still in the phase of doing the necessary eliminative groundwork, and it may be that all these results will eventually prove negative or of little consequence. It is no secret among us that the crisis in behavioral science consists of the fact that time-honored methods of physical sciences and the tools of conventional mathematics have not advanced us much in dealing with persons. Perhaps we have not exploited

these methods intelligently enough, or perhaps we have already exhausted their yield in the domain of persons.

If only we could summon up greater ingenuity in the application of classical methods. Or alternatively, if we could develop some new perspective, invent some new angle of approach, construct a more serviceable paradigm theory to guide our research. Beginning efforts in this latter direction, I shall suggest, may be implicit in the imagery of Dr. Krasner's title "The Therapist as a Social Reinforcement Machine" and I am stressing the word "machine."

It may seem contradictory to you to hear someone who has been emphasizing therapy as an art now encourage a look at machines, since a machine appears antithetical to anything which might be termed art. But let us give Dr. Krasner's concept of a therapist as a social reinforcement machine some moments of cool attention. (I say cool because the issue of machines in human behavior arouses strong emotions which can be noted at dinner parties of both clinicians and chi-square scientists.)

Dr. Krasner suggests that we view the psychotherapist as a controller of behavior whose influence is achieved through the mechanism of generalized reinforcement and then gives us an excellent review of the documented work using this approach. Some therapists might not like this image of themselves as influencers and controllers, perhaps since it connotes something which has been considered disreputable in the history of psychotherapy, namely, suggestion. Suggestion has had a sinister connotation of influencing a person against his will, without allowing him to bring his critical faculties to bear on what is being done, often to his detriment rather than benefit. But there should be no objection to viewing a therapist as an influencer. Influence is not necessarily a term of opprobrium. The therapist does attempt to influence a patient, and the patient wants him to; otherwise, he would not be there. The modern exploratory psychotherapist tries to design treatment in a way that the patient does participate and does use his critical faculties in subjecting what is done to rational inquiry. We have some degree of control and influence over a patient. When it comes to psychotic and neurotic states I certainly wish we had greater influence than we do in relieving persons of this type of mental suffering. The difficulty seems to be, granted that we influence and control, what is effective and what are its mechanisms of action?

That a mechanism of action involves reinforcement I find plausible enough, but it does not go far enough to be a satisfactory explanation. I shall be as unsparing of psychology as I have been of psychiatry and say that the criticism I have for the category "schizophrenia" I also have for the category "reinforcement." What is to be included under this term and what are the limits of the category? It lacks specification of detail and is neither exclusive nor exhaustive enough. If everything one person says or does to another qualifies as reinforcement, then the category is too general to be useful. Also missing in the reinforcement view of therapy is an explicit answer to the question, what is being reinforced by a therapist? Hopefully the probability of every response is not being strengthened, since this would accentuate the imbalance of an already unstable system. One might say that in therapy we are extinguishing neurotic responses while strengthening healthy responses. But this crude a dichotomy would be too vague, too global an attempt to differentiate response classes. It may remove the mysticism from therapy, but it does not remove the mystery of the beneficial effect of person on person, at least for me.

Experimental work in operant conditioning certainly strongly supports the view that we can influence behavior in therapy. But in clinical discourse what is it that is effective and in what direction does this influence operate? The probabilities of behavior strengthened in therapy seem to involve response classes far more vital and combinatorially complex than the frequency of plural nouns or an increase of self-references. The strengthening of these latter response classes has been demonstrated first perhaps since they are easiest to measure. But in clinical discourse when a therapist says to a woman "you try to weaken a strong man in revenge for your father leaving you" and the patient responds for 20 minutes with affectively intense, shifting, but colligated associations to this utterance, we find ourselves in a maze of response classes of quite a different order of magnitude. In this situation of a series of compound inputs, of a continuous flow of associational information, of long sequences of utterances bearing meanings, of the processing of meaning through an exchange of messages, reinforcement theory is at present too abstract. For this situation, in which the factors are singularly plural, we need a greater specification of detail, a greater concern with the *meaning* of utterances, a facing up to the semantic problem of two-person discourse. It is at this point, to return to the last term in Dr. Krasner's title, that a machine, the computer or a computer-like artifact, might help us.

Again let us identify a crucial difficulty of the therapist which prevents him from doing more, from being more effective. He often finds himself lost in the great mass of semantic information provided by a patient in the course of therapy. In building up his internal working model or imago of a patient, he uses dozens of categories and stores in them hundreds, even thousands, of items. At any given moment only a fraction of this model is accessible to working retrieval by the therapist, not necessarily because of neurotic factors in him—although this can happen—but because of intrinsic human limitations in processing large amounts of information. Therapy bogs down and often reaches an impasse when a therapist, more a sink than a source of information, seems to have exhausted the conceptual alternatives, when he cannot find a new heuristic, a way of reducing the search space, in order to advance his working model and to aid the patient in an increasing access to unrecognized but highly consequential nonrational beliefs. The therapist seems unable to get through to the patient with utterances of incisive significance to him. Could a computer be used as a research tool to investigate this problem? Could we simulate a therapist's mental operations by means of a computer program which contains the desired combinatorial complexity far greater than that which can be handled by ordinary verbal and statistical techniques? Would this be of any practical use?—the clinician in me asks. I don't know, it might be—the basic scientist in me answers. Certainly we should try to find better ways of reaching patients with spoken inputs which have a greater impact on them. We all sense that in therapy we are not fully utilizing the potential of person-on-person effect. We are missing something due perhaps to our own limitations as information processors.

Using computer metaphors, let us say that persons are programed, like machines, by experiences with other persons who in turn have been programed by still other persons. Where this all begins sounds like the chicken and egg problem, but this has never seemed to be much of a problem to me as long as one specified which chicken and which egg. If therapists modify the programs of patients, the research advantage of a computer program as a model of this process is that it is highly explicit, operational, and can be experimentally tested within a reasonable time using a set of understood physical mechanisms.

This is not the place nor am I the person to elaborate on the advantages and limitations of this machine perspective. When we make such analogies we hope to increase our knowledge of at least one of the analogous pair. In the machine-therapist analogy we may be finding out more about what we believe a machine is rather than what we believe a therapist is. But as children of our time, it is difficult not to be excited by the computer and the possibilities of adapting it to aid us in coping more successfully with the problematique of psychotherapy.

I feel Dr. Krasner is quite correct in stating that psychotherapy represents only one aspect of the general problem of behavior and person control by means of communication. Elucidating difficulties in psychotherapy may contribute to an entirely new science of independent status, a science of persons as information processors, as Pasteur's discovery of microorganisms in wine helped the wine-making art somewhat but mainly contributed to the new science of bacteriology. If this is so, and particularly if computer-like machines fulfill their sense of promise, we must consider Dr. Krasner's final ethical warnings very seriously or we in the humanistic sciences will be caught unprepared for the social and political consequences of our work as were atomic scientists 25 years ago. To compare ourselves now with atomic scientists represents perhaps a presumptuous and prestige-borrowing overevaluation of our powers. But the more I witness of the population explosion, the more I read of the exponential increase of scientific work, and the more I learn about the speed, storage, learning, and creative capacities of the computer, the more I wonder if we shall be prepared.

At the start of my discussion I mentioned that our trouble lay in deciding the next worthwhile research steps in studying therapists. I commented on those fruitful relations which historically have held between a practical art and science and suggested we use our knowledge of them as charts for these steps. Then I offered opinions as to what two of the next steps might be in (*a*) studying the therapists working mental operations and (*b*) simulating them in mind-like arti-facts such as computer programs. These suggestions obviously stem from personal commitments which I am prepared to defend, to reinforce, or to abandon in the course of our group discussions. If they must be abandoned, I would certainly hope to go home having acquired some better ones.

# Therapist's Contribution

DR. HUNT: I find myself wondering if it would not provide the best use of our time to give the authors of the four papers an opportunity to respond to Dr. Colby's remarks before we open the circle to permit general discussion. I should like to start by calling on Dr. Betz.

DR. BETZ: I will speak briefly to the comments on my studies. The matter of homogeneity and diagnosis is an important one about which it is difficult to get perfect agreement among clinicians. The criteria in our clinic are, I would think, roughly the same as those in other comparable American university hospitals, perhaps somewhat on the conservative side. In addition to diagnosis based on clinical manifestations, we also utilize what we call a "personal diagnostic formulation." This involves taking into consideration certain personal issues or interpersonal difficulties which seem crucial in producing the clinical manifestations. For instance, a difficulty in establishing a non-oppositional relationship with another human being, so that aloofness or separateness are conspicuous interpersonal features, weighs heavily with us toward the schizophrenic diagnosis. Our main concern in these studies has been for reliable comparability between the patients treated by doctors with high or low success rates. To assure comparability, we used a common standard for the two groups, official hospital records. In our hospital case records, the diagnosis and condition on discharge are written into the record, at discharge, not by the patient's therapist, but by the Chief Resident in Psychiatry, after consultation with

the staff and with the approval of the Chief of service.

At the present time, Dr. Astrup, from Oslo, Norway, who is spending a year in our clinic, is making an independent diagnostic survey of our research case records, following Langfeldt's distinction between true schizophrenia and schizophreniform psychosis. This will provide an opportunity to compare our diagnostic practices with those of the Scandinavian psychiatrists.

Dr. Colby's hypothesis that the B doctors may be more frightened by patients who lose control, and so perhaps curb spontaneity in the sicker patients has a valid ring. In counseling doctors with a view to assisting them with their schizophrenic patients, one can often discern in some who are having difficulties, a more marked uneasiness in their contact with the patients, than in others who are not much bothered by the same type of behavior. The B doctors often have a good deal of intellectual understanding of what needs to be done, and perhaps how to go about it, but have difficulty in implementing this understanding when *with* the patients. They seem more able to think about what has gone on with the patient *after* the fact rather than while events are in progress, whereas the A doctors can participate rather immediately in interchange with the patient. This seems to me a phenomenon of considerable interest, meriting further study.

DR. HUNT: Thank you, Dr. Betz. I know many of you would like to ask questions or make comments. So would I.

102

But let us hear next Dr. Krasner's response to Dr. Colby's remarks.

DR. KRASNER: While listening to and enjoying Dr. Colby's paper, I had my pencil poised to reply to the comments I anticipated he would make about my paper. Much to my surprise, I agreed with most of what he said.

First, I want to clarify my view of the nature of the studies described in my paper. Conditioning studies have been termed "laboratory" studies or experimental analogues of psychotherapy. I feel that these terms may be misnomers. Most of us are so involved in the psychotherapy process, both in research and in clinical practice, that there has developed an aura of sacredness about the process. For example, in Dr. Strupp's fine paper there is almost a note of apology that his research was not done in the actual therapy situation. Many investigators imply that the process of psychotherapy, as now practiced, is the royal and only road to changing people's behavior. The yardstick for the acceptability for research then becomes "how close is this to the real psychotherapy process?" I feel strongly that we are losing sight of the purpose of psychotherapy, which is to change people's behavior. The purpose of psychotherapy is *not* "to do" psychotherapy, as such. Therapists often write and talk about psychotherapy as an important process from which they obtain considerable satisfaction. It is good for the therapist to enjoy psychotherapy and to feel that he is doing something important, but this is not the purpose of psychotherapy. The apologetic tone in papers which experimentally investigate behavior is uncalled for. These so-called laboratory studies have important implications for the psychotherapy process and derive some of their hypotheses from psychotherapy. However, I am less and less inclined to call them "experimental analogues" of psychotherapy. Rather, I see

them as part of a broader psychology of behavior control which is oriented toward devising techniques for the deliberate control, manipulation, and change of behavior. I would agree with Dr. Colby's point about the inconsequentiality of plural nouns. In our own studies we use emotional words primarily because of hypotheses derived from psychotherapy. But our basic aim is not to create an analogue of psychotherapy, but to devise techniques of behavior control.

I would also agree with Dr. Colby's comments about the apparent inadequacies in current reinforcement theory *completely* explaining psychotherapy. I have the same reaction to papers which "explain" psychotherapy in learning terms. What is accomplished in such papers is the substitution of one brand of explanation for another brand. I do not think that this is what we are doing in these operant conditioning studies. We are not trying "to explain" psychotherapy. We are not saying psychotherapy is a reinforcement process and these are the studies that prove it. Rather, we are saying that operant conditioning studies are related to studies in brainwashing, hypnosis, attitude influence, psychotherapy, and other subbranches of a more general psychology of behavior control.

Of course, the kinds of terminology used in behavior control studies often cause strong reactions from therapists. I have received a number of reactions from therapists to my paper which include: "I enjoyed reading your paper but I disagreed with everything in it." "Why do you use words such as 'machine,' 'manipulation,' and so on?" These are words that make therapists very uneasy. Although Dr. Colby admits that it is pretty well agreed that therapists do control behavior, many therapists really do not accept this notion. They refuse to acknowledge that they are actually manipulators of behavior. I would call it the "look, no hands" phenomena: "I am not really doing anything to you." Manipulation and control are words which go against the therapist's grain.

There are two other points I would like to make: one concerning training, the other ethics. I think that operant conditioning studies have major implications for training, both in psychotherapy specifically and psychology in general. There are many implications of these studies for the programing of future therapists. I might also add that for better or worse, operant conditioning has a strong attraction for students doing doctoral dissertations, and I suspect there will continue to be a veritable flood of such dissertations. In any case, the kind of thinking involved in these studies will have an important influence on the training of future psychology graduate students.

One final point, which Dr. Colby has made, and which I would like to emphasize: in investigating behavior control, there must be concern with ethical and value problems. Many investigators feel that to "manipulate" behavior is "bad." Carl Rogers, for one, has contended that to manipulate is to destroy. Within the last few years we have seen an increasing growth in behavior control studies: brainwashing, sensory deprivation, conditioning, and use of drugs. Psychotherapists increasingly are becoming interested in conditioning techniques as evidenced by the growth of interest in Wolpe's and similar work. Razran has recently written a fine paper on Russian conditioning techniques. You may have seen an article in a recent issue of *Harpers* which expressed concern about where research in psychology and psychiatry was headed and tried to anticipate the potential dangers to mankind inherent in studies of behavior control. Most of the studies in these areas are preliminary, and there is a long way to go before there is a really effective psychology of behavior control. Yet we must

give serious thought to the long-range implications and potential dangers in these kinds of studies. As a matter of interest, Oppenheimer some years back raised this very point and said that the danger to society inherent in investigation of techniques of behavior control is greater than investigations in the atomic energy area. If we conceive of the psychotherapist as a behavior controller, then the question of his ethics and value systems becomes of crucial importance. Further, the problem is whether you can investigate values through behavioral analysis. I think that it can be done, and we are trying some preliminary approaches to this problem. But, again, I think therapists are deceiving themselves if they are unwilling to face the issues here. There is now enough evidence to clearly show that the therapist value system cannot be kept out of psychotherapy.

DR. HUNT: Thank you, Dr. Krasner. Although I am tempted again to open the floor for discussion now, because I find myself wanting to ask questions and I suspect that all of you are pretty much like me, I shall repress this impulse (I can see by the expression on Dr. Shakow's face that it would technically be more correct for me to say *suppress* this impulse), and I shall ask Dr. Strupp for his response to Dr. Colby's remarks.

DR. STRUPP: Thank you. I would like to keep my comments brief to give others an opportunity. I was very much intrigued by two points in Dr. Colby's paper, namely: (*a*) his recommendations for the next steps involving naturalistic observations of expert craftsman therapists—as yet we have too few observations of this kind—and (*b*) his reference to experiments simulating the therapists' operations. I'd like to make a few observations about this.

First, the difficulties in naturalistic observations have been set forth extremely well in Dr. Butler's paper. He points out, among other things, that in making naturalistic observations you adopt already a frame of reference, a theoretical framework, and it is very difficult to make observations without being committed in advance to a definite point of view. Thus, one runs the danger of merely observing what one wants to observe or what one has already decided to observe.

Moreover, there seems to be a great upsurge of interest on the part of many researchers in naturalistic observation. I believe it was Dr. Luborksy, who pointed out in his *Annual Review* article a couple of years ago, that there has been a marked decline in good case history studies based upon naturalistic observation in clinical situations. However, during the past 2-3 years there has been a renewed interest along these lines. The study by Scheflen[1] of Dr. Rosen's work and the research conducted by Dr. Franz Alexander's group, and Dr. Shakow's group are good examples of this trend. This brings me to a basic question in this area, namely, experimentation versus naturalistic observation. I think we have more and more turned away during the last few years from crude *ad hoc* quantifications and from what I consider premature experimental attempts; rather, we prefer to look first more closely at the phenomena. This, I believe, is a very salutary development, because in many ways experimentation in this area is decidedly premature. The conceptualization of many experiments, especially in the verbal conditioning area, reveals a great hiatus between the clinical phenomena and the experimental operations; all too often, it seems to me, translations are very loosely made, and there is not sufficient understanding on the part of the experimenters of the clinical phenomena. The choice is not between experiments and naturalistic observation—clearly we are not dealing with an "either/or" proposition—but I believe we still have a great deal to learn from naturalistic observation, and it is a good thing that some of us are coming back to it.

DR. STEVENSON: I'd like to ask Dr. Betz a question. Dr. Betz, I was interested in Dr. Astrup's review of your cases, having in mind particularly other studies in Norway by Professor Langfeldt about different prognoses of these two types of schizophrenic-like illnesses, and as you know from Professor Langfeldt's work, which I think Dr. Astrup has also confirmed, the prognoses of what they call schizophrenia and schizophreniform psychosis is markedly different.

DR. BETZ: That has been the prevailing viewpoint, carrying with it a certain fatalistic implication about prognosis for the "process" schizophrenia group. It has the implication that this group, perhaps on a genetic or constitutional basis, is so constituted that effective therapeutic intervention is not possible. As more knowledge is gained, in dynamic terms, about this group and about therapeutic conditions favoring good outcome, this assumption may prove not to be absolutely valid. A somewhat analagous therapeutic outlook can be found in late nineteenth century medical textbooks about pernicious anemia and diabetes. Better knowledge about the nature of these illnesses has justified a more favorable prognostic view of these disabilities. One implication of the Phipps studies on schizophrenia is that what happens *next* may be more important than what has gone before, genetically or experientially. A potentiality to overcome a constitutional handicap may be present, if it can be elicited by appropriate therapeutic intervention.

DR. STEVENSON: I hadn't really reached my question, which is related to what I was saying about the different

<hr>

[1]Scheflen, A. E. *A psychotherapy of schizophrenia: Direct analysis.* Springfield, Ill.: Charles C Thomas, 1961.

prognoses in different groups of patients. I have wondered whether or not your residents had any influence on the selection of the cases assigned to them.

DR. BETZ: No.

DR. STEVENSON: I have been making some naturalistic observations of our residents, and it does seem that certain residents do select out certain kinds of patients, and they can influence the chief resident to channel certain kinds of patients in their direction and shift patients sometimes after the original assignment. I don't know to what extent this is a factor, but I wondered whether you had gone into this.

DR. BETZ: We have avoided shifting patients from one doctor to another. Our studies have been naturalistic rather than experimental.

DR. STEVENSON: Well, is your assignment completely randomized?

DR. BETZ: The assignment is random. The policy is for strict rotation. If there are occasionally little leaks in that, I don't think it is enough to count.

DR. HUNT: The First Conference on Research in Psychotherapy started with a great deal of emotionally loaded fencing back and forth among us participants, but it ended with a high level of communication among us. This communication was partly emotional. We achieved a stage where you could express an idea without fearing that someone would take a devastating poke at it, or at you. The communication was also substantive. I believe a considerable share of the change which I saw taking place during that first conference has endured and is to be found in the manner in which we are starting today. We appear to be starting this conference at the same high level of mutual confidence and understanding at which we ended three years ago.

As our authors have been responding to Dr. Colby's remarks, various of you have indicated to me that you have questions to ask or comments to make. I have been putting your names down here. I have the largest number of names under my notes on Dr. Krasner's responding remarks.

DR. SNYDER: I would like to address my remarks to Dr. Krasner. I found his article exciting, intriguing, stimulating, interesting, and everything else! I very much appreciated it, but I think I should say that, while he points out a fascinating idea, and discusses the similarity of these manipulative techniques to psychotherapy (and so far as that goes, isn't every human action a manipulative technique?), the differences are not brought out—the fact that brainwashing and psychotherapy are very different, also. For example, most people who are brainwashed are having this process done to them whether they want it or not—in fact, when they do not want it. Secondly, they are forced to do something that is not in line with what they conceive to be for their own good, which is different from what happens in much psychotherapy. So that I think the analogue cannot be considered total and complete; we still have differences, and I would be inclined to say, "Thank God, we aren't brainwashing yet. Let's try to avoid it."

DR. KRASNER: My reaction is to agree with you. I think that there are a number of similarities which cannot be ignored. However, this adds to the importance of investigations in this area which seek to determine both the elements of similarity and dissimilarity. To stress the ethical problem again, it is necessary for investigators with "good ethics" to learn more about these controlling techniques so that they can be used for the "good" of mankind. That there are some inherent dangers in these kinds of studies has been stressed previously. However, research in these fields must be, and will be, continued. What we are stressing is the need for thought to be given to the social applications and implications of these researches. To comment on the point about "doing something to a person against his will," isn't there a considerable element of this in psychotherapy? The person who winds up in psychotherapy is usually the person who has most consistently and successfully fought against having his behavior influenced via social pressures, and he still carries the battle over into the therapy situation. As a "naturalistic" observation I think that many patients who are in therapy do not really want their behavior changed, and in this sense, the therapist is trying to do something against their will. Dr. Frank has some interesting comments in his excellent new book on this viewpoint about psychotherapy and brainwashing, and perhaps he would like to comment on this.

DR. BUTLER: I really have a comment or two, not directly about Dr. Krasner's paper, but Dr. Strupp mentioned naturalistic observations versus experimental science. It seems to me that we often think of these as being somewhat different enterprises and it seems to me they can be different enterprises, but they shouldn't be. There is a sense in which you are going to get out of an experiment just what you put into it. Experiments test hypotheses; that's good. But they don't lead to discovery unless something goes wrong, unless there is some sort of a surprise. In the operant conditioning approach there are very precise ideas about methods of controlling and shaping behavior. The ideas about human nature and the process of psychotherapy connected with this approach seem to me not to be very precise. I think there should be a kind of interplay between observation, that is, taking in what is mysterious and surprising in such a way that substantial hypotheses and theories are contrived. These contrivances could then be tested,

perhaps, in the context of the approach Dr. Krasner is advocating. I think for some time there should be room for rather loose-jointed procedures so that the real mysteries can emerge and take form. There can be, as I say, a kind of limitation of discovery by experimentation; I think that possibly is what Dr. Strupp means by premature experimentation, experimentation based on method rather than on positive knowledge.

DR. LUBORSKY: I would like to make a comment, also, about Dr. Krasner's survey of research studies. One of the crucial necessities, I think, to make them more relevant to psychotherapy is the understanding of the patient or subject that the experimenter or the therapist has an interest in helping him. I believe that we were all in agreement with Dr. Frank's point about the tremendous importance of the therapist's intent to help a person and the person's recognition of that intent. Most or all of the studies you surveyed involved a relationship in which a subject is to be experimented upon. These studies might be more relevant if more of them added the helping intent as another ingredient of atmosphere. Otherwise, the studies could still be carried out in the usual style.

DR. KRASNER: These studies are in their early stages with their potentiality limited only by the ingenuity of the experimenter. One study I have recently heard about is that of Slack,[2] in which the operant conditioning approach was used to manipulate the usually unmanipulatable behavior of juvenile delinquents. This is the kind of study that moves in this direction. What would be your observation to that?

DR. BORDIN: I think Slack's procedure represented an ingenious process of bringing someone into a cooperative

[2] Slack, C. W. Experimenter-subject psychotherapy. *Ment. Hygiene,* 1960, **44**, 238-256.

relationship leading toward personality
change under conditions where the kinds
of persons he was dealing with would
not ordinarily do so. Now, if you recall
the conditions, he would bring them in
first as subjects in the experiment, but the
whole process is one of eventually under-
mining their doubts about other people
and their willingness to become part of a
changed process. Gradually, the subject
moves into conscious active collaboration.

DR. SHAKOW: Could I just make a
comment on what Dr. Butler just said?
We see so much overemphasis of method
in psychology—doctoral dissertation after
doctoral dissertation that does not really
grow out of theory but rather out of an
elegant and controllable method. I think
that we should consider the experimental
approach in the context of the kinds of
*goals* which Dr. Butler has just presented
rather than from the point of view of the
method, as it has been true so frequently
in the past.

DR. BORDIN: May I make a comment on this once again? I think there
would be a danger if we did not take account of three parts of the process of
adding to knowledge. One of them I
would put as curiosity, the second one, the
kind of creative action in discovery, and
the third one, the process of verification.

Now, I think that we underestimate—
and I am responding to Dr. Butler here—
we underestimate the importance of curiosity. In the search for knowledge, we too
readily assume that going through the
verification process cuts off discovery. If
curosity is strong enough, when one fails
to obtain verification, it can overcome the
tendency to rationalize the failure and can
lead to an examination of one's presuppositions. The failure to get verification
should lead to the re-examination of one's
own fund of naturalistic observation on
which presuppositions are based, with the
possibility of discovery coming in response to the failure to verify. So it seems

to me that it would be dangerous to
assume that discovery can only occur in
the naturalistic observation process. It
can occur as part of the cycle of verification and modification of hypotheses.

DR. KRASNER: By using manipulative reinforcing techniques to obtain our
goal.

DR. BORDIN: In general terms.

DR. BLOCH: I'd like to comment
briefly on that. I think the Slack work is
very relevant: one of the questions there
is who manipulates whom. The purpose
for which this particular system of paid
delinquent and conditioning intervener is
established may very well be for the intervener to change the delinquent. In talking
with Dr. Slack about it I had the impression that maybe it is the delinquent who
is interested in proving that the world is
really a manipulative place and people
will only use you for their own purposes
and, indeed, cannot be trusted. The stated
and open basis on which the agreement is
reached doesn't contain in it all the significant elements of the transaction. There
may indeed be other important things
going on.

DR. SHLIEN: As Dr. Bloch says, there
is a moot question of who is manipulating
whom. The patient is probably alert to the
possibility and nature of rewards, and
often knows what behaviors he must emit
to obtain approval, if he wants it. One
could argue that the patient controls the
therapist as much as the therapist controls
the patient, and this might seem to equal-
ize matters and take the curse off the
whole problem of control. I don't think
so. War is evil even when both sides are
evenly matched for mutual "influence."
Further, why assume without question
that control is necessary and inevitable in
all interaction, or that direction and control are therapeutic and therefore proper
objects of our study? There may be situations in which genuine freedom is pos-

sible, and freedom could be therapeutic. We might find attention, for instance, a generalized reinforcer which enables the patient to choose his own adaptation to a wider range of problems than we experimentally present.

I know that Dr. Krasner is duly sensitive to the ethical problems. Some of the logical problems worry me more. His paper has already been called provocative. I find parts of it downright outrageous. Of course this means it scares me, and of what am I afraid? I'm afraid, for one thing, that there is an attractive simplicity in such work that will lure people into mechanical techniques prematurely. I am more afraid that because these techniques do have some effect we will assume that people are predictable and controllable to a degree beyond that which they truly are. For my part, I feel that if they are really predictable and controllable, O.K.—go ahead and predict and control them to the utmost. But if they are not so predictable, then it is a crime against nature to set up a system which operates wholly on the assumption that you can predict and control.

Dr. Krasner suggests that the scientific problem is to find techniques whereby one can change the behavior of others. To my mind, that is a political problem. The scientific problem is to find and understand the internal mechanisms of behavior change. Once we know the basic mechanism, there may be many applications.

I wonder what Dr. Krasner would think about this point. It appears to me that the significant factor in change is the invention of the operant. Now I understand that we are not really talking about true operants, but about previously conditioned behaviors; however, using this language, I would say that the reinforcement is not the effective mechanism. It is only the external assistance given to a highly significant internal event. When a quiet student finally speaks in class, it may be based on an internal decision not yet reinforced or influenced by anything the teacher has done. What the teacher does next will probably influence how much more the student talks in the future, but what really counts is the invention, the first instance, of the operant. I think *that* is the primary element in change, and the emphasis on reinforcement seems to me to conceal what is primary.

Finally, I'd like to ask this question: If the therapist is a reinforcement machine, is the reinforcement machine a therapist? That is, if A is equal to B, is B also equal to A? If not, and I would guess that Dr. Krasner would not say that the machine is a human being, then B is not equal to A, but only part of A. I would ask, and think it very important to know, what is left in the therapist not accounted for by the machinery analogy.

DR. KRASNER: Well, I think there are three points involved. You are saying things that are similar to what Dr. Colby said. Implicit in what you are saying is that psychotherapy is not really approachable via assumptions that behavior is lawful and predictable. The evidence against this idea is quite strong and is supported by several of the studies reported here. In fact, the basic assumption in having a conference such as this one is that there are lawful relationships in psychotherapy. Whether in the long run you can account for all of psychotherapy in such lawful terms, or whether there will always be a certain amount of "humanity" which we cannot get at, certainly remains a question. I almost hope that you are right, but I do not think that we can assume this.

Secondly, insofar as the operant is concerned, again I think you are right. In order to reinforce operant behavior, an operant must first make its appearance. However, you can use these techniques to increase the likelihood of such an occurrence. By manipulating instructional set you can influence the kind of behavior you want. The same thing of course occurs in this other situation called psychotherapy. For example, how do you get a patient to talk about a specific topic you feel is relevant, such as sex? Generally, you wait until he says something and then you reinforce it. You may ask questions, you may probe, but you still aim to influence the frequency of this operant behavior after it has occurred.

Thirdly, I want to comment about the therapist being a human being. I do not really think that the therapist is a "machine" in the sense of being nonhuman. There are, however, certain analogies to machines that are relevant. I would particularly like to stress "programing," which involves the training of this therapist "machine." There have been recent studies which have demonstrated that by controlling the training techniques you can greatly alter the "machine's" behavior. I would like to see the kinds of techniques I have been describing influence training techniques so that there is a greater awareness on the part of the therapist of what he is doing and what he is potentially able to do in altering behavior. Does this make him any more or less human? Referring to the therapist as a "machine" very much arouses strong feelings in therapists who are kind, warm, helping people. However, I feel strongly that by stressing the kinds of potential techniques that can make the therapist more effective in his task of changing behavior, we are fulfilling our obligations as therapists and as human beings. I would contend almost paradoxically that thinking in terms which are optimistic about the potentiality of change in human behavior makes us more human.

I want to make another point that I think is relevant here. Most of the studies I have cited are being done by clinical psychologists. All too frequently there is an inclination on the part of "applied" people to resent experimental psychologists interpreting clinical phenomena by

extrapolating from the rats to human beings. However, in the operant conditioning studies most of the investigators are trained in clinical work, with the same value systems and interests as psychotherapy researchers. I think this fact should be noted in evaluating the "machine" conceptualization.

DR. FRANK: To go back to John Shlien and put it most sharply, it seems to me that one way to find out just how spontaneous people are and what the limits of influence are is to try to influence them. I think we will find that there are real limits. Even the effects of brainwashing do not last very long when people come back to their environment, for example. Similarly, when you talk about trying to understand the change of behavior—one of the ways to understand is to try to change it. Kurt Lewin called this action research. The most useful ways of learning about something is to try to modify it because then you know what you are introducing into the system and you see what happens. Then, finally, I would like to ask a question for information. It is my understanding that the operant conditioning procedure works only on behavior and is not a method for influencing emotional states, and in psychotherapy we are trying to influence feelings and not just verbalizations. Is this a real limitation of operant conditioning or is it not?

DR. KRASNER: I don't think so. One of the most important areas of investigation is that of the relationship between changes in words and simultaneous changes in emotions. It would be reasonable to assume that if you are changing a person's talking about emotions, then you are changing his emotions. It certainly is worth investigating. Some of this was implicit in your comments last night.

DR. STEVENSON: I just wanted to touch on what seems to be another important point with regard to the operant conditioning studies. This is, that they don't demonstrate, as I see it, new influences on human behavior but rather how it can influence past behavior covertly. If you want to have a patient talk about sex, one of the best ways is to ask him to do so. You can also say "un-hunh" every time he makes a reference to sex, but this is a very time-consuming way. Several members of our staff are interested in verbal reinforcement. We had a woman patient who was wearing pants and slacks around the ward and we decided that she ought to differentiate herself more sharply as a woman. We were trying to influence her to wear dresses and skirts, and we set up an elaborately designed program for the nurses to praise her every time she was in a dress and to be cool to her whenever she wore slacks. While we were getting this design established, one of the residents, who was rather brusque went to the patient and said, "Look, I don't want to see you wearing slacks and pants any more. Get in dresses and stay in dresses." That was all that was required.

DR. SASLOW: I wanted to say a word on a point which Dr. Frank just made to Dr. Krasner. I thought of the observations of Pisoni and Salzinger in which they reinforce affectively laden statements and demonstrated that affectively laden statements were increased by this simple method. You don't have this in mind?

DR. FRANK: That is different.

DR. SHAKOW: They were affective words, weren't they? The words don't necessarily have to be laden. There were words like "mother" and "home." In discussing their paper at the Brussels meeting I said, "You've got all affective words, but did you have 'affect'?" This they couldn't answer. Now, whether they have carried out studies later which give evidence of the latter I don't know, but thus far all I see is the label.

DR. SASLOW: One other comment. It

is not an uncommon observation, especially when you are teaching younger people, that when a patient gives you a communication filled with much emotion, it isn't difficult to teach a resident to look upon the communications as being a multilevel message with one level the emotional level, another the concept level, and so on. You can teach him to respond or not to respond to any one or more of these levels. If he can learn how to practice nonresponse to an extremely hostile component of the message or to respond to the content without the emotional response, in a very short time you will have an entirely different kind of behavior, including some affective change in the patient. Subsequently you can reopen the topic that you wished to have discussed.

DR. FRANK: Let me say that I am quite sure that we influence our patients. I am not sure this is the mechanism by which it happens, and that is the only question I was raising.

DR. LENNARD: I think we might also consider that the patient in turn influences the therapist, even though the extent and type of influence may be very different. There has been very little work on this process, though there is the suggestion based on studies of doctor-patient relationships that the direction of influence is not all one-sided. It may not be any particular patient who exerts the influence but the types of patients seen by a physician over longer periods of time. For example, physicians whose practice is mainly limited to patients of lower socioeconomic status will in time differ, insofar as some elements of treatment procedure and approach are concerned, from a physician who is mainly seeing a group of wealthy patients. Such differences may be attributed to the physician's response to particular expectations and demands which subsequently result in modification in procedure and approach. I would not at all be surprised if studies of psycho-

therapists and types of practice (in terms
of their social composition or diagnostic
specialization) would not yield similar
findings. I suggest that the influence of
the therapists' "patient set" upon his
therapeutic and personal outlook is worthy
of attention.

DR. STRUPP: I would like to come
back to one comment by Dr. Krasner
which struck me very much. I refer to his
statement that the typical patient who
comes to psychotherapy is the sort of person who for a variety of reasons, which
often can be traced genetically, has learned
in childhood to resist social influence (by
parents and other authority figures). Now,
it seems to me that a good part of the
therapist's effort is directed at breaking
down these resistive patterns and to show
the patient that it isn't expedient and
adaptive to resist authority figures in this
way. As the patient comes to experience
that it is in fact safe and that he is better
off to follow a different path, he becomes
more open to experience and in general
he "feels better." All this is by way of
saying that in breaking down resistances
the therapist is, as it were, "conditioning"
the patient explicitly and indirectly at the
same time. I am also asking, as did Dr.
Frank, are we conditioning verbal behavior, or are we conditioning emotions?
Perhaps a method could be devised to
test this.

DR. HUNT: I would like to change
here because we have comments on Frank,
Colby, and Betz here that I would like to
come back into. Is there another quick
comment on this?

DR. LUBORSKY: Yes, one of the
points made by Dr. Frank had to do with
the tiny role of the truth of an interpretation in the effectiveness of that interpretation. I wondered how far he would go
in maintaining that. One of the hardest
things in the course of learning to engage
in psychotherapy is to listen. And I have

noticed that the patient himself is usually
listening. When one says something that
is to the point of what the patient is expressing, one gets more response from the
patient. Your statement was that it is not
the truth but the belief of the patient that
is crucial. What I want to add is that cap-
turing an aspect of the truth will make a
great difference too.

DR. FRANK: During the coffee break
Dr. Colby pointed out that what I was
saying was a truism. All truth is nothing
but consensus anyway. I think that the
point I was making is that we sometimes
search too hard to find exactly the precise
and correct interpretation, assuming there
is something that it applies to, whereas
what really counts is plausibility in terms
of what the patient has said and what
makes sense to you. I suppose this is
where the skill of the therapist comes in.

DR. LUBORSKY: It does have a different ring if stated that way. One hopes
for at least an aspect of the truth in an
interpretation; your address included an
illustration of a very plausible interpretation.

DR. MAHL: I was going to ask Dr.
Frank the same question about his paper
last night that Dr. Luborsky asked.

I want to respond to the concern shown
earlier that there might be many Ph.D.
theses done applying the operant conditioning technique to the interview simply
because there was now a method available.
Those who expressed concern about pushing the method to the limit implied that
in principle this would be a bad thing. I
don't share that concern. As I remember
Dr. Conant's review of the history of the
concepts of atmospheric pressure and of
Boyle's law of gases, these principles
didn't develop until people had spent
many years playing around with the barometer and with the vacuum pump. Boyle,
according to Dr. Conant, did studies num-
bering in the hundreds with the vacuum

pump, and as a result of thus pushing this method to the extreme he was able to arrive at the basic laws of gases. The same thing happened with the barometer and the concept of atmospheric pressure. Freud certainly pushed the "free association" method, applying it to symptoms, spontaneous verbal and ideational material, dreams, tongue-slips, lapses of memory, "meaningless" acts, etc. When he was making his great discoveries, he apparently did this at the drop of a hat. I think that we shouldn't in principle condemn this massive exploration of a new method. We might ask information theorists about the ratio of new discoveries to quantity of information input.

Dr. Colby's discussion prompts the following comments. His remarks about the partial identifications every therapist makes with his patients struck a certain resonance in me. I wonder if this process isn't more important than his brief comments about it would indicate. Does this capacity to make partial identifications in a controlled way have anything to do with the distinction between Dr. Betz's A and B therapists and with the dimension of spontaneity and freedom of expression Dr. Butler wrote about in his paper? The capacity for partial identifications might make a therapist more successful. It's a form of sublimated libidinal tie with a patient which I believe is bedrock for any successful therapeutic venture. The analytic writing on empathy, understanding, and the basis for interpretation emphasizes a capacity for controlled identification by the therapist with the patient. It is regarded as one of the processes giving birth to empathy and one's ability to understand the patient. I have wondered, Dr. Betz, if you had any observations about differences in capacity for controlled, partial identifications between your A and B doctors.

DR. BETZ: The question is important but difficult to answer with evidence. I

have talked with residents informally, attempting to learn about what is going on in them while they are working with schizophrenic patients. From such conversations I have had some leads. For instance, one resident who has a high success rate with his schizophrenic patients, told me that when he feels in contact with a patient, the patient at that moment seems to represent to him some prototype from his own earlier experience—either a personal identification, or some person who had been important and meaningful to him with whom he had felt a very sympathetic response.

What is it that engages the therapist's interest in a profound way, so that the patient gets some sense of contact? I think that it is an important consideration—what these matters are in the therapist that enable this to occur.

DR. MAHL: But I think this is something so important that it would underlie many of the profound manifestations of the therapist's characteristics and it ought to be studied.

DR. BORDIN: I would like to add some suggestions to those that have already been made as to where one might seek the answer to why it is that these A and B doctors seem to have a different impact. The suggestions I have to offer grow out of work we have been doing on how personality factors condition vocational choice. The not very original idea, of course, is that the people do choose those occupations whose activities permit them to indulge in their preferred ways of both expressing and controlling their impulses and their emotions. Some of our research has involved comparisons of lawyers with dentists, some comparisons of accountants, not CPAs, and creative writers, as well as physicists and clinical psychologists. I am using my impression of what is involved in these occupations as developed from this research. One direction would be to choose which of the possible ways in which the relevant occupations differ are the crucial ones in terms of this therapeutic situation. For example, it is obvious that a lawyer makes use of words. Is it that the A doctor is more verbal? Some of your comments about them referred to being able to respond and not being at loss for words—this is changing slightly what you said. This is one occupational group. Another one is creative writers who on the Strong would seem to fall into the same general group as lawyers, the verbal group. Research has suggested that creative writers are persons who were searching for identifications. Perhaps part of being a creative writer is being able to put yourself in the place of other persons, to see the world the way other people do. Creative writers seem to be, in this case as contrasted with accountants, persons who did not form a very tight identification. The accountants seemed to have a very tight identification and did not tend to look at the world from different points of view; instead, the creative writers were the ones who were trying on how other people thought, and perhaps this is part of this partial identification process.

Another one has to do with the issue of how directly a person expresses his interpersonal curiosity. We suggest that clinical psychologists, for example, express their interpersonal curiosity very directly. I have the impression that lawyers do. The very practice of law, with its access to people's secrets provides this special opportunity. By comparison, the accountant mostly has access to people's financial secrets, which represents a displacement from one of the original sources of curiosity, curiosity about interpersonal relationships. This, then, may be another factor to consider.

Another one which I saw as being of possible relevance is the willingness to respond spontaneously. We see some suggestions of difference between the accountant who is much more conventional and less free as compared to lawyers, creative writers, and apparently clinical psychologists. I don't know about psychiatrists; we haven't studied them. So these are the kinds of ideas that strike me as possibly being worth pursuing. What you have is alternative interpretations of your data, and I think this is part of what Dr. Colby was talking about.

# II.

## RESEARCH PROBLEMS RELATING TO MEASURING PERSONALITY CHANGE IN PSYCHOTHERAPY

---

# The Patient's Personality and Psychotherapeutic Change[1]

### LESTER LUBORSKY, PH.D.

### OVERVIEW

In 1954, after five years of prior planning and constructing of instruments, the Psychotherapy Research Project of the Menninger Foundation took its present shape. Despite the numerous "outcome" research reports in the literature, we felt there was an immense need for an intensive "outcome-process" research on psychoanalysis and other *long-term* psychotherapies. We aimed to find and refine hypotheses on *what* changes in psychotherapy and *how* and *why* these changes come about.

This is a progress report on some leads suggested by a segment of data from the Psychotherapy Research Project. An overview of the project is necessary to introduce the present topic. Briefly, our plan called for assessment of 42 patients by teams of clinicians before treatment, at the end of treatment, and two years later. Our approach entailed naturalistic observation (which implies minimal interference with clinical processes) from three angles simultaneously (patient, treatment, and therapist, and life-situational variables), combined with length of observation (the whole period of long-term treatment plus a two-year follow-up) and a

[1] This paper is from the Psychotherapy Research Project of the Menninger Foundation. Although analysis of these data and writing were done separately in Philadelphia, in a very real sense, all 19 members of the Psychotherapy Research Project have been co-workers and co-contributors (Robert S. Wallerstein, Lewis L. Robbins, Gerald A. Ehrenreich, Michalina Fabian, Mildred Faris, Helene D. Gerall, Bernard H. Hall, Leonard Horwitz, T. W. Mathews, Martin Mayman, Herbert C. Modlin, Gardner Murphy, Majorie Orth, Irwin Rosen, Helen Sargent, Richard S. Siegal, Ernst Ticho, Gertrude R. Ticho, and Harold M. Voth). Drs. Robert Wallerstein, Gardner Murphy, and Bernard Hall especially contributed suggestions for final revisions. Dr. Wayne Holtz-man has been an active and stimulating consultant to the project for many years and specifically has participated crucially in the formulation of this report. Dr. Irving Janis and Dr. Albert Stunkard have been over a draft of the manuscript and aided its development. Miss Lolafaye Coyne has had the principal load of the considerable statistical work and has contributed to its elucidation in this report. Mr. Kenneth Berg has shared some of the statistical work. My colleague, Dr. Robert Downing, has discussed aspects of the report with me.

The work of the project has been generously supported initially by the Foundations' Fund for Research in Psychiatry and subsequently by the Ford Foundation.

balance between clinical and quantitative description.

There is no need to go into the details of our aims, method, rationale (Wallerstein, Robbins, Sargent, & Luborsky, 1956; Luborsky, Fabian, Hall, Ticho & Ticho, 1958; Sargent, Modlin, Faris, & Voth, 1958), and operational problems of method (Hall & Wallerstein, 1960; Wallerstein & Robbins, 1960), for much has been published on these topics. The present report is the first in which we are able to give a portion of our results.

*Patients, Therapists, and Research Staff*

At this time (December, 1960) we have completed assessments of 24 patients before treatment and at termination. Sixteen of these were again followed up and studied two years later. To go through our research procedures on this number of patients has required five years of work and waiting. We estimate another four years at least before all 42 patients have completed treatment and we have completed the assessment on them at all three points.

The patients were selected from among those assigned to psychotherapy and psychoanalysis by the Menninger Clinic's Psychotherapy Service. Because of the problems of finding adequate cases in the clinical population, the selection is not completely random (Wallerstein & Robbins, 1960, pp. 167-170). Only those cases who had been given a complete examination by the Outpatient Service or the Hospital Service were included in the research. Of our total group of 42 patients, half were to be in psychoanalysis and half in other forms of long-term psychotherapy. The 24 cases in this report approximately follow this proportion (11 were in psychoanalysis and 13 in other forms of psychotherapy).

The therapists were those assigned to the patients by the regular Menninger Foundation procedures. Although certain criteria were applied for inclusion of the therapists in the project, the group is probably roughly representative of the therapists at the Menninger Foundation (Wallerstein & Robbins, 1960, pp. 178-180). By usual standards the group of therapists would be considered experienced psychotherapists.

A research team of two or three clinicians from the Psychotherapy Research Project was assigned to do the research assessment: Lewis Robbins and Robert Wallerstein assumed responsibility for the patient variables at the time of initial studies (and predictions about anticipated course and outcome of treatment); Bernard Hall, Lester Luborsky, Ernst Ticho, Gertrude Ticho, and Michalina Fabian have divided up the work on the patient variables and treatment variables for both the termination and follow-up studies; for the situational variables, Harold Voth, Herbert Modlin, Helen Sargent, Mildred Faris, and Marjorie Orth have shared the work at initial, termination, and follow-up points.

*Aims and Methods*

The general aim of the present report is to examine some patient variables which may be connected with change in patients in long-term treatment. In carrying out this aim, we will:

(*a*) Examine the scores derived from the initial clinical assessments of the patient variables, in particular their reliabilities, intercorrelations, and principal factors. Each of these patient variables had been chosen originally because of hypotheses relating them to the course and outcome of psychotherapy.

(*b*) Examine relationships between the patient variables and an estimate of change during treatment. At this stage of the project, the available measure of change is derived from the Health-Sickness Rating Scale (which is described below under the heading of "Change in Health-Sickness Rating").

(c) Illustrate by (a) and (b) some of the problems of selecting estimates of change and describe our preferred methods for expressing change in patient variables, to be used in the final analysis of the results.

The worth of a judgment about a person rests partly on the quality of the information from which the judgments are made. Before going into the specific methods of estimating the variables or change in the variables, we must say more about the observations. The collection and organization of the information in the various forms was the work of the three teams of clinician-researchers. For the description of the patient, treatment, and life situation at "Initial," "Termination," and "Follow-up," the teams drew upon the views of a number of informants: the patient, therapist, supervisor of the therapy, psychological tester, the patient's relatives, and at times the patient's employer. Thus we have a broad base of observation from which to derive judgments of the variables and changes in these.

Three major ways of assessing our data are planned. One will be a clinical synthesis for each of 42 individual case histories. A second major approach will be the detailed categorization of predictions by a formal logical system, with the examination of our line of reasoning for each individual confirmation or refutation. The third major way will be the statistical handling of the data that derive from the paired comparisons (to be described below). It is from a portion of this last method that the material for this paper was drawn.

PATIENT VARIABLES

*Choice of Variables*

As part of putting the project into its present shape, we distilled into 28 vari-

ables the best clinical experience from psychoanalytic and other sources on patients' qualities relevant to the course and outcome of treatment. These variables are defined and described elsewhere (Wallerstein, Robbins, Sargent, & Luborsky, 1956). When the time came to apply our major quantitative method of paired comparisons to these patient variables, we selected for the purpose only 12 variables. These were the ones which seemed most suitable for paired comparison judgments. "Somatization," for example, did not seem able to stand by itself as a variable, since most of our patients had little or none of it. Although we used only 12 of these variables in the paired comparisons, we continued to write our qualitative descriptions for every one of the original 28 variables (that is, our Form B).

The twelve variables are listed below (the numbers in parentheses refer to the concepts described on pp. 241-250 in the above reference):

1. Anxiety Level (II-1)
2. Severity of Symptoms (II-2, 3)
3. Self-Directed Aggression (II-4)
4. Extent to which the Environment Suffers (II-5), (i.e., as a direct result of the patient's illness)
5. Externalization (IV-5)
6. Psychosexual Development (III)
7. Integration of Defenses (IV-2)
8. Anxiety Tolerance (IV-3)
9. Insight (IV-4)
10. Ego Strength (IV-6)
11. Motivation (VI)
12. Quality of Interpersonal Relationships (VII)

*The Paired Comparisons Method of Judging Variables*

Our research requirements seemed best met by rank order statistics, specifically by an adaptation of the classical Fechnerian method of paired comparisons by Sargent (1956). We were investigating the effects of many variables with a relatively small number of patients (rather than a few well-defined variables on many patients). We needed a method that, by providing a quick examination of many variables, would help tell us which were worth the huge work of exact measurement. We made a beginning at such work in the construction of our instrument for assessing the Health-Sickness dimension. Ordinal scaling also has the advantage of assuming only that the individual is higher or lower on a scale; metric scaling requires measurable distances between points. Ordinal scaling refers more specifically to the relationships within the population. Finally, the preferred style of quantitative thinking by clinicians is most often in terms of a patient at hand having more or less of a quality than another patient.[2]

To pair every patient with every other

_____

[2] To be precise, the paired comparisons technique eventuates in a scale that is more than ordinal but less than equal interval. To explain this further: if a judge could clearly differentiate all 12 patients in a batch and make consistent choices, Patient A would get 11 choices, the next patient 10 choices, and so on down to the last one who would have zero choices. There would be no ties. However, the paired comparisons method allows for natural inconsistencies to appear (which the less time consuming ranking method would not); e.g., A is chosen over B, B over C, but C is chosen over A. Such inconsistencies may result in ties. (This may be thought of as low internal consistency or, more penetratingly, a reflection of the difficulty of distinguishing patients in a certain range.) Thus we will have more than an ordinal scale, since extreme differences in the patients will show in a stretch out of the distribution and small differences will show in bunching-up of the distribution of number of choices. We therefore learn something about which patients are closer to others and which further apart. We still cannot say, for example, that two patients who are five numbers apart in the low end of the scale are the same distance apart as two patients who are five numbers apart in the high end of the scale, but we do know more than that one patient is higher than the other.

patient in a group the size of ours would be an impossibly difficult task. In Sargent's form of the paired comparisons procedure, the name of each patient was paired with every other in a batch of only 12 patients. The 42 cases had been broken down by random sorting into overlapping batches of 12 patients each. Each batch contained 6 patients in psychoanalysis and 6 in other forms of psychotherapy; this rule of thumb division was intended to stretch the variety of patients in each batch. The clinician had only to decide for each pair "which of these two patients has more (of the variable)?" The clinician was not expected to make a new assessment of the patient but rather to refer constantly to the forms compiled by the research team. The list of pairs was filled out independently by two judges. So far, these judges have been members of the Psychotherapy Research Project.

It will be of special interest to those who might use the paired comparisons method to know that clinicians find themselves quite comfortable in making these choices, much more so than when they are asked for ratings of the variables. A problem in this method appears when too many pairs are being judged at one sitting; the process becomes quite tedious.

*Interjudge Agreement*

To establish the comparability of batches, each patient appeared in two different ones. With our 42 cases, 7 overlapping batches were composed. The seventh was formed by blending the last 6 cases with the first 6 cases. Every batch was rated by two judges. Since 11 is the highest number of choices a patient can receive from each judge, and each patient appears in two batches, total scores range from 0–44.

After completing the paired comparisons for all patient variables at the initial point, we had to make some slight adjustments for batch incomparability.[3] Patients may have been chosen a different number of times because they were being compared with a different group of patients or because the judge's judgments began to drift away from his earlier standards.

The agreement of the two judges who composed the research team at the initial point (LLR & RSW) was high.[4] What we have here is a form of "clinical reliability." Although the two judges did the paired comparisons without discussion of the position of the patient in the paired comparisons, they had worked closely together in selecting and defining the variables and had based their conclusions recorded in the forms on extensive discussions of the case. Although these interjudge consistency figures do not tell us what can be done by two judges working in complete isolation, they indicate the degree of agreement that two judges can achieve after sharing the digestion of the

[3] The choices on the six overlapping patients in successive batches can differ in two ways: in *rank order* and *mean number of choices*. The first can be measured by a rank order correlation between the six patients on the two occasions; this type of incomparability was *not* changed by our scaling corrections. The second was corrected for the group by the scaling technique—all 12 variables went through one cycle of scaling in which the means for groups of overlapping cases on the total sample were equated by the addition or subtraction of a correction factor. (This does not mean that an individual patient will be corrected so that he has the same number of choices in both batches.) At this point the merger between the last batch and the first batch was tested. For 7 of the 12 variables, this merger was not good enough (after the one cycle of corrections had already been made) so that a slight adjustment of previous corrections had to be made.

[4] Consistency of pooled judges was estimated in two ways: by correlating each judge's scores on each variable in each batch and by correlating agreement of scores for each patient in successive batches of six patients. By both methods the median correlations over all batches for each variable were high—*all* correlations were above .85.

data and then making the paired comparison judgments independently.

*Intercorrelations*

The intercorrelations of the 14 variables (that is, with the addition of "Predicted HSR" and "Initial HSR") are generally high (see Table 1). The immediately obvious exceptions are "Anxiety Level" and "Self-Directed Aggression." We had expected considerable interrelationship since all variables were selected for their presumed bearing on the course and outcome of treatment. Possibly a halo effect contributes in part to the correlations; only more experience with these variables will tell us the extent to which this is applicable. However, it is important to note that even the highest correlations in this matrix do not imply completely overlapping variables; for example, a correlation as high as .70 only accounts for approximately 50% of the variance.

*Factor Analysis*

In picking a group of variables it is hard to tell the extent of their overlap and composition without trying them. Factor analysis is an excellent method for finding the major groupings of variables (specifically the least number of factors which would explain the intercorrelations) and the components of each patient variable (see Table 2).[5] By the Principal Components Method (Hotelling, 1933), the first factor will be the principal component.

We had expected, from our preliminary intercorrelation study on the first 12 patients (Luborsky & Sargent, 1956), that the first factor might also be the only factor, since the previous level of intercorrelation was even higher than the one

[5] To be precise, we did a *components analysis* which differs from factor analysis in that it finds the least number of factors (components) that can explain the *total variance* in all the variables.

reported here for 42 patients. Actually, there was much meaningful variation left beyond the first factor in the unrotated matrix: the principal component still left 40 percent of the common variance unexplained. Factoring was considered completed after five factors had been extracted, since by that point 90 percent of the estimated common variance had been taken out.

With the aim of finding simple structure of the factors, they were rotated by the Normal Varimax Method (Kaiser, 1958). This rotation method tends to maximize the heaviest loadings (with 42 cases, a rough rule of thumb would be that any loading of approximately .40 is sig-

nificant, while a loading of .30 or less is negligible) and minimize the lightest loadings across a factor.

We have tried to fit names to these factors and have listed them below, together with the variables having the largest loadings (i.e., over .50):

I. Personality Development and Strength (interpersonal relationships, psychosexual development, anxiety tolerance, ego strength, predicted HSR, integration of defenses, initial HSR). Note that the variables in this largest factor tend to be more encompassing variables referring to the patient's general level of functioning and resilience.

TABLE 1

INTERCORRELATION OF PATIENT VARIABLES AT THE INITIAL POINT
(Pearson Correlations, $N=42$)

|  | 1 | 2 | 3 | 4 | 5 | 6 | 7 | 8 | 9 | 10 | 11 | 12 | 13 | 14 |
|---|---|---|---|---|---|---|---|---|---|---|---|---|---|---|
| 1. Anxiety Level | x | | | | | | | | | | | | | |
| 2. Severity of Symptoms | .60 | x | | | | | | | | | | | | |
| 3. Self-Directed Aggression | .09 | .45 | x | | | | | | | | | | | |
| 4. Extent to which environment suffers | .38 | .75 | .23 | x | | | | | | | | | | |
| 5. Externalization | .34 | .60 | .10 | .86 | x | | | | | | | | | |
| 6. Level of Psycho-sexual Development | −.16 | −.56 | −.24 | −.44 | −.44 | x | | | | | | | | |
| 7. Patterning of Defenses | −.46 | −.84 | −.40 | −.67 | −.61 | .72 | x | | | | | | | |
| 8. Anxiety Tolerance | −.03 | −.53 | −.14 | −.59 | −.59 | .73 | .72 | x | | | | | | |
| 9. Insight | −.23 | −.38 | −.29 | −.36 | −.46 | .30 | .50 | .49 | x | | | | | |
| 10. Ego strength | −.41 | −.77 | −.21 | −.68 | −.63 | .74 | .93 | .81 | .49 | x | | | | |
| 11. Motivation | −.18 | −.58 | −.34 | −.63 | −.67 | .63 | .69 | .63 | .67 | .65 | x | | | |
| 12. Quality of Inter-personal Relationships | −.10 | −.62 | −.20 | −.56 | −.52 | .86 | .80 | .84 | .36 | .86 | .65 | x | | |
| 13. Initial Health-Sickness Rating | −.46 | −.84 | −.33 | −.72 | −.62 | .64 | .84 | .69 | .43 | .81 | .67 | .72 | x | |
| 14. Predicted Health-Sickness Rating | −.11 | −.62 | −.41 | −.57 | −.48 | .72 | .69 | .72 | .33 | .68 | .64 | .78 | .74 | x |

TABLE 2

ROTATED FACTOR LOADINGS OF PATIENT VARIABLES AT THE INITIAL POINT
(NORMALIZED VARIMAX)

| | I | II | III | IV | V | $h^2$ |
|---|---|---|---|---|---|---|
| 1. Anxiety Level | −.02 | .95 | .01 | −.09 | .15 | .94 |
| 2. Severity of Symptoms | −.50 | .58 | .37 | −.08 | .43 | .92 |
| 3. Self-Directed Aggression | −.12 | .06 | .96 | −.14 | .04 | .96 |
| 4. Extent to which environment suffers | −.35 | .26 | .13 | −.10 | .85 | .94 |
| 5. Externalization | −.30 | .17 | −.04 | −.28 | .35 | .92 |
| 6. Level of Psychosexual Development | .89 | −.08 | −.09 | .12 | −.09 | .83 |
| 7. Patterning of Defenses | .72 | −.44 | −.23 | .26 | −.29 | .91 |
| 8. Anxiety Tolerance | .82 | .06 | .04 | .29 | −.33 | .87 |
| 9. Insight | .19 | −.13 | −.13 | .93 | −.16 | .96 |
| 10. Ego Strength | .79 | −.38 | −.03 | .25 | −.31 | .92 |
| 11. Motivation | .50 | −.02 | −.22 | .58 | −.45 | .83 |
| 12. Quality of Interpersonal Relationships | .93 | −.05 | −.05 | .14 | −.22 | .93 |
| 13. Initial Health-Sickness Rating | .65 | −.41 | −.23 | .16 | −.42 | .84 |
| 14. Predicted Health-Sickness Rating | .77 | .01 | −.36 | .06 | −.32 | .82 |
| Percent of variance | 41.5 | 14.9 | 11.0 | 12.7 | 20.0 | 90.0 |

II. Anxiety Level (anxiety level, severity of symptoms).

III. Self - Directed Aggression (self-directed aggression).

IV. Insight (insight, motivation).

V. Externally focused illness (extent to which the environment suffers, externalization).

These five are the essences remaining after the factor analytic boiling down. In evaluating a patient's potential for change in treatment, the two judges in our project relied especially upon the main factor, "Personality Development and Strength," together with the other four factors.

METHODS FOR ESTIMATING CHANGE

We had supposed that the variables—probably in a unique combination for each patient—would help in predicting the outcome of the treatment. To take the next step of actually relating these patient variables (and the factors) to change requires a tough decision about what to accept as an estimate of change. The most

usual solution is to rely upon the therapist's rating of "improvement." This usually requires nothing more sophisticated than a four-to-eight point poorly defined scale; i.e., the judge is permitted to weight in his own way any aspects of change which he values in his concept of mental health. The rating cannot reveal either the point at which the patient started or the nature of the change. Used by itself, it is generally considered to be a crude and often misleading measure of change (Miller, 1951; Sanford, 1953; Luborsky, 1954; Parloff, Kelman, & Frank, 1954).

Many refinements of improvement scales have been attempted (Lorr, 1954). A highly developed one is the "Hunt Movement Scale" (Hunt, 1950). The University of Chicago Counseling Center project tried, among other methods, a rating by the therapist of "success" (Seeman, 1954) and a scale for "adjustment" as judged from the TAT (Dymond, 1954). The recent Phipps Psychiatric Clinic study (Frank, 1959) relied upon well-defined criteria of improvement; they used differences before and after treatment in the patient's position on "discomfort" and "social ineffectiveness" scales.

A different approach to investigating change is represented by Muench (1947). He was one of the first to investigate the variety of changes in the patient (as opposed to restricting attention to improvement in mental health) in his study of test score differences before and after treatment. An exacting method has been proposed for registering change on dimensions which are tailor-made for each individual (Luborsky, 1953): intercorrelating intra-individual measurements taken from the therapy at intervals, factoring these and expressing change on these factors. If, for example, two symptoms fluctuate together over time, we may suspect they spring from a similar dynamic source; change measures could then be in terms of the principal dynamic sources. In the last conference on psychotherapy Rogers (1959) described facets of the patient's experiencing of himself which could be scored from segments of the recorded psychotherapy. These were actually dimensions of change which he then could relate to "improvement." Other methods have been described by Miller (1951) and Zax and Klein (1960).

Both approaches — investigating the variety of changes and focusing on changes which are explicitly relevant to mental health—are included in the Menninger Foundation Project. This distinction has been more fully explicated by Wallerstein (1959). For the present paper, we will report on one method of estimating change in mental health: "Change in Health-Sickness Rating." Another method, "Changes in Patient Variables," will be briefly delineated but not used until the final results of the project are available.

*Change in Health-Sickness Rating*

For more than a decade, a number of us at the Menninger Foundation have tried to perfect a shorthand quantitative survey instrument for estimating a patient's mental health and the changes in it (Luborsky, 1962). In applying this method, the judge considers the patient in terms of seven criteria[6] and decides approximately where the patient would fall within a ranked standard series of sample patients; then he assigns the patient a single rating from 0-100 as the Health-Sickness Rating (HSR). In no instance is the rater also the therapist.

We currently have available HSR scores at the initial point (by the Initial Team) and the termination point (by the Termination Team) for 24 patients and also at the follow-up point on 16 patients.[7]

The HSR is a special and limited segment of our assessment; its seven criteria are all obviously value-laden—they all

---

[6] The seven criteria in brief are: (1) ability to function autonomously, (2) seriousness of the symptoms, (3) degree of discomfort, (4) effect upon the environment, (5) utilization of abilities, (6) quality of interpersonal relationships, and (7) breadth and depth of interests.

[7] The teams work separately. The Initial Team does not have access to later information about the patient. The Termination Team sees none of the Initial Team's quantitative scores but has access to the qualitative information. The members of the Termination Team record their HSR first without discussion of it with each other and then make a consensus rating. These separate HRS judgments tend to agree closely; e.g., the correlation of any two Termination Team members with each other is .95 (N=22).

As a further sample of the degree of agreement reached in the application of the scale: The Situational Variables team rated the HSR on the basis of their own discussions. They did their own evaluation and collection of data but had access to the information of the Initial and Termination Teams. Their consensus HSR ratings correlated .91 (N=24) with those of the Termination Team.

An example of an application of the scale where complete independence was maintained is provided by Stone and Dellis (1960). HSR ratings based upon psychological tests showed considerable agreement between raters: from .69 based upon the Wechsler alone to .85 based upon the Rorschach alone.

share in the concept of mental health of the clinicians who developed the scale. Our full assessment, on the other hand, includes aspects of change with no clear relationship to mental health. Nevertheless, most of the common variance can be explained by the first principal component which contains high loadings by the Initial HSR and Predicted HSR. These two variables are also moderately highly correlated with most of the other variables in Table 1. This confirms our hunch about the value of a generalized concept of health-sickness which runs through many of our variables.

*Change in the Patient Variables (as Estimated by Paired Comparisons)*

When the paired comparisons at termination and follow-up are complete on all 42 cases, we will have available our preferred method for estimating change. Although we now have 24 complete termination studies, paired comparisons cannot be used until batch comparability has been judged, and this cannot be done without the complete group. We will do the same type of analysis on the variables as judged at termination as we report here for the initial patient variables. If the judges have a high reliability and the judgments have a similar factor structure, we may be able to extract vectors of change. We will have differences in the patient variables at initial, termination, and follow-up which are directly meaningful. We may have, for example, a scaled score based on paired comparison judgments for "Anxiety Level" which is directly comparable at the three points.

INITIAL PATIENT VARIABLES
AND CHANGE

Of all the influences which are thought to determine the change a patient can make through treatment, the patient's personality is most often thought to be predominant. Here we will not look into the other influences, i.e., the treatment, therapist, or the life situation. Within the area

of the patient variables, the most common hypothesis in the research literature (Luborsky, 1959) is that *the greater the patient's assets, the greater the benefit he will derive from treatment.* Freud (1937) lists those principal factors which determine how much change a patient can make: (*a*) the degree to which the illness is the result of a trauma (the more purely traumatic, the more change can be made); (*b*) the strength of the instincts (the more excessive the instinctual demands, the more difficult it is to improve one's functioning); and (*c*) the degree of "modification of the ego" (the more distortion of the ego, the more difficulty in obtaining a cure). The last of these is similar to the common hypothesis. The American Psychiatric Association nomenclature includes this view in its well-known triad: *"Prognosis"* is a function of *"premorbid personality"* and *"precipitating stress."* Illness is thus considered a reaction in which the better the premorbid personaliy, the better the prognosis. Barron (1953) concludes on the basis of his MMPI Ego Strength Scale that those who are better off to begin with are likely to improve the most. Sullivan, Miller, and Smelser (1958) report similarly that patients judged improved were more likely to be those with higher occupational achievements and less psychopathology (also based upon MMPI).[8]

[8] Another apparently contradictory possibility is that *the fewer the assets and the more severe the patient's illness, the greater the gains he will make from psychotherapy.* We found this trend in our 1952 survey of psychotherapy of the Department of Adult Psychiatry (Luborsky, 1962). The HSR was applied by all therapists to their patients currently in psychotherapy at the Menninger Foundation. The amount of change in HSR depended upon the initial level of HSR: the lower the initial level, the greater the improvement. (However, in the 1952 findings we were dealing with the difference between the initial HSR and the *current* point in treatment rather than the termination point). These two hypotheses seem completely opposed, but each contains the same two elements in reversed proportions: the first hypothesis refers to high *capacity* for change but little

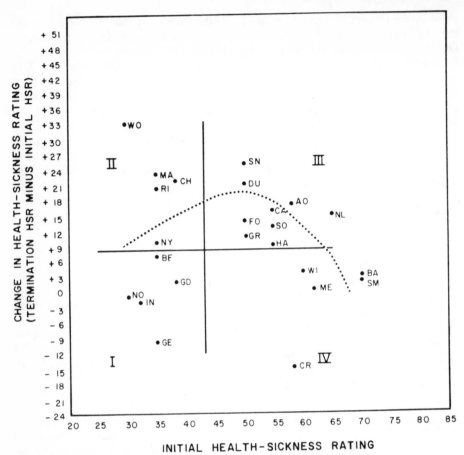

Figure 1.   Scattergram of Initial Health-Sickness Rating against Change in Health-Sickness Rating (Termination HSR minus Initial HSR) $(N=24; r=-.18)$.

To see how this common hypothesis holds for our present patient sample, we will explore the "Initial HSR" in relation

room for change (as the upper part of the scale of mental health is composed); the second hypothesis refers to low *capacity* for change with much *room* for change. The second hypothesis may be partly a product of the familiar "ceiling effect": those who start with most dysfunction have most room for improvement and those who start with most assets have least room. But we do not mean to imply by the term "ceiling effect" that the relationship is entirely artifactual. Possibly those who are highest in HSR may be suffering less and be more self-satisfied and consequently less amenable to change. However, these data alone will not permit a conclusion on the issue of artifactuality.

to change in the HSR during treatment. After that we can go into the relationship of the patient's position on each of the 12 patient variables and change in HSR during treatment.

### Initial HSR vs. Change in HSR

The common hypothesis does not apply *if* we consider only the negligible correlation with Change of −.18. However, a scattergram of these scores (Figure 1) is more informative than a correlation by itself. Considerable dispersion is revealed, but we do not see as random a dispersion as a correlation of −.18 would imply. A longer look reveals a moderately curvilinear relationship.

We then can discern a grouping of cases that form a trend line corresponding to a "ceiling effect" (that is, the higher the Initial HSR, the lower the improvement and vice versa). This line, however, does not fit the data very closely. It is obscured by several cases with few assets who made little or no change.

At the risk of overinterpreting slight trends in our search for hypotheses, we will take another look at the scattergram. It shows up the rudiments of the common trend reported in the literature. The patients with more assets initially *more often* show a *moderate* positive change than those who start with fewer assets. We define "more assets" initially as "Initial HSR of 50 or above." (In using HSR 50 as a cutting point we are dividing patients along an important dimension. HSR 50 is defined as "definitely needs treatment to continue to work satisfactorily and has increasing difficulty in maintaining self autonomously. . . ." In fact, 9 of the 10 patients in the "below 50" group—all actually HSR 38 and below—were in the hospital at the start of their psychotherapy; *none* of the 14 at HSR 50 or above were in the hospital at any point during psychotherapy. Eight of the 9 who were in the hospital at the start of psychotherapy were able to leave the hospital and continue psychotherapy on an outpatient basis). The clear gap on the scattergram between HSR 38 and 50 happens to coincide with the cutting point we have selected. If we divide the change at +9 or above, the "more assets" group has 9 patients above this point and 5 below. This certainly would not make a significant fourfold contingency table, but it shows the trend. The 10 patients with fewer assets initially (HSR below 50) seem to be more polarized: they either make little or no change, or they make a large change.[9]

Averages of the amount of change in the "more" and "less" assets subgroups are not significantly different from each other. Neither from the results by this method nor from the results by the correlation method using the whole group is the common hypothesis applicable.

Klein's recent report (1960) on psychoanalytic patients compares amount of change in patients with initial "moderate dysfunction" and those with initial "severe dysfunction." The degree of dysfunction is derived from a rating scale based upon data of the "pretreatment history, admissions procedure, and the opening phase of treatment." It heavily stresses social functioning, self-esteem, symptoms, integration, and insight. A five-point scale was used for categorizing the amount of change in these areas. Klein reports no significant difference between the two groups in the amount of change, although the difference slightly favored the "moderate dysfunction" group as she had expected (that is, the common hypothesis). In her patient group, therefore, *regardless of the level of dysfunction at which they began treatment, patients moved approximately the same number of points,* so that she raised the question of the limits of modifiability of patients. A similar finding is reported from the Chicago study (Seeman, 1954): therapist's ratings of the client's initial status on "personality integration (vs. highly disorganized)" correlated only .08 with the therapist's rating of success of the treatment. The same lack of a significant relationship emerged for patient's estimates of a somewhat similar variable: $Q$-adjustment scores before therapy and change scores on the same measure correlated $-.25$ (Cartwright & Roth, 1957).

In conclusion, three other psychotherapy projects, as well as our own (for the group taken as a whole), came up with a negative result for the common hypothesis. The only suggestion for a predictive trend came from the slight differ-

[9] If we plot the Initial Rating assigned *retrospectively* by the Termination Team and use the same cutting points, only *one* patient who started below HSR 43 improved more than +9.

ences in the scatter within the group—a person starting out above HSR 50 has a slightly greater chance of making a moderate gain than a person starting out below HSR 50. For the next steps, it might repay study to examine the patients in these subgroups even more carefully. Can one see, for example, differences in the "fewer assets" group between the five who improved and the five who remained essentially unchanged? Through inspection alone of the patients in Figure 1, we note that the five in Quadrant I include all the patients with the most severe addictive symptoms (IN, GD, BE, and even NY who is just across the dividing line) and the patient with the most severe paranoid symptoms (NO). Nothing as severe is to be found in the five patients of Quadrant II, or in fact, in any of the other patients in the entire group of 24.

The brief analysis above points up an aspect of the scale that has to be taken into account: mental health is not a uniform continuum. Therefore, changes which started at different points on the scale must have different meanings. A patient who started at HSR 30 (WO) and lost her depression and became capable of functioning again, registered a huge change. But is this change the same as for a patient who started at 55 (CA) and was functioning fairly adequately except for her anxiety about caring for her child and being a proper mother for it? Resolution of this patient's difficulties would not register a change as great as for the one who began at HSR 30. Are the changes in the two patients comparable? Similarly, 10 points registered for NY, who started at 35, meant nothing significant for his functioning; the 3 points for BA, who started at 70, meant much more. This quality of the mental health continuum points up a major limitation in the global approach to the initial state of the patient as well as a limitation in the global approach to "amount of change." In the

analysis to follow, the defect of the global approach to the patient's initial state will be partially corrected.[10]

*Initial Patient Variables vs. Change in HSR*

The 12 initial patient variables scores were each correlated with change in HSR. As anticipated, none of them individually had a high relationship with Change in HSR (see Table 3).[11] Only "Anxiety Level" had a significant relationship (.44).

[10] An afterthought led us to try an improvement rating for this present report. We were curious to see whether the usual type of improvement score would correlate with our HSR change score. Two judges (BH & LL) made independent ratings of the 24 patients on a five-point crudely specified scale ranging from "no improvement" to "much improvement." However, these improvement ratings may still be only distant relatives of the usual improvement scores in the literature, for our improvement ratings were made by judges who knew the cases thoroughly and *after* the assessments were complete on all cases. Naturally, therefore, the interjudge agreement was high ($r=.88$).

The improvement ratings and the HSR change scores did not correlate very highly, however ($r=.48$). (The HSR ratings at the initial point were made by different raters than the HSR at termination. When we tried a change score in which the initial point was based upon the judgments of the same people who made the termination ratings [i.e., a "retrospective initial HSR rating"], the correlation with improvement was higher [.65].)

Initial HSR correlated .54 with the improvement ratings, while it correlated only −.18 with HSR change scores! Possibly the relationship was influenced by the contamination of the judges making the improvement ratings by knowledge of the Initial HSR ratings. Even more likely, the judges gave more weight in their judgments of "improvement" to changes by patients who were in the top part of the HSR scale.

[11] A similar finding has been reported: none of a long list of patients' qualities as judged by diagnostic interviewers were correlated significantly with amount of improvement (a type of Hunt Movement Score) as judged by therapists (Hunt, Ewing, LaForge, & Gilbert, 1959).

TABLE 3

CORRELATIONS OF INITIAL PATIENT
VARIABLE WITH CHANGE IN HEALTH-
SICKNESS RATINGS
N=24

| | HSR Change (Termination minus Initial HSR) | Corrected HSR Change (Termination HSR with Initial partialled out) |
|---|---|---|
| 1. Anxiety Level | .44* | .37 |
| 2. Severity of Symptoms | −.02 | −.16 |
| 3. Self-Directed Aggression | −.08 | −.14 |
| 4. Extent to which Environment Suffers | .04 | −.10 |
| 5. Externalization | .01 | −.12 |
| 6. Level of Psycho-sexual Development | .22 | .33 |
| 7. Patterning of Defenses | .20 | .34 |
| 8. Anxiety Tolerance | .05 | .18 |
| 9. Insight | −.09 | −.04 |
| 10. Ego Strength | .07 | .13 |
| 11. Motivation | .22 | .34 |
| 12. Quality of Inter-personal Relationships | .23 | .36 |
| 13. Initial Health-Sickness Rating | −.18 | |
| 14. Predicted Health-Sickness Rating | .13 | .26 |

* $P_2 < .05$.

We wondered whether a correction for the initial position of the patient would show more clearly the unalloyed relationships with Change in HSR. These correlations are presented in the same table; no dramatic alterations were produced by this type of correction. Although quality of interpersonal relationship, level of psychosexual development, and patterning of defenses got pulled up, they did not reach a significant level; but it is of interest that these are the ones which figured most highly in Factor I.[12] We constructed a scattergram (Figure 2) of "Anxiety Level" against "Change in HSR" and found that the correlation does not adequately reflect the strength of the trend line. One patient, NO, who had the most psychotic coloring to her illness of any in the entire group, reduced the correlation markedly.

The correlation of "Anxiety Level" with "Change in HSR" was unexpectedly higher than was true for the other variables. Yet some relationship was not a complete surprise to us or to others. Rogers (1957) included among six conditions of therapeutic change, "the client is in a state of incongruence, being vulnerable or anxious." Freud (1919) offered a rationale which clarifies this relationship. He believed an optimum level of "suffering" is conducive to change; premature improvements can reduce the motive for change. The therapist's focus, therefore, should not be upon making life pleasant for the patient. The role of anxiety is especially clear in the treatment of patients with phobias. For cure to occur, Freud recommended that the patient put up with the anxiety of engaging in the activities which arouse the phobic anxiety. This toleration of the anxiety gains for the patient an access to the relevant associations and memories which permit the phobia to be resolved.

DISCUSSION AND CONCLUSIONS

With our experimental design we were not out to *prove* hypotheses but to *find*

[12] We noted that most of the common variance can be explained in terms of this first principal component. It is natural to wonder how a combined factor score (of Variables 6, 7, 8, 10, 12, 13) would relate to the change measure. The correlation .36 does not quite reach .05 significance level (but is higher than the correlation of Initial HSR with the change measure).

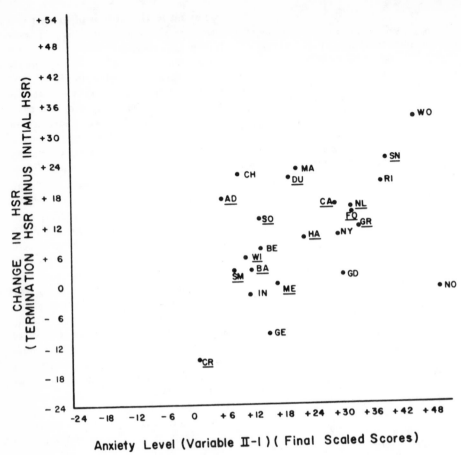

Figure 2. Scattergram of "Anxiety Level" scores against "Change in Health-Sickness Ratings" (Termination HSR minus Initial HSR) ($N = 24$; $r = .44$) (underlined patients have HSR of 50 or above).

hypotheses about the relationship of initial patient variables to change during psychotherapy. So far in this report we have examined two fragments of our data: (*a*) initial patient variables (assessed by the paired comparisons method) which we had expected to be related to change through psychotherapy and (*b*) correlations of these variables with an estimate of change. We will go on now to examine further the method for estimating change as well as to set forth some of the hypotheses that appear most promising.

We can conclude that:

1. Helen Sargent's adaptation of the method of paired comparisons works adequately (although with some corrections necessary) in the estimation of the initial patient variables.

2. Five principal factors appear to be the essential core of the initial evaluation of the patient, as a factor analysis of the intercorrelations of the scores on these patient variables brings out. *These five factors reflect the main hypotheses of our judges on the dimensions which are most*

*relevant in estimating psychotherapeutic change. Of these five, the factor entitled "Personality Development and Strength" is the most heavily weighted.*

However, these factors are a representative sample of our bases for estimating a patient's treatment outcome only if an adequate selection of the variables was put into the factor analytic machine. We also assume that the abstraction into variables is a legitimate one; the actual process of estimating a patient's potential for psychotherapy may be better represented by the way we use specific items of information in making our predictions (Sargent & Horwitz, 1960).

3. The initial patient variables in general do not correlate highly with the measure of change, Change in Health-Sickness Rating. The one exception, however, was the variable "Anxiety Level" which had a significant correlation with the change measure. We may, therefore, consider as a fair hypothesis that *the higher the initial anxiety level, the greater amount of change a patient will make in psychotherapy. Also, the "Initial HSR," which is a global estimate of the patient's initial position on the mental health dimension, does not relate highly to the change measure.*

It would seem reasonable at this point to conclude that *the initial position of the patient on the health-sickness dimension or on a variety of personality variables has little to do with the* amount *of change he will make in psychotherapy.* This would in fact correspond with our results as well as those of Klein (1959) and Katz, Lorr, and Rubinstein (1958). However, there are cogent reasons why we think the foundations of these relationships are shaky. These principal reasons involve principles that apply as well to much similar psychotherapy research:

1. There must be an *interaction* between the initial position of the patient and the various therapeutic processes (and other influences) which intervene between the initial position and final estimates. We therefore never anticipated that change could be fully predicted from the initial patient variables in isolation; the treatment, therapist, and life situation also play a part.

2. It is an important clinical assumption that the *pattern* of the initial patient variables is highly relevant. For this reason we stressed profile comparisons as the quantitative method which most closely fitted clinical assumptions (Luborsky & Sargent, 1956). We anticipated that single initial variables would only correlate moderately with change for we were aware of relying upon various combinations of variables in our assessments.

3. "Change in Health-Sickness Rating" is only one among several possible types of measures of change. Our results might have been different with other measures, for recent studies have shown that change measures *sometimes* do not correlate highly with each other (e.g., Rogers & Dymond, 1954; Gibson, Snyder, & Ray, 1955; Cartwright & Roth, 1957). Cartwright and Roth found that therapist and patient estimates of change fall into uncorrelated factors; however, the separate therapist measures (plus lay observer and the TAT measures) hang together in one factor while the patient measures are together in another factor. Further work with our HSR change measure will probably place it nearer to therapist measures than to patient measures.

4. For any measure of change in psychotherapy, one should be able to specify the beginning and ending point and the nature of the territory covered in the change. This is one of the values of the HSR method and a major deficit in the usual improvement rating. However, any scale should represent degrees of the same quality. Our change measure is probably not a unitary dimension but means different things at different parts of the scale.

5. The amount of change on the Health-Sickness Rating Scale may not take into account the personal meaning of certain changes. The changes may be small in terms of the mental health dimension but quite significant to the person. This point has been made by Brenman (1952) and by Schafer (1958). For example, after Termination, Patient CA was able to adopt a child and care for the child adequately, despite the expense of increased anxiety. The shift which made this change possible was of paramount importance to CA, but it may not be commensurately reflected in the Health-Sickness Rating (HSR at Termination, 71; at Follow-up, 77).

6. Changes from an initial to end of treatment point are not sufficient to indicate whether the changes are reasonably lasting. In future analyses changes also will be investigated from termination to the follow-up two years later. (From the 16 patients who have reached Follow-up, we learn that gains are maintained with only a slight nonsignificant loss *on the average* from Termination to Follow-up with about half losing and half gaining slightly—Mean Initial HSR, 48.0; Mean Termination HSR, 57.9; Mean Follow-up HSR, 56.9). A slight nonsignificant average decrease from end of treatment to follow-up is also noted by Rogers and Dymond (1954).

The analysis of the data of the Psychotherapy Research Project is in its infancy; we are proceeding with the happy view that "the" best is yet to be. Eventually we will try other assessments of change: (a) clinical comparisons of the patients at the three points in time, (b) confirmation or refutation of predictions of change, and (c) comparison of changes in the profiles of paired comparison scores at the three points. The last will provide a more configurational measure which should relate more directly to the interactions among the three sets of variables. Thus the efforts in the present report to relate an initial position on single variables to a single measure of change are but tentative beginnings of a larger effort to study interactions among configurations of three sets of variables that change over time.

All these principles represent "promissory notes" for analyses which we will eventually report. To keep up the market value of these notes we will show how some of these can be applied to the refinement of the hypotheses we have formulated.

### Refinement of the "Anxiety Level" Hypothesis

The Anxiety Level Hypothesis was based upon the entire range of the HSR. However, if HSR is not a unitary dimension, relationships may not hold over the entire range. If we divide the HSR scale at its midpoint, we find that the change for patients who start below HSR 50 ($n=10$) covers an almost totally different area of the scale than the group who start at HSR 50 and above ($n=14$). Only four patients in the low group overlap at all, and the overlap is very slight. We therefore suspected what emerged: the correlation with Anxiety Level differed for each subgroup ($r$ for the total group$=.44$; for the high HSR group alone$=.66$; low group alone$=.11$). A more refined statement of the hypothesis might be: *For the patients who start treatment with at least a moderately high capacity for autonomous functioning, etc., the higher the level of anxiety the greater the change that is likely.*[13]

---

[13] *After* completing the present report, it was a pleasure to read the similar formulation of my colleagues Siegal and Rosen (1961) who independently concluded from the psychological tests that the significance of anxiety varies in different patients; crucial for therapeutic change is the "capacity to experience anxiety as a signal that further ego activity is required."

*Refinement of Hypothesis about the
Initial Level of Mental Health*

We noted earlier that the Initial HSR (and most Initial Patient variables) did not correlate significantly with *Change in HSR*. Nevertheless, we saw that greater relationships may exist for certain segments of the HSR scale. It might also be that *the amount of change* is less predictable than the *end point* of the change.

When we examined the predictions by the two Initial judges of the end state (i.e., Termination HSR) we found they seemed to be operating on the hypothesis that *the best estimate of the end state was the Initial state plus a moderate increment*—their Initial HSR correlated .73

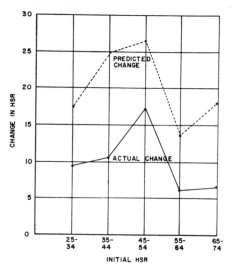

Figure 3. Initial HSR against amount of predicted and actual change in HSR (*N*= 24).

with their Predicted HSR. Their predictions actually turned out to be fairly accurate; i.e., their Initial HSR correlated .71 with the Termination HSR! And, in fact, two of the three worst predictive errors seemed due to neglecting their own hypothesis—they predicted huge changes for two patients who started out quite low in HSR. The *increment* of change was less predictable than the *end level* (the corre-

lation of the increment predicted and the actual increment is .40). This may seem paradoxical at first glance. However, it is easily resolved: the judges were not able to predict amount of change accurately, but whatever increment they added did not change the patient's position on the HSR scale in relation to the other patients (hence the high correlation between Initial HSR and Termination HSR). Finally, we should recognize in this finding the probable reason for the major factor "Personality Development and Strength": the judges were working—we see now, correctly—on the hypothesis that *a correct assessment of the present level of mental health gives the best estimate of the future level.*[14]

[14] The judges of the Initial study team held out hopes of positive change for *every* one of the 24 patients; for only two of the patients did they predict less change than occurred. The predicted increment was not constant at all points on the scale: the relationship was clearly curvilinear between the Initial HSR and the amount of change predicted. Those who were initially low in HSR were given low predictions of change, those in the middle range of HSR were given the highest prediction of change, and those in the top range of HSR were given moderate to low predictions of change. This somewhat bell-shaped curve *actually* holds between Initial HSR and *actual* amount of change! (See Figure 3.)

REFERENCES

Barron, F. Some test correlates of response to psychotherapy. *J. consult. Psychol.,* 1953, **17**, 235-241.

Brenman, Margaret. On teasing and being teased and the problem of moral masochism. In R. S. Eissler et al. (Eds.) *The psychoanalytic study of the child,* Vol. 7. New York: International Universities Press, 1952. Pp. 264-285.

Cartwright, D. S., & Roth, I. Success and satisfaction in psychotherapy. *J. clin. Psychol.,* 1957, **13**, 20-26.

Dymond, Rosalind F. Adjustment changes over therapy from Thematic Apperception Test ratings. In C. R. Rogers & Rosalind F. Dymond (Eds.), *Psychotherapy and personality change.* Chicago: Univer. Chicago Press, 1954. Pp. 109-120.

Frank, J. D. Problems of controls in psychotherapy as exemplified by the psychotherapy research project of the Phipps Psychiatric Clinic. In E. A. Rubinstein & M. B. Parloff (Eds.), *Research in psychotherapy*, Proceedings of a Conference, Washington, D. C., April 9-12, 1958. Washington: American Psychological Association, 1959.

Freud, S. Lines of advance in psychoanalytic therapy. (Originally published 1919) Standard Ed. Vol. 17. Pp. 159-168. London: Hogarth Press & Institute for Psychoanalysis, 1955.

Freud, S. Analysis terminable and interminable. (Originally published 1937) In *Collected Papers*. Vol. 5. Pp. 316-357. London: Hogarth Press & Institute of Psychoanalysis, 1950.

Gibson, R. L., Snyder, W. U., & Ray, W. S. A factor analysis of measures of change following client-centered therapy. *J. consult. Psychol.*, 1955, **2**, 83-90.

Hall, B. H., & Wallerstein, R. S. Operational problems of psychotherapy research: II. Termination studies. *Bull. Menninger Clin.*, 1960, **24**, 190-216.

Hotelling, H. Analysis of a complex of statistical variables into principal components. *J. educ. Psychol.*, 1933, **24**, 417-441 & 498-520.

Hunt, J. McV. Measuring movement in casework. In A. H. Brayfield (Ed.), *Readings in modern methods of counseling*. New York: Appleton-Century-Crofts, 1950.

Hunt, J. McV., Ewing, T., LaForge, R., & Gilbert, W. An integrated approach to research on therapeutic counseling with samples of results. *J. counsel. Psychol.*, 1959, **6**, 46-54.

Kaiser, H. F. The varimax criterion for analytic rotation in factor analysis. *Psychometrika*, 1958, **23**, 187-200.

Katz, M. M., Lorr, M., & Rubinstein, E. A. Remainer patient attributes and their relation to subsequent improvement in psychotherapy. *J. consult. Psychol.*, 1958, **22**, 411-413.

Klein, Henriette R. A study of changes occurring in patients during and after psychoanalytic treatment. In *Current approaches to psychoanalysis*. New York: Grune & Stratton, 1960.

Lorr, M. Rating scales and check lists for the evaluation of psychopathology. *Psychol. Bull.*, 1954, **51**, 119-127.

Luborsky, L. Intra-individual repetitive measurements (P-technique) in understanding psychotherapeutic change. In O. H. Mowrer (Ed.), *Psychotherapy: Theory and research*. New York: Ronald, 1953. Pp. 389-413.

Luborsky, L. A note on Eysenck's article: "The effects of psychotherapy: An evaluation." *British J. Psychol.*, 1954, **45**, 129-131.

Luborsky, L. Psychotherapy. In P. R. Farnsworth & Q. McNemar (Eds.), *Annual review of psychology*. Vol. 10. Palo Alto, Calif.: Annual Reviews, 1959. Pp. 317-344.

Luborsky, L. Clinicians' judgments of mental health: A proposed scale. *Arch. gen. Psychiat.*, in press.

Luborsky, L., & Sargent, Helen D. Sample use of method. *Bull. Menninger Clin.*, 1956, **20**, 263-276.

Luborsky, L., Fabian, Michalina, Hall, B., Ticho, T., & Ticho, Gertrude. Treatment variables. *Bull. Menninger Clin.*, 1958, **22**, 126-147.

Miller, J. G. Objective methods of evaluating process and outcome in psychotherapy. *Amer. J. Psychiat.*, 1951, **103**, 258-263.

Muench, G. A. An evaluation of non-directive psychotherapy by means of the Rorschach and other tests. *Appl. Psychol. Monogr.*, 1947, **13**, 1-163.

Parloff, M. B., Kelman, H. C., & Frank, J. D. Comfort, effectiveness, and self-awareness as criteria of improvement in psychotherapy. *Amer. J. Psychiat.*, 1954, **111**, 343-351.

Parloff, M. B., & Rubinstein, E. A. Research problems in psychotherapy. In E. A. Rubinstein & M. B. Parloff (Eds.), *Research in psychotherapy*. Proceedings of a Conference, Washington, D. C., April 9-12, 1958. Washington: American Psychological Association, 1959.

Rogers, C. R. The necessary and sufficient conditions of therapeutic personality change. *J. consult. Psychol.*, 1957, **21**, 95-103.

Rogers, C. R. A tentative scale for the measurement of process in psychotherapy. In E. A. Rubinstein & M. B. Parloff (Eds.), *Research in psychotherapy*. Proceedings of a conference, Washington, D. C., April 9-12, 1958. Washington: American Psychological Association, 1959.

Rogers, C. R., & Dymond, Rosalind F. *Psychotherapy and personality change*. Chicago: Univer. Chicago Press, 1954.

Sanford, N. Clinical methods: Psychotherapy. In P. R. Farnsworth & Q. McNemar (Eds.), *Annual review of psychology.* Vol. 4. Palo Alto, Calif.: Annual Reviews, 1953. Pp. 317-342.

Sargent, Helen D. Insight test prognosis in successful and unsuccessful rehabilitation of the blind. *J. proj. Tech.,* 1956, **20**, 429-441.

Sargent, Helen D., & Horwitz, L. The prediction study of the Psychotherapy Research Project: Progress, problems, and plans, 1961. (In preparation)

Sargent, Helen D., Modlin, H. C., Faris, M. T., & Voth, H. M. Situational variables. *Bull. Menninger Clin.,* 1958, **22**, 148-166.

Schafer, R. On the psychoanalytic study of retest results. *J. proj. Tech.,* 1958, **22**, 102-109.

Seeman, J. Counselor judgments of therapeutic process and outcome. In C. R. Rogers & Rosalind F. Dymond (Eds.), *Psychotherapy and personality change.* Chicago: Univer. Chicago Press, 1954. Pp. 99-108.

Siegal, R. S., & Rosen, I. C. Character style and anxiety tolerance: A study in intrapsychic change. Paper prepared for the Second Conference on Psychotherapy, Chapel Hill, N. C., 1961. (Included in this volume)

Stone, H. K., & Dellis, N. P. An exploratory investigation into the levels hypothesis. *J. proj. Tech.,* 1960, **24**, 333-340.

Sullivan, P. L., Miller, Christine, & Smelser, W. Factors in length of stay and progress in psychotherapy. *J. consult. Psychol.,* 1958, **22**, 1-9.

Wallerstein, R. S. The problem of assessment of change in psychotherapy. *Psychoanalytic Quart.,* in press.

Wallerstein, R. S., & Robbins, L. L. Operational problems of psychotherapy research I: Initial studies. *Bull. Menninger Clin.,* 1960, **24**, 164-189.

Wallerstein, R. S., Robbins, L. L., Sargent, Helen D,, & Luborsky, L. The psychotherapy research project of the Menninger Foundation: Rationale, method, and sample use. *Bull. Menninger Clin.,* 1956, **20**, 221-278.

Zax, M., & Klein, A. Measurement of personality and behavior changes following psychotherapy. *Psychol. Bull.,* 1960, **57**, 435-448.

# Relation of Treatment Frequency and Duration to Psychotherapeutic Outcome

MAURICE LORR, PH.D.

Investigation of the relation of therapeutic outcome to frequency and duration of psychotherapy is analogous in many ways to the study of drug dosage and its effects. For a given drug it is possible to vary the size of the dose, the number of administrations, the frequency of administration, and the duration of a course of treatment. Psychotherapeutic outcome may be studied similarly, in relation to duration of a single interview, number of interviews in a course of treatment, frequency of treatments per week or month, and duration of a course of treatment. Yet it is surprising how rarely therapeutic gain has been investigated in relation to these potentially influential variables. Their prescription by the therapist or the clinic appears to be based on clinical experience and tradition, although social class status also plays an important unrecognized role. Other considerations that limit contacts are therapist time and the income of the patient.

Current practice in public clinics is to schedule most psychiatric patients for individual psychotherapy once or twice a week for about 50 minutes on each occasion (Feldman, Lorr, & Russell, 1958; Hollingshead & Redlich, 1958). Patients seen for psychotherapy in private practice are likely to be scheduled at similar rates. However, the length of a patient's therapeutic interview is related to his social class position (Hollingshead & Redlich, 1958). Lower class patients are usually seen for 15 to 30 minutes, while upper class patients are rarely seen for less than 50 to 60 minutes. The number of visits per week made by patients receiving individual psychotherapy from private practitioners is definitely correlated with class status. The higher the class the more frequently the treatment is administered. In veterans clinics (Feldman et al., 1958) education, a crude index of class status, is similarly correlated with the scheduled number of visits. The length of time a patient remains in treatment is linked to social class although the patient's diagnosis and the goals of psychotherapy seem equally important determinants.

The most widely held view appears to be that therapeutic progress in individual psychotherapy that is directed at reorienting or changing the person will be a positive function of the intensity and frequency of contacts. Clara Thompson (1950) and others have argued that duration of treatment rather than frequency of contact is the crucial factor in such treatment. The purpose of this paper is to critically review some of the studies available that seek to relate frequency of contact and duration to therapeutic change. Studies concerned with the relation of the number of treatments to improvement will be described first. Then, a digest of a recently completed study of the influence of treatment frequency and duration on treatment outcome will be presented.

Seeman (1954) reported a study of counselor judgments of therapeutic outcome in relation to case length for 23 clients who received nondirective counseling. He reports a trend in favor of higher success ratings for longer cases. The shorter cases spanned the entire range of success ratings from 1 to 9, while the longer cases were judged to fall on two high points of the scale (7 and 8). He concludes that if a client is in therapy for at least 20 interviews, there is a strong assurance, as judged by the counselor, of gain in therapy. Since Seeman fails to provide any statistical data it is not possible to judge the validity of his findings.

Myers and Auld (1955) examined the records of 23 cases that came to a community clinic over a one-year period. All were seen by senior staff and resident psychiatrists for "expressive" psychotherapy. The manner in which therapy was terminated was classified as follows: the patient simply quit; was discharged as unimproved; was terminated as improved; was continued on treatment elsewhere. The data show that discharge status of unimproved does not vary with number of interviews. However, of 16 patients discharged as improved, there were zero with 1–9 treatments, seven with 10–19 treatments, and nine with 20 or more treatments. This suggests that a minimum number of treatments are required for a rating of improvement by a therapist. It should be noted that duration of treatment, which is not reported, may be confounded with number of interviews.

Imber et al. (1957) were concerned with the relation between amount of contact between patient and psychotherapist and improvement rate. They hypothesized that patients having fewer and briefer sessions of psychotherapy would show significantly less improvement than patients with more and longer sessions over the same period of time. Fifty-four psychiatric patients were assigned at random to three psychiatrists, each of whom treated equal numbers of patients in group psychotherapy and in two forms of individual psychotherapy. The group psychotherapy patients were seen once a week for about one and one-half hours. The analytically oriented individual therapy patients were seen once a week for an hour. The minimal contact therapy patients were seen

individually for no more than half an hour once every two weeks. The average number of sessions was 17.7 for those patients in analytic-type individual treatment, 15.8 for the group therapy patients, and 9.3 for the minimal contact patients. Patients in the three groups were re-evaluated six months after treatment commenced. An analysis of covariance of ineffectiveness scores showed that group therapy patients improved more than minimal contact patients but not more than the analytically oriented individual therapy patients. The latter group also improved more than the minimal contact group. The authors conclude that their hypothesis had been confirmed.

Unfortunately, length of interview, frequency of treatment, and type of treatment are confounded in the study design. Thus, despite the study's many merits, it is simply not possible to infer which variable was the effective agent. Minimal contact patients received a treatment that was different from that received by the other two groups. Single therapeutic sessions for the three groups varied from 30 to 90 minutes in length and thus are confounded with the number of treatments received over the six-month period. The effective condition that separated the restricted therapeutic contact group from the other two groups could have been fewer sessions, briefer sessions, or type of treatment.

Ends and Page (1959) have reported a study aimed at testing the usefulness of group psychotherapy with alcoholic patients, and the intensity of its application. More specifically, they asked whether doubling the number of group therapeutic sessions from 15 to 30 within the same time interval would result in significantly greater therapeutic movement. They conclude that doubling the number of sessions without increasing the total elapsed time in treatment results in significantly greater therapeutic movement. However, the 15 and 30 interview groups were not run in the same study. The data on the 15 interview group were collected in an earlier phase of the project, and the results with this group were known before the 30 interview group was studied. Further, the two groups were from obviously different populations on such variables as age, duration of drinking, and initial scores on the study criteria. No effort to statistically control these differences was attempted. Finally the fact that the 15 interview group showed even fewer changes than a control group run simultaneously with the 30 interview group is even stronger evidence of the population difference. Thus, the conclusions of this study regarding treatment frequency are extremely doubtful.

Cartwright (1955) studied counselor ratings of success in client-centered psychotherapy in relation to length of therapy. The total sample of closed cases was analyzed into two groups: one group of short-case clients (1–12 interviews) and the other of long-case clients (13–77 interviews). Within each group there was a strong positive relation between number of interviews and success rating. A "failure zone" between the 13th and 21st interview was interpreted as a period during which potentially long-case clients dropped out of therapy. Taylor (1955) came to a similar conclusion from a study of 309 closed cases from a psychoanalytically oriented clinic. Thus, rated improvement appears to be positively related to the number of treatments within each type of group.

The most recent report encountered is one by Nichols and Beck (1960). They were concerned with personality change in 75 undergraduates who received psychotherapy in a psychological clinic. The therapists were 14 third and fourth year graduate students. Clients were seen for an average of 14.7 interviews, and no student was seen for less than 5 interviews.

The authors factored 30 change scores obtained from 18 California Psychological Inventory measures, 4 Sentence Completion measures, 4 client ratings, and 4 therapist ratings. Six factors were found. Only Factor B, which is defined by therapist ratings of change in symptoms and complaints, understanding of self, feeling toward life (happiness), and over-all improvement, correlated with the number of interviews received. This correlation is .29 (one-tailed test). Thus, only therapist judgment of improvement, which could be biased under the conditions of ratings, is associated with number of treatments. Further, as Nichols and Beck (1960) indicate, the correlation is also confounded with time between tests and with placebo effect. The net results provide little to support the notion that increasing the number of contacts will improve the patient proportionally.

*Treatment Frequency and Change*

The last study to be described (Lorr, McNair, Michaux, & Raskin, 1962) aimed to test the broad hypothesis that therapeutic gains resulting from individual psychotherapy increase with the number of treatment interviews received over fixed time intervals. The following were the specific hypotheses: the greater the number of psychotherapeutic interviews the greater (*a*) the reduction in manifest anxiety; (*b*) the reduction in the number and severity of patient complaints and problems; (*c*) the increase in ego strength; (*d*) the increase in self-acceptance; (*e*) the increase in sociability; (*f*) the reduction in hostility towards others; (*g*) the increase in independent behavior; (*h*) the number of positive behavioral changes reported by the therapist; (*i*) the level of self-awareness.

The study design called for the random assignment of patients, at each of seven mental hygiene clinics, to one of three different treatment schedules—twice weekly, once weekly, and once biweekly. Each patient selected for the study was interviewed and tested just before initiation of treatment and again at the end of 16 weeks and 32 weeks of psychotherapy. The sample in each clinic was confined to male veterans with service-connected disabilities, less than 51 years of age, and without any current indication of brain injury. None had received psychotherapy within the 90 days prior to inclusion in the study. The typical patient, of the 133 included, was 37 years of age. Approximately half were high school or college graduates, and of the 75 percent employed, the average annual earnings were $3500.

Seventy-five different therapists participated in the study. Of these, 64 were staff members and 11 were residents or trainees. There were approximately equal numbers of psychiatrists, social workers, and clinical psychologists. The typical therapist had four and one-half years of experience as a psychotherapist. The treatment, called "intensive," consisted of interviews 50–60 minutes in duration and directed toward changing the patient, assisting him to modify his personal adjustment patterns, and aiding him to make more constructive use of his assets. Most therapists were psychoanalytic in orientation, although Sullivanian and modified Rogerian approaches were represented.

*The Criteria*

Since the various measures are described fully in the monograph, they will only be listed here. Ten patient criteria were used to evaluate the changes hypothesized. Included were the following: (*a*) Manifest Anxiety Scale; (*b*) Symptom Check List (20 items); (*c*) Ego Strength Scale (Barron); (*d*) Sociability Scale; (*e*) Friendliness Scale; (*f*) Self-Rating Scale (16 five-point scales); (*g*) The Interpersonal Check List (ICL). The ICL provided measures of assertiveness, cooperativeness, hostility, and dependence.

The therapist rated his patient on Severity of Illness which was derived from ratings on seven four-point scales. He also described his patient on the ICL. A Change Inventory was completed by the therapist at the time of each re-evaluation. The Inventory consisted of 92 statements, marked true or not true, which are descriptive of specific changes frequently observed in patients. Included was a score on Interview Relationship (IR), a score on Interpersonal Changes (IC), and a third measure of Symptom Reduction (SR). The social worker interviewed the patient at the time of intake and at the close of 16 weeks of treatment. He rated the patient on a number of scales, but only ratings on social adjustment and severity of illness were used in the analysis.

The statistical model for evaluating the effect of increasing amounts of psychotherapy on the various criteria was analysis of covariance within a simple randomized design. Final criterion mean scores were adjusted for initial status on the criterion being analyzed. In each instance the correlations between initial criterion scores and various predictor and background variables were examined for possible statistical control. The control variables considered included schooling, earnings, employment status, vocabulary, and similar characteristics of the patient. Other variables inspected were length of experience and rated competence of the therapist as well as his liking for the patient.

*The Four-Month Results*

During the first 16 weeks of therapy the twice-weekly frequency group actually attended an average of 25.5 therapy sessions; the once-weekly group, an average of 14.5 sessions; and the biweekly group, an average of 8.6 interviews. The three treatment groups did not differ significantly when treatment began on any of the criteria or on predictor or background variables. Nevertheless, the influence of initial scores on the four-month scores was statistically eliminated except for the Therapist Change Inventories.

None of the *F* tests on the six patient criteria, the five therapist criteria, or the two social work criteria were significant at the .05 level. Patient, therapist, and social worker concurred in observing no differences ascribable to treatment frequency. Thus the major hypothesis received no support for the patients studied over a 16-week interval. A check on a possible differential dropout rate by treatment frequency was negative. In order to test for treatment gains, all treatment groups were pooled and tests were made on the combined group scores. There were no significant changes on the patient measures over the first four-month period. However, both therapists and social workers independently observed a significant decrease in severity of illness of the study sample. There was also significantly greater congruence between therapist and patient in their ICL descriptions of the patient.

*The Eight-Month Results*

The eight-month analysis was based on 58 patients who remained in the study on the original randomly assigned treatment frequency schedules. There were 16 patients in the twice-weekly group with an average of 50.8 therapy sessions. Thirty patients in the once-weekly group had an average of 27.7 sessions, and 12 patients in the biweekly group had an average of 14.4 hours of treatment. The groups did not differ significantly on initial criterion, predictor, or background variables. The relation between treatment frequency and remaining or terminating was not significant. However, the pretreatment status of patients remaining in the study for 32 weeks at assigned treatment schedules differed significantly in certain re-

spects from patients who did not. The eight-month sample had higher Manifest Anxiety scores and less favorable self-descriptions. Their therapists observed significantly less IC + SR change during the first four months of therapy than for the dropout group.

Analysis of 15 criteria of response to psychotherapy indicated that none of the differences between treatment frequency groups were significant at the .05 level. Thus, once more the research hypothesis that treatment effects will be greater with more frequent treatments was not supported after 32 weeks of psychotherapy. Patient and therapist agree on this finding. The treatment groups were next combined and tests were made to identify any gains from initial status to eight-month status. Of the patient measures, the Ego Strength Scale scores increased significantly in the expected direction. Patients also used fewer dependency adjectives in describing themselves on the ICL. The therapists reported a significant decrease in severity of illness and noted significantly more symptom and interpersonal changes at eight months than at four months.

*One-Year Follow-Up*

One year after beginning psychotherapy, all of the patients who had completed at least four months of psychotherapy were asked to submit to a follow-up re-evaluation. Of 102 patients retested, 55 had remained in psychotherapy for the entire year (In Group) and 47 had completed or terminated psychotherapy some time after four months of treatment (Out Group). The 31 patients who did not respond to the follow-up request did not differ significantly in background characteristics from those retested.

Both the In Group and the Out Group were dichotomized into two groups on the basis of the number of interviews received. Patients receiving less than the median number of interviews were classed as Lows; all others were classed as Highs.

## In Group Comparisons

The High In Group consisted of 28 patients seen an average of 62 interviews. The Low In Group consisted of 27 patients seen an average of 27 interviews. Tests showed that the High and Low Groups differed significantly on some background variables. The High Group was younger, more frequently unemployed and single, and reported fewer symptoms. Tests for differences between the two groups at one year (initial scores controlled) showed that the High Group scored significantly lower on Cooperativeness and Friendliness. None of the therapist measures discriminated between the two groups. An item analysis showed that reduced "Friendliness" means less frequent endorsement of such platitudes as "It pays to turn the other cheek rather than to fight," and more frequent endorsement of such statements as "It is often necessary to fight for what is right," and "If I resent someone's action I promptly tell him so." The reduced "Cooperativeness" scores were due to less frequent endorsement of such self-descriptions as "Accepts advice readily," "Kind and reassuring," and "Often helped by others." Thus the High Group became more outspoken, independent, and determined to protect its own interest.

Significant changes from pretreatment status occurred on three of the patient measures for the In Group. Manifest Anxiety score and number of symptoms decreased while Ego Strength scores increased. Therapists report a significant decrease in severity of illness, more interpersonal changes, and more symptom reductions compared with changes during the first four months of psychotherapy. Thus patients in treatment status at the close of one year show a pattern of change

that is broader than at four or eight months.

## Out Group Comparisons

The High Interview Out Group consisted of 23 patients who had been seen an average of 34 interviews. The Low Out Group consisted of 24 patients seen an average of 16 sessions. There was no difference between High and Low Groups in actual duration of treatment. The mean length of therapy was 29 weeks for both groups. The High Group differed from the Low Group only on Severity of Illness on initial scores and background variables. The covariance analysis of the differences between High and Low Out Group at the end of one year showed up three significant differences. As with the In Group, the High Out Group was lower on Friendliness and Cooperativeness. In addition, the High Out Group patients showed a significantly greater reduction in number of dependency adjectives used in self-descriptions. These findings tend to confirm the finding that patients with more interviews see themselves as more assertive and outspoken in pursuing their own interests, less dependent, and less willing to be imposed upon by others.

To determine whether these were significant shifts made by the entire group from pretreatment status, tests were made on variables unrelated to number of treatments. None of the differences were significant. Thus among the Out Group, only those patients with an above median number of interviews present evidence of change from pretreatment status.

Thus, for patients remaining in treatment for as long as eight months, there is little evidence from the study just cited that the number of times the patient is seen effects the outcome. Duration of therapy, rather than treatment frequency, is associated with change over an eight-month period. For the one-year period the basis of treatment effects is uncertain because comparisons are no longer based on groups to which patients have been randomly assigned and maintained under set treatment conditions. On the other hand, the agreement as to the kinds of changes exhibited by the High In Group and the High Out Group suggests that the number of treatments does have some influence on outcome after a one-year period. Of the two factors, duration of psychotherapy appears more influential than treatment frequency. The patterns of change become broader and more consistent at each assessment period.

The Cartwright (1955) and Taylor (1956) finding that the number of treatments clients receive is related (nonlinearly) to therapist's ratings of improvement receives only partial support in the treatment frequency study (Lorr et al., 1961). Data on patients out of treatment at the end of one year suggest that a minimum number of treatments are required to effect an assessable change. The Low Out Group did not change after an average of 16 interviews, while the High Out Group did after 34 sessions. However, neither the Cartwright nor the Taylor study appears to have controlled duration of treatment. Neither author provides data concerning the number of weeks their patients remained in treatment nor their treatment schedules. A patient wtih 14 treatments at the time of termination could have been treated for seven weeks on a twice-a-week schedule, or for 14 weeks on a once-a-week schedule.

Clara Thompson's comments in her *Psychoanalysis* (1950) have a bearing here. She says:

Originally it was thought that six times a week was essential in order thoroughly to immerse the patient in the contemplation of his problems . . . . When analysis developed in the United States, I suspect the tendency to take long week ends contributed to the decision that analysis could be done five times a week. But whatever motive brought the change

about, the change itself demonstrated that five times a week still produced effective analysis. The recent war with its great shortage of psychoanalysts, coupled with an increased demand for treatment, has encouraged further experimentation, and it has been found that effective psychoanalysis can be done in many cases on a three-times-a-week basis—in very rare cases even on a once-a-week basis . . . . The three-times-a-week experiment is responsible for another discovery. In actual duration of treatment, in terms of months and years, the patient going five times a week takes about as long to be cured as the patient going three times.

Change would appear to require the passage of time. Insights are put into practice in daily living. New ways of reacting interpersonally must be tested again and again in natural settings before what has been learned becomes consolidated. Trial and error testing seems a prerequisite for the process of growth and change. Especially in adults, there is no reason for expecting striking characterological changes in the matter of weeks.

In conclusion, the review of studies available suggests that duration of treatment is a more influential parameter than sheer number of treatments. It would appear that traditional treatment frequency schedules should be examined more critically. Therapist time can be spread over more patients with fewer contacts and at less cost to patients.

REFERENCES

Cartwright, D. S. Success in psychotherapy as a function of certain actuarial variables. *J. consult. Psychol.,* 1955, **19**, 357-363.

Ends, E. J., & Page, C. W. Group psychotherapy and concomitant psychological change. *Psychol. Monogr.,* 1959, **73**(10, Whole No. 480).

Feldman, R., Lorr, M., & Russell, S. B. A mental hygiene clinic case survey. *J. clin. Psychol.,* 1958, **14**, 245-250.

Hollingshead, A. B., & Redlich, F. C. *Social class and mental illness: A community study.* New York: Wiley, 1958.

Imber, S. D., Frank, J. D., Nash, E. H., Stone, A. R., & Gliedman, L. H. Improvement and amount of therapeutic contact: An alternative to the use of no treatment controls in psychotherapy. *J. consult. Psychol.*, 1957, **21**, 309-315.

Lorr, M., McNair, D. M., Michaux, W. W., & Raskin, A. Frequency of treatment and change in psychotherapy. *J. abnorm. soc. Psychol.*, 1962, **64**, 281-292.

Myers, J. K., & Auld, F. Some variables related to outcome of psychotherapy. *J. clin. Psychol.*, 1955, **11**, 51-54.

Nichols, R. C., & Beck, K. W. Factors in

psychotherapy change. *J. consult. Psychol.*, 1960, **24**, 388-399.

Seeman, J. Counselor judgments of therapeutic process and outcome. In C. R. Rogers & Rosalind F. Dymond (Eds.), *Psychotherapy and personality change.* Chicago: Univer. Chicago Press, 1954.

Taylor, J. W. Relationship of success and length in psychotherapy. *J. consult. Psychol.*, 1956, **20**, 332.

Thompson, Clara. *Psychoanalysis: Evolution and development.* New York: Hermitage House, 1950.

# Toward What Level of Abstraction in Criteria?[1]

JOHN M. SHLIEN, PH.D.

The problem under main consideration here is that of the level of abstraction to which a concept in personality measurement may be raised, or should be raised, and the ways in which different levels of abstraction gain or lose in value for the researcher, according to his aims. This problem is one of many which developed in a practical research setting. That setting will be briefly described to give the context and history of this single instance of research, which in turn is presented as a particular illustration of the general problem: at what level of abstraction shall personality change be measured?

The context is one of outcome evaluation and comparison. Despite increasing and eminently worthwhile studies of process, there is serious doubt as to whether outcome studies are really behind us. Especially there is still much work to be done in the comparisons between outcomes produced by different forms of therapy. One can see evidence of growing inclinations among therapists of divergent schools of thought to put their work to test against not only controls, but each other, and this not in a hindering competitive spirit, but out of a cooperative and venturesome interest. We can expect more of such studies in the next decade, and obviously these will require a set of measurements with at least some common application in every experiment. One might hope that a conference such as this one would eventually produce a core battery of change measures, and stimulate the comparative research of which such a group of conferees would be capable.

[1] Prepared with the aid of a grant from the Ford Foundation (Psychotherapy Research Project) to the Counseling Center, University of Chicago.

## SECONDARY PROBLEM IN CONTEXT

The study of psychotherapy which provides the background for this problem is one in which comparisons were made, first between *two different* kinds of *structure* within the same *orientation*. That orientation was client-centered, and the structures were those of ( *a* ) an unlimited number of interviews, with voluntary termination, compared with ( *b* ) time-limited therapy in which the number of interviews was limited to 20, with termination set in advance (Shlien, 1957). In a second study, the *same structure* of time limits was compared in *two different types of therapy,* client-centered and Adlerian. For the moment, the history of the first study is a significant one. There, the main focus was a test of the value of time-limits in therapy—of their effectiveness as compared with controls, and of their efficiency when compared with longer unlimited cases.[2] The results were almost unanimously confirming of effective and efficient outcomes for time-limited therapy: six of the seven criteria used were in agreement on this point (Shlien, 1956).

That "almost" deserves some discussion, though it is not the main problem of this paper. The seventh criterion, the TAT, showed no change during therapy, but a

[2] Oversimplified, the theory of time limits in therapy is that healing is not a function of time, but of energy, or quality of experience. Whatever health-giving that can happen "sooner or later" can happen sooner. This could be flippantly put as the inverse of Parkinson's Law, "work expands in proportion to the amount of time available for its completion." But there is a serious and profound theory, culminating in Taft's (1933) well-known statement of the "single contact," which deserves careful attention and which was the theoretical basis for this study.

startling and unmistakable decline in the follow-up period (Henry & Shlien, 1958). Such contradictions of criteria, when all had been adopted in equally good faith, are perplexing, intriguing, and cannot be passed over lightly.

## CONTRADICTION OF CRITERIA

What can our position be when faced with such a contradiction? We cannot take the role of the student of human nature, who can balance the problem of the "whole man" in all his diverse aspects against the possible unity of the "integrated personality." We have no such easy accommodation. For us, these are *criteria*. We measure our work by these standards. Shall we expect contradictions as a part of nature, or try to resolve them? In the present state of clinical measurement, cultural diversity, and incomplete psychological conceptualization, I believe that we must expect some contradiction. When a study such as that by Little and Shneidman (1959) can conclude that for some of our major instruments—the Rorschach, TAT, MAPS, and MMPI— "agreement on diagnoses will be only slightly better than chance," there cannot be much hope for still better agreement between such clinical instruments and other types of ratings, reports, or scores. As things now stand, we could introduce a contradiction almost at will, simply by continuing to add another test (of the many established ones) to the battery until the desired result was achieved. For that matter, a battery of total agreement would rest uneasy upon the researcher, who might feel dismayed rather than fortunate to find all his measures so well related, for as Campbell and Fiske (1959) point out, a test must show some *discriminant* capacity in order to justify itself. Then there are discriminations within discriminations. Not only are diagnostic instruments at some variance, but there are somewhat separate "vantage

points" from which criteria come, or are viewed, and within which those instruments may operate differently. Cartwright and Roth (1957) report posttherapy factors in an analysis of ten outcome variables. There are three factors: client satisfaction, therapist view of success, and client response to others, and on the second factor, "the therapist stood alone in his views." Recently, a larger scale study by Cartwright, Fiske, and Kirtner indicates that the TAT may stand alone also.[3] From these technical considerations, one might indeed expect criteria to contradict each other some of the time.

Just beyond the clinical instruments lies the culture, full of conflict and ignorance about what constitutes criteria of "adjustment," "mental health," etc. Popular norms still judge the concrete behaviors which order a citizen's rank in mental health, and we psychologists by and large accept their judgment. In this sense, clinical psychology is in a rudimentary stage. Scott (1958), writing on research definitions of mental health, says, "The public picks the cases still." *They* send patients, and the hospital makes its diagnoses *somehow*. Scott suggests that the public will continue to define mental health or personality defect until we diagnose everyone. This is an interesting notion, but to carry it out would not create so much change in the situation as it would consternation in the public; our diagnostic or "change measuring" instruments (being one and the same—a mistake in itself) are usually built of the very same concrete, specific, and mundane behavioral traits that "the public" has used. Thus our inventories ask, "does your stomach rumble"; "are you afraid of mice"; "are you intelligent"; "feel ready

[3] Preliminary evidence from a factor analysis of a very broad range of criteria indicates that the TAT factor is remarkably separate, with no loadings on anything else, nor other factors loading on it. (Personal communication from D. Cartwright and D. Fiske).

144                                        RESEARCH IN PSYCHOTHERAPY

to go to pieces"; "like mannish women";
"disgusted by sex"; "never finish work";
"have temper tantrums"; "want to be a
florist"; "smoke too much"; and the like.
So far, most of our "operational" definitions of healthy personality are linked, in
a way which negates psychology, to "success"—high grades, achieving power,
making money, for instance. The problem
here is that we have yet to develop psychological or psychiatric definitions of
health which are *independent* of the cultural values of modern life (even though
to many psychotherapists that life is considered to be in many ways a failure).
There are too few efforts to develop positive concepts and measures, and they will
have to fight their way clear. There is too
little confidence in *psychological* values.
Unfortunately we are forced into culture-
bound concreteness, and since the culture
is somewhat ignorant, the specifics it offers
as criteria are not appropriate to take the
full measure of change in psychotherapy,
for the most part. The important end of
the therapy process, as far as measurement
is concerned, is the termination point,
not the beginning. But the public gives
us criteria which are no moré than complaints having to do with the *beginning*—
those things which repel, irritate, frighten
—whatever makes one person so trouble-
some to others that he is called "mentally
sick." Elimination of such troublesome-
ness is not the achievement of health, but
many of our criteria are built as if it were.
Then dimensions which were not even
present at the beginning of therapy enter
in when health is achieved, and these
dimensions have no opportunity for expression in even a passive sense. As a
theoretical example, the elimination of
slavery is not immediately translatable, by
subtraction, as freedom. Slavery is rather
easy to define in concrete and specific
ways. Freedom is a more abstract realm of
behavior, not because it is mystical, but
precisely because the behaviors it will
contain are far less easy to observe, speci-

fy, or predict. That is part of the nature of
freedom. Control is in the hands of the
free person. So it is with sickness and
health. Sickness lends itself to observation
and description easily; health does not. In
more literal psychological terms, when insecurity ends and security is achieved, a
contingent dimension (according to W. I.
Thomas) comes into play—i.e., venturesome seeking of new experience. But we
are not given "venturesome" at one end
of the security–insecurity scale. For the
most part, clinical scales are still in the
elementary stage of the discomfort–relief
type of conception, and after the discomfort is relieved, what then?

It seems that so long as clinical instruments remain unreliable, and "noncon-
vergent," some behaviorally concrete and
some conceptually abstract, most residual
and a few positive, most reflecting the
ordinary cultural concerns and a few
being psychologically independent, there
will be contradiction among criteria. This
need not be a complete roadblock to conclusions in research, but neither is it a
situation which leaves one content. In the
experiment on time-limited therapy in
which this problem was encountered, the
force of the contradiction was to lead us
to a replication[4] for a second test. That
is, of course, not a solution. It is only a
pause for reappraisal. It was in the course
of this replication that another phase of
the "level of abstraction" problem developed.

PRIMARY PROBLEM IN CONTEXT

From this point on, I will be dealing
with the barest outline of the total experiment, and some sketchy descriptions of a
particular part of it, not to give detailed
proof but to illustrate the case of one
variable pursued through different levels
of abstraction. The variable in question is
self-esteem. The outline of some results

[4] Not exact, in that one condition—the brand
of therapy—was changed.

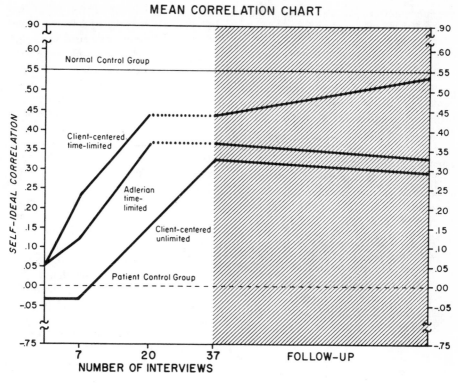

Figure 1. Average levels of self-ideal correlation in three experimental groups.

which led to this pursuit is seen in Figure 1. That chart shows average levels of self-ideal correlation for three experimental groups—one unlimited in time and composed of clients who voluntarily terminated, and two other groups which were limited in time to 20 interviews. The first question about level of abstraction arises from a comparison of two of these groups; the two which are client-centered, one time-limited, the other unlimited. An answer to this question will lead to a complication in the second comparison—between Adlerian time-limited therapy and client-centered time-limited therapy. All of these results are in terms of correlations between self and ideal "Q sorts," but this discussion is *not* about Q technique, or Q methodology. The "Q sort" was born to be factor analyzed (Stephen-

son, 1953) and here we are considering only the correlation between self and ideal descriptions, which could be (and have often been) given via any sort of inventory. It is the instruction ("describe yourself as you are" and "describe yourself as you would like to be") that matters. The correlation between these two descriptions can be called discrepancy or congruence (and is often called both by the same writer).

Can such a correlation or ratio justifiably be called *self-esteem,* as Butler and Haigh (1954) suggest? This is precisely the way it has long been conceived and "operationally" derived. Fifty years ago, William James wrote, "It is determined by the ratio of our actualities to our supposed potentialities; a fraction, of which our pretensions are the denominator and the numerator our success: thus

$$\text{Self-esteem} = \frac{\text{Success}}{\text{Pretensions}}.\text{"}$$

Kurt Lewin's ratio of "level of aspiration" to "level of achievement" is a similar derivation for self-esteem. Is self-esteem a variable of significance in psychotherapy? I have never met a therapist of any persuasion who did not think it absolutely essential, of the highest importance. As a final note, it is a psychological construct, a personal feeling, independent of any particular content or culture, and thus capable of being raised beyond the level of specific behavioral traits.

Returning to this problem as it arose in context: In the original comparison between the two client-centered therapy experiments, one time-limited and the other unlimited (Figure 1), each population had been measured on the self-esteem variable by use of a somewhat different Q-sort deck, though the same self and ideal instructions were given in every instance. The question at this point was simply—can these two populations be compared? Can these two decks be considered a single instrument? For the unlimited group, the original Butler-Haigh 100-item deck was used (Butler & Haigh, 1954). For the time-limited group, that deck was modified, reduced to 80 items, balanced for positive and negative statements, some items eliminated because they were "chronic neutrals," and a few new items added.[5] The question was an-

---

[5] The primary reason for this modification is of practical interest for researchers. It was to reduce the amount of time required for administration of the test, which was given at four points, and required up to an hour for each administration. Increase or decrease of items from a base of 100 seems to increase or decrease in roughly geometrical proportion the amount of time required. We found that an 80-item deck required on the average one-half the time it took to sort the 100-item deck. It was our principle, to put it wryly, that "the testing battery should not take more

swered easily enough. Three population samples, providing the appropriate client and control range of distribution of "scores," (i.e., self-ideal correlations) were given both the 100- and the 80-item decks to sort, half taking the 80 items first. Within a few days, each individual sorted the remaining deck, always using the same self and ideal instructions. The self-ideal correlations from each deck, when correlated for each individual in the three samples (total $N=45$), yielded $r$'s ranging from .77 to .91, averaging $r=.82$.[6] These are on the average as high as the best reported reliabilities for $Q$ sorts, and we may feel fairly comfortable in comparing as equivalent those self-ideal correlations from $Q$ sorts which have the same design and a good deal of overlap in "trait universe." But here a more interesting problem comes into view. How much difference *can* there be in a set of items before the items begin to influence or outweigh the sorter? As Briggs and Wirt (1960) put it, "The $Q$-sort technique produces an amalgamation of sorter, subject, and $Q$-deck characteristics which are difficult to refract." The problem can be put in an even more intriguing way. *Is there an abstract entity, an internal self-ideal relationship* (congruence or discrepancy) *which exists within each person's consciousness of himself in a general sense, and which will be projected upon or represented through any set of items?* To what extent is this measure of self-esteem a core of feelings, independent of the cultural traits usually offered as concrete avenues of its expression? And if there is such a psychological entity, which cuts

---

of the client's time than he had hours in therapy." This is a serious matter. To ignore it may mean that one collects a great deal of data which is clouded in its meaning by factors of fatigue, resentment, and carelessness. The average client in research spends 10 to 25 hours taking tests.

[6] $Z$ transformations have been used throughout where needed.

across a variety of self descriptive items, would there still be a particular set of items which would be most truly representative of the self-ideal relationship within a given individual?

## SEARCH FOR EVIDENCE OF AN ABSTRACT ENTITY

To explore these possibilities, three other sets of items were casually selected. One was a set of 50 items taken at random from Hilden's Manual of 1,000 items (Hilden, 1954). Another set was found in the list of 49 value adjectives, presented as a check list form by Bills, Vance, and McLean (1951). It is rated on a five-point scale, and can be easily administered under self and ideal instructions. Finally, after these sorts were executed, each subject was asked to make up a list of 25 statements about himself—statements he (or she) would consider personally significant, whether positive or negative.[7] One might expect that this last set of items would have the most stability (in an ordinary test–retest reliability sense, though it might show the greatest volatility in a change inducing situation such as therapy) and most meaningful and accurate representation of self-ideal congruence. On the other hand, however much one might expect generality and overlap of these private items from person to person (and I had no expectations on this point, in either direction) there was amazingly little. Of course, these people had just been through four other inventories of a more conventional sort, running the usual gamut of

categories, and may have been trying to "say something different" about themselves. At any rate, there was practically no overlap in items from one person to another, and no item common to all. Even with broad categorical interpretation, at least 50% of the private items would remain unique.[8]

From this, you can see what is to follow. We have five "decks," all to be sorted by the same individuals, using always the "self" and "ideal" instructions. These five are abbreviated as the 100-$Q$, 80-$Q$, 50-H$Q$, Bills Index, and 25 idio-$Q$.

A group of subjects was given the task of sorting, for self and ideal, all five of the decks. This is a task of considerable cost in effort and time and was performed in two or three sittings, ranging over a period of three to ten days. The subjects numbered 27 (though only 19 gave completely usable data on all five sorts) and they were obtained on a volunteer basis, without client status, research obligations, or any special motivation.[9] The tasks were carried out in the order given on Table 1. Table 1 is a set of illustrative data, showing a sample of ten cases which include the lowest and highest "scores" (Self-ideal $r$) from the total sample, plus eight other

---

[7] Surely this is very close to the recommendation given by Stephenson for the most valid approach to the unique qualities of each person's attitudes and experiences. The reader can get an idea of how unique these items might be by referring to the case of "Dora." There, for instance, items read, "I have a tragic mouth," "I can be ill from longing," "Physicians I spurn," etc. It is striking to compare these to the conventional $Q$ or questionnaire items (Stephenson, 1953).

[8] Professor George Klein has suggested that if people could sort each other's items, for themselves, with the same results as were obtained on a general, conventional deck, that would be overwhelming proof of existence of an abstract entity. I did not try this, and feel that it would be interesting, indeed overwhelming, but likely to fail. The "entity" need not be *that* abstract, nor is blindness to the other's unique items a required proof of "abstractness."

[9] Much gratitude is due to Drs. Galatia Halkides and Virgil Willis who, as research assistants, obtained this and other data from friends, relatives, students, hospital patients, or other willing sources. The fact that the investigation was not conducted with more vigor is no fault of theirs. This was a side issue to a main project, and was carried out in spare time through motives of new curiosity as each step developed.

cases taken at random from the total sample of complete cases, all ordered by their first column rank. Scanning across five columns for each individual, Table 1 shows evidence of a conspicuous degree of stability for the sorter. One can predict any person's score from deck to deck better than one could predict from person to person within any column. From inspection of this sample, one can tentatively conclude that there is some internal sense of self-ideal congruence (or discrepancy) which has a greater influence upon the sorting than does the effect of the written statement presented as opportunities for that expression. That does not posit an unvarying psychological entity, nor does the evidence suggest anything of the kind. The table of intercorrelations (Table 2) tells us that there is a moderately high level of agreement between the ranks of most self-ideal correlations on all decks or sorts or inventories used, and inspection of the two directions of variability in Table 1 suggests that the agreement comes more from the outlook of the

TABLE 1

ILLUSTRATIVE SAMPLE SHOWING TEN SUBJECTS' SELF-IDEAL CORRELATIONS ON FIVE DIFFERENT Q-SORT DECKS OR INVENTORIES (PARTIAL DATA)

| Subject | 100-Q | 80-Q | 50-HQ | Bills Index | 25 idio-Q |
|---|---|---|---|---|---|
| Fi | −.32 | .21 | .02 | .16 | −.12 |
| Jo | .08 | .30 | .09 | −.06 | .13 |
| Ro | .14 | .40 | .21 | .33 | .31 |
| De | .32 | −.19 | −.16 | .50 | .35 |
| Kl | .53 | .74 | .65 | −.34 | .58 |
| Ad | .57 | .70 | .66 | .49 | .48 |
| Ne | .67 | .64 | .74 | .65 | −.59[a] |
| Gr | .78 | .70 | .83 | .92 | .68 |
| Ot | .81 | .72 | .43 | .79 | .67 |
| Sp | .91 | .95 | .96 | .90 | .93 |

[a] This minus coefficient seems highly inconsistent; it may be one of those occasional mishaps in which the order of piles is inadvertently reversed either by the sorter or the psychometrist.

TABLE 2

INTERCORRELATIONS

| | 100-Q | 80-Q | 50-HQ | Bills Index |
|---|---|---|---|---|
| 80-Q | .82 | | | |
| 50-HQ | .65 | .69 | | |
| Bills Index | .50 | .65 | .66 | |
| 25 idio-Q | .58 | .68 | .75 | .56 |

Note.—This table is made up of all the data available, so that some of the intercorrelations are based on an N=45, some less, as few as N=19. Again in keeping with the instructions to the conference, this is not intended to be a detailed description of research, but an illustration of the theoretical problem under discussion.

sorter than the influence of the items sorted. If, from this, one takes the notion that the abstract entity does exist, and that it weighs more heavily than do the concrete trait descriptions, one is moved to wonder if this effect cannot be more highly abstracted. If completely removed from the level of imposed verbal trait descriptions, what stability would such a measure have, and what would it mean?

After brief consideration, and still on an exploratory basis, an apparatus was constructed (Figure 2) to present the possibility of a ratio of correlation on a nonverbal level. Presumably each individual would use his own total estimate or his situational response as a measure of his self-ideal congruence. This apparatus is simple, and consists of two semi-transparent curved circles which can be moved through 180 degrees by the subject, so that they are back to back, completely opposite (a −1.00 correlation), or centered together, so that they completely overlap, (a +1.00 correlation) or any point between these extremes. The subject is told to think of one circle as representing his "self," the other his "ideal," paraphrasing the usual sorting instructions. He faces the circles, moves them to suit himself, until he is satisfied. On the back stand, hidden from his view, are notched pointers, one attached to each

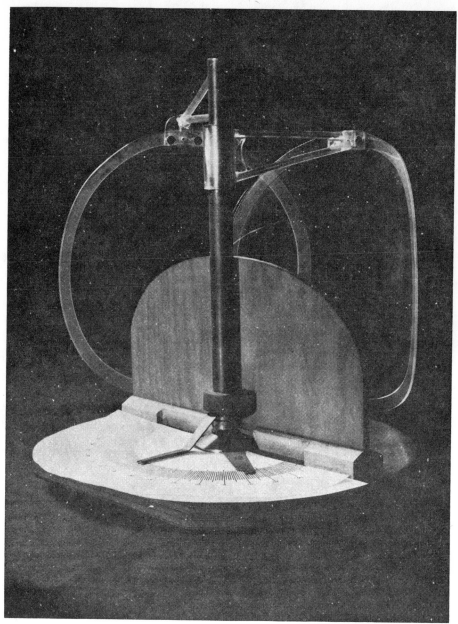

Figure 2. Abstract Apparatus 1 (rear view).

circle arm so that they indicate the angle of separation between the circles. The psychometrist makes a pencil mark in each notch, notes the angle, translates it from an adjoining table as the cosine of the angle between two vectors, and records it as a correlation coefficient. (Actually, there is no advantage to this over any other ranking system, except that it permits us to continue to speak of the "self-ideal correlation," and gives an over-worked psychometrist the feeling of having accomplished a tedious computation in no time. The entire procedure, from portal to portal, takes three minutes or less.)

In order to test the stability of this level of abstraction as a measure, a second instrument was devised. It is still more simple, composed of two frosted 12-inch squares of plexiglass, which slide in parallel tracks so that they can touch edges, overlap completely, or be fixed at any in-between point. Again the self-ideal instructions are given, and the degree of overlapping variance is read off a hidden scale on the back. This second apparatus (not shown, but henceforth called Apparatus 2) is, like Apparatus 1 (Figure 2) an admittedly crude and imperfect piece, not as refined as need be for extensive use, but satisfying for the exploratory nature of this investigation.

When the abstract measures, Apparatus 1 and Apparatus 2, were given to a group of 20 undergraduate psychology students, with the 80-item $Q$ sort given between the two abstract measures, the correlation between the two abstract measures was .81. This abstract level, then, has as much stability as the average reliability of the $Q$ sorts, or as much convergence as the 100- and 80-item $Q$ sorts which have considerable overlap in items. Clearly, whatever goes into the subject's *abstract* judgment of self-ideal discrepancy, it is as stable as if he were using a forced sort and a deck of *concrete* items.

However, when these two abstract measures are correlated with the intervening conventional 80-item $Q$-sort self-ideal given to those 20 students, the relation is lower. Between Apparatus 1 and the 80-item self-ideal correlation, $r=.39$; between Apparatus 2 and the 80-item self-ideal correlation, $r=.48$. (Another sample of 20 cases, half "normal controls" and half Veterans Administration "mental

patients," used the 80-item self-ideal sorts and Apparatus 1, yielding a product-moment correlation of .42.) When 12 of those 20 students were recaptured within the month and prevailed upon to write the 25 personal statements significant about themselves, and to sort those personal statements under self and ideal instructions, again the items were highly unique. The rho between the personal 25-item self-ideal correlation and the "score" on Apparatus 1, pooled with those same cases and Apparatus 2 (for a total N of 24) yielded a rho of .67. This is roughly twice as large, in terms of predictive power, as the relation between the abstract apparatus measure and the 80-item deck of concrete conventional items.[10] That is to say, the concrete items made up by each individual, unique and personal to him, are much more related to the demonstrated abstract entity than are the conventional concrete items which are more common to the population. It would seem that these private items are the sorts of considerations which compose one's self-ideal disparity. For the sake of the theoretical argument in this paper, I will make an exaggerated interpretation of these findings and assert: the most abstract is also the most concrete (though in a very special sense).[11] The "abstract"

---

[10] Butler (1956) has found a single *ideal* factor which he calls a "common cultural ideal." When Dymond (1954) had six judges sort the 100-item deck into two piles, one "well-adjusted," the other not, the range of discrepancy between any two judges was between two and four items. The conventional deck does seem to have a heavy component of what Edwards (1957) calls the "social desirability variable," and this is much less evident in the "idio-$Q$" or personal items invented by each subject for himself.

[11] Granted that this is what one could say unequivocally only if repeated experiments produced a correlation of 1.00 instead of the .67 given. But I am reminded that one of the most enduring and forceful ideas in psychology, the frustration-aggression hypothesis, was based on evidence such as a correlation of −.66 between cotton prices and lynchings in the South.

is not really empty; it has implicit concrete meanings in the consciousness of the individual, and at least some of these can be made explicit. Perhaps it would be better to say that the abstract is the most general, in that each individual can apply it to his own unique concrete.

## REVIEW

Thus far, we have followed the development of an important variable in personality change through several stages. Self-esteem was a theoretical "given" to begin with. It is supposedly universal, but of what content each man's personal measure is composed we do not know, unless we ask. It cannot be observed directly, but may be derived from a ratio of some personal judgment having to do with what one is, and what one wants to be. This we are given, at the beginning, as a psychological concept by theorists such as William James, Kurt Lewin, and Karen Horney. Later, researchers developed an empirical substantiation of this concept and its derivation, using the self-ideal $Q$ sort (Butler & Haigh, 1954). Such substantiation brings the concept "down to earth" for a test, grounding it in a list of commonly observed concrete behavioral descriptions. This paper has discussed an exploratory study which gives evidence to the effect that the individual concept of self-esteem does not depend upon, or vary greatly when confronted with, different sets of common behavioral descriptions. This suggests that self-esteem operates and can be measured at a higher level of abstraction. At a further stage of inquiry, self-esteem is demonstrated to be measurable without the use of any explicitly stated behavioral descriptions. This appears to be a very high level of abstraction, returning in apparently contentless form to the ratio given by those original conceptualizers. Yet it seems that the abstract form is not truly without reference to any content at all, for in the most crucial point of the exploration, the

abstract is found to be more closely linked to the behaviors invented by each person to describe himself than to the conventional behaviors common to a population. For purposes of argument, I have drawn these conclusions:

1. There is such a thing as an abstract psychological entity, approachable by measure.

2. In this case the example of self-esteem, derived from the self-ideal relation, is a model of such an entity.

3. The highest level of abstraction is the most general, i.e., best applied to the uniquely concrete by each individual. It will *contain* the personally significant concrete, though it will not specify it.

## RESEARCH-WISE, WHAT OF IT?

If you can accept the foregoing as a demonstration that self-esteem can be measured at either a more abstract or more concrete level, which way is dictated by what aims? Look again at Figure 1, representing the experiment from which this problem developed. There is another comparison to be made between two groups; one Adlerian and time-limited, the other client-centered and also time-limited (Shlien, Mosak, & Dreikurs, 1960). In this comparison, both groups used the identical 80-item $Q$ sort. With respect to the means for each population, the groups were not distinguishable at any of the three testing points from pre- to posttherapy. That is the complication mentioned earlier. These results tell us something significant we wanted to know about time limits in therapy, but do they tell us all we need to know? If they do, I believe that we could have obtained the same group means through use of the abstract apparatus, with a saving in time which would have enabled us to use another test (perhaps to encounter another contradiction!). But we used the $Q$ sort, having in mind to subject it to analysis for different clusters or factors in each population, because we *know* there are differences—in the therapy, in the populations, in the outcome, in some way. We would "know" this even if the item analysis did not show it to be so. Or would we? Perhaps we are in danger of being like the essayist who wrote, "All food is the same, being limited to a narrow range within which gourmets pretend to find exquisite distinctions." In that case, all of our close analysis is an exercise in technical virtuosity, and the abstract measure of outcome is sufficient. On the other hand, such a measure is at least vulnerable to the criticism of "placebo effect" without means to test or counter it. Then we are in danger, if there are differences as we believe, of overlooking them. In that case the development of the abstract measure is itself only an exercise.

It would seem, then, that a compromise solution is most reasonable. The variable of self-esteem has been tested and proved on the ground and in the air, as it were. The *Q* sort or an inventory can provide both the ratio and the concrete behaviors which will separate groups or individuals having identical "total scores." Then the question is—are these the significant ways in which one wants to discriminate? Does it matter whether one "smokes too much," etc. Unless these behavioral items cluster into a complex which itself is a higher level of abstraction, these concrete differences are only at the level of "complaints," not personality variables. The lowest level of concreteness may be necessary as a base of observation for the beginning of measures of change, but until they cluster into intercorrelating sectors, they do not begin to qualify as measures of "personality" change, and I would argue that until the measure has been raised to a higher level of abstraction, it is not significant. For research in psychotherapy this is a special problem; we speak of change as taking place in terms of concrete "items" (he no longer "smokes too much"). But this, I

believe, is only apparently so. "Manifestations" are simply easier to observe and describe than are "causes." That does not signify their importance. Any variable which can be observed only at a concrete behavioral level is not a very important psychological basis on which to discriminate between people. Still, the necessity to make discriminations remains. The abstract level of measurement could accomplish this only under ideal circumstances, as yet far from achieved. If the important variables could be raised to a high level of abstraction, and could be made practically economical, theoretically sound, technically pure, they could in combination make the kind of change measures which would enable significant discriminations without resort to elementary behavioral items. Until this is achieved, the abstract measure has limitations for the researcher which make it useful only in gross ways. Even so, it is not just a worthless exercise. Any variable, whether it originates in the armchair or Univac, should be validated as a psychological concept. In the instance of the example in this discussion, self-esteem was followed through its course from armchair to behavioral items and then to a demonstration of its abstract reality. "Tolerance for ambiguity," "Ego-Strength," or other thought-originated concepts could be treated in the same way. On the other hand, variables which begin "on the ground," as it were, in "hypothesis generating" studies (from factor analysis, for instance), could profit from the test of being raised to a higher level of abstraction. If they cannot meet this test, perhaps they are transitory and insignificant.

I have the hunch that the most important personality variables we could deal with are those at least capable of, perhaps even demanding, a high level of abstraction for their best measurement, and the most important variables are best measured abstractly. Self-esteem is one. There are others—for example, honesty and courage. These are variables of personality, capable of change, susceptible of influence by psychotherapy. As for their importance: if and when they are achieved to a high degree, there is very little more a therapist can do, as a therapist, for his client or patient. (For that matter, if everyone were honest and courageous, would there be any need for psychotherapy at all?) If these variables are so significant, why are they not being measured and used? I believe it is because the concepts are highly abstract, and need to be measured at that level, where we have least confidence and experience in careful measurement. We cannot offer a check list of behavioral items to tap the content of these qualities in each individual. The content is too various, and we cannot know the range or weights of the general list of behaviors. Moreover, these abstract concepts have never been formulated in a way comparable to the theory of self-esteem, as that concept gave us a model for this discussion.

## SUMMARY

Two problems resulting from a comparative study were discussed. With regard to the contradiction of criteria, it seems that there is not enough unity among instruments, sources of opinion, or level of abstraction to permit us to anticipate complete agreement. A particular case of the problem of level of abstraction was illustrated, using self-esteem as the example. It was argued that such a variable can be demonstrated to have an abstract status, somewhat independent of conventional lists of behaviors, and most highly related to the behavioral items specific and unique to each person. The abstract measure is valuable where gross comparisons are sought, though it will not separate individuals where differences at more concrete levels may exist. The researcher's aims will dictate which level is most useful. Above all, it is argued that the most important variables are *psychological*, i.e., not the elementary behaviors which can be observed only on the most concrete level, but those concepts which can apply generally to a wide variety of concrete behaviors. Whether or not the most abstract level of measurement is used, the fact that it can be abstracted is a standard of its psychological significance. The final solution may lie in the development of measures at a high level of abstraction in several distinct areas, so that desired discriminations may be made by combination without resort to descriptions of behaviors which are by themselves not significant.

## REFERENCES

Bills, R. E., Vance, E. C., & McLean, O. S. An index of adjustment and values. *J. consult. Psychol.*, 1951, **15**, 257-261.

Briggs, P. F., & Wirt, R. D. Intra-Q deck relationships as influences and realities in personality assessment. *J. consult. Psychol.*, 1960, **24**, 61-66.

Butler, J. M. Factorial studies of client-centered psychotherapy: A preliminary report. *U. Chicago Lib. Counsel. Cent. Disc. Pap.*, 1956, **2**, No. 9.

Butler, J. M., & Haigh, G. V. Changes in the relation between self-concepts and ideal concepts consequent upon client-centered counseling. In C. R. Rogers & Rosalind F. Dymond (Eds.), *Psychotherapy and personality change*. Chicago: Univer. Chicago Press, 1954.

Campbell, D. T., & Fiske, D. W. Convergent and discriminant validation by the multitrait-multimethod matrix. *Psychol. Bull.*, 1959, **56**, 81-105.

Cartwright, D. S., & Roth, I. Success and satisfaction in psychotherapy. *J. clin. Psychol.*, 1957, **13**, 20-26.

Dymond, Rosalind F. Adjustment changes over therapy from self-sorts. In C. R. Rogers & Rosalind F. Dymond (Eds.), *Psychotherapy and personality change*. Chicago: Univer. Chicago Press, 1954.

Edwards, A. L. *The social desirability variable in personality assessment and research*. New York: Dryden, 1957.

Henry, W. E., & Shlien, J. M. Affective complexity and psychotherapy: Some comparisons of time-limited and unlimited treatment. *J. proj. Tech.*, 1958, **22**, 153-162.

Hilden, A. H. *Manual for Q-sort and random sets of personal concepts.* St. Louis: Washington Univer. Press, 1954.

James, W. *Principles of psychology.* Vol. 1. New York: Henry Holt, 1950.

Little, K. B., & Shneidman, E. S. Congruencies among interpretations of psychological test and anamestic data. *Psychol. Monogr.*, 1959, **73** (6, Whole No. 476).

Scott, W. A. Research definitions of mental health and mental illness. *Psychol. Bull.*, 1958, **55**, 65-87.

Shlien, J. M. An experimental investigation of time-limited client-centered therapy. *U. Chicago Lib. Counsel. Cent. Disc. Pap.*, 1956, **2**, No. 23.

Shlien, J. M. Time-limited psychotherapy: An experimental investigation of practical values and theoretical implications. *J. counsel. Psychol.*, 1957, **4**, 318-322.

Shlien, J. M., Mosak, H. H., & Dreikurs, R. Effect of time limits: A comparison of client-centered and Adlerian psychotherapy. *U. Chicago Lib. Counsel. Cent. Disc. Pap.* 1960, **6**, No. 8.

Smith, G. M. Six measures of self concept discrepancy and instability: Their interrelations, reliability, and relations to other personality measures. *J. consult. Psychol.*, 1958, **22**, 101-112.

Stephenson, W. *The study of behavior: Q-technique and its methodology.* Chicago: Univer. Chicago Press, 1953.

Taft, Jessie. *Dynamics of therapy in a controlled relationship.* New York: Macmillan, 1933.

# Discussion of Papers on
# Measuring Personality Change

## NEVITT SANFORD, PH.D.

It has seemed to me that sooner or later we would need an over-all scheme embracing variables in the patient, in the therapist, and in the processes of their interaction. It is not possible to segregate the several topics that we have been assigned. The task of our group, as you know, is to talk about variables in the patient's personality, but it seems clear that if we are going to formulate personality we should use the same terms for the therapist that we use for the patient. Again, Dr. Lorr's paper is concerned mainly with certain aspects of the process of therapy—with the frequency of therapy sessions, and duration of the whole enterprise—but he studies these things in relation to a judiciously chosen set of objective measures of personality. Dr. Luborsky sticks pretty closely to variables in patients, measured on two different occasions, but looking at his variables it is not too difficult to make some inferences as to what the therapy must have been. We can be pretty sure that there was long-term therapy, and psychoanalysis. Dr. Shlien is concerned with the philosophy and strategy of selecting variables for study, and he naturally relates these problems to the processes of therapy and to the interests of the therapist. It seems to me that we need a scheme of the sort that I have sketched below (Figure 1).

Now I would argue that the same general scheme that holds for psychotherapy holds also for other kinds of change-agents or agencies that are brought to bear from time to time in our society. Psychotherapy probably ought to be regarded as a special case of interpersonal relationships; and changes in the person that occur in psy-

chotherapy ought to be regarded as special cases of change in general. After all, we are interested in changing people, or in enabling people to change, or in creating conditions under which they can change in directions that they favor. We will do well to look for alternatives to psychotherapy. Our aim should be to know enough about personality—how it develops, how it functions, how it changes— so that other kinds of instrumentalities in addition to psychotherapy can be made available to people. We may hope to utilize what has been and is being used in psychotherapy, but probably there will never be enough psychotherapists to help all the people who want or need it. More than this, if we look now for alternatives, we may get some fresh ideas about what might be done in the therapeutic relationship.

In our model there is a person who enters into some kind of situation that has been designed with the general objective of changing him or promoting his growth. This scheme holds not only for psychotherapy but for various other situations as well. It holds for an educational institution or program, and for a correctional

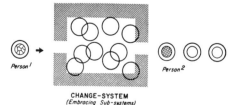

CHANGE-SYSTEM
(Embracing Sub-systems)

Figure 1. Model of psychotherapy or of any social system designed to change the person who passes through it.

155

institution or a summer camp or encampment for citizenship. It holds for interviews and for bringing up in the family. In all these cases there is some kind of agency or system or set of processes designed with the object of inducing changes that will accord with somebody's hopes or expectations.

Concerning objectives, it seems safe to say that we, as psychologists, want to see people develop, we want to help them become whatever they can become. These are the terms we use in education and they seem to be readily applicable to psychotherapy as well. We do not have to look very far, however, to see that different people have in mind quite different kinds of objectives.

One of the most interesting aspects of the whole scheme is the change-inducing process or processes. In psychotherapy the therapist is, of course, central, but he is not everything. If our concern is with group psychotherapy, other clients or patients have roles in the process. Even in person-to-person psychotherapy there are various conditions governing the relationship between the entering person and the change-inducing system. For one thing, there is the question of how hard it was to get into the system. The opening, we might say, varies in elasticity. Whether we are concerned with a school or with a psychotherapeutic relationship, the question of how hard it was to get into it might have an important bearing on what the final outcome will be. If one can secure the services of a highly regarded therapist, the processes of interaction may well be different from what they would be if one settled for some less sought after therapist, and this regardless of the competence of the two therapists. The same holds for colleges. Some colleges have such prestige that students may well believe that once they have gained admittance everything will be done for them. Possibly the same thing holds in the case of the

highly regarded therapist. If the therapist were a less highly regarded one, one might enter therapy with the expectation that he would really have to work, and the outcome might be different.

What has just been said concerns any agency set up in order to change people. The same general considerations would hold for arrangements in which we undertook to investigate people over a period of time; we would still have to deal with the effects of the investigator in producing any change that has occurred.

Dr. Lorr, of course, is concerned with certain aspects of the change agency—the duration of the person's stay within it and the frequency of contacts with the therapist. The issues that Dr. Lorr raises have also been raised in education: should we have a system in which everything is speeded up in order to get people through in a hurry or to teach them as much as possible in a limited time, or should education proceed at a more leisurely pace so that experiences can "sink in" and new insights can be integrated with the student's actual life? Dr. Lorr finds that the frequency of the interviews doesn't really make much difference when the over-all time is constant. If the over-all time is a year, then probably as much is accomplished by weekly interviews as with interviews twice a week. It is possible that educators can learn something from this finding.

The processes that are brought to bear on the patient or client or student might be characterized as *rational* or *irrational*. Those who operate an agency for change usually have some kind of theory governing what they do. They bring to bear certain influences which, according to some theory, will change the person in some desired way. But other influences may enter the picture, independently of the therapist or not intended by him, and they may have an important bearing on what happens. This corresponds well with what is commonly to be observed in institutions. Institutions are designed, in the first instance, rationally. Their activities are supposed, on reasonable grounds, to produce certain kinds of effects. But analysis of an institution after it has been in operation for a time will show that many of its activities have no conceivable relation to its stated objectives. For one thing, all institutions, once they have been set going, have to devote time and energy to self-maintenance; for another, institutions change their purposes, and instrumentalities designed for an earlier purpose lose their function; but this does not mean that the instrumentalities will be given up; on the contrary, interest becomes vested in them, they come to serve various individual needs of the institution's members, and hence they persist as irrational features of the system. Small wonder that what happens to people who pass through the system is often unanticipated, and actual outcomes cannot be related to procedures that were deliberately undertaken. Similarly, a person may pass through a long series of therapeutic interviews that were designed to reduce his symptoms or to relieve his suffering. It might be that neither of these things happens, but that he becomes in the end a psychotherapist himself.

In considering the outcomes of passages through change-agencies or change-systems, there are several possibilities that must be kept in mind. There may be change or no change. Change may be desirable or undesirable—from various points of view. Changes that are desirable, from the point of view of the therapist or educator or reformer, may or may not be due to activities deliberately undertaken.

This last confronts us with a difficulty of experimental control that is not always overcome in researches on psychotherapy. It is not only that a desired outcome might be due to some unrecognized ac-

tivity of the therapist, but it may be due to events outside the therapeutic situation altogether—events not taken into account in the experimental design. As for research on the effects of college, I believe it still remains to be demonstrated that changes observed in college students were due to educational activities of the college rather than to something else, and that similar changes might not be occurring in people of the same age in quite different situations.

There are two further points about change. One is that the new state of the individual may be temporary or enduring. The only way to tell which is the case is by means of follow-up studies, examining individuals at various times after they have completed their passage through the change-system. It is common to examine people two years after they have completed psychotherapy. In Dr. Luborsky's work there was follow-up after two years. Finally, it is important to ask whether it is change itself or the achievement of some absolute standard of health or maturity or excellence that we are interested in. In colleges nowadays there is enormous emphasis upon this latter objective, for example, upon the kind of excellence that insures that a student will be admitted to a good graduate school. Since it is suspected that the major determinants of this eventuality are in the student at the time he enters college, the tendency of colleges is to be very careful about selecting students, less careful about what is done to or for them during their college course. Few colleges would care to base their reputations upon their ability to change poor students into mediocre ones. The same kinds of choices are, to some extent, open to the psychotherapist. It is one thing to work with patients who are interesting, attractive, possessed of many resources and socially valuable traits, and who were already practically cured once they had made up their minds to enter psychotherapy; it is something else to work with unpromising characters who might change a great deal but still be rather unpromising characters. It is too much to ask that psychotherapists avoid patients of the first type, but perhaps it is not too much to ask that, like Freud, they accept various kinds of patients including some of the unpromising ones.

Now let us turn to the major problem confronting the authors of the papers in this first group. To measure personality change in psychotherapy we have to have variables of personality, and this means that we must first find some suitable basis for selecting—and for defining—such variables. Dr. Shlien has been concerned with the problem of selecting variables.

It seems to me that our approach to this problem ought to be guided by a general theory of personality. This is not the place to offer such a theory, but we may at least note some of the considerations that affect our choices of variables.

Let it be noted first that in Figure 1 I have borrowed from Kurt Lewin in offering a conception of the person. Whether or not we put the "psychological environment" inside the personality, as I would be inclined to do, Lewin's distinction between the psychological environment and "the person"—or "core personality" as others might say—is well worth making when it comes to the definition of variables relevant to psychotherapy. And in our formulation of "patient variables" we should include also variables in the patient's situation of the moment, that is, in his nonpsychological, or geographical, environment. For example, strains arising from this environment may have an important bearing on the outcome of psychotherapy.

Most psychologists are willing to think of personality as an organized complexity, a whole constituted of parts that are somehow organized. It is hardly controversial to speak of interactions among the parts

and of interactions between the personality as a whole and the environment. The great difficulty comes when we ask ourselves how we are going to conceive of the parts or elements of the personality. You will recall Allport's text (1937) in which he gave a great deal of attention to what he called "the search for elements." This search for elements is still going on. Although progress has been made since 1937, many of the issues pointed up by Allport are still with us. One way to approach the problem is to make use of Angyal's analysis (1941), in which he describes the possible ways of dividing a whole—any whole—a person, an animal, a plant, or anything. He refers first to simply making arbitrary cuts and dividing the whole into fragments. This is what we often do in practical work. We choose some variable that we think is related to some important function in which we are interested. Psychologists can agree, for example, to rate "leadership" or "good social relations" when these traits are regarded as important in some future role. Scientists of quite different theoretical persuasions can work on these arbitrarily chosen aspects or fragments of the whole. There is no necessity for agreeing first about "fundamentals." We can proceed this way in research on psychotherapy, without getting into any theoretical arguments, and focusing on some agreed "targets."

Another way to divide a whole is according to a rigid fixed principle, for example, we might divide a tree into inch cubes. I don't suppose we have good examples of this in contemporary psychology, but the old habit psychology proceeded in such a way as this. A person was an aggregate of habits or S-R bonds, all of which were essentially alike in their structure. We needn't dwell on this because the practice has been virtually abandoned. The third way of dividing, according to Angyal, is by abstracting features of the whole, as when we speak of the health-sickness ratio, or of a person's ability, maturity, or soundness. In rating variables of this kind our reference is to the whole person. It is remarkable how willing we are to rate them without knowing very much about the person in question. A rating of "stability" or "integration" should be based upon an enormous amount of knowledge of the person, but often we rate these things as easily as we rate gregariousness. Usually, of course, the reliability of such ratings exceeds their validity. But be that as it may, it seems that we can hardly do without such variables in the study of psychotherapy. We must refer to the whole person sometimes, and this is one way in which we can do it.

The final way to divide a whole is according to its structural articulation. One starts with a conception of the whole and asks how it is put together. Any element is defined in terms of its relations to other elements and to the whole. This is fairly un-American and I don't believe it is often done in this country. To find good examples in the work of psychologists, we have to go back to Freud and Jung, in whose work it was simply taken for granted that the psyche was a whole and that analysis called for its being divided into interacting elements or systems. I think this is one of the reasons for the durability of Freud's scheme. It is one of the few schemes we can use when we wish to talk about the whole personality. The whole is structurally articulated in the sense that one can't really describe any one of the elements at any particular time without paying attention to its relations to the other elements and to the whole personality. If we were to throw out Freud's tripartite scheme—Id, Superego, Ego—we would have to substitute some other equally comprehensive and equally articulated theoretical structure.

Dr. Luborsky seems to have been caught on the horns of a dilemma here.

The variables used in the research he describes are derived from the Freudian scheme. But the researchers must have been worried about what kind of quantitative treatment could be accorded these variables, for what we have in this research is not a theoretically integrated scheme but rather an aggregation of concepts that are mentioned from time to time by psychoanalysts and by other people of psychoanalytic orientation. It turns out, to no one's surprise, that one of these variables is correlated .93 with one other. One may ask why the researchers didn't have, in the first place, one variable to stand for whatever it is that has been measured twice. I think the researchers pulled back from the point of view of structural articulation, and chose instead the procedure of rating a lot of things and then seeing what comes out in the factor analysis. What comes out in the factor analysis tells us less about the structural articulation of personality than it tells us about the attitudes and preferences of psychologists. It is plain that the raters prefer a particular kind of person, one that we might call the well-developed or well-functioning person.

(This desirability factor seems to come out in all factor analyses of rated traits. Psychologists have an ideal of the developed person. We ought to make this more explicit and use this as one way of dealing with the problem posed by Dr. Krasner. Let us admit that there are certain kinds of things that we value; for example, that we are interested in more people becoming better developed.)

In general, it seems that psychologists in their search for elements or variables of personality have at one time or another used every possible way of dividing the whole. We seem to have used most often the method of taking random cuts and next most often the method of abstracting features of the whole. We have got over the practice of dividing according to a fixed principle, but we still do not take readily to the method that has most to recommend it, that is, division according to theoretical structure.

This last method requires, of course, that elements be derived from a general theory of personality. As Dr. Wallerstein pointed out, we do not have much consensus in this matter. Still, there is ground for hope. If we look over what has been happening since 1937, when Allport published his survey, it seems that we may note some convergent trends in personality theory. Theorists pay more attention to each other than they did 25 years ago. The boundaries separating schools are less sharply drawn than they used to be. Everybody is more aware of the complexity of personality than formerly, and there are fewer claims that a particular scheme will take care of everything.

Concerning specific proposals for elements, it seems that what Allport called "dynamic elements of the nomothetic order," e.g., needs, motives, striving, are still the prime variables of personality. This is true, I think, despite the fresh, and apparently still growing, emphasis upon cognitive variables. Cognitive variables have come in for their innings not merely as instrumentalities of needs, but as motives in their own right. It is also fair to say, I think, that there has been a trend toward increasing accent on the higher mental processes, or perhaps on what is distinctively human as opposed to animal in personality functioning. Going along with this is an increased accent on the concept of the self and on the concept of ego considered as a "conflict-free" sphere. Associated with this last is an increasing tolerance of holism. Psychologists who talk about the self or ego seem quite willing to think of these systems of the personality as wholes, whose parts are always under the influence of system-wide processes. Finally, every-body seems to be becoming more social in his conception of the personality. It would be almost unthinkable, for example, that a personality theorist today should omit all references to social role, role disposition, role conception, and so on.

To these brief comments on trends in theory may be added a few considerations other than theoretical ones which help determine our choice of variables for describing personality. One such consideration is the coarseness of the categories we use in analyzing behavior. One of the reasons for the hiatus between psychotherapists and academic psychologists, I think, is that the psychotherapist is almost bound to use coarser analytic categories. He has such an enormous array of material to deal with that he has to work at the level of long units of behavior and to talk about things like needs, anxiety, and the like. He finds it impossible to reduce his material to elements as fine as S-R bonds, for example. All that we can ask of him is that he use categories that lend themselves to further analysis. And we may ask of the laboratory scientist that he use elements that can be built up into something that is meaningful at the level of practice.

Another consideration has to do with the abstractness of the variables used. The psychotherapist is focused more upon the concrete than the experimentalist is—and this is another reason for the difficulties between them. The psychotherapist has to talk with patients in their own language, and this will have reference to a very great many very specific and concrete details. It is very difficult to move from this realm of discourse to the highly abstract terms used in reinforcement theory or a theory having to do with transactions among subsystems of the personality. I suppose we ought to try, nevertheless.

This brings us to Dr. Shlien's ideas

about abstractness or concreteness in the self-conception. It seems to me that he may be confronting here the persistent issue of generality vs. specificity in personality functioning. I think he is showing, for one thing, that the self-esteem measure is general, that a lot of little manifestations of self-esteem can be made the basis for a generalized picture. I am puzzled about whether his nonverbal measure is really more abstract. (Here the subject indicates by means of a piece of apparatus, in one operation, what he regards as the discrepancy between his real self and his ideal self.) It turns out that the measure obtained in this way correlates with the self-ideal self discrepancy as revealed by $Q$ sorts. What is most significant and highly interesting is that the measure correlates best of all with the discrepancy index based on items which the subject himself has chosen as important in human life. What I would like to ask Dr. Shlien is whether this nonverbal measure is really abstract or whether it is not simply another particular kind of response that the subject is asked to make, and whether it cannot be used as an index of a hypothetical generalized level of self-esteem. It seems to me that it might be regarded as another response, to be correlated with the total scale for measuring self-esteem. This raises the question of how stable the nonverbal measure is. If one took this measure from time to time during the course of a day, or a week, one might get a lot of variability. If this should turn out to be so, then one would be inclined to doubt the value of the measure as an indicator of change in psychotherapy.

In my own thinking about self-esteem, which is a favorite variable, I have had to deal with another consideration, one that confronts us all in selecting variables: that is, how close to the objectively observable do we insist that the variable be?

How great is our willingness to entertain hypothetical constructs? My impression is that we don't worry as much about operational definitions today as we did 20 or 25 years ago. Today we take a much more liberal view of the matter, not insisting that everything be defined strictly in terms of operations. Operationism today means only that the hypothetical construct must be somehow related to something that is observable. This is all that is really required. In the case of self-esteem, my inclination would be to regard it as a hypothetical construct, or as a central variable in the personality which shows itself in behavior in a great diversity of ways. On the other hand, one may look at variables as entities which are quite open to observation. I am willing to call these entities variables, but I would not suppose that they stand in any one-to-one relation to any subsystems of the personality. I would prefer to reserve the term "variables of personality" for the hypothetical constructs that stand for processes inside the person, processes which may be expressed in different degrees in various objective measures.

Another thing that affects our choice of variables is preference in respect to methodology. Dr. Luborsky has offered the best example of "method-centering." Of 28 variables that he could have used he chose 12, because they lent themselves to rating by the method of paired comparisons. Well, we all do this sometimes; there are times when we have to use measures that are available. No doubt the variables actually rated have some theoretical significance. But suppose Dr. Luborsky was forced to choose between variables that could be rated by this method of paired comparisons and variables that on theoretical grounds were integral to the whole structure of personality. I gather that he would be thrown into something of a quandary. Since I am not doing research on psychotherapy I may announce that I stand foursquare for theoretical significance. Let the methodologists devise methods that are adequate to genuine problems; and let us resist all pressures to use certain methods just because they exist.

Now let us return to the model shown in Figure 1. Typically in research on psychotherapy we focus on differences that turn up when we compare the person at the time of his entry into the change-system with himself at the time he leaves it. Often we attempt to assess him at later times also. I would call attention to the fact that the person is always being perceived and evaluated by other people—his psychotherapist, his employer, his friends and relations—and by himself. There is, of course, the truth about the person— the person as he really is—and this we seek to ascertain by scientific methods; but there is also truth in these perceptions and evaluations, and my suggestion is that we use *these* as criterion variables, bringing them in relation to predictor variables in the change-system and in the person at the time he enters it.

Another suggestion: the whole process that extends from the time of a preliminary interview to the time of follow-up some years after the person leaves the system is subject to division into numerous subprocesses and substages. Instead of trying to predict from the beginning to the end, let us concentrate upon, and study intensively, some of these subprocesses or substages. For example, we might test a prediction, made on theoretical grounds, that patients who in a preliminary interview exhibited traits $a$, $b$, and $c$ would when confronted with activity $t$ in an early stage of psychotherapy respond with behavior $x$. And so for any two times during the process of psychotherapy. And so, for that matter, for times after the therapy has been terminated. What we are after,

it seems to me, is general knowledge about the conditions and processes of change in personality, knowledge that will be applicable not only to psychotherapy but to various other situations in which change is sought. To obtain this knowledge we should study change wherever it occurs—and developmental change wherever it can be made to occur. This is quite a different objective from that of trying to show that psychotherapy does some good or that a particular brand of psychotherapy has something to recommend it.

A final point. In my view, investigation and activity designed to change or to develop people are not really separable in practice. It goes without saying that we can't change people deliberately without understanding them. Or more precisely, our understanding and changing activities go on together. We learn enough about a person so that we believe a certain intervention by us might induce a desired change. Then we try and see. When due attention is given to the rules of evidence, there is probably no better way to increase our understanding of people than through the practice of psychotherapy—and of other techniques of planned change. What is perhaps not so well understood is that the study of people over time—just studying them without any other kind of intervention—is very likely to change them. This was our experience at Vassar College. It was our distinct impression that interviewing students, doing nothing but asking them questions, several times a year over a period of four years had the same kind of general effect as does counseling or psychotherapy. This means that the investigator who proposes to look deeply into the processes of his subjects must take the same kind of responsibility as does the psychotherapist or the educator. This brings us back to the question of value that was debated, with feeling, this morning. My position is that as psychotherapists, or teachers, or parents, or psychological investigators we cannot avoid responsibility for changing people. This means that we must work within a system of values—implicitly or explicitly. The only way to promote good effects and to avoid harmful ones—as judged according to the system of values—is to know enough about the conditions and mechanisms of change so that we can predict the effects of each particular action.

## REFERENCES

Allport, G. W. *Personality: A psychological interpretation.* New York: Holt, 1937.

Angyal, A. *Foundations for a science of personality.* New York: Commonwealth Fund, 1941.

# Measuring Personality Change

DR. HUNT: I want to give the discussed authors a chance to respond to the discussant. Dr. Lorr says he has no comments to make, so I will give you Dr. Luborsky.

DR. LUBORSKY: I'm indebted to you, Dr. Sanford, for your discussion. I would like you to carry it further; in particular, I'd like to hear more of your reaction to the main correlations that are presented in the paper—for example, the one about the relationship of anxiety to my change measure. I would like to hear your interpretation of the correlation. As you could tell from the paper, it certainly struck my fancy when it turned out that way. It generated a number of ideas as to how one would go further in understanding the correlation.

You noted the relationship of our variables to the psychoanalytic theory. I would say we were liberal in choosing these variables, for we did not systematically or solely derive these variables from psychoanalytic theory. The variables came from psychoanalytic theory plus experience with a variety of psychotherapies.

About the selection of only 12 variables for paired comparisons: Every method requires selection from the data. As I mentioned in the paper, we did not stop making assessments of *all* variables. Future analyses of data by other methods will supplement the paired comparisons.

DR. SHLIEN: There was one question about the meaning of "abstract." I used it as referring to something which can be conceptualized, and which can be raised above the level of specific content. Without those two qualities, it does not

deserve to be called a general personality variable. There are many kinds of concrete statements in our personality inventories which are nothing but complaints— no more personality variables than "beats his wife" or "speeding through red light" found on the police blotter. They are just the culture's complaints against the individual. Then there are individual concretes which are unique, and they are not personality variables either. But they are the content of an abstract statement which could be a personality variable. A personality variable which can be raised to a high level of abstraction isn't so much a dependent consequence as it is a prime mover which will be projected upon all sorts of testing situations. There is a study by Levy[1] in which he asked some subjects to describe an ideal home town and their own home town and also an actual self and ideal self. In each set of descriptions he had a self (or actual) and ideal correlation. The correlation between these two actual–ideal correlations was quite high ($+.75$ or so), which sounds to me as if this demonstrates a real, abstract personality variable, expressing itself in terms of self perception, or town perception, or other possible concretes.

DR. FRANK: This is what I thought would explain your results, but how does this explain the fact that the most abstract correlates more highly with the most concrete $Q$ sort? I should think it would correlate equally with the less specific $Q$ sort.

[1] Levy, L. H. The meaning and generality of perceived actual–ideal discrepancies. *J. consult. Psychol.*, 1956, **20**, 396-398.

DR. SHLIEN: Well, it seems to me that in a way that is a play on words, which is most concrete. I think the meaningful concrete is the concrete for each individual and those concretes which we generally use—"Does your stomach rumble?" or "Do you want to be a florist?" and that sort of thing—these have a lot of error variance in them. They don't mean very much to me personally. That is how I would explain the difference.

DR. FRANK: If the tendency is to put a certain distance between the real and the ideal in a personality trait, why shouldn't it apply to all three of these test situations?

DR. SHLIEN: Well, it isn't as easily projected upon concretes which are maladjusted to that person.

DR. BETZ: I like Dr. Shlien's paper very much. It recalled to my mind Alfred North Whitehead's discussion of "generalities" and "particulars"—that certain particulars carry within them an entire generality. This has been thought-provoking to me as a physician conversing with patients, because global, theoretical conceptions often don't lend themselves to lively conversational interchange. But neither do trivial particulars. If the right "particular" can be found—some current experience on the ward, for example— that contains within it a basic "generality" (theme or issue) of that patient's difficulty, it can be effectively utilized for a discussion that is particular, but not trivial —that has larger overtones. If such a particular can be successfully utilized, the general problem frequently resolves itself. It is of help in carrying on meaningful conversations with schizophrenic patients if the doctor can recognize a generality in a particular. To me, Dr. Shlien's work demonstrates the possibility that there may be ways to approach generality and "meaning" directly, rather than just by inference from collections of separate items or traits.

DR. SANFORD: We might as well go on with this. It seems to me that all personality traits are abstract; anything that we infer as a more or less durable disposition in the person is abstract, and I don't know just how to define degrees of abstractness. Nearly all of these traits that we mentioned are highly abstract concepts, but your conception, Dr. Shlien, makes me think not so much in terms of abstractness vs. concreteness as in terms of centrality vs. superficiality or inwardness vs. outwardness. It seems to me that what you are saying is that the nonvariable measure gets at a more inward aspect of the person, inward in the sense that it is less dependent on immediate field conditions than would be some of these particular things that you are calling concrete. The "rumbling of the stomach" and that sort of thing would be pretty closely related to a very concrete and tangible experience; and I thought that the reason the nonvariable measure went with the more idiographic picture was just because the person was giving in this picture something a little more inward and durable, a more characteristic part of his unique self; and that you gauged this more directly by means of the nonvariable measure. It seems to me that this is an inward–outward dimension rather than an abstract–concrete one.

DR. BORDIN: I would put it in terms of specificity–generality. That seems to be the issue rather than abstract–concrete. The question might be put this way; how heterogeneous is the domain of responses that is being sampled in which you are finding a high interrelationship? Ideally you would want to hit on a concept that will have the maximum generality in a most heterogeneous domain of responses. I had the feeling that Dr. Sanford's responses earlier this morning were raising one of these issues. In fact, how heterogeneous was your domain of responses that you were observing? It strikes me that there was not as much heterogeneity as I would like to see, in the sense that all measures represent a task where the individual is to describe himself via words, via manipulating some object, or something of this sort. How homogeneous or heterogeneous you consider this domain depends partly on how you define the domain. I define all of these tasks as falling into the class of conscious self-description. To make the domain more heterogeneous, we ought to have situations in which the task given him is not to describe himself, but where his behavior would offer an opportunity to infer how he is seeing himself in terms of ideal versus actual.

DR. SHLIEN: Don't you think I just gave you an example of that?—in Levy's study in which he asked people to describe an ideal town or their own home town.

DR. BORDIN: Well, as soon as you start putting it into ideal or actual I have some concern here.

DR. HUNT: Is this concern between self-acceptance and self-comfort, is it between the nature of these items in the general issue?

DR. BORDIN: Well, for example, if you ask someone to describe his patients, isn't he describing a part of himself? So if you study how he talks, how he would like his patients to be and how they actually are, don't you expect that under those circumstances you are getting partly a description of how he sees himself? This is what would make me a little uncomfortable, that such observations are not far enough removed from the observation situation where the individual sets out to describe himself to someone else. I would like to get as far away as possible from that situation. I would admit that describing one's town is not identical with describing oneself, but it seems to run the risk of partaking too much of the initial situation where you ask the individual directly to describe himself.

DR. SANFORD: It is very helpful to me. I explored this a little bit this morning, this generality vs. specificity thing, and I think it is helpful. To me it seems very much like the old issue that Gordon Allport discussed at length some years ago. Consider honesty, for example. The reason that we are interested in generalized honesty is because this would permit us to predict individual behavior in a great diversity of situations. It would be a dependable feature of the person in that sense, if indeed such a trait exists. Nowadays we are more willing than formerly to agree that such generality exists, but the issue is still alive. It is very interesting to have it revived in this way. If we use honesty as an example, it seems to me that what you would be doing, Dr. Shlien, is finding a particular response that somehow partakes of the totality of honesty. To go back to self-esteem, the empirical question is whether the self-esteem that you get at by means of a non-variable procedure really is general in the usual sense of the word; can we depend upon it to predict high level self-esteem responses in a great diversity of future situations?

DR. SHLIEN: I think a single self-esteem measure probably is dependable. That is the significance of this study, and it is a probable model for other measures. Let me point out also that what I am trying to say here is that the aims of the researcher will determine to a large extent what level of abstraction he uses. If I only wanted to compare Adlerian and client-centered outcomes, I could just as well have used this highly abstract self-ideal apparatus. But if one wants to know also about differences within subgroups of those two populations, one needs a set of descriptions at a lower level of abstraction. This is something we want, so Dr. Butler and I are working on a factor analysis of the arrays of concrete items from which we drew this abstract over-all measure of self-esteem. There you see the effect of the researchers' aims upon the level of abstraction we choose for measurement.

DR. BUTLER: This seems to me to be an important issue, important enough for me to register a dissent on this. I think Dr. Shlien is right, not because he is a colleague who is close to me, but because he is right. It is a real abstractive process. My first guess is that they were overjoyed to find so much consistency in situations so different.

My second reaction is that we should consider the nature of the abstractive process in relation to the conditions under which the abstractions or generalizations arose. If a person says "I am inferior," it is a high level of abstraction, although it may be a trait. There are then specific situations, "concretes," as Dr. Shlien calls them, specific sets of experiences, leading to the generalization "I am inferior," or something like that. In varying degrees we think that this is a core abstraction or a guiding abstraction, which governs behavior and therefore is very important. I think we should consider the conditions which brought about the self-description and the ideal description of the person. Whatever they were, they had little to do with a piece of plexiglass apparatus. The fact is that the self-ideal description in terms of traits and the self-ideal description in terms of overlap of pieces of plastic labeled self and ideal were related. It seems to me, therefore, that the direction of generalization runs from specific experiences in specific situations to the linguistic self and ideal descriptions to the self and ideal descriptions symbolized by the overlap between plates of plexiglass. How otherwise is a person able to fit these pieces of glass together in a meaningful way? The same thing holds, I think, for the relation between self-ideal descriptions and actual home town *vs.* ideal home town relations. It seems, on

these grounds, that Dr. Shlien's usage meets the criteria of people studying generalization.

DR. BLOCK: I think it is a distressing property of this field that different people can interpret the same data not orthogonally but diametrically. As I recall the Levy study, precisely the opposite point was made; namely, here was an artificial and deliberately distant measure that correlated too highly with self-ideal correspondence, thereby attenuating the meaning to be ascribed to the self-ideal measure. In reading Dr. Shlien's paper, I kept feeling, as I read about the plexiglass and the superimposition of the panes of glass to get a percent of variance, etc., that while the measures were becoming more and more abstract and divorced from specific procedural details, the measures were also becoming less important. It seems to me that in showing self-ideal correspondence as measured by the angle between two panes of plexiglass relates to self-ideal self correspondence as measured by $Q$ sorts, one shows that $Q$ sort measured self-ideal self correspondence means less than we had hoped it might mean. The findings of generality as measured in these several ways can be extended even further so that the measure could be derived simply by asking people to place themselves on a seven-point scale—"How do you like yourself today?" The question then becomes "So what will these findings of generality mean?" My own feeling is that such findings of generality suggesting self-ideal self correspondence per se has a rather limited and superficial meaning unless it is connected to other measures or placed in a context of understanding. Self-ideal self correspondence has a significance only after confounding variables are partialed out—variables such as defensiveness or tendency to create a favorable impression in the person who will be looking at the protocols, and so on. Unless this is done, it seems to me that the demonstration of a correspondence among several uncorrected self-ideal self correspondence measures does not imply support for an abstraction or construct of importance.

DR. SHLIEN: I think as you take a measure which you can abstract at higher and higher levels you really demonstrate its importance rather than its unimportance. I feel that just as you would not want simply to treat symptoms, why simply measure symptoms?

DR. LUBORSKY: I wonder for what types of problems your abstraction principle is important? The paper itself does not clarify this. In the first few pages there is a discussion of contradiction among various criteria. The rest of the paper is on self-ideal ratio as a criterion. The discussion never does come back to the relationship of this criterion to the other criteria, so that the title really should be: "Toward what level of abstraction in self-ideal ratio as a criterion?" That is the main thing considered. You are not comparing the self-ideal ratio's level of abstraction with the level of abstraction of other criteria in psychotherapy, so that we do not really have a basis for answering "toward what level of abstraction in a criterion." It does tell us interesting things about the generality vs. specificity of the concept of self-ideal. Your data tell us that people will show the same behavior on this variable no matter how you ask them the question.

The finding reminds me of a story about a man who came to a wise old man (whose role has fallen upon present day therapists) and wanted to know how he would fare if he went across the border and lived in another country. The sage asked him, "How was it in the country from which you came?" And the man replied, "I had a hard time there." The sage then answered, "Well, that's the way life is in the other country too."

DR. SHLIEN: I am only putting that forward as a model, and I am suggesting that this same kind of analysis could and should be applied to other personality variables.

DR. SANFORD: I believe you said, Dr. Shlien, that this might be applied to variable ideal strengths. Wasn't that one of the possibilities? This brings us to one of the issues now on the floor. I think probably you're accenting experience-phenomenology. That makes some sense to me. The feeling about oneself in relation to one's ideals could be a broad phenomenal field. It could be described in holistic terms; and you are suggesting that you can get at this total field in this way perhaps much better than you can by befogging the issue of self vs. ideal and all these variable constituent concepts. A concept like ego strength makes no reference to the phenomenal field at all. It is simply a concept designed to order an enormous diversity of observed events. I might say, half facetiously, that you might walk up to the person and ask, "How is your self-ideal–self ratio today? How is your morale today?" But you wouldn't walk up to a person and ask, "How is your ego strength today?" Or if you did, you wouldn't be approaching what the people who invented this concept mean by it. On the other hand, if you define self-esteem in phenomenal terms, you could make some sense of asking people in some more or less direct way how they are phenomenally.

DR. HUNT: Are you differentiating trait and state in a sense, trait being enduring and state being momentary?

DR. SANFORD: I think it is like that, and I think this is connected with my question about the stability of self-esteem. It would seem to me highly variable, particularly in young people, who are so readily plunged into the depths by failure and elevated to great heights by momentary success.

DR. BETZ: Could this be used as an instrument like a thermometer by which one might gauge the variability of self-esteem within a certain range for certain people? There might be a range like normal temperature, and then there might be ranges outside of that.

DR. SANFORD: It seems to me it would be wonderful for getting rapid soundings during the course of an enterprise, for possible fluctuations during such an undertaking.

DR. ROSEN: Aren't there many different and equally appropriate levels of abstraction, depending on the question "Appropriate for what?" The level of abstraction on which one talks with a patient during a psychotherapy hour is somewhat different, I think, than the level of abstraction on which one discusses a case perhaps with one's supervisor or with one's colleagues, which again may be different from the level of abstraction on which one discusses a particular phenomenon when one attempts to do research and discuss it at a conference.

DR. BUTLER: I hope you will forebear another comment by me. I am somewhat ego involved in this question because I began pushing self-ideal comparisons about 1947 (when I joined Rogers and colleagues) on the basis of a description of L. Sweet's work in 1931 by Percival Symonds; and I think there are experimental, factual results which bear on these questions.

In the first place, as we follow successful cases through therapy and establish criteria we find that self-ideal correlations on $Q$ sorts increase for those cases labeled successful, by and large. By and large for those cases labeled unsuccessful on the basis of many criteria, the self-ideal correlations tend to decrease or remain at the pretherapy level. Now, that is one thing. Experimentally this has been criticized because of the possible fact that the content of the $Q$ sort is the same thing as what is talked about in therapy. The cards may not look like what the therapist and the client or patient are talking about, but they may be topics which may have been touched upon. Now, if you take another operation entirely, for example, the plexiglass apparatus, therapist and client were not talking about putting spheres together, and substitute that for a $Q$ sort, then you have avoided that criticism, and I think this is a worthwhile experimental point. It is a different kind of behavior rather than a similar kind of reaction to verbal stimuli from cards and verbal interchanges in a therapy situation. I think from this point of view the finding that self-ideal correlations are consistent over a rather wide range of different behavioral situations, different kinds of reaction with the environment, is quite interesting. So far you have been only able to get at self-ideal by verbal means. Now we find this kind of consistency which allows us to substitute one kind of task for a distinctively different kind of task. It opens up possibilities for studies which simply have not been available before.

DR. FRANK: I am still troubled about one thing here. You are assuming that this is a function of the thing that is being judged, that is, the reality versus the ideal. Suppose people have a constant discrepancy for any two judgments when neither one is anchored. Suppose you ask what is the difference between an angel and an archangel, for example. Would some people show bigger discrepancies, and some smaller discrepancies? Is there any way of trying to test this out?

DR. SHLIEN: No. Somebody mentioned that before. That is a curiosity. That is a good question.

DR. FRANK: What you are measuring may be the habitual tendency to see a certain amount of difference between two things, neither of which is anchored.

DR. SIEGAL: We know that people have response sets in the way that they answer rating scales. There are people who are willing to use scale extremes and some who stick to the innocuous middle.

DR. SHLIEN: Well, then, it appears that this means something.

DR. FRANK: It does mean something. It may be something entirely different than a statement about the ideal and real $Q$ sorts.

DR. BORDIN: I would feel better about it if one could do it that way. I don't seem to have gotten part of my message across, at least I don't think to Dr. Butler, because most of the time when he is talking, he speaks of specificity–generality of a communication. Another issue is the mode of communication. There are different ways you can communicate a message. You can communicate it in verbal terms. You can say, "I think your ideas are all wet," or you can just go—(gestures with hand). One has been with words, and one has been with action. Is this general or specific? The lack of generality lies in the content. The lack of generality in these situations, no matter what the form of communication, is that you are asking the person to say something about himself that involves a concept of an ideal and a concept of how he actually is. This is the lack of generality that exists in all of these situations. Although some of them involve words and some of them involve plexiglass, they all have in common that you are saying to the subject, "Respond to me, do something," in these terms of communication, "that tells me something about how you see your ideal self, how you see your actual self."

DR. SHLIEN: One thing I get out of your message is that you are in favor of a high level of generality in behavior. Is that true?

DR. BORDIN: This comes back to the other issue of "for what." I have a different view of it, I think, than Dr. Luborsky

has. I think that the "gang" at Chicago has offered certain specifications with regard to the discrepancy between ideal and actual views of oneself. Rogers has offered certain specifications about how one's response to oneself in ideal and actual terms is influenced by the responses of caretakers during childhood. I am shifting on the other side and defending the concept as such. But there is the necessity of moving beyond—and we were talking about this before—making lots more specifications about the nature of this as a personality variable.

DR. BLOCK: I thought the Levy study has been relevant to this discussion more than a little, and I think it is pertinent to introduce still other data in the field. First note that since by and large the ideal selves of individuals seem to be pretty similar, the great proportion of the variance of self-ideal self-congruency measures is ascribable to differences in the self-pictures people offer of themselves. There is a lot of information on self-descriptions and the correlates of self-description. For example, in experiments on social perception, it is found time and again that people who describe themselves favorably (and who therefore will have a high correspondence between self and ideal) also will describe other people favorably whether they know them or not. These ascribers of unqualifiedly favorable characteristics themselves have unfortunate personal qualities and they make less discriminations in social perception experiments than people who are taking chances in their predictions. There are many other such findings related to self-descriptions which should be brought to bear upon an understanding of self-ideal self correspondence measures. The significance of these results is this: to use self-ideal correspondence as an operational translation of the self concept, one has to qualify the measure or handle it quite carefully. I don't think the arguments so far question the usefulness of the concept of self. The notion organizes many facets of the individual and relates to his behavior in some fairly intricate, yet specifiable ways. I think the problem before us is that the particular ways of measuring self-ideal self correspondence, although different, are all frankly rather patent. We need to become more sophisticated so as to get at and control some of the unfortunate influences upon the self-ideal self discrepancy, thereby making this index a more faithful reflection of the underlying concept.

DR. GORHAM: One of the difficulties of using actual-ideal $Q$ sorts as a measure of psychotherapeutic change is the confounding influence of the therapist. Increase in actual-ideal correlations may represent progress to some therapists, while the same change indicates increasing of unhealthy rigidity to others. The direction in which the therapist is trying to lead the patient is probably related in some way to the degree of his own personal actual-ideal ratio.

DR. BETZ: Could this instrument not be used on the therapist as well as on the patient?

DR. GORHAM: This is exactly what is being done by the Rogerian group. So far so good. However, it is assumed by them that if the patient ideal is approaching that of the therapist, improvement is taking place.

DR. SHLIEN: Well, the assumption is that self-ideal ratio is a measure of self-esteem. If you want to argue now that self-esteem is not the significant variable, do so.

DR. GORHAM: Indeed, I think it is a very significant variable. It seems to be misinterpreted here, because what means self-esteem to some means rigidity or perfectionism to others.

DR. SHLIEN: We do know about that; we know that there are defensive sorts which are unreasonably high and that sort of thing, but those are technical questions about the meanings of different levels of self-ideal correlations. The kind of question that I am really trying to speak to is the kind of question raised by Dr. Rosen who says there are different levels of abstraction and which one do you want to apply to which part of the conduct. My feeling is that though you may in your therapeutic sessions talk at a low level of abstraction, you are really trying to work toward a more general outcome, that is to say, when the patient says, "Gee, I wish I had enough guts to talk back to my teacher," I think if you were just accepting this statement at face value, you would really be dealing with the level of symptom reduction. I don't think that is what any therapist wants to do. I think you really want this person to turn out to be a generally courageous person. If that is what he wants, then why isn't the measure "courage" a properly higher level of abstraction?

DR. SANFORD: I have one further comment about self-esteem. One of the biggest differences we found at Vassar between the seniors and freshmen was that the seniors had a much higher ideal self/self ratio, that is to say, the opinion of the self, the real self, was much lower than the ideal, whereas in freshmen there was a great similarity between the two estimates. One could put this down to the greater sophistication of the seniors, their greater willingness or inclination to admit unfavorable things about themselves, or perhaps some inclination even to be ironical about themselves, to make wry comments about what they are and what they would like to be, whereas, the freshmen showed more uniformity in all of these appreciations. For the freshmen the real self was more like the ideal woman and the ideal self was more like the average woman. Now, we may raise the question, Which of these groups of people, freshmen or seniors, had the higher health-sickness ratio? The low ideal self/self ratio, of course, was one of the numerous signs that the seniors were less healthy in some sense of the word than the freshmen. I think, then, that in a way we are talking here about different conceptions of the aims of therapy or different conceptions of desired states. Our impression was that the freshmen were more healthy. They were more harmonious internally; life was somewhat simpler for them. They saw themselves in a fairly clear way; they saw where they had been, where they were going, whereas the seniors were definitely more upset, confused, disrupted, in conflict. But we were not too disturbed about this because we thought that these were signs of growth in the seniors. Growth is a succession of upsets and integrations at higher levels. Eventually, probably, the seniors will achieve stability. But if it is stability we are after, one can see the role of this sense of all-of-a-piece-ness, of harmony and comfort about oneself; but if one is thinking of the personalities moving in the direction of greater complexity, which would naturally bring more disharmony, then his aim is somewhat different, and the ideal self/self ratio has a different implication.

DR. BORDIN: Did you have social desirability measures on your groups of freshmen and seniors? You had given them MMPIs, hadn't you?

DR. SANFORD: Yes.

DR. BORDIN: And did they differ on that?

DR. SANFORD: In the same way.

DR. BORDIN: In the same way. It seems to me that this is important because the social desirability measure could be interpreted as a situational relevant measure, the person's willingness to respond in a conventional way. This is one way to interpret it. I am not sure I would be willing to argue that it is the only deter-

minant of the measure. But, to the extent that it reflects that, then the question enters of the situational factor in this ideal-self relationship.

DR. STRUPP: What Dr. Shlien's demonstration and much of the research as well as a good deal of the discussion indicates to me is that there is considerable unclarity about the precise meaning of the self-ideal correlation, as indeed there is much question as to what the correlations in $Q$ methodology mean anyway. We seem to be dealing here with a highly general and very vague factor which has some construct validity—at least in client-centered therapy — and which correlates with favorable outcomes of therapy and similar measures. But, I think we are as yet far from understanding what this correlation means. Dr. Shlien's demonstration in fact lends credence to my assertion that we do not precisely understand what this correlation indicates. It is interesting that as far as I know this measure has not been tried in other forms of psychotherapy. It may be indicative of a general sense of well-being or, contrariwise, of malaise or moroseness, but what it means beyond that is largely guesswork.

DR. LUBORSKY: My comments are on the meaning of the self-ideal discrepancy. They relate partly to Dr. Lorr's paper. He reports that patients who remained in treatment (at the eight-month point) had higher manifest anxiety and less favorable self-descriptions than patients who did not remain. These two qualities may belong together. Several investigators, including Rogers, have concluded that the self-ideal gap implies disequilibrium so that people with a large self-ideal gap should show anxiety. I would expect this to be true, by and large, in the college seniors described by Dr. Sanford. Facing the future after graduation engenders self-questioning and therefore also anxiety. I am saying in total that a high self-ideal gap may imply a readiness for anxiety and possibly also, therefore, a readiness for change—I think that ties in with the point that Dr. Siegal and I both make in our papers.

DR. SHLIEN: May I say one more thing? It seems to me that the questions that Dr. Saslow raises about comparability and that Dr. Strupp raises about the improvised means of self-ideal correlation could be applied to all other kinds of criteria we used. It troubles me a little to think that self-esteem has been just a little the property of the Counseling Center or that we alone take a precious attitude toward self-ideal correlations, and that sort of thing. I feel personally that the kind of problem the paper raises is your problem as well as our own and applies to all of your criteria as well as our own.

DR. HUNT: I think I am going to call a halt on this discussion. All right, Dr. Luborsky on Dr. Lorr's paper.

DR. LUBORSKY: I believe that Dr. Lorr's study is the best designed one in the psychotherapy literature dealing with frequency of appointments in relation to change. It attempts to control for the selection of patients, and the comparison of initially equally "sick" patient groups. I was therefore quite interested in the results, for they bear on a prevalent practical problem.

Dr. Lorr qualifies his results as applicable to the patient population he studied, which is a blessing in any paper. I say this because I suspect in his patient group, which is part of the outpatient VA clinic population, that if we applied the Health-Sickness Rating Scale, we would not find the entire range of patient population included. Probably relatively few patients who would be acceptable for psychoanalysis were represented. The heaviest concentration may have been in the "borderline psychotic" range. The relationship of frequency of appointments to change differs for patients who are at different levels of what we call "mental health." Also, some treatment structures may work best at a certain frequency of appointments, e.g., four to five hours per week is supposed to be optimal for psychoanalysis; for sicker patients, we often suggest supportive therapy with relatively infrequent appointments over a long time span.

How do you explain the fact that 31 patients (out of 133) didn't respond to the follow-up request? For patients who have completed a period of psychotherapy, this seems to be a high percentage. Whenever the percentage is so high one must suspect a selective factor—and possibly one that operates beyond the reach of the available information you have about these patients.

DR. LORR: On the matter of which patients remain, a distinction should be made between those who terminate prematurely and those who remain about six weeks or longer. Our studies as well as all I have seen in the literature indicate that the patient who terminates prematurely without or against the advice of the therapist is strikingly different from the patient who does not quit treatment. The former is less anxious, more psychopathic and nomadic, more ethnocentric, less dissatisfied, and less well educated than the typical remainer.

Of the cases lost from the study at the end of eight months, some had completed or terminated treatment, and others who remained in psychotherapy were excluded because their treatment frequency had been altered by the therapist. The pretreatment status of patients remaining in the study at eight months at assigned treatment schedules differed from the patients who dropped out. The eight-month sample was seen as more disturbed and Manifest Anxiety scores were higher. Thus the eight-month sample was not quite the same as the sample at the end of four months.

We are quite conscious of the fact that our patients are chronically ill and some have been in psychotherapy before. We would be reluctant to generalize to groups not similar to them.

DR. SANFORD: Dr. Luborsky was asking earlier for some response to the substance of his paper. (I wasn't able to summarize the papers in my discussion earlier, for which I apologize.) He was calling attention to the major finding that of the numerous variables assessed at intake, anxiety level was about the only one that really correlated with the posttherapy assessment of improvement. The correlation was .44, I believe. Then at the end he came to what I think he regards as the really important point, which is that the best outcomes were achieved by patients who at the beginning were high on "good development" or something of that kind, and who also had a high anxiety level. This, I think, is what Dr. Luborsky is most interested in. It is the suggestion that anxiety may be a good thing. It is a particularly good sign of a favorable outcome if it is occurring in a person who doesn't need therapy very much. Aside from this, Dr. Luborsky addresses himself to a major hypothesis: that people who do best in therapy are generally those who need it the least, that is, those people who are already most well developed are those who will go further. And also he is saying that if these people have some anxiety at the same time, then the prospects for a good outcome are particularly good. This makes a lot of sense. Now, Dr. Luborsky has brought this into relation with self-esteem and also into relation with the frequency of the therapy sessions; this leads me to say one thing about Dr. Lorr's paper. His finding on frequency of sessions is one of the few things that has ever come out of psychotherapy research that seems to me very useful to the practitioner. But we have to be very careful about this. I don't believe Dr. Lorr's find-

ing suggests that we ought to adopt as a general rule some given frequency of sessions for all patients. I know Dr. Lorr doesn't believe this either. Actually, the frequency of sessions in practice, I believe, has a lot to do with the therapist's assessment of the anxiety level. If a patient is having a bad time and is having a lot of anxiety, the natural recourse is to frequent sessions.

DR. HUNT: Or the opposite. I wonder if this is possible.

DR. SANFORD: —Unless you can quickly reduce the anxiety; in which case, according to Dr. Luborsky, you reduce your chances of therapeutic gain.

DR. HUNT: My point was that if you are really getting into this, the more interviews you have, the more likely the anxiety is to pile up.

DR. SANFORD: Well, much depends on what the therapist is doing. I think he usually has in his armamentarium some means for generating anxiety and some means for reducing anxiety. He uses these in accordance with his conception of what the traffic will bear. I think that frequency of sessions cannot follow a rigid rule, but it is something to be adapted to general circumstances as the therapist understands them.

DR. LUBORSKY: There are many unanswered questions about frequency of sessions. One concerns the consequences of *very* frequent vs. infrequent appointments. A study should compare *three or more* with *two or less* appointments per week. I would think this would be important to help us to reach broader application of the research results.

DR. STRUPP: This finding of Dr. Luborsky's, that anxiety is significantly correlated with and highly predictive of outcome, is rather startling, because it runs counter to what has been reported in the literature about the relationships between judgments of the patient's suitability for psychotherapy and outcome. In one of our studies,[2] anxiety was very unreliably correlated with suitability for therapy and expected outcome, as judged by a psychiatrist. This leads me to wonder whether anxiety in the Menninger study was not in turn correlated with judgments about the patient's motivation for psychotherapy. Partly, the correlation may be due to the fact that patients had been selected who were considered highly motivated for therapy. The findings of other studies may be different because very different patient populations were involved. I would appreciate your comment on this point.

DR. SIEGAL: May I just make a remark. I think it is much too simple to say that Dr. Luborsky's study shows that anxiety is a good thing across the board. I think that what this study shows and what our study shows is that judging from anxiety alone you don't know where you stand. You have to know in whom the anxiety is occurring. I think all of us know this clinically. It's very different if you have a neurotic patient who is anxious and you are going to analyze him. That is quite different than having a very disorganized psychotic patient who is anxious. I wouldn't just let it go by saying that a correlation of .44 between initial anxiety level and degree of change after treatment means, across the board, that anxiety is a good thing.

DR. LUBORSKY: We had examples of those extremes.

DR. SIEGAL: Yes.

DR. ROSEN: That is the point I wanted to ask Dr. Strupp about. Was your correlation an across-the-board one pertaining to all patients. I think that Dr. Luborsky's finding had to do with anxiety in patients with a certain degree of ego-autonomy. The presence of anxiety proved

to have some predictive value, but this did not hold over the whole health-sickness continuum for patients.

DR. STRUPP: The study I referred to had nothing to say about outcome. These were judgments by psychiatrists of patients who were seen in initial interviews. We tried to explore the factors which our raters considered predictive of successful outcome. There is also a study by Garfield and Affleck,[3] which showed that ratings of anxiety bear only a limited relationship to ratings of prognosis. So, in terms of these findings which apparently diverge from Dr. Luborsky's, I was wondering how the differences might be explained.

DR. LORR: One observation is worth making: four or five correlational analyses of patient and therapist reports have been published.[4] It is striking that in each instance the therapist judgments of improvement are independent of patient reports. Further, test scores (Rorschach, inventories) are independent of both therapist and self-reports. In other words, there appears little or no agreement among therapist, patient, external observer, or test as to how much or little the patient has changed or improved.

DR. LUBORSKY: In our studies most of the principal quantitative measures are really from observers' judgments, which are based upon information from patient, therapist, supervisor, etc. These observers'

[2] Strupp, H. H., & Williams, Joan V. Some determinants of clinical evaluations of different psychiatrists. AMA Arch. gen. Psychiat., 1960, 2, 434-440.

[3] Garfield, S. L., & Affleck, D. C. Therapists' judgments concerning patients considered for psychotherapy. J. consult. Psychol., 1961, 25, 505-509.

[4] See, for example:

(a) Rogers, C. R., & Dymond, Rosalind F. Psychotherapy and personality change. Chicago: Univer. Chicago Press, 1954.

(b) Gibson, R. L., Snyder, W. U., & Ray, W. S. A factor analysis of measures of change following client-centered therapy. J. counsel. Psychol., 1955, 2, 83-90.

(c) Cartwright, D. S., & Roth, I. Success and satisfaction in psychotherapy. J. clin. Psychol., 1957, 13, 20-26.

judgments probably correlate more highly
with therapist's judgments than with the
patient's judgment. Similarly, the Anxiety
Level score is based upon independent
observers' ratings; however, it probably
correlates highly with therapist's judgments. The same is probably true for the
change scores used in our paper. We have
not yet intercorrelated these measures;
however, I have also wondered, Dr. Lorr,
whether the same orthogonality would appear in our data and why it has so often
in other studies.

DR. BUTLER: I find all these comments fascinating, but it so happens that
they tie in with the comments on Dr.
Shlien's paper. We find, first, starting from
Dr. Bordin's remarks, that there is a difference between the self-ideal correspondence as a theoretical notion and the self-
ideal correlation as a measure which is an
empirical operational expression of that
notion in this sense—Chodorkoff[5] has
found that people with high self-ideal
correlations above a certain level tend to
be more rather than less maladjusted. And
I think his is a very nice study.

Now, in our results we started out with
average self-ideal correlation of zero between clients' pretherapy, and higher self-
ideal correlations for success cases at
follow-up on a variety of criteria. If we
factor the results we find 11 kinds of
clients before therapy on self sorts. Eleven
types! You might think of these types,
for example, as differing in organizational
defenses, but however you think of them,
the significant fact in relation to many of
these points that have been brought out—
in Dr. Siegal's paper also—is that these
different self-factors have differential relations with the ideal or the ideal factor.

That is, one group of people characterized by a factor will have a high negative
correlation with the ideal. Another group
with another extreme will have a pretty
high positive correlation. It seems there
is a kind of continuum there. The way it
turns out, people with the extremes on
the correlations between self factors and
the ideal factors are the people who are
the difficult cases in therapy. The top
ones tend to be very rigid people as
Dr. Gorham suggested, and the bottom
ones tend to be quite disorganized, and
there seems to be an optimum range in
between, so the median self-ideal correlation of zero as a measure obscures the
self-ideal correspondence as a variable
because it is not precise enough. If you
use the factorial techniques which bring
this out, then the relationship to outcome
turns out to be predictive. This fits your
findings in a way I think, Dr. Luborsky,
in that the cases that tend to have low but
not markedly negative or markedly positive self-ideal correlations are those with
whom the therapy seems to work.

Now, with respect to Dr. Lorr's paper,
this last comment shows also that the
finding relates to his in the inverse sense.
We found, and this seems to me to be a
striking and interesting fact, that the TAT
ratings, personality ratings by friends who
did not know the subject was in psychotherapy, ratings by the therapist on gain
in personal integration, and success ratings
on an absolute level, all tended to be consistent if, but only if, the self factors after
therapy were used instead of the correlation of self with ideal. In other words, the
factor loading of an individual on a self
factor separated the variance in such a
way that the therapist's judgments, the
observer's judgments, and the diagnostician's judgments as measured by the
projective tests, and so on, all tended to
go in the same direction (which incidentally says something of the power and
sensitivity of the factoring methods). I

[5] Chodorkoff, B. Self-perception, perceptual
defense, and adjustment. *J. abnorm. soc. Psychol.,* 1954, **49**, 508-512.

Chodorkoff, B. Adjustment and the discrepancy between perceived and ideal self. *J. clin.
Psychol.,* 1954, **10**, 266-268.

think the basic point here for theoretical discussion is that the self-ideal correlation is not the same thing as the theoretical variable, that other variables can come in. I think the basic question then is, with respect to the things that come in, are those things consistent with theory? Is it consistent with theory that a person with a very high self-ideal correlation might be a person who is very maladjusted? I suspect that it is. I suspect that the paranoids, for example, are very low. These various results show that there is as yet no empirical ideal variable.

## III.

## RESEARCH PROBLEMS RELATING TO THE DEFINITION, MEASUREMENT, AND ANALYSIS OF SIGNIFICANT VARIABLES IN PSYCHOTHERAPY

# On the Naturalistic Definition of Variables: An Analogue of Clinical Analysis[1]

JOHN M. BUTLER, PH.D., LAURA N. RICE, PH.D.
AND ALICE K. WAGSTAFF, PH.D.

In what follows, the clinical analysis of psychotherapy will be considered as a particular aspect of naturalistic observation and research. Our intention is not to defend or justify naturalistic observation and research (the clinical process). Rather, it is an attempt to formulate some aspects of the process leading to unambiguous methods of analysis, the methods yielding results partaking of the character of hypotheses which function so as to lead to more refined hypotheses (or to experimental arrangements which are validating or invalidating).

When one considers the philosophy and teaching of science, it is significant that little, if any, formal attention is paid to naturalistic observation and research, although it is quite clear that they are the foundation of all science. In modern science, discussion is usually concentrated upon questions of verification and the nature of scientific knowledge. Yet the

science of physics is profoundly indebted to the uncontrolled observations of superstitious Babylonian and Chaldean priests. In the year just past we have witnessed world-wide observances of the centennial of that triumph of naturalistic observation and research, the Darwinian theory of evolution, which is still revolutionizing our perspectives of the biological world and, indeed, of ourselves. Yet, in current discussions of scientific philosophy, there appears to be a stress upon two aspects of science: experimental method and the personal element, the latter being discussed under such headings as "genius," "creativity," "scientific imagination," and/ or luck.

Actually, scientific method, verification, is valued in itself, but those who practice scientific method are not. It seems to be agreed that verification may call for an admirable degree of ingenuity. But no matter how admirable the ingenuity, it remains ingenuity; the experimentalist is really somewhat below the salt. The highest rank he can attain is that of Boyle. The deepest admiration is reserved for the scientists like Newton or Einstein or Darwin who, by the creative use of their

[1] The investigations reported here were supported by funds from the Ford Foundation.

We wish to express our appreciation to Drs. Desmond Cartwright and Donald W. Fiske for making case recordings and test data available to us.

178

imagination, in the context of the world of science, erect revolutionary theories or contrive somehow, like Fleming, to see the significance of accidental events and to capitalize on them. It turns out then, that in order to significantly advance science, we must have flashes of genius or be lucky. This approach to understanding science creates a rather prickly and uncomfortable situation for the majority of scientists who, however much they aspire to be geniuses, are not; and who, however much they wish to be lucky, are forced like the rest to wait their turn for the event which is unlikely to happen.

The sense of discomfort increases if one is in a borderline science, if one is essaying a domain in which basic and fruitful concepts like those of Einstein, of Newton, and of Darwin have not been formulated; where experimentation, as in certain areas of psychology, seems to be reduced to empty formalism because positive knowledge does not exist which tells us what should be controlled.

When a scientist enters into an inquiry in a new domain, his ideas, however precise as ideas, are hazy with respect to the domain simply because it is a new domain. When the phenomena under consideration are not well described, when relationships at the phenomenal level are not known, the person who insists on starting out with precise experiments lacks the imagination required to observe, to look around and see, at the first level, what seems to be going on. Experiments which precede rather than succeed observation amount to being precise about vagueness and suggest a disproportionate concern for the opinions of other scientists with a disproportionate lack of concern for truth which, above all, should characterize the scientist. It seems to the writers that the scientist who wishes to bring a new domain under the sway of science should seek to observe, to arrive at preliminary hypotheses or systems of

hypotheses on the basis of his observations. His ultimate aim, of course, should be the ultimate aim of any scientist, that of generating sets of propositions which, at crucial points, are verifiable in the sense of scientific method. His immediate aim then should be to arrive at fruitful hypotheses.

In our present stage of understanding science, the creation of fruitful hypotheses must await the moment of insight of the genius or the lucky event which only the genius appreciates. Nevertheless, as psychological experimentation has shown quite clearly, the appropriate arrangement of situations can lead to insight into situations or can retard and prevent the occurrence of insight. The aim here will be to describe an approach to the data of naturalistic observation which, it is hoped, will encourage the development of fruitful hypotheses with respect to the domain of inquiry.

## NATURALISTIC OBSERVATION

As conceived here, the naturalistic observer approaches his domain of inquiry, considered to be some behavioral situation, with several sets of convictions, beliefs, frames of reference, biases, prejudices—call them what you will—which will hereafter be called a classification system. To a first approximation, at least, the observer knows what behavior is. That is, he has a definition, explicit or implicit, of what behavior is and he knows in a preliminary way what behavior he is interested in observing. Suppose now that he observes a single organism behavior over a series of occasions and that each occasion covers a period of time such that several behaviors are observed. Then the observer has collected two sequences of observations, the sequence within occasions, and the sequence of occasions. It seems to be a reasonable assumption that if the observer is to come out with some hypotheses based on the organism's behavior, he will consider the behavior within occasions. And he will consider not only what does occur, but what does not occur that could be expected to occur. Also he will notice which events follow on each other and which events do not follow on each other. Such considerations might lead to conclusions or hypotheses about what might be called the behavioral structure of an occasion. But there is also a sequence of occasions. Therefore, there will be a set of occasions, each having its own structure. The set of occasions constitute the data of our naturalist.

In addition to considering the sequence of occasions as such, the naturalist undoubtedly takes into account not only the sequence of occasions, but tries to see relationships among the behaviors over the whole set of occasions without regard to the structure of each occasion.

In other words, what is noticed among other things, is which events follow on each other and which events do not follow on each other over all the occasions. It can be seen then, if the naturalist is observing many behaviors over many occasions, that his observations can aggregate to an impressive number. And they can easily aggregate to an overwhelming amount as the number of organisms observed increases.

Now suppose what probably is actually not often the case, that the categories of observations of the naturalist are mutually exclusive. Were this so, it could be shown that the nature of classification systems is such that it might well appear to the observer that there is order in the data in the sense that scientists think of order as "underlying relations." Also, from well-known experimentation in psychology on memory, learning, and forgetting, it is clear that the classification system of the observer may change continually as observation proceeds, so that the very process of observations may be, and really always is,

conditioned by the preceding observations. Thus, the very process of data formation, from one point of view, changes. From another point of view it can be said that the classification system of the observer is continually conditioned by the observations. Thus we see that all is in flux, the observer has a frame of reference which is not fixed, which can change as a result of the very process of observation. Furthermore, what we know about memory indicates that additional changes in the frame of reference and of the data conceived as the ordering of observation into the frame of reference of the observer, come about as a function of time. Bartlett's fascinating study of remembering, as well as a host of others, indicates that upon reflection after the events, the inner nature of the events seems to have changed.

Consider that naturalistic observer, the psychotherapist. He is, mainly at least, observing the communicative or linguistic behavior of a patient or group of patients over periods of perhaps hundreds of therapy hours. Therefore, even were his classification subclasses few in number and mutually exclusive, the observations would amount to a really overwhelming array of data. Even when the psychotherapist takes notes, these can really be regarded, no matter how voluminous, as at best, aids to memory. The therapist, a Freud for example, then must remember over long periods of time and over many patients, what happened, what didn't happen, etc., in addition to considering information not obtained in the therapy hour. Then he creates on what he conceives to be his observations, a theory of psychotherapy and a psychological theory of personality. No matter how plausible and convincing these theories may be, it is clear that the interaction of observer and observed, the personal or subjective element, can and probably does play a large part in the creation of the theory—and in such a way that we do not know to what extent the theories describe the theorists or the patients.

It would indeed be a humbling and corrective experience for a psychotherapist to have copies of the original situations, such as sound recording or sound motion pictures, played back after a case description and analysis. For he would no doubt discover that while there were "essential truths" in his formulation, what was described as having a dramatic unity had in fact far less unity, was much more scattered throughout the observations than his formulations indicated. And he would also find that what on listening or viewing seemed to be important events, had been neglected in his formulation. In other words, faithful copies of the events lead, upon presentation to the original observer, to a change in the classification system or hypotheses consequent upon his original observation. Even were the psychotherapist unbiased or uninvolved, the case would be the same because of the large numbers of responses displayed by his patient.

The considerations outlined above suggest the basic function of naturalistic observation. The function of naturalistic observation and research is to generate hypotheses concerning the underlying structure, when present, in behavioral domains. It is not to test hypotheses. The testing of hypotheses is in the province of the experimental method and, in certain situations, of statistical methods. Generally speaking, the use of experimental method depends upon control, and by control is meant the control of *relevant* conditions or variables. Seldom it is, if ever, that everything can be controlled. Thus the use of experimental method depends upon previous positive knowledge or upon insight gained in uncontrolled situations. But uncontrolled situations are just those covered by naturalistic observations. Thus, if we can improve naturalistic observation, we are more likely to

be in a position to have insight into what should be controlled in advancing an experimental attack upon the domain of inquiry.

The function of naturalistic observation being the generation of hypotheses, a basic problem of such observation is at once apparent. That is what might be called objectifying the observations or moving from the act of observation to the recording of data. The recording of data is thought of as obtaining a record of behavior in symbolic form. Getting such data implies:

(*a*) a standard definition of what constitutes a response;

(*b*) a classification scheme or system into which responses are ordered as they occur.

In what follows it will be assumed that the investigator has a standard and specifiable definition of a response.

The function of the classification system in naturalistic observation and analysis is to provide an objective record of behavior such that once the period of observation has ended, one can tell with certainty what was observed. Therefore, the classification should be objective in the sense that two observers would to a very high degree classify behavior the same way; the classification scheme should be specifiable and reliable. To the extent that it is not, the classification system is personal and unreliable. Secondly, the classification system should have mutually exclusive subcategories, unless the classifying behavior of the investigator is the object of investigation. When the classes are not mutually exclusive, cross-classification may be dependent; some of the possible cross-classification will be mere artifacts.

It seems that reliability and mutually exclusive subclasses represent minimal characteristics of a satisfactory classification system. A reliable classification system with mutually exclusive classes would provide an objective record of behavior over a series of observations and would push the problems of subjectivity and insight back where they belong; namely, into the creation of the classification system itself and to the generation of hypotheses based upon analysis of the classified behavior.

Since the number of classified behaviors or data may be very large, it seems that an additional criterion of a minimally satisfactory classification system would be that it be susceptible of objective analysis, preferably analysis of a type which treats the classification system and the data as a unit.

The three criteria of a minimally satisfactory classification system by no means exhaust the problems inherent in classifying behavior. For it is clear that an arbitrary number of classification systems can be applied in the same observational situation. And the same applies to the definitions of response. When we have two different universes of discourse, connected, possibly, only by a standard definition of response, then two criteria of the relative validity of the systems might be called internal productivity and external productivity; internal productivity being some index of the amount of order in the behavioral data and external productivity being some index or set of indices indicating relationships between the behavioral data and other data. A somewhat analogous distinction is made in mental test theory between the kind of validity described by the correlation between a test and the factor (or factors) it represents and the kind of validity described by the correlation between a test and an external variable. Given two classification systems, the first having more internal and external productivity than the second, it seems clear that the first is preferable to the second. It should be noted, however, that one system might have more internal productivity and less external productivity

than the other, and vice versa; in that case the two criteria might not point to the same decision.

A further distinction to be made concerns the "grain" of the classification systems. A fine-grained system is one with relatively many subclasses and a coarse-grained system, one with relatively few (and as few as two) categories. A system with only two subclasses really has but one, for a two-class system can describe at most but one kind of organism-environment transaction, all other kinds being lumped together in the remainder class. Thus the two-class system represents the ultimate in coarse-grained systems for, of course, a one-class system is completely determined. A completely determined system can yield no information. Since the behavior of organisms is complex, it would seem that a three-class system, and other relatively coarse-grained systems, would be less likely to be productive, other things being equal, than relatively fine-grained systems. For fine-grained systems are less likely to have responses classified into the remainder class.

In coarse-grained systems, behavior is likely to be classified into the remainder class because attention is centered on a few kinds of behavior; in fine-grained systems, however, such classifications are likely to be made because of inability to identify the class into which to order the response. In such a case the class "unclassifiable" becomes a subclass of the remainder class. In actual investigations it is probably desirable to record, in addition to the explicitly defined categories, the unclassifiable and remainder classes, for they will often be of considerable interest and could yield valuable information.

A criterion related to that discussed above is exhaustiveness. An exhaustive system is one in which all responses are classified into the explicit categories and none are classified into the unclassifiable and remainder classes. It seems reasonable to suppose that the more exhaustive a system is, the more productive it is likely to be.

In general, then, a satisfactory classification scheme will have mutually exclusive subclasses, be susceptible to routine analysis, and will possess internal and external productivity. Productivity is in turn likely to be dependent upon "grain" and exhaustiveness. These rather rough, ready, and commonsensical criteria are somewhat vague and lack the sense of closure obtained by means of a complete intellectual scheme. However, they seem to be serviceable criteria and can be used to some extent for developing a classification system before observation formally begins. Some of the criteria, especially productivity, will be more sharply delineated later.

It will be remembered that the behavior being considered here is completely uncontrolled by the investigator. Nevertheless, the classification system is somewhat analogous to a control of behavior in the sense that the observer is insisting on perceiving the behavior observed in terms of the classification system he is employing. Thus the observer is willy-nilly controlling his experience, as in an experiment, but, perhaps, in an undesirable manner. That is, his classification scheme may simply be an objectified set of prejudices having much to do with the misguided imagination of the observer but containing no insight about the kind of organism observed. In this case, it is likely that analysis of the data will reveal only the folly of the originator of the classification system. A properly conceived and executed experiment, however, does not fail to yield real information. This is in the very nature of the process of experimentation. It therefore behooves the naturalistic observer to be as carefully imaginative in constructing his classification system as he can possibly be; to fuse his creativity and experience to the end

of constructing a more than minimally satisfactory classification system.

The desirability of extreme care and maximal creativity in constructing a classification system can be seen by considering a situation in which behavior is physically controlled by limiting the behavior of the organism to series of finite alternatives. The maze in which the organism is restricted to right and left turn behavior is a good example; so are Fabre's caterpillars endlessly circling the post on which he placed them. Such simple situations, hardly to be conceived as constituting full experimental control, have yielded a wealth of information about response acquisition and instinctive behavior. Now in the maze, for example, the alternatives can be considered as a two-class classification system, and analysis of the sequence of alternatives expressed in the behavior of the organism can be handled, as will be shown later, in the same manner as with the classification systems which do not imply the imposition of physical limitations upon behavior of the organisms being observed. To make the point in a rather fanciful manner, when the organism is merely observed, the organism "selects" as behavioral alternatives the subclasses of the observer's classification system. When there is more control, choices are forced upon the ogranism by environmental conditions imposed by the investigator. In neither case is it remarkable that a "choice" is made. In the first case, however, "selection of alternatives" may have nothing to do with the organism observed and everything to do with the observer. In the second case selection of alternatives actually represents transactions, however "artificial" the environment may be. In other words, in the second case the behavior represents an actual organism-environment transaction. In the first case the classified behavior *may* show only that behavior occurred; the classifications may not represent any actual transaction between organism and environment. This is the defect of uncontrolled observation; it may be observation of no more than the fact that responses occurred a given number of times. Thus the necessity for the basic criterion of productivity. For productivity guards against just the possibility that a given classification system is irrelevant to a given group of organism-environment transactions or responses. For it is here conceived that an irrelevant but specifiable and reliable classification system would for a given set of responses be unproductive. That is to say, an irrelevant system would result in data exhibiting no order.

A naturalistic investigation is concluded when analysis of the data results in a demonstration that the system is unproductive or productive as the case may be. If the system is productive, the end result should be a sharpened and refined set of hypotheses leading to a better classification system with which to approach the domain. Or it may result in a set of hypotheses so refined as to indicate what is to be controlled and varied in an experimental attack upon the domain of inquiry.

The nature of exploratory investigation being what it is, it starts and ends with personal creation. Usually personal creation, the subjective element, pervades the entire process, often to the detriment of the investigation. The personal, subjective element should be confined to the beginning of the investigation when the classification system is being devised and made explicit, and to the end when the routines of analysis have provided the formal results upon which personal creativity should operate.

## MATHEMATICAL ANALOGUE

A mathematical counterpart of the ideas presented in the preceding discussion can be constructed rather straight-forwardly. Consider a classification system with $q$ mutually exclusive subclasses and a group of $t$ subjects for each of whom just $n$ responses have been classified. Each response of a subject may be represented by a column vector with one unit entry and $q-1$ zero entries, and the $n$ responses of each subject may be represented as a column vector with $n$ unit entries and $n(q-1)$ zero entries. Arranging all of the $t$ columns into a data table then gives the $nq \times t$ data matrix

$$s_{ij} = 1 \text{ or } 0 \qquad [1]$$

where $s_{ij}$ is the element in the i-th row and the j-th column of the data matrix, hereafter denoted by S. S is what we call the standard or primitive form of the data, for it represents the behavior of the subjects as it occurred; in other words it shows just what the subject did and did not do and when.

The data matrix, S, represents the behavior in such a way that corresponding to the i-th response of the $t$ subjects there is a $q \times t$ submatrix of S containing $t$ unit entries and $t(q-1)$ zero entries. From this circumstance it can be shown that the rank of S is at most $nq - n + 1$ when $t$ is greater than $n(q-1)$. The difference between $nq$ and $nq - n + 1$ is a consequence of considering alternative subclasses of the classification system as mutually exclusive.

Given S, attention can be shifted to the question of the internal productivity of S and to the question of the underlying structural relations, if any, embodied in S. These questions have been considered in detail in Butler, Wagstaff, Rice, and Counts (1960). Here we will emphasize the fundamental conclusions.

We conceive of the responses of the subjects as being determined by response tendencies or dispositions. These tendencies to respond are not mutually exclusive although the actual responses are. Corresponding to S is a matrix S* which is a representation of the response tendencies generating S. For the i-th response in S there is a $q \times t$ submatrix, the row vectors of which are necessarily orthogonal. The corresponding vectors in the corresponding $q \times t$ submatrix of S* are not necessarily orthogonal. Therefore, S* cannot refer to actual behavior since the behavioral alternatives are mutually exclusive.

Consider now the matrix

$$R_o = 1/t \; SS' \qquad [2]$$

This matrix is $nq \times nq$ and is square symmetric. The elements of [2] are $P_{1j}$ where $P_{1j}$ is the proportion of subjects behaving the same way in rows i and j of S. Being a proportion $P_{1j}$ may vary between zero and unity. Given the i-th row of $R_o$ and summing across the first $q$ columns, then the second $q$ columns, etc. yields for each set of $q$ columns the value $P_{11}$, the diagonal value of the i-th row in $R_o$. Thus the sum of each row of $R_o$ is $nP_{11}$.

We now require that, in order to be able to state that the classification system is internally productive and that there is an underlying set of structural relations or response tendencies, the following relations hold:

$$R_o - R_o^* = D \qquad [3]$$

where D is a diagonal of square blocks of order $q \times q$ which correspond to the $n$ responses and $R_o^*$ in an $nq \times nq$ square symmetric matrix with elements $P_{1j}$ except for the elements in the $n$ different $q \times q$ principal submatrices corresponding to the $n$ responses. $R_o^*$ is obtained from S* in the same way as $R_o$ is obtained from S.

The entries in [3] imply that the empirical proportions based on the behavior of the subjects are reproduced by S* with the exception of those proportions in the $q \times q$ blocks around the main diagonal of $R_o$. The proportions in these blocks are fixed as $P_{11}$ and as zero by the restriction that responses be mutually exclusive.

Adding the requirement, which seems to be a natural one, that the row entries of each of the $n$ $q \times q$ principal submatrices of $R_o^*$ sum to $P_{11}$, we have the circumstance that the rows of $R_o^*$ sum to $nP_{11}$ as do the rows of $R_o$. Since the entries of $R_o^*$ and of $R_o$ are the same outside of the $q \times q$ diagonal blocks, $R_o^*$ and $R_o$ have the same first centroid. Furthermore, comparison of $R_o$ and of $R_o^*$ shows that if they are to be different, then, from the restrictions stated, the $q \times q$ blocks in $R_o^*$ must be nondiagonal since the $q \times q$ blocks in $R_o$ are diagonal. Now $R_o$ and $R_o^*$ must be different if the classification system is internally productive except for the limiting and ideal case when the row vectors of S having any unit entries in common are identical and when those that are different have nothing in common. This is surely the ideal case in which the classification system has maximum internal productivity, for then the differentiation between classes of behavior is maximal.

When the ideal case does not obtain, the row vectors of S overlap but are not identical; then S* will differ from S and the rank of S* will be less than the rank of S if the system is at all productive. As in factor analysis, S* is not directly obtainable. However, factoring of $R_o^*$, analogous to factoring the reduced correlation matrix of factor analysis, expresses the vectors of S* in a linear basis or coordinate system. The problem in exploratory analysis is similar to that in the factor analysis of quantitative variates. By substituting communalities for the diagonal values of $R_o$ one gets $R_o^*$. Then one may go through the routines of factoring to obtain a factor matrix expressing the vectors of $R_o^*$ in a basis. Since the entries of $R_o$ are all zero or positive, a factor matrix may be obtained, the entries of which are all zero or positive: we restrict our attention to such matrices, for those with negative entries have no direct behavioral interpretation. Behavior appears or it does not appear. This restriction guarantees a unique factor matrix when the configuration of vectors is orthogonal. When the configuration is not orthogonal, a factor matrix which is unique, in the sense that it contains the least possible linear dependence, may be obtained. This factor matrix, hereafter called the simple factor matrix or the factor matrix of the simple basis, is obtained by making each factor collinear with one of the vectors of the configuration. Since negative entries are not permitted, these vectors are the outer vectors of the configuration. When the configuration is orthogonal, the factors comprise a simple basis or coordinate system which is unique because any rotation of factors would produce a factor matrix with negative entries possessing no direct behavioral meaning.

Loadings on the basis vectors (factors) serve as the beginning point for inference and hypothesis formation just as in the factor analysis of quantitative variates. Internal productivity is assessed in two ways. First the rank differential, $r/nq - n + 1$, where $r$ is the rank of $R_o^*$, is computed. The expression in the denominator is the maximal possible rank. The lower limit of the rank differential is $1/nq - n + 1$, which indicates high internal productivity, and the upper limit is unity, which indicates no internal productivity. The second and more significant sign of internal productivity is the index of internal productivity, $1 - [u/(r^2 - r)]$ where $u$ is the sum of the off-diagonal elements of the matrix of inner products of the unit length factors. When the vectors of the simple basis are orthogonal, the matrix of inner products of basis vectors is an identity matrix, then the index has a value of unity for $u$ has a value of zero. The lower limiting value of the index is zero for the upper limit of $u$ is $r^2 - r$.

Factoring $R_o^*$ simultaneously provides for assessment of internal productivity and for the factor matrix which is the beginning point for hypothesis formation. When the rank differential is unfavorable (high value) and the index of internal productivity is low, computing the factor matrix for the simple basis is a superfluous effort.

Analysis of $R_o$ is equivalent to analyzing the relations between the rows of S. Analysis of the rows might be characterized, somewhat crudely to be sure, as a "trait" analysis. Sometimes one might wish to make a "type" analysis. This is equivalent to analyzing the columns of S or matrix S', the transpose of S. A suitable matrix for analysis is then

$$1/n \, S'S = R_o \qquad [4]$$

where n is the number of responses. The entries of [4] show on a scale from zero to unity the similarity of behavior from subject to subject. Considerations similar to those of the analysis of S apply. Estimating communalities and factoring will provide a simple basis from which internal productivity can be assessed.

## PLACE OF THEORY IN NATURALISTIC OBSERVATION

In the introductory section we have said that observation should precede experimentation, and yet we recommend that the naturalistic observer should bring to the construction of his classification system all the creativity and experience he can muster. It is precisely here, in our opinion, that the function of theorizing enters in. We conceive of theorizing— more accurately, perhaps, construction building—at this stage, not as a source of testable propositions, but as a systematization of experience, one's own and that of others, which can stimulate and enhance our individual creativity. It should serve to guide us in deciding which of literally hundreds of aspects of the behavior might be interesting to observe.

If one takes seriously the function of naturalistic observation and research as a method of discovery, then it follows that the classification system devised should remain as close as possible to the behavioral level. That is, a given class should contain behaviors that are similar as behavior rather than containing units that are dissimilar behaviorally but are thought to be conceptually related. An example of the latter would be such a class as "resistance" which might include silence, change of topic, and sundry other behaviors thought to be indices of some inner state, called "resistance." Clearly, as soon as such a concept intervenes, a hypothesis has already been built in and we are one step removed from behavior; the first step of discovery has been bypassed. Of course the unit of behavior we observe is complex, and of course we observe some things rather than others, influenced by our own prejudices, preconceptions or theories, but as long as we are including in a given class units that are directly observable as involving the same behavior, we can *discover* what goes with what. Whatever we choose to call such classes and however many hunches we have concerning the clinical significance of a given class of behaviors, the real definition of the class lies in the behavioral descriptions used by the judges in placing a unit of response in Class A rather than in Class B.

## STIMULUS HUNGER AS A BASIC DRIVE

This section summarizes briefly the ideas presented in our paper "Self-actualization, new experience, and psychotherapy" (Butler & Rice, 1960). As a result of some of the questions that we, as therapists, asked ourselves, we undertook a survey of some of the literature in experimental and comparative psychology,

covering studies at the prehuman level, embryological studies, and studies of neonates and children. We arrived at the conviction that self-actualizing processes have a primitive base, that this primitive base has many of the characteristics of the so-called physiological drives; that it is as independent of the physiological drives as the physiological drives are of each other; and that as a derivative or result, self-actualization depends primarily upon the satisfaction of this drive. We consider that this drive, which we have called "stimulus hunger" is the basis for much of what is constructive, creative, and self-actualizing in human life, and on the negative side for much, though far from all, of what is negative, destructive, and self-limiting.

This drive, stimulus hunger, shows in behavior as an ever-present tendency for the organism to get new experience, either in the form of new stimulus objects or in the form of change in the level and mode of stimulation. In the naive or primitive organism this is almost wholly a tendency to get new sensory influx. In a symbol-using, symbol-creating organism such as the human child, we emphasize the broader meaning of "new experience" rather than simply input from the environment. We are not emphasizing the sensorium, but rather the commerce of the entire nervous system of the organism with the stimuli. That is, we are talking about behavior and its immediate precursors—perceptions, ideas, sensations, and the like. We take the position that both thinking (a central process) and motor outflow have as much right to be regarded as experience as has sensory influx. Furthermore sensory processes, thinking, motor outflow, and behavior are processes which cannot be sharply delineated from a neurological standpoint.

It seems plausible, therefore, that there is a tendency to think new thoughts which is not in principle different from the tendency to get new stimuli. And what inhibits thinking is what inhibits adient behavior to new stimuli, namely punishment.

Self-actualizing tendencies, then, are just the tendencies to think new thoughts; thinking creates experience in much the same fashion that approaching stimuli creates new experience. It is the approaching, behaving, adjusting, preparing to respond, *in relation to the stimuli* which is the experience or experiences, not the new stimuli; it is the thinking processes (and their motor patterns) which are the experience, not just the thought contents. Stimulus hunger has to do with a wide range and variety of thinking, and as a process the range and variety of thinking or conceptualizing provides new experience for the organism in much the same sense as the presence of new stimulus configurations.

The line of reasoning presented above has immediate implications for psychotherapy. We see therapy as a continuing search for new elements and the forming of creative recombinations of new and old elements. At its best there is a tremendous amount of new experience, proving painful, certainly, but also intensely satisfying. The effect of a stimulating therapist style is to arouse or re-arouse within the individual more associations, images, trains of thought, etc. It enables the client to generate new experience for himself. It seems obvious that the stimulus (therapist communication and behavior) with the greatest connotative range, with the most far-reaching reverberations within the organism, results in a maximum of satisfying experience.

There is one qualification, however, which must be made. Aversive stimulation, especially anxiety and fear, inhibit and channel both thinking and behavior. Aversive stimulation seems to be prepotent over adience. Certain forms of

therapists' communications might be highly stimulating but also be carriers of inhibiting and channelizing effects. As a case in point the psychoanalysts have described defensive and regressive reactions to interpretations of motives, impulses, etc. Such interventions, although they may be stimulating, may also leave the client with little control over the kind and quantity of internal arousal. When the therapist communicates within the frame of reference established by the client, the client has control of this kind because the therapist is not perceived as a to-be-coped-with event.

The preceding ideas lead us to the following proposition:

Given *n* semantically equivalent statements, the one possessing the greatest range of connotation is that which is the most stimulating. Alternatively we might say that given *n* paraphrases of the same message, one may possess a greater range of connotations than the others, thus providing a basis for an increased range of thinking or experiencing in a respondent.

Let us assume for example, that five experienced therapists are responding to the same client message. Let us further assume that they are all equally accurate and equally accepting in their attitude toward the client. Our contention is that each of the five might well respond in a style that was different from the styles of the others, and that each of these styles might have different experiential consequences for the client and consequently different behavioral consequences in the further participation of the client.

Under the three conditions of prizing, understanding, and stimulating, we hypothesize that the self-actualizing tendencies of clients will function. They can begin to create new experience for themselves; they can be "open to the creation of new experience" and thus can break through the endless repetition of experience so characteristic of maladjusted persons.

## IMPLICATIONS FOR CONDUCT OF THERAPY

The specific implications of this viewpoint will be discussed later in the paper, inasmuch as they are embodied in the dimensions of the Therapist Classification System. The more general impact of this thinking is that it leads us to view the therapy relationship as a situation in which each member serves as a particular kind of stimulus for the other. Each is putting certain constraints on the behavior of the other, each may be facilitating in the other behavior that might not otherwise be possible. Our exploration of the therapy process, then, focuses on the question: What kinds of stimuli are the client and therapist being, each for the other, during the therapy hour?

First let us distinguish between participative style and specific content. In client-centered therapy the therapist controls the content of his responses in the sense that he chooses to stay within the frame of reference of the client. This is a deliberate choice on the part of the therapist, based on theoretical considerations. Although this might seem to reduce the stimulus value of the therapist, there are some excellent reasons for doing this: (a) it reduces the interpersonal anxiety, thereby providing for greater tolerance of intrapersonal anxiety and for the kind of climate in which conjunctive communication can flourish; (b) it helps to keep the balance of initiative on the side of the client; (c) it is consistent with the hypothesis, to be discussed later, that the "meaning" of a client's key experiences resides in the experiences themselves. These "meanings" need not be interpreted from outside but are potentially available to the client for reorganization if he can be helped to re-experience them under certain therapeutic conditions.

Even though the impact of the therapist may be lessened (we entertain this possibility; we do not hold it) by his staying within the client's frame of reference, this still leaves the therapist with, at least potentially, a very high stimulus value simply in his style of participation. It is just here, however, that the therapist tends to become client controlled, though not usually as a conscious or deliberate choice.

Take, for example, the inexpressive client, who speaks in a flat (or speechmaking) voice, who deals with each subject of discussion in an abstracting, analytical way, using extremely inexpressive language. Granted that these stylistic characteristics may stem from his emotional problem, they have, in our opinion, an effect on the therapist which lessens the chance of a successful therapy, beyond the difficulty that would be expected from the extent of the emotional disturbance. The therapist's style of participation tends to become inexpressive and similar to that of the client, and the therapist then becomes a weaker and less adequate stimulus for the client, further damping the style of the client.

On the other hand the client who speaks in a voice of intense involvement, who expresses feelings with directness, using language that generates vivid imagery in the hearer, stimulates his therapist to the end that he becomes more expressive, thus in turn re-stimulating the client. Therapy then becomes an exciting and productive experience for each participant.

The implications of this thinking for the conduct of therapy might be as follows: (1) While the content of his responses is controlled by the conscious choice of the therapist, his style of participation is not usually a matter of choice and tends to become similar to that of the client. (2) The client is in turn influenced by the style of the therapist, tending to move toward his style, though probably at a slower rate. (3) In addition to their impact on the therapist, certain dimensions of the client's style of participation are in themselves vehicles of therapeutic change, and can be shown to be related to measures of therapy outcome. (4) If the therapist could establish stylistic independence of the client on a fairly expressive level, the client would be stimulated toward more expressive participation. (5) This change in style of participation of the client would in turn be accompanied by a more favorable outcome than would be predicted under usual circumstances.

## CONSTRUCTION OF THE CLASSIFICATION SYSTEMS

The client classification system and the therapist classification system are both based on a combination of the empirical and the theoretical. In the case of the client system, classes of behavior were chosen which seemed to differentiate between interviews which were considered "good," mediocre, or "bad" by client and/ or therapist. From listening to these we tried to identify styles of participation that varied in a meaningful way in relation to the seeming value of the interview. Then each of the preliminary classes was considered from the standpoint of our theorizing about therapy. Does each subclass of each class make clinical sense, or are they perhaps just concomitants of some more significant stylistic variable?

In the case of the therapist classification system, the situation was somewhat reversed. We first thought of aspects which seemed likely to be crucial in the impact of the therapist on the client, and then listened to selected tapes to see if therapists did indeed seem to vary significantly along these dimensions. In both classification systems, however, the relationship between the observed behavior and the theory is the same. The subclasses

of each class are specified by the behaviors to be included and not by the supposed clinical meaning. It is the discrimination between kinds of behavior which is central, not the verbalized description or definition of the categories. Clinical hypotheses were not being tested but were to be generated by the analysis.

One further general point is in order here. The subclasses within each aspect are not intended to be scales. Some behaviors are, of course, thought to be more therapeutic than others, but the subclasses contain qualitatively different kinds of behavior which may prove to be important in their own right.

### A. Client Classification System

1. *Level of Expression.* This aspect involves the level at which the client is dealing with and expressing whatever subject matter is under discussion. The subclasses are as follows:

a. *Analysis of action (including cognitive action):*

Statements placed here are those that attempt, either naively or with sophistication, to look beneath the surface, to analyze, interpret, explain, classify, evaluate, or generalize about action, including cognitive action.

b. *Analysis of feeling:*

The analysis of feeling category is somewhat similar to (a) above in its form; that is, the statements analyze, interpret, explain, classify, evaluate, or generalize. The focus here, however, is on the feelings of the client as feelings, not as classes of behavior.

c. *Responsiveness:*

Responsiveness is the category for statements that express directly a feeling or inner experience. The focus is on internal experience— feelings, images, fantasy, impulses, expressed or described more or less directly rather than being first analyzed, conceptualized, or categorized. A statement that is rated here is one that could have been made only by the person himself or by someone who had put himself in the person's frame of reference. In R statements the client is seeking expression for something that is present "right now" even though it may be present in the past tense when the feeling first occurred in the past.

2. *Voice Qualities and Manner of Speaking.* This aspect classifies client responses according to qualities of voice— inflection, pitch, pace, etc., without regard to the content of what is being said. It is a complex class, compounded of varying degrees of three different qualities: (*a*) amount of energy in the voice; (*b*) the direction in which the energy is turned; (*c*) whether the energy is controlled or discharged. For the training of judges, verbal descriptions of subclasses are supplemented by taped examples.

a. *Emotional:*

Responses placed here have a high energy level, but the energy tends to overflow into discharge rather than being used in a controlled way. The energy seems to overflow from within rather than being aimed toward the outside world. The voice breaks, trembles, is choked with crying, expressed discharge of acute tension, etc.

b. *Focused:*

Responses placed here have high energy, but the energy is used in a controlled problem-solving way rather than being discharged. The voice gives an impression of pondering or exploration. The energy seems to be turned inward rather than being propelled outward. Speech is characterized by hesitations and irregularities of pace.

There is little fluctuation in pitch of voice, but great irregularities in stress of syllables.

c. *Externalizing:*

Responses placed here are characterized by fairly high energy, which is directed outward, seemingly toward having some effect on the outside world. It is characterized by a soapbox quality, in the sense of having a cadence or rhythmic pattern, as if the grooves were already on the disk and the record only had to be set going. The speech pattern is much smoother than in (*b*) above, with emphatic though often mechanical inflection, together with a fairly wide range of pitch.

d. *Limited:*

Responses placed here are characterized by low energy used in a matter-of-fact, even incidental tone. It is clearly a communication to the therapist, but it is not clearly directional in the sense of (*b*) or (*c*). The pace is even and relatively unstressed.

3. *Quality of Participation.* This aspect concerns the participation of the client in whatever he is discussing.

a. *Participating:*

This includes responses in which the client is a participator in whatever he is discussing, even though he may not be the prime mover in the action.

b. *Observing:*

The client is on the sidelines as an observer of the scene, rather than being an integral part of the scene. Statements in which the self is mentioned only as being an observer of the scene, and statements referring to self only implicitly are rated here as well as statements completely unrelated to the self.

## B. Therapist Classification System

1. *Freshness of Words and Combinations.* The most highly connotative language possible seems to be poetic, metaphorical language in which much sensory imagery is used. This does not include analogy where the emphasis is on the isomorphism of the two experiences, but rather the use of metaphor which adds vividness and color to the primary experience. This main class contains five subclasses.

 *a.* Responses placed here are those which present rather vivid metaphors, having a high degree of imagery. This does not include statements of analogy but, rather, responses having a strong picture-building character. The imagery is most often visual or auditory, but it may also be kinesthetic.

 *b.* Responses placed here contain one or more fresh, colorful words or combinations, often of a sensory character. The words may carry images in themselves, but the total response does not have the vivid, picture character of (*a*).

 *c.* Responses rated here have an overall punchy, stimulating character, but are without the use of unusually fresh sensory words or images. This may involve unique phrasing, juxtaposition, or sounds or combinations of sounds.

 *e.* Responses placed here consist of commonplace expressions. The words and phrases, as well as the general structure of the response have an everyday, garden-variety quality.

 *f.* Responses placed here are empty or formalized. Generally there is an absence of denotative reference, which may be formalized or simply contentless.

2. *Voice Quality.* Although interpersonal anxiety is presumably cut down by the fact that the therapist stays within the frame of reference of the client, therapy is essentially an interpersonal process. There must be a real person for the client to encounter. If the client gets back his own messages from the therapist with nothing coming from him as a person, it can become like a stimulus deprivation experiment. This dimension is addressed to the question of how much the therapist's voice is bringing to the therapy situation. Is he actually bringing something as a person, something that provides or generates new interpersonal experience for the client? Is he simply "present and accounted for"? Or is he actually removing something from the situation, through dullness, weakness, or through empty and forced attempts to be something which at that moment he isn't? This class contains seven subclasses.

 *a.* Here the voice brings to life the feelings of the client—fear, anger, pleasure, etc., but not to the extent of losing himself in the emotion; that is, there is control rather than overflow of energy. There is a good deal of energy present.

 *b.* Here again there is high energy in the therapist's voice, but it is characterized not by emotion but by vigor, confidence, warmth, etc.

 *c.* The therapist's voice has high energy, used in a controlled, problem solving way. It is characterized by a pondering, exploring quality. There is unevenness of inflection and often hesitation, but not the hesitation of indecisiveness. The response may end on a questioning note, but not on a vague or weak one.

 *d.* The voice carries a note of newness or closure just arrived at, the interest of something newly seen or seen a different way. There tends to be a higher pitch and a rising energy level.

e. There is a moderate amount of energy, expressed in a serious but only moderately inflected voice. The inflection is natural, though with more seriousness and less animation than in many conversations.

f. There is high energy present, but the words are accented for effect rather than for spontaneous meaning. It may take the form of a slight cadence or like an actor reading lines. The thing to watch for is the shifting of accent from the location of natural meaning.

g. This subclass resembles (f) above except that energy is low. A cadenced or singsong quality predominates. They have the sound of a preformed pattern in which meaning is secondary.

h. Very little energy is present. The response sounds thin, wispy or breathless, as if the therapist would run out of energy before the response was finished. The sentences are comparatively uninflected.

3. *Functional Level of Response.* This dimension is more complexly determined than are the other two. While we think that the concept of stimulus hunger as a basic drive is a crucial one in therapy, there are clearly other aspects that interact with or channel it. When one reads Greek drama, for instance, there can be a tremendous arousal of new experience, and as has been repeatedly recognized, one can feel intense catharsis. Nevertheless, there are ingredients missing that are present in psychotherapy. One such essential ingredient is the self-directed search for the idiosyncratic "meaning" or impact of one's own inner experience.

Once aroused, these experiences must be focused on and experienced out to the very edges, if their shape is to be spread out before one, and made usable for reorganization.

This class, then, has to do with the functional level of the therapist's response. We distinguish seven subclasses or levels.

a. The first distinction is between a focus outside or inside the client. Although these responses are within the frame of reference of the client, the therapist is joining with the client in focusing on something that is outside. Responses may refer to the client and still be placed here, if it is a behavioral description of oneself as an external object.

b. Responses placed in this second subclass focus on the client's concept of himself and of the stimuli immediately impinging on him. These responses are certainly "inside" the client, since the client and the therapist are examining the client's own motivations, attitudes, perceptions, and behavior. On the other hand, they contain a kind of objectification, in which, momentarily at least, there is a two-part division of the self, with one part observing the other. This is in contrast to the "feeling" categories where the focus is on "how I feel," "what's it like right now."

c. Responses placed here concern feelings, but the feelings are being labeled rather than explored. The emphasis is on finding a name for it, classifying it, rather than on exploring "what is it like inside?" For instance, a therapist who responds "you are angry" is summing a whole range of experience under this common label. It leaves out the whole range of inner experience that makes one person's experience of anger so different from that of another.

d. This subclass includes responses in which the therapist is expressing feeling or inner experience without using feeling or sensory words. He is attempting to bring it alive by verbally acting it out. Speaking in a slightly different context, we could say that the therapist is attempting to get into the slipstream of the person's inner awareness without organizing it or making it static. It has the fluid quality of a momentary impression or free association.

e. Responses placed here attempt to explore the stimulus for a feeling. It is not an attempt to pin down causality, but to explore the personal impact of the stimulus.

f. In this subclass and the one that follows, the therapist is attempting to help the client to explore the idiosyncratic edges of his own feelings. Responses placed in this subclass involved the sensing edge of the client's inner awareness, responding to the flavor of the experience. They need not be literally sensory, but may involve images, etc., but they tend to involve "body language."

g. Responses placed here are on the impulse edge of inner awareness. They involve an outward push, what the client would like to do right then. They are on a primitive impulse level, rather than having a considered ego-integrated quality.

### DATA ANALYSIS

The study to be reported consists of the application of classification systems to the behavior of clients and therapists. Our strategy was to apply and analyze separately the classification systems for client and therapist, treating the responses of client and therapist separately, and then to treat each dyad of client-therapist response as a unit. Treating the dyads of responses as units results in an analysis of response by response interaction between client and therapist.

The experimental population of clients consisted of 24 completed cases selected from a larger block of research cases. All cases were treated by therapists with a Rogerian orientation and were selected so as to provide an equal number of tape recorded interviews from cases rated as success and failure cases by their therapists. A group of cases rated at the mean of the nine-point scale used in rating were also included in the study. Length of treatment was balanced among the cases, and four attrition cases (discontinuing therapy before the sixth interview) were included among the failure cases.

The interviews selected for analysis were the second and next-to-last interviews, this selection being based on a desire to minimize "hello-goodby" effects. Only the second interviews were used for the attrition cases. Once the interviews had been selected, they were divided into thirds, by time. Then ten successive responses of client and therapist were taken from each third of the interview and classified. All classifications were based on listening to tapes; transcripts were not used. The unit of response used was what we conceived to be a "natural" or functional unit. That is, the response of the client was what was said between two therapist responses, and the response of the therapist was what was said between two client responses.

Reliability of classification was controlled by training. Judges were given written specifications of the classification systems and taped samples of responses with their classification. The judges were trained until they reached a standard set by the investigators. Periodically, the judges were required to classify a standard set of responses taped onto "drift" records. The drift records were designed to insure that standards of judgment did not change.

After the client responses had been classified, they were brought into the standard form of the matrix S. The data matrix S, with unit and zero entries, showing just what each client did and did not do in terms of the classification system employed was 720 × 44, with $n = 30$, $q = 24$, and $t = 44$. In the final standard form, then, the classification system had 24 independent, mutually exclusive subclasses.

The matrix $1/n$ S′ S (Butler, Wagstaff, Rice, & Counts, 1960) was used in the analysis. The elements of this matrix are a measure of the similarity between interviews on a scale from zero to unity. In this study sequence within thirds of the interviews was not retained; only the sequence between thirds was retained. Thus a rearrangement of the S matrix was necessitated. The rearrangement was carried out according to the method outlined in Wagstaff and Butler (1959). As a result, the final measure of similarity between interviews was based on a sequence of thirds of interviews rather than on a sequence of responses, one after another.

The matrix of interview similarity is shown in Table 1 (see Wagstaff, 1959, p. 43). The matrix was factored by the multiple group method. Communalities used for the groups are given in the diagonals of Table 1. Communalities were estimated by taking the centroid of each group, using the highest off-diagonal value of the variables in each group in the diagonal.

The factoring process was stopped when the sum of squares of the projections on the first centroid vector, as shown in the factor matrix, was .97. Since this vector has unit communality and is contributed to by all dimensions, it seemed that the data were essentially accounted for. As a check, a sample of 150 residuals was computed. These had a mean of .02 and a median of .018. Since the distribution was reasonably symmetrical, no further basis vectors were extracted.

Table 2 shows the matrix of the cosines of the angular separation between the

vectors of the simple basis. The rank differential is .07 and the index of internal productivity is .89. Thus we conclude that the classification system has considerable internal productivity.

After the simple basis had been determined, the matrix of projections of the interviews on the orthogonal basis best fitting the simple basis was found by the method described in Butler, Wagstaff, Rice, and Counts (1960). It should be noted that these loadings of necessity closely resemble those for the corresponding matrix of projections onto the vectors of the simple basis. The matrix of the projections onto the orthogonal factors approximating the simple basis is shown in Table 3. The second interviews are the odd-numbered loadings, and the succeeding even-numbered loadings are the next-to-last interviews. Interviews 41, 42, 43, and 44 are the second interviews of the attrition cases for which there were no late interviews to classify. The loadings of the interviews on the basis vectors represent the similarity between the actual interviews and mathematically defined "hypothetical interviews."

In obtaining characterizations of the mathematically defined interviews, those interviews having loadings of .40 or more on a given basis vector with no other loading greater than .20 were selected. Then those response classifications appearing most frequently in the interviews were selected until there were ten response ratings for each third of the interview. It will be remembered that there were ten responses in each section of the interview. Table 4 shows the frequency of responses classified within each class for each basis vector at the first, second, and third sections of the interviews.

The four interviews serving as the base for the characterization of the first factor are 2, 9, 10, and 6. The characteristic behaviors are such that the client almost always includes himself in what he is expressing rather than expressing himself as an observer. The typical response is that in which the client is analyzing feelings having relevance to him, sometimes his voice being expressive of feeling. Even when communicating about ideas or actions the client expresses himself in a focused, energetic manner. In roughly one-fourth of his responses, the Factor I client expresses feelings or experiences quite directly with a voice quality which is focused or emotional. The direct ver-

TABLE 1

MATRIX $1/N$ s′ s:

Proportionate Correspondences[a] between Interviews

| | 1 | 2 | 3 | 4 | 5 | 6 | 7 | 8 | 9 | 10 | 11 | 12 | 13 | 14 | 15 | 16 | 17 | 18 | 19 | 20 | 21 | 22 |
|---|---|---|---|---|---|---|---|---|---|---|---|---|---|---|---|---|---|---|---|---|---|---|
| 1 | — | | | | | | | | | | | | | | | | | | | | | |
| 2 | 30 | 50[b] | | | | | | | | | | | | | | | | | | | | |
| 3 | 17 | 03 | — | | | | | | | | | | | | | | | | | | | |
| 4 | 23 | 07 | 50 | — | | | | | | | | | | | | | | | | | | |
| 5 | 20 | 10 | 47 | 33 | — | | | | | | | | | | | | | | | | | |
| 6 | 40 | 37 | 23 | 20 | 30 | 36 | | | | | | | | | | | | | | | | |
| 7 | 33 | 00 | 50 | 40 | 63 | 23 | — | | | | | | | | | | | | | | | |
| 8 | 23 | 00 | 57 | 60 | 33 | 13 | 47 | — | | | | | | | | | | | | | | |
| 9 | 33 | 50 | 10 | 07 | 13 | 43 | 13 | 03 | 51 | | | | | | | | | | | | | |
| 10 | 13 | 40 | 00 | 03 | 07 | 37 | 03 | 00 | 33 | — | | | | | | | | | | | | |
| 11 | 17 | 07 | 37 | 27 | 37 | 13 | 30 | 43 | 03 | 00 | 44 | | | | | | | | | | | |
| 12 | 40 | 40 | 13 | 07 | 20 | 30 | 20 | 17 | 37 | 17 | 27 | — | | | | | | | | | | |
| 13 | 30 | 23 | 23 | 07 | 43 | 50 | 30 | 10 | 37 | 27 | 40 | 43 | — | | | | | | | | | |
| 14 | 20 | 23 | 23 | 13 | 33 | 27 | 27 | 17 | 23 | 13 | 57 | 40 | 63 | — | | | | | | | | |
| 15 | 53 | 23 | 20 | 20 | 27 | 40 | 30 | 13 | 40 | 17 | 17 | 33 | 40 | 30 | — | | | | | | | |
| 16 | 43 | 27 | 23 | 13 | 33 | 57 | 33 | 20 | 30 | 23 | 23 | 40 | 53 | 43 | 47 | — | | | | | | |
| 17 | 43 | 03 | 50 | 30 | 47 | 23 | 67 | 50 | 20 | 03 | 27 | 17 | 27 | 20 | 37 | 37 | — | | | | | |
| 18 | 37 | 20 | 20 | 07 | 27 | 43 | 23 | 07 | 33 | 13 | 13 | 37 | 40 | 30 | 43 | 43 | 30 | — | | | | |
| 19 | 23 | 10 | 40 | 17 | 53 | 27 | 47 | 23 | 17 | 07 | 33 | 33 | 53 | 50 | 27 | 43 | 33 | 27 | — | | | |
| 20 | 50 | 27 | 23 | 13 | 37 | 40 | 33 | 20 | 30 | 13 | 33 | 50 | 47 | 43 | 43 | 50 | 30 | 50 | 47 | — | | |
| 21 | 30 | 07 | 47 | 60 | 40 | 23 | 47 | 57 | 07 | 00 | 53 | 20 | 23 | 30 | 20 | 30 | 33 | 17 | 23 | 33 | — | |
| 22 | 27 | 10 | 63 | 43 | 33 | 23 | 37 | 70 | 07 | 00 | 53 | 20 | 20 | 27 | 20 | 23 | 43 | 17 | 20 | 27 | 60 | — |
| 23 | 37 | 03 | 40 | 53 | 53 | 17 | 73 | 50 | 10 | 00 | 27 | 13 | 13 | 13 | 23 | 20 | 57 | 17 | 23 | 20 | 40 | 30 |
| 24 | 30 | 07 | 43 | 27 | 53 | 27 | 47 | 40 | 13 | 00 | 47 | 27 | 47 | 43 | 23 | 33 | 30 | 20 | 63 | 40 | 40 | 33 |
| 25 | 33 | 03 | 33 | 17 | 47 | 33 | 57 | 23 | 10 | 07 | 27 | 23 | 30 | 27 | 30 | 27 | 33 | 23 | 33 | 33 | 30 | 23 |
| 26 | 13 | 13 | 23 | 10 | 27 | 17 | 23 | 13 | 10 | 00 | 50 | 43 | 47 | 60 | 10 | 30 | 13 | 23 | 40 | 33 | 27 | 27 |
| 27 | 33 | 03 | 50 | 53 | 63 | 23 | 70 | 60 | 10 | 00 | 33 | 17 | 20 | 23 | 30 | 27 | 50 | 20 | 40 | 33 | 53 | 40 |
| 28 | 17 | 03 | 63 | 43 | 47 | 27 | 50 | 57 | 07 | 00 | 43 | 13 | 23 | 20 | 23 | 50 | 30 | 27 | 30 | 17 | 23 | 33 |
| 29 | 37 | 03 | 47 | 53 | 43 | 23 | 57 | 60 | 17 | 00 | 20 | 07 | 13 | 07 | 33 | 27 | 63 | 27 | 30 | 17 | 30 | 37 |
| 30 | 27 | 00 | 43 | 50 | 33 | 13 | 50 | 67 | 07 | 03 | 17 | 00 | 07 | 03 | 13 | 13 | 57 | 07 | 17 | 03 | 30 | 37 |
| 31 | 10 | 07 | 37 | 20 | 53 | 10 | 40 | 27 | 03 | 00 | 53 | 20 | 40 | 53 | 13 | 23 | 30 | 13 | 53 | 33 | 30 | 33 |
| 32 | 33 | 07 | 57 | 57 | 53 | 23 | 70 | 63 | 13 | 03 | 27 | 13 | 13 | 13 | 27 | 27 | 60 | 20 | 30 | 20 | 43 | 40 |
| 33 | 40 | 13 | 57 | 43 | 50 | 40 | 60 | 40 | 23 | 03 | 30 | 13 | 27 | 20 | 40 | 33 | 60 | 30 | 37 | 23 | 37 | 37 |
| 34 | 40 | 13 | 47 | 33 | 67 | 33 | 63 | 43 | 23 | 10 | 43 | 40 | 50 | 43 | 37 | 40 | 47 | 30 | 60 | 47 | 40 | 33 |
| 35 | 43 | 03 | 50 | 47 | 53 | 27 | 73 | 50 | 13 | 00 | 23 | 03 | 10 | 03 | 27 | 23 | 60 | 20 | 30 | 20 | 40 | 37 |
| 36 | 43 | 03 | 40 | 23 | 40 | 17 | 53 | 33 | 17 | 03 | 37 | 27 | 33 | 23 | 47 | 40 | 57 | 37 | 43 | 53 | 33 | 33 |
| 37 | 20 | 10 | 30 | 23 | 33 | 17 | 37 | 27 | 17 | 07 | 53 | 40 | 53 | 70 | 23 | 37 | 30 | 23 | 57 | 40 | 37 | 33 |
| 38 | 20 | 10 | 47 | 30 | 60 | 20 | 60 | 37 | 20 | 03 | 37 | 33 | 47 | 43 | 27 | 40 | 43 | 30 | 60 | 40 | 33 | 30 |
| 39 | 37 | 03 | 40 | 47 | 53 | 20 | 70 | 50 | 13 | '03 | 27 | 17 | 23 | 30 | 30 | 33 | 53 | 20 | 37 | 23 | 43 | 30 |
| 40 | 30 | 00 | 37 | 57 | 37 | 13 | 53 | 60 | 10 | 00 | 23 | 10 | 10 | 13 | 20 | 20 | 43 | 10 | 20 | 10 | 43 | 30 |
| 41 | 20 | 10 | 27 | 20 | 33 | 17 | 30 | 27 | 13 | 03 | 50 | 43 | 47 | 57 | 23 | 37 | 30 | 27 | 50 | 47 | 23 | 27 |
| 42 | 37 | 10 | 47 | 40 | 57 | 30 | 70 | 40 | 20 | 00 | 33 | 17 | 27 | 20 | 30 | 27 | 63 | 23 | 40 | 30 | 33 | 37 |
| 43 | 37 | 07 | 43 | 33 | 53 | 27 | 60 | 30 | 17 | 00 | 20 | 10 | 17 | 10 | 27 | 23 | 37 | 30 | 30 | 23 | 33 | 30 |
| 44 | 30 | 27 | 50 | 43 | 43 | 27 | 43 | 47 | 20 | 07 | 47 | 47 | 43 | 47 | 23 | 40 | 33 | 20 | 47 | 40 | 43 | 50 |

balization of experience accompanied by the expression of emotion in the voice is found only in the Factor I client.

Time trends within the interview are not prominent for Factor I clients. There is a slight increase in responsiveness and emotional involvement and also some increase in externalizing and observing responses.

Factor II characterizations were based on Interviews 26, 41, 37, 3, 11, and 19. Here nearly all of the client responses are classified as participating. However, responsiveness, the direct expression of feeling is absent, and analysis of actions and ideas are present almost to the exclusion of analysis of feelings. In the involvement class, over two-thirds of the responses were classified as showing a low energy level, the voice sounding rather matter-of-factly serious and lacking in searching or exploring quality.

Sequence effects for Factor II show a definite trend for the involvement class, with an increase in focused or exploring

behavior during the hour. Externalizing responses all appear in the last third of the hour with a decrease in responses showing limited energy output. Clearly the clients typically leave the hour showing more energy output than at the beginning. The outstanding characteristic seems to be the low energy level of responses throughout most of the interview with some, but not much, increase as the hour progresses.

The eight interviews upon which the characterization of Factor III depends are 30, 23, 29, 35, 40, 4, 32, and 43. About half of the responses have a participating quality and about half have an observing quality.

In the level of expression class the client, in 90% of his responses, is discussing ideas or actions; he never expresses feelings directly. In those responses in which feelings are discussed in relation to self, the voice has an externalizing rather than an exploring quality. In fact, in most responses, the client sounds as

*Table 1 continued*

|    | 23 | 24 | 25 | 26 | 27 | 28 | 29 | 30 | 31 | 32 | 33 | 34 | 35 | 36 | 37 | 38 | 39 | 40 | 41 | 42 | 43 | 44 |
|----|----|----|----|----|----|----|----|----|----|----|----|----|----|----|----|----|----|----|----|----|----|----|
| 23 | 69 |    |    |    |    |    |    |    |    |    |    |    |    |    |    |    |    |    |    |    |    |    |
| 24 | 37 | —  |    |    |    |    |    |    |    |    |    |    |    |    |    |    |    |    |    |    |    |    |
| 25 | 53 | 50 | —  |    |    |    |    |    |    |    |    |    |    |    |    |    |    |    |    |    |    |    |
| 26 | 10 | 40 | 27 | 61 |    |    |    |    |    |    |    |    |    |    |    |    |    |    |    |    |    |    |
| 27 | 70 | 47 | 43 | 20 | —  |    |    |    |    |    |    |    |    |    |    |    |    |    |    |    |    |    |
| 28 | 43 | 50 | 47 | 30 | 53 | —  |    |    |    |    |    |    |    |    |    |    |    |    |    |    |    |    |
| 29 | 67 | 37 | 33 | 03 | 57 | 53 | 70 |    |    |    |    |    |    |    |    |    |    |    |    |    |    |    |
| 30 | 63 | 30 | 23 | 00 | 53 | 43 | 73 | 68 |    |    |    |    |    |    |    |    |    |    |    |    |    |    |
| 31 | 30 | 47 | 20 | 57 | 47 | 33 | 17 | 20 | —  |    |    |    |    |    |    |    |    |    |    |    |    |    |
| 32 | 70 | 43 | 40 | 13 | 70 | 57 | 70 | 63 | 30 | —  |    |    |    |    |    |    |    |    |    |    |    |    |
| 33 | 57 | 43 | 33 | 10 | 57 | 43 | 57 | 50 | 33 | 67 | —  |    |    |    |    |    |    |    |    |    |    |    |
| 34 | 50 | 63 | 57 | 37 | 60 | 53 | 40 | 30 | 40 | 53 | 47 | —  |    |    |    |    |    |    |    |    |    |    |
| 35 | 77 | 40 | 50 | 00 | 63 | 50 | 70 | 60 | 27 | 77 | 67 | 47 | —  |    |    |    |    |    |    |    |    |    |
| 36 | 40 | 47 | 40 | 20 | 43 | 47 | 40 | 23 | 30 | 40 | 37 | 50 | 43 | —  |    |    |    |    |    |    |    |    |
| 37 | 20 | 43 | 27 | 63 | 33 | 33 | 20 | 10 | 53 | 23 | 20 | 47 | 13 | 40 | 70 |    |    |    |    |    |    |    |
| 38 | 50 | 63 | 43 | 43 | 60 | 50 | 43 | 30 | 53 | 57 | 47 | 70 | 47 | 50 | 53 | —  |    |    |    |    |    |    |
| 39 | 67 | 43 | 37 | 23 | 70 | 50 | 63 | 60 | 40 | 70 | 53 | 50 | 60 | 37 | 37 | 50 | —  |    |    |    |    |    |
| 40 | 73 | 33 | 40 | 10 | 63 | 40 | 63 | 67 | 23 | 63 | 47 | 40 | 57 | 27 | 23 | 40 | 67 | 67 |    |    |    |    |
| 41 | 20 | 40 | 13 | 63 | 27 | 30 | 20 | 10 | 60 | 23 | 20 | 47 | 13 | 37 | 70 | 47 | 27 | 23 | 65 |    |    |    |
| 42 | 67 | 43 | 40 | 17 | 57 | 43 | 60 | 53 | 33 | 60 | 67 | 57 | 73 | 43 | 27 | 47 | 47 | 43 | 30 | —  |    |    |
| 43 | 60 | 33 | 43 | 10 | 50 | 37 | 50 | 40 | 33 | 53 | 57 | 40 | 67 | 33 | 23 | 40 | 47 | 47 | 23 | 67 | —  |    |
| 44 | 37 | 47 | 30 | 43 | 47 | 47 | 30 | 27 | 43 | 37 | 37 | 63 | 30 | 43 | 47 | 53 | 37 | 37 | 50 | 40 | 23 | —  |

[a] Decimal points are omitted.

[b] Communalities are given only for interviews used in groups.

TABLE 2

COSINES OF ANGLES OF VECTORS
OF THE SIMPLE BASIS[a]

|   | A | B | C |
|---|---|---|---|
| A | 1.00 | | |
| B | 24 | 1.00 | |
| C | 18 | 25 | 1.00 |

[a] Decimal points are omitted.

though he were dramatizing or making a speech (externalizing). This persistently externalizing voice quality is the outstanding characteristic of clients having high loadings on the third basis vector.

In comparing the clients whose interviews define the three factors, there are well-defined similarities and differences. The clients loaded on the first two factors are usually participants rather than observers of the scene. However, on Factor I, the client is talking about his feelings with high energy, while on Factor II the client is operating on a low energy level about his ideas or some activity in which he is participating. The voice of the Factor II client lacks force and does not have an exploring quality like that of the Factor I client. The Factor III client may have high energy output but he is externalizing; he is not a participant like the Factor I and Factor II clients.

In the level of expression class, the Factor II and Factor III clients seem very similar. Both exhibit practically no discussion of feelings and experiences. However, the Factor II client is communicating about his own actions or ideas, whereas the Factor III client is frequently talking about events completely outside himself. Moreover, the Factor III client has high energy output; the Factor II client a low one.

In summary, it might be said that the Factor I behavior was more optimal for therapy than the other types. The client's energy, openness of expression, and ability to directly communicate experience

seem to point toward the likelihood of favorable personal reorganization. Factor II behavior seems more questionable. On the one hand the client communicates

TABLE 3

MATRIX OF ORTHOGONAL APPROXIMATION
TO SIMPLE BASIS[a]

| Interviews | I | II | III |
|---|---|---|---|
| 1 | 48 | 14 | 35 |
| 2 | 69 | 06 | –04 |
| 3 | 11 | 32 | 46 |
| 4 | 10 | 18 | 62 |
| 5 | 20 | 35 | 45 |
| 6 | 56 | 13 | 14 |
| 7 | 10 | 30 | 67 |
| 8 | 00 | 28 | 69 |
| 9 | 72 | 05 | 07 |
| 10 | 56 | –03 | –03 |
| 11 | 03 | 63 | 19 |
| 12 | 49 | 45 | 00 |
| 13 | 49 | 56 | 03 |
| 14 | 28 | 78 | 00 |
| 15 | 49 | 16 | 22 |
| 16 | 52 | 34 | 16 |
| 17 | 16 | 24 | 63 |
| 18 | 46 | 22 | 12 |
| 19 | 19 | 55 | 20 |
| 20 | 44 | 45 | 07 |
| 21 | 11 | 40 | 38 |
| 22 | 13 | 41 | 34 |
| 23 | 07 | 15 | 81 |
| 24 | 15 | 50 | 35 |
| 25 | 18 | 24 | 42 |
| 26 | 12 | 78 | –03 |
| 27 | 10 | 28 | 70 |
| 28 | 10 | 38 | 50 |
| 29 | 15 | 10 | 82 |
| 30 | 04 | 02 | 83 |
| 31 | 01 | 72 | 19 |
| 32 | 14 | 18 | 79 |
| 33 | 32 | 16 | 60 |
| 34 | 27 | 50 | 41 |
| 35 | 15 | 05 | 79 |
| 36 | 12 | 39 | 34 |
| 37 | 12 | 82 | 12 |
| 38 | 16 | 53 | 42 |
| 39 | 10 | 28 | 75 |
| 40 | 04 | 16 | 81 |
| 41 | 10 | 80 | 12 |
| 42 | 23 | 25 | 64 |
| 43 | 19 | 16 | 57 |
| 44 | 29 | 55 | 31 |
| LV | 43 | 59 | 66 |

[a] Decimal points have been omitted.

relevant material in a somewhat expressive way, but some of the important ingredients of expressiveness seem to be missing. Factor III behavior by contrast seems more unequivocal. The self-avoidant, nonparticipating, describing, verbal behavior with its externalizing quality, seems unlikely to be associated with favorable outcomes in therapy. Thus the type of behavior shown by the factorial structure seems to have clear implications for therapeutic outcome.

In order to check the plausibility of the inferences drawn from the factorial structure, the external productivity of the classification system was checked by way of the factorial structure. Relationships of the factor loadings to the following external indices were found:

a. Therapist experience
b. Success rating by therapist
c. Outcome rating by client
d. Taylor Anxiety Scale
e. Barron Ego Strength Scale

The findings may be summarized as follows:

*Factor I*

1. Excluding attrition cases, success-rated cases (ratings of 6 or above) tended to be higher on Factor I for the early in therapy interviews when compared with the nonsuccess cases ($U$ test, .05 level).

2. The late interviews of success-rated cases tended to be higher on Factor I than for nonsuccess-rated cases ($U$ test, .025 level).

3. The early interviews having loadings of .40 or more on Factor I were success-rated cases.

4. Of the seven failure-rated (ratings of 4 or below) cases, six had loadings of .20 or less on Factor I ($U$ test, .062 level). The seventh case had a loading greater than .20 early in therapy, but the loading had decreased somewhat at the end of therapy.

5. Clients of therapists with two or more years of experience tended to have higher loadings on Factor I than on Factor III for both early and late interviews ($U$ test, .05 level) than did the clients of less experienced therapists. The same comparison between Factor I and Factor II did not yield significant results.

6. Client evaluation of outcome of therapy was not significantly related to loading of early interviews on Factor I ($\rho = .05$, N.S.).

7. Client evaluation of outcome of therapy was not significantly related to loading of late interviews on Factor I

TABLE 4

FREQUENCY OF RESPONSE FOR EACH MAIN CLIENT CLASS

| Interview section | Factor | | | | | | | | |
|---|---|---|---|---|---|---|---|---|---|
| | I | | | II | | | III | | |
| | A | B | C | A | B | C | A | B | C |
| Quality of Participation | | | | | | | | | |
| Participating | 10 | 9 | 10 | 9 | 8 | 10 | 6 | 5 | 6 |
| Observing | 0 | 1 | 0 | 1 | 2 | 0 | 4 | 5 | 4 |
| Level of Expression | | | | | | | | | |
| Responsiveness | 2 | 3 | 2 | 0 | 0 | 0 | 0 | 0 | 0 |
| Analysis of feeling | 5 | 5 | 6 | 1 | 1 | 1 | 1 | 1 | 1 |
| Analysis of action | 3 | 2 | 2 | 9 | 9 | 9 | 9 | 9 | 9 |
| Voice Quality | | | | | | | | | |
| Emotional | 1 | 3 | 2 | 0 | 0 | 0 | 0 | 0 | 0 |
| Focused | 9 | 5 | 7 | 1 | 2 | 3 | 0 | 0 | 0 |
| Externalizing | 0 | 2 | 1 | 0 | 0 | 3 | 9 | 9 | 10 |
| Limited | 0 | 0 | 0 | 9 | 8 | 4 | 1 | 1 | 0 |

($\rho = .27$, .05 level $= .38$). Rank correlation between correlations of $Q$ sorts (self-sort and ideal common factor) was not significantly related to loading on Factor I for early and late interviews although in the expected direction early in therapy ($-.28$) and although the change was in the expected direction.

8. Change in favorable self-description as revealed by correlations between self $Q$ sorts before and after therapy had significant rank order correlations, with rank of loading on Factor I for early but not for late interviews ($\rho = .46$ and .30, respectively, .05 level $= .38$).

9. Decrease in anxiety score on the Taylor Anxiety Scale had a significant rank correlation with rank of loading on early Factor I interviews but not for late Factor I interviews, ($\rho = .47$ and .13 respectively).

10. For clients with pure loadings on Factor I and pure loadings on Factor III, the difference between means on the Barron score was significant in favor of the Factor I clients ($U$ test, significance level $= .033$). The comparison between Factor I and Factor II clients did not yield significant results.

Although some of the results on Factor I are not in the expected direction, the positive results are consistent with the factor characterization. No unexpected findings in the sense of the opposite of expectation occurred. It can be said, therefore, that the characterization of Factor I is consistent with the definite findings and not inconsistent with the nondefinite findings. To this extent the characterization of Factor I is supported by data extrinsic to the classification system used.

*Factor II*

1. In comparing ranks of loadings on late and early interviews of the clients, no significant difference between early and late interviews was found (Wilcoxon test).

2. When loadings of the late interviews of clients loaded on Factor II were compared on the basis of success ratings, partially successful (ratings of 5) against all other ratings, the combined success and failure ratings, it was found that the mean rank of the clients with ratings of 5 was higher than the mean for clients with other ratings ($U$ test, significance level $= .025$). When the clients with ratings of 5 were compared separately with those clients whose ratings were above 5 and below 5 respectively, the mean differences were still significant at the .025 and the .055 levels, respectively. Thus Factor II seems to be characteristic of late interviews of partially successful cases.

3. Therapist experience was not related to factor loadings on Factor II.

4. Rank order correlation of loading on Factor II with client evaluation of outcome was .42 and .18 for early and late interviews respectively. The first correlation is significant at the .05 level.

5. Rank order correlation between correlations of $Q$ sorts on self and the ideal factor were not significant for early or late interviews.

6. Rank order correlations between favorable change on pretherapy and posttherapy self $Q$ sorts for early and late interviews were not significant and in fact were practically zero.

7. Rank order correlations between loadings on Factor II and change in Taylor Anxiety score, pretherapy Taylor score and posttherapy Taylor score were not significant.

8. Rank order correlations between loadings on Factor II and change in Barron Ego Strength score, pretherapy Ego-Strength score, and posttherapy ego strength score were not significant.

*Factor III*

1. Early interviews of completed failure cases were higher on Factor III than early interviews of success cases ($U$ test significance level $= .05$).

2. Late interviews of failure cases were higher on Factor III than late interviews of other cases (*U* test significance level = .01).

3. Success cases had lower loadings on Factor III late in therapy than they had early in therapy (Wilcoxon test, significance level = .025).

4. All failure-rated cases had substantial loadings on Factor III for their late interviews. The lowest loading was .34, the remaining six had loadings greater than .40.

5. Late interviews of clients having experienced therapists had lower loadings on Factor III than late interviews of clients having the less experienced therapists (*U* test, significance level = .025). This is the opposite of the finding for Factor I.

6. Rank order correlation between client evaluation of outcome and rank of loading on Factor III was −.54 for early interviews and −.31 for late interviews. The first correlation is significant at the .05 level; the second, not.

7. Rank correlation between loading on Factor III and correlation between self *Q* sorts and ideal factor was not significant.

8. Rank of loading on Factor III was not correlated significantly with rank of pretherapy score, posttherapy score, or change in score on the Taylor Anxiety Scale for early and late interviews.

9. The rank correlation between loadings on Factor III for late interviews and Barron Ego-Strength score was −.56. This is significant at the .01 level. For the early interviews the correlation was not significant.

The findings on the various measures for the three factors found might be summarized as follows:

1. Clients showing Factor I behavior early in therapy were more likely to be rated as success than as failure cases. It is even more likely when the Factor I behavior appears late in therapy. When Factor II behavior appears early in therapy it could not be predicted how the case would turn out. Clients at all levels of success, therapist experience, and length of case appear in Factor II early in therapy. However, by the end of therapy, Factor II behavior is characteristic only of partially successful cases. Clients with Factor III behavior early in therapy tend to be failure cases. This relationship holds for late therapy cases. However, two long success-rated cases both score on Factor III and had high loadings on it at the end of therapy. These cases had therapists in the less experienced group.

2. Clients on Factor I tended to have more experienced therapists; on Factor III, less experienced. Experience was not related to Factor II.

3. Client evaluation of outcome of therapy is related positively to Factor II (early interviews only) and negatively to Factor III (early interviews only). It is not related to Factor I.

4. Correlations of self *Q* sorts with an ideal factor derived from another sample of clients were not related to magnitude of factor loadings on Factors I, II, and III.

5. Favorable change in self-description as assessed by correlations between pretherapy and posttherapy self *Q* sorts was correlated positively with magnitude of loading on Factor I (early interviews only). Favorable change was not significantly related to magnitude of loading on Factors II and III.

6. Decrease in anxiety as measured by change in score from pretherapy to posttherapy was positively correlated with magnitude of loading on Factor I (early interviews only). Decrease of anxiety and level of anxiety was not related to size of loadings on Factors II and III.

7. Ego strength, measured by the Barron scale at posttherapy was positively correlated with Factor I behavior (late interviews only) and negatively with Factor III behavior (late interviews

only). Ego-strength change was not significantly correlated with loadings on any factor. However, the difference between means of Ego-strength scores of clients pure on Factors I and III was significant at the .033 level, with the Factor I clients having the higher Ego-strength score.

In comparing the factors each with the other, it seems that the factors represent classes of behavior which can be arranged on a continuum of expressiveness of linguistic behavior in the Order I, II, III and that the placement of clients on the continuum is related to outcome of therapy from the vantage point of the therapist, of the client, and of test instruments which are essentially diagnostic in nature. The degree of expressiveness is also related to therapist experience which suggests, not so much that it is important to control the experience variable in the study of therapy, but that the performance of the therapist is the variable that should be experimentally controlled. Our findings allow us to state only that relationships exist, not that they are causal. It is our hypothesis, nonetheless, that therapist expressiveness represents a set of causal influences affecting the process and outcome of therapy and that the more experienced therapists are more expressive than the less experienced. It should be noted, however, that expressiveness is a complex variable. For example, as the classification system shows, there are several ways in which a Factor I type client might be expressive, and thus distinctively different kinds of behavior might yield the same score on an expressiveness continuum. Whether these different expressive modes giving the same score might have the same effect, we do not know. The point, however, is that we have empirical leverage on the problem of defining a variable, and the information at hand is that the variable might be very complex.

At the time of writing, analysis of the therapists' responses in relation to the responses of the clients studied has not been completed. However, the dimensionality of the therapists' responses, analyzed in the same fashion as those of the clients, has been found to be four. Data on three main classes of the therapist classification system have been studied in relation to the factor structure of the client's behavior. These therapists' classes are Categories 3, 1, and 2 of the classification system previously described in the section on Therapist Classification System.

Table 5 shows the rank order correlations between combined frequencies of the subclasses of Therapist Classes 3, 1, and 2 judged to be optimal for therapy, and the magnitude of loading on Client Factor I, II, and III for early and late interviews considered separately. A correlation of .38 and above is significant at the .05 level.

Table 5 shows rather clearly that the rank of the frequency of Categories 3, 1, and 2 of therapist responses is related positively to the rank of loading on Client Factor I. Thus the therapist behavior judged to be optimal tends to be associated with client behavior judged to be optimal. Since the therapists of clients loading high on Factor I tend to be among the more experienced, it seems we can say with a fair degree of confidence that the more experienced therapists tend to exhibit more of the behavior judged to be optimal, although the exact relationship has not yet been determined. The relationships are higher for the early interviews; why this should be is not apparent, although different alternatives could be advanced.

On turning to consideration of Client Factor II, it is seen that the relationship between Factor II and therapist response is negative for Classes 3 and 1 and near zero for Category 2. It appears that with the passage of time, therapists with Factor II clients exhibit relatively more of the optimal responses, particularly in the subcategories of Category 1. However, this interpretation must be qualified to an unknown degree because *some* clients move from Factors I and III early in therapy to Factor II late in therapy.

For Factor III the relationship with frequency of optimal therapist responses is negative for therapist Categories 3 and 2. For Category 1 the relationships are not significant although very nearly so late in therapy. For Categories 1 and 3, the magnitude of the relationship increases as therapy goes on. At the end of therapy, optimal therapist responses to Factor III clients tend to decrease. Since Factor III clients tend to be unsuccessful cases and since their therapists tend to be relatively inexperienced, it may be that in-therapy behavior of Factor III clients militates against the appearance of optimal responses in their therapists. This is especially suggested by the results on therapist Category 2, voice quality, where the correlations are high negative.

The results of the analysis of client and therapist responses, as viewed through the perspectives of the classification systems employed, suggest that there are causal relationships between client expressiveness, therapist expressiveness, the process of psychotherapy, and the outcomes of psychotherapy. We are of the opinion that after the therapist responses have been analyzed in detail and after the dyads of client-therapist responses have been analyzed, we will be traveling on two roads simultaneously. One road will, we think, lead us to increasingly precise definitions of expressiveness variables in behavioral terms. The other will lead us to experimental modification of the therapy hour. As a matter of fact, we already have some ideas on how to modify therapy hours and have put some of them into effect with results which we find to be provocative.

What we have tried to present to this conference is a viewpoint on naturalistic research which has led us quite naturally to a mathematical counterpart of our intuitive ideas. The mathematical model results in behavior classes or classes of individuals derived from behavior. We regard these classes of behavior or of individuals as being the possible precursors of meaningful variables related to client and therapist behavior and as being

TABLE 5

RANK ORDER CORRELATIONS

(Therapist Response Categories and Client Factor Loadings For Early Therapy and Late Therapy Interviews[a])

| Therapist Classes | | 3 | | 1 | | 2 | |
|---|---|---|---|---|---|---|---|
| Client Factor | | E | L | E | L | E | L |
| Factor I | E | 70 | | 57 | | 64 | |
| | L | | 40 | | 33 | | 60 |
| Factor II | E | −31 | | −68 | | 14 | |
| | L | | −28 | | −07 | | 04 |
| Factor III | E | −27 | | 05 | | −76 | |
| | L | | −40 | | −37 | | −60 |

[a] Decimal points are omitted.

promising precursors when external productivity of the classification system has been demonstrated. Our aim in presenting a specimen analysis has been to show that naturalistic investigation can be objective, can be operational, and can lead to clinically meaningful results. The specimen investigation presented has not been a complete one. A complete investigation would include the isolation of classes of clients and classes of therapists based on separate analyses of their behaviors, and classes based on client-therapist dyads for both row and column ("trait" and "type") analyses of the data of classification arranged in the standard form of the data matrix S.

BIBLIOGRAPHY

Arrow, K. J. *Social choice and individual values.* New York: Wiley, 1951.

Auld, F. J., Jr., & Murray, E. J. Content-analysis studies of psychotherapy. *Psychol. Bull.*, 1950, **52**, 378-395.

Berelson, B. *Content analysis in communication research.* Glencoe, Ill.: Free Press, 1952.

Brice, N. The facilitation and obstruction of progress in psychotherapy: A statistical analysis of a single case. Unpublished doctoral dissertation, University of Chicago, 1957.

Butler, J. M. Empty research proposal: Category analysis. University of Chicago Counseling Center Staff Paper, 1951.

Butler, J. M. Assessing psychotherapeutic protocols with context coefficients. *J. clin. Psychol.*, 1952, **8**.

Butler, J. M. Measuring the effectiveness of counseling and psychotherapy. *Personnel Guid. J.*, 1953, **32**, 88-92.

Butler, J. M. The analysis of successive sets of behavior data. *Univer. Chicago Counseling Center Discussion Paper, (Library)*, 1955, **1**, 1.

Butler, J. M. On the structure of groups and institutions. *Univer. of Chicago Counseling Center Discussion Paper, (Library)*, 1956, **2**, 13.

Butler, J. M. Client-centered therapy. In L. Abt & D. Brower (Eds.), *Clinical psychology III*. New York: Grune & Stratton, 1959, in press. (a)

Butler, J. M. Introduction to successive set analysis. *Univer. of Chicago Counseling Center Discussion Papers, (Library)*, 1959, **5**, 16. (b)

Butler, J. M. An orthogonalization computing method for successive set analysis. *Univer. of Chicago Counseling Center Discussion Paper, (Library)*, 1959, **6**, 5. (c)

Butler, J. M. Orthogonalization processes for oblique simple structures. *Univer. of Chicago Counseling Center Discussion Papers, (Library)*, 1959, **5**, 5. (d)

Butler, J. M., & Rice, Laura. Self-actualization, new experience, and psychotherapy, *Univer. of Chicago Counseling Center Discussion Papers, (Library)*, 1960, **6**, 12.

Butler, J. M., & Wagstaff, Alice. A standard form for classification systems in successive set analysis. *Univer. of Chicago Counseling Center Discussion Papers, (Library)*, 1959, **5**, 7.

Butler, J. M., Wagstaff, Alice, Rice, Laura, & Counts, Sarah. Naturalistic observation and research. *Univer. of Chicago Counseling Center Discussion Papers, (Library)*, 1960, **6**, 17.

Cartwright, D. S., Kirtner, W., & Fox, S. An operator-display analysis of psychotherapy. *Univer. of Chicago Counseling Center Discussion Papers, (Library)*, 1956, **2**, 17.

Coombs, C. H. A theory of data. *Psychol. Rev.*, 1960, **67**, 143-159.

Coombs, C. H., & Kao, R. C. Non-metric factor analysis. *Univer. of Michigan Eng. Res. Inst. Bull.*, 1955, No. 38.

Coombs, C. H., Raiffa, H., & Thrall, R. M. Some views on mathematical models and measurement theory. *Psychol. Rev.*, 1954, **61**, 132-144.

Dollard, J., & Mowrer, O. H. A method of measuring tension in written documents. *J. abnorm. soc. Psychol.*, 1947, **42**, 3-32.

Fox, Margaret. A quantitative study of changes in verbal behavior occurring in client-centered counseling. Unpublished doctoral dissertation, University of Chicago, 1951.

Gibson, W. A. Application of the mathematics of multiple factor analysis to problems of latent structure analysis. Unpublished doctoral dissertation, University of Chicago, 1951.

Gibson, W. A. Orthogonal and oblique simple structures. *Psychometrika*, 1952, **17**, 317-323.

Green, B. F. The orthogonal approximation of an oblique structure in factor analysis. *Psychometrika*, 1952, **17**, 429-440.

Green, B. F. A general solution for the latent class model of latent structure analysis. *Psychometrika*, 1953, **16**, 151-166.

Guttman, L. The quantification of a class of atrributes: A theory and method of scale construction. In P. Horst (Ed.), *The prediction of personal adjustment*. New York: Social Science Research Council, 1941.

Holzinger, K. J., & Harman, H. *Factor analysis*. Chicago: Univer. Chicago Press, 1943.

Hood, W. C., & Koopmans, T. C. (Eds.), *Studies in econometric method*. New York: Wiley, 1953.

Koopmans, T. C. Identification problems in latent structure analysis. *Cowles Commission Discussion Paper*, 1951.

Lasswell, H. D. A provisional classification of symbol data. *Psychiatry*, 1938, **1**, 197-204.

Lasswell, H. D., Leites, N., et al. (Eds.), *Language of politics*. New York: Stewart, 1949.

Lazarsfeld, P. *Mathematical thinking in the social sciences*. Glencoe, Ill.: Free Press, 1957.

Rice, Laura, Wagstaff, Alice, & Butler, J. M. Successive set project, Part I: Preliminary analysis of data from one dimension of client category system. *Univer. of Chicago Counseling Center Discussion Paper, (Library)*, 1959, **5**, 4.

Simmel, Marianne, & Counts, Sarah. Some stable response determinants of perception, thinking, and learning: A study based on the analysis of a single test. *Genet. Psychol. Monogr.*, 1957, **56**, 3-157.

Simon, H. A. Logic of causal relations. *Cowles Commission Discussion Papers*. New series No. 70, 1952.

Simon, H. A. Causal ordering and identifiability. In W. Hood & T. Koopmans (Eds.), *Studies in econometric method*. New York: Wiley, 1953.

Tate, F. K. A rank pattern analysis of verbal behavior in client-centered psychotherapy. Unpublished doctoral dissertation, University of Chicago, 1953.

Thurstone, L. L. *Multiple factor analysis*. Chicago: Univer. Chicago Press, 1947.

Wagstaff, Alice, & Butler, J. M. A summary matrix for successive set analysis. *Univer. of Chicago Counseling Center Discussion Papers, (Library)*, 1959, **5**, 9.

Wagstaff, Alice. Successive set analysis of verbal styles in psychotherapy. Unpublished doctoral dissertation, University of Chicago, 1959.

White, R. K. Black boy: A value analysis. *J. abnorm. soc. Psychol.*, 1947, **42**, 440-461.

Yule, G. U., & Kendall, M. G. *An introduction to the theory of statistics*. (13th ed.) London: Griffin, 1953.

# Character Style and Anxiety Tolerance: A Study in Intrapsychic Change[1]

RICHARD S. SIEGAL, PH.D. AND IRWIN C. ROSEN, PH.D.

The gradually unfolding nature of the psychotherapeutic and psychoanalytic process looked at from one highly restricted point of view can be understood as the inexorable disclosure by the patient of secrets; secrets he keeps from himself as well as from others by means of the complex, intricate, and hidden methods whose understanding forms the stock in trade of the psychotherapist. Research into the processes and outcomes of psychotherapy or into any other natural or artificial phenomena, can also be looked at as a struggle on the part of the researcher to find ways which make it possible for the objects of his research to disclose their secrets. Just as the psychotherapist harbors within himself secret thoughts and feelings with regard to his patient, his relationship to the patient, and the process they are engaging in, all of which are traditionally viewed under the heading of countertransference, so the researcher keeps hidden, both from himself and his scientific

public, ideas and feelings in regard to the research enterprise. The influence upon the treatment of the process and progress notes the therapist prepares and the case presentations he agrees to participate in is commonly acknowledged to be significant (Ekstein & Wallerstein, 1958).

The foregoing considerations are offered by way of preparation for our disclosure of the secret that the invitation to participate in this conference is playing a role in the research endeavor in which we are engaged. It offers us the opportunity to begin to explore and to share with you a way of ordering the almost overwhelming abundance of data we have collected.

We have had, from the inception of the data gathering, predetermined ways of handling our data which we hope will compel them to yield up some of their hidden implications. All of this has been previously described (Wallerstein, Robbins, Sargent, & Luborsky, 1956) and we shall presume your familiarity with it. Briefly stated, our project has already arrived at two ways of treating the data which comprise separate and independent research approaches: (a) the Prediction Study, in which clinicians predict the course and outcome of psychotherapy on the basis of their initial pretherapy examinations; the predictions then being formalized and the precise nature of the evidence set down in advance for the verification or invalidation of such predictions; and (b) the Paired Comparisons Study, which is designed to enable us to arrive at interindividual comparisons of patients, of psychotherapeutic modalities,

[1] The work of the Psychotherapy Project of The Menninger Foundation has been generously supported, initially by the Foundations' Fund for Research in Psychiatry, and subsequently by the Ford Foundation.

This report represents, we feel, a closer than usual collaboration. Our ideas are the product of truly mutual participation in a shared effort.

We wish to acknowledge the assistance of Frederick Hacker, M.D., and René Spitz, M.D. Both men generously gave us time to discuss with them the ideas embodied in this paper.

We are especially indebted to Robert Wallerstein, M.D., co-chairman of our project, for his consistent encouragement and help in the task of translating a clinical impression (shared by himself) concerning the significance of anxiety tolerance, into the form and structure of the present paper.

and of life-situational contexts. Brief reflection on the nature of these two ways of organizing our data will reveal something of their clinical "naturalness." The therapist beginning treatment with his patient implicitly makes predictions and sets before himself anticipations as his growing understanding of his patient becomes the guide to future therapeutic interventions and hoped-for outcomes. Thus, a prediction study (even with the rigorous rules of evidence imposed by our design) is a congenial research extension of an essentially clinical attitude. Similarly, the method of paired comparisons represents, in a more rigorous and specific way, a manner of thinking that clinicians feel is also compatible with their predetermined ways of organizing their thoughts. Again, for example, the clinician considering his new patient will often compare him with others who are in some ways similar to and in other ways different from this individual. Moreover, he will do this with respect to certain selected variables important to his theoretical framework. Indeed, this implicit and not necessarily conscious sifting through of his previous experiences with other patients forms, of course, one method by which the clinician brings to bear upon the current clinical situation his accumulated skill and knowledge.

In both methods, however, the focus of the clinician's attention remains on the individual patient, even though both methods can be extended in a research design to yield, with appropriate statistical treatment, clinically meaningful groupings of patients.

There is, however, another step to be taken, and one which is approached by the clinician with considerable reluctance. Influenced both by personal preference and training to direct his attention to the individual patient, the clinician approaches with wariness the problem of assigning individuals to groups on the

basis of common characteristics. He has learned to be skeptical of diagnostic labels; he has become mistrustful of global classifications of individuals into groups like "improved and unimproved" at the termination of treatment; he recognizes the wide range of individual difference that characterizes most clinically derived groupings. We thus share with you another secret, our own initial reluctance, since we are clinicians as well as researchers, to make statements about groups rather than about individual patients in our project. At the same time, we view the present paper as a way of exploring the possibility of utilizing one of our selected patient variables, anxiety tolerance, and attempting to see how far one can go in making clinically meaningful statements about groups of patients classified according to change in this one dimension of intrapsychic functioning.

We should like next to touch upon the way in which psychological tests are used in our project. While we cannot in this paper give any complete account of our psychological test procedures and rationale, we should emphasize that the test battery is in all respects identical with that used in our day-to-day clinical work at The Menninger Foundation. We include the Wechsler-Bellevue, Rorschach, Word Association, Thematic Apperception Test, and a test of concept formation. Detailed explications of our procedures and of our rationale for test interpretation have been set forth elsewhere (Ehrenreich & Siegal, 1958; Siegal & Ehrenreich, 1959; Siegal, Rosen, & Ehrenreich, 1960).

As originally conceived, the Psychological Test Study of our project patients was to be an independent study parallel with the nontest, "clinical" study of the patient and the therapy. The tests were to be kept independent of other sources of information. That is, on the basis solely of psychological test data and inferences derived from these, we anticipated that we too would utilize the methods of the Prediction Study and the methods of the Paired Comparisons Study. For various reasons, this plan will probably not prove feasible. We have neither the manpower nor the independence from other lines of investigation to carry this through (although we probably shall be able to complete a prediction study of a somewhat more limited kind than the project as a whole is conducting). True to the clinical spirit of our research, our psychiatric and psychological colleagues, attempting to assess intrapsychic factors within the patient and to predict course and outcome of psychotherapy, have been unwilling to do so without the benefit of psychological test reports. To separate testing and clinical psychiatric investigation in our setting would be clinically "unnatural." This has necessitated making test-retest comparisons on terminated patients, in some cases before we have been able to make independent predictions of psychotherapy course and outcome. It is our plan, if time permits, to make predictions on some of the patients before termination occurs, at a point at which we still know nothing about the psychotherapy. We have then, as data, 18 test-retest reports on patients who have currently come to termination. (There are 42 patients in the study of whom 26 have terminated psychotherapy.) These reports vary in the amount of time which has been devoted to their preparation and in the explicitness and faithfulness with which they follow the outline of variables assessed at three points in time, initial, termination, and follow-up (Wallerstein et al., 1956). Some of them follow this form exactly, assessing each of the variables we feel we can assess from psychological tests alone; and some, on the other hand, are much briefer attempts to summarize the significant changes in the psychological test picture referring explicitly to some but not all of the variables.

We are utilizing the occasion for this paper to begin the search for clinical ways

of examining the data which will make it possible to arrive at some more or less generalizable understanding of our cases. We started, then, simply by inspecting the data at our disposal at this stage of the research. And here we must introduce the notion that we consider our data to be the inferences drawn from the psychological test protocols. Neither the patients' responses nor the scores we attach to these responses are the object of our research scrutiny. This is, we realize, rather different from the usual approach to psychological test-retest studies in psychotherapy research. It corresponds to Sargent's idea (1961) explicitly accepted and utilized by the project, that the essential data of the project as a whole are not the observations made by the psychiatrist or social worker or psychologist who examines the patient, but rather the inferences and predictions he arrives at after he has gone through the process of clinical inference. We believe this is the hardheaded, realistic approach, since it is evident and has been pointed out many times that observation is inevitably selective and the very act of observing includes the drawing of inferences. Of course, this point is arguable, and it is not our intention here to introduce considerations of epistemological theory. We are convinced, however, that before one can profitably utilize test responses and scores he must first assign meaning to them in accord with the theory of personality to which he is committed. The same score, the same response, the same verbalization, the same percept represents and conveys different meanings depending on the personality, the test context in which it appears, and the theoretical framework within which these data are conceptualized. The same intrapsychic process or entity or variable manifests itself in different ways in different patients. Anxiety, or ego strength, or insight, or psychological-mindedness shows in tests in a multiplicity of ways. Our preference is not to look for some particular test indication of insight, for example, but rather to make whatever inferences we can about the intrapsychic variable we are interested in and to compare this assessment with our assessment of the same variable for some other individual. We feel we may compare patients in terms of intrapsychic variables much more accurately, readily, and meaningfully than we can in terms of test responses or test scores. In beginning to examine our data, then, we start with the inferences we have drawn, as stated in the test-retest reports.

Turning to these in preparation for writing this paper it became evident to us that we might have commented on changes in insight in one patient in much greater detail than in another, upon changes in the way guilt manifests itself in one patient but not in another, etc. This, as we explained in our introduction, is a product of the necessity to integrate our test studies with the other investigative approaches to the patient. One variable, however, upon which we commented in each case was anxiety tolerance. Extracting from each report those statements relevant to the variable anxiety tolerance, we became aware of the importance of this concept in our thinking. We began to notice the explicit and implicit connotations of high or low anxiety tolerance in our clinical practice as well as our research reports. We began to think about the concept, its meaning, its history, its value, its unclarities. We began to wonder: What does it mean if we say the patient's anxiety tolerance has increased or decreased? How is it possible to increase anxiety tolerance? What shifts, or changes or reorganizations in personality can bring this about?

We propose to examine the changes which have taken place from pretherapy to posttherapy studies of 18 patients as reflected in psychological tests, from the restricted and limited point of view of anxiety tolerance. How can we concep-

tualize changes in anxiety tolerance, and how far will this single concept take us in understanding what has changed within the patient and how this change has come about?

Anxiety tolerance was defined for the project by Wallerstein and Robbins (Wallerstein et al., 1956) as "the capacity to experience anxiety without having to act to discharge it." They went on to say, "this can be judged in many ways; by reactions to discussions of painful problems, by observations of levels of overt anxiety, its height, duration, and the pressure to rapid and impulsive discharge; nature of behavioral, internal psychologic, and of somatic patterns of discharge." This definition, which accurately reflects our current clinical usage, leads to certain theoretical and practical difficulties. It seems to us to limit unduly the application of the construct anxiety tolerance.

The operative word in restricting its range of application is "act." Act can be variously defined. It seems to us, however, that the connotations of the term in this definition involve only a certain kind of "acting." Consider, for example, a well-compensated, tightly organized obsessive-compulsive neurotic who successfully maintains himself without extreme or disabling conscious anxiety through continual yielding to internal demands that he perform compulsive acts of a mild sort. Here is an individual who *acts* in order to free himself from anxiety or reduce the quantity of anxiety he experiences. Yet, to describe this man as lacking in anxiety tolerance would not be consistent with the clinical probability that were he to be deprived of the opportunity to carry through his compulsive rituals, he would probably experience a significant increase in the amount and intensity of manifest anxiety without any increased tendency to "act." Under such circumstances we would be dealing with a partially decompensated obsessive-compulsive neurotic experiencing more manifest anxiety, who would probably tend to become more ruminative, circumstantial, obsessional, and indecisive. In this clinically plausible hypothetical case the intensity of experienced anxiety would have increased while the individual's tendency *to act* to diminish the anxiety would have decreased. Does this situation reflect a rise in anxiety tolerance?

If the same individual continues to decompensate, his characterological defense patterns will be used more vigorously, more frequently, more arbitrarily, and with diminishing effectiveness in reducing the impact and intensity of anxiety. His thinking may display more and more primary process characteristics and, in short, he may become near psychotic or psychotic. While the course of the decompensation and its results in symptomatology and behavior are not wholly predictable, one possible course is towards increased ideational activity which may be more and more autistic, perhaps paranoid or perhaps simply overideational. No significant increase in the tendency to dispel anxiety via action need occur because the preferred obsessive-compulsive characterological modes of defense and control rely heavily upon binding anxiety in ideational activity. Even with increasingly ineffective ideational binding of anxiety, the characterological tendency to inhibit motor discharge may remain more or less operative. There is no intent here to disregard the clinical reality that the tendency to act to reduce anxiety is heightened in some cases. The course of decompensation obviously differs among individuals. It is sufficient to make our point that there *are* individuals who decompensate without an increasing tendency to discharge anxiety through action. Are we to characterize anxiety tolerance as having increased in the course of a decompensation to a more regressed level of thinking and behaving?

This line of thought made it increasingly clear to us that the kind of action referred to in the project's definition of anxiety tolerance is the kind loosely characterized as arising from an alloplastic orientation, a disposition to discharge anxiety-provoking tension, or tendency to "act out." (This latter is perhaps the most loosely used technical term in the clinical vocabulary.) It makes perfectly good sense and is in clear accord with our everyday clinical usage to characterize an individual who tends to prevent himself from experiencing anxiety by running away, drinking, avoiding anxiety-arousing situations, and so on, as one in whom anxiety tolerance is low. This is the limited area of application of the concept of anxiety tolerance as heretofore defined.

One of the undesirable concomitants of limiting the use of the term in this way is that it violates one's feeling that organizing concepts should apply to the whole range of phenomena involved. The concept of physiological tolerance, the tolerance of the organism for a certain drug, let us say, is one which does apply to a whole range of phenomena and individuals.

In doing an experiment on the tolerance of rats for a given drug, one might observe that rats of a certain strain, or rats reared under certain conditions, or rats of a certain color, differ in their tolerance for the drug. One might even find that intolerance for the drug is manifest in differing symptoms depending on the size or color or physical condition of the laboratory animal. Even so, the concept of physiological tolerance applies equally to all of the laboratory animals.

How does the concept anxiety tolerance apply to autoplastically oriented individuals, for example, particularly those who are psychotic?

Let us examine, before we proceed further, the meaning of alloplasticity and its converse, autoplasticity. The variable allo-plasticity was defined for our project by Wallerstein and Robbins (1956) as, "The nature and extent of the expression of the illness on the environment and the *deleterious* consequences to the environment." Our use of the concept is somewhat different since this definition makes it a concept which has only partial reference to intrapsychic processes. If one has to evaluate to what extent deleterious consequences of the patient's actions exist, one must investigate the environment rather than the patient. Psychological tests do not yield this information. We need a concept, however, which captures the understanding of intrapsychic processes implicit in the thinking of so many clinicians when they try to distinguish between individuals who will "act out" (speaking loosely) and those who will not.We have, without redefining the term in any explicit way, used the category *alloplasticity* to describe the extent of the individual's tendency to discharge anxiety, or to avoid it, rather than to attempt to bind it or to suffer it.

We, of course, realize that one can't accurately characterize people in this respect as either-or. The most alloplastic individual utilizes some autoplastic methods of dealing with anxiety and the reverse is true. An underlying continuum is implied and we are aware of the arbitrariness in calling an individual auto- or alloplastically oriented. We feel, however, that this may not be wholly inappropriate in a preliminary exploration of the kind we are undertaking here. Further, since we intend to describe shifts towards or away from alloplasticity it should be clear that we will be describing directions of change.

When we describe an individual as having shifted in an alloplastic direction, this does not imply that he is "an alloplastic individual." He may remain predominantly autoplastic in his way of defending himself against anxiety and yet he may have moved in the direction of alloplasticity. The same applies to the "autoplastic individual." The individual who is described as moving in the direction of increasing autoplasticity may not have moved far enough, so to speak, to be considered autoplastic and yet there may have been a development of autoplastic devices for dealing with anxiety. [2]

By alloplastic we mean the tendency to attempt to dispel experienced anxiety or to ward off threatening anxiety by acting upon and changing the environment. The autoplastically oriented individual's defensive efforts, in contrast, are directed toward altering himself, or some aspect of himself, to dispel or bind anxiety. The individual who repeatedly reacts to threatened eruptions of anxiety by getting drunk, changing jobs, driving 90 miles an hour, or getting into fights is alloplastically oriented. The individual, on the other hand, who tends to react to intense anxiety by ruminating, developing phobias, intrusive thoughts, or delusions, is reacting autoplastically. The individual who finds himself responding to more or less mild anxiety with a fantasy or daydream, on the autoplastic side, may be contrasted with the individual who responds to mild anxiety by taking an extra before-dinner cocktail or impulsively setting up a late afternoon nine holes of golf.

There are, of course, difficulties in assessing anxiety tolerance. We do not mean simply the lack of reliability or validity of the instruments one has available but, rather, the difficulties *in principle* of assessing anxiety tolerance. For example, it is easy to assess if one is confronted with an

---

[2] Since presenting this in Chapel Hill it has become clear to us (through examination of cases in which independent judges disagreed on the direction of change after psychotherapy) that allo- and autoplasticity are not simply opposite poles of the same continuum. It is possible, we have seen, for patients to increase in both auto- and alloplasticity. Further conceptual refinement is thus clearly in order.

individual who is quite anxious yet simply suffers the anxiety. By definition his anxiety tolerance is high. What of the individual, however, who is to a great extent anxiety free? What, in other words, is the role of experienced anxiety itself in assessing anxiety tolerance?

How is one to assess anxiety tolerance if only mild anxiety is manifest? Anxiety tolerance, it seems to us, is a concept analogous to, say, potential energy in physics. If one investigates a boulder precariously balanced on the lip of a precipice he need not wait until the boulder plunges over to calculate the forces involved. Measuring various aspects of the physical structure of this situation, the mass of the boulder, the distance it will drop, etc., and performing a few computations will yield the answer. In theory, we should be able to assess anxiety tolerance, or more accurately put, potential anxiety tolerance, without waiting for the boulder to drop or the patient to become anxious to the limits of his tolerance for anxiety. To do so requires investigation and assessment of the structural factors in the situation (the patient's defenses and controls) and the dynamic-economic aspects of the situation (the forces involved). In the boulder-precipice situation the dynamic aspects are well known and are encompassed by the formula for the acceleration of a free-falling body. We have no such constant as gravity to work with and here, of course, the analogy breaks down since we have no reason to assume the forces we are dealing with are constant from individual to individual.

Looking through the relevant parts of our test-retest reports, we noted the frequent occurrence of such statements as, "she is less frightened of losing control over her impulses"; "the patient is no longer so threatened by the possibility of being overwhelmed by his impulses or by anxiety"; "the patient's marked decrease in vulnerability to primitive poorly modu-

lated infantile outbursts"; "extremely vulnerable to waves of disorganizing anxiety and panic." In 12 of 18 reports some phrase appeared, concerning either the picture before or after therapy, referring to the possibility of "loss of control," "disorganization," or being "overwhelmed." In many reports the word anxiety was invariably accompanied by such modifiers as "disorganizing," "of panic proportions," or some phrase suggesting not only that the anxiety alluded to was especially intense but that in fact it was likely to be overwhelming.

Turning to the psychoanalytic literature, we found that Rosenberg (1949) pointed out that from its earliest period, psychoanalytic theory of the nature of anxiety has approached the subject from two points of view. On the one hand, the relationship of anxiety to instinctual frustrations has been stressed. Although Freud (1927) made considerable modifications in his conception and orientation in this respect, he continued to stress the close relationship of anxiety to quantities of frustrated instinctual tension. In *Inhibitions, Symptoms and Anxiety,* he distinguished between two types of anxiety. He recognized and explicitly stated the value of anxiety as a response to an internal danger situation. He did not, however, abandon his earlier emphasis on accumulations of excitation which cannot be discharged. He thus gave the name *primary anxiety* or the traumatic factor to the condition directly brought about by helplessness in the face of overwhelming excitation. Secondary anxiety, in contrast, was defined as an ego reaction which becomes manifest as a signal that a danger situation may arise. Jones (1957, p. 256) comments:

In the traumatic situation all the protective barriers are overrun, and a panicky helplessness results, a response which Freud called inevitable but inexpedient. Most clinical instances of anxiety, however, may be called expedient, because they are essentially signals of approaching danger which for the most part may then be avoided in various ways. Among these is the action of repression itself, which Freud now regarded as being set in action by the anxiety instead of, as he had previously thought, being the cause of the anxiety.

Anna Freud (1937) as well, in *The Ego and the Mechanism of Defense* included in a list of "motives" for the defense against instincts, "instinctual anxiety or dread of the strength of instincts." She quoted Robert Waelder who described "the danger that the ego's whole organization may be destroyed or submerged." Miss Freud (1937, Ch. V) stated,

. . . the only pathological states which fail to react favorably to analysis are those based on the defense promoted by the patient's dread of the strength of his instincts. In such a case there is a danger that we may annul the defensive measures of the ego without being able immediately to come to its assistance. In analysis we always reassure the patient who is afraid of admitting his id impulses into consciousness by telling him that, once they are conscious they are less dangerous and more amenable to control than when unconscious. The only situation in which this promise may prove illusory is that in which the defense has been undertaken because the patient dreads the strength of his instincts.

Whether, in fact, there exist two qualitatively different variants of anxiety or whether the distinction between "primary" and "secondary" anxiety is simply a quantitative one, it is clear that the implications of experienced anxiety differ from patient to patient. That is, anxiety of a certain intensity in individuals with certain defensive ego structures is disorganizing (or "primary," if you like). Other individuals are able to utilize the anxiety as a signal of danger to the ego.

The capacity to experience signal anxiety, in other words, varies among individuals. It is just this capacity, we propose, that constitutes anxiety tolerance. To define anxiety tolerance as *the capacity to experience signal (or "secondary") anxiety,*[3] simple though it may sound, is to

make the concept applicable to all individuals, not just those who respond alloplastically to the threatened arousal of anxiety. The autoplastically oriented individual for whom anxiety has become disorganizing (or primary, if you will) without an increased tendency to motor activity, has just as little capacity for the experience of signal anxiety as his alloplastically oriented, impulse-ridden counterpart.

This definition, we feel, represents explicitly something that most clinicians recognize implicitly: that the meaning and consequences of experienced anxiety differ depending on the individual's ego structure (and thus the course of his ego development) (Greenacre, 1941).

Let us now apply the redefined concept anxiety tolerance to our group of subjects attempting to describe the patterns of change noted from pre- to posttherapy psychological tests. (Again, note that there is no intention to imply arbitrary dichotomies. We are concerned here more with direction of change in anxiety tolerance than with the magnitude).

Our studies of change in anxiety tolerance in 18 patients upon whom we have currently completed pre- and posttherapy psychological test studies show us, of course, that the pattern of change varies from patient to patient and that the differences in individual patterns of change far outweigh their similarities. When we say, for example, that there has been an increase in anxiety tolerance and an increasing reliance upon autoplastic ego activities, we realize that this statement, applied to a group of patients in our study, is, of course, a highly abstract, and perhaps overly general one. Each individual of

---

[3] Our colleague, Gerald A. Ehrenreich, points out that this definition includes implicitly, the ego function of discriminating the signal as such; that is, not solely the tolerance for the *experience* of anxiety but the ability, in addition, to *recognize* it as a signal. Therefore, an increase in anxiety tolerance implies improved ego functioning.

whom this statement is partially true reveals under intensive study his unique pattern of change, generally involving complex and interrelated alterations in virtually all of the intrapsychic variables considered in the project. Defensive realign-
ments occur, energy redistributions are
seen, impulse-defense configurations have
undergone reorganization. The precise
alteration of defenses (i.e., the increasing
or decreasing utilization of a specific defense, along with changes in the rigidity
of such a defense, or the pervasiveness of
its use, or its brittleness) all vary widely
from individual to individual. Nevertheless, certain commonalities appear which
seem to form the basis for four distinguishable patterns of change.[4]

*I: Increased Anxiety Tolerance with In-
creased Prominence of Autoplasticity*

We note first a group of five patients
of whom it may generally be said that
anxiety tolerance has increased along with
an increasing tendency toward the utilization of autoplastic ego operations. These
five patients seemed to share some com-

[4] In Chapel Hill the conferees very cogently
questioned the lack of evidence of reliability.
Subsequently, independent judgments by a
psychiatrist, based on the same test reports as
were our consensus judgments, proved to be in
agreement with us in 78% of the anxiety tolerance and 67% of the allo-autoplasticity instances.
To make independent judgments based directly on test data would necessitate an experienced psychologist going over, in detail, the
entire pre- and posttherapy test protocols in
order to arrive at some more or less explicitly
integrated picture of the personality structure
and its changes following therapy. Then, and
only then, would in-context, meaningful judgments of changes in anxiety tolerance be made.
Hundreds of man-hours might be involved in
this task. This forces one, as do many questions
raised in Chapel Hill, to confront the choice of
where first to invest limited energies and resources. Shall one start by seeking more certain
knowledge or broader conceptual clarity? Concepts defined in ways to achieve maximal reliability are likely, at this stage of our knowledge, to possess low construct validity.

mon characteristics. In general, there
seemed to be a simultaneous strengthening of defensive ego operations, and an
increasing flexibility characteristic of
them. Impulse controls tended to be more
stable, less erratic. Patients in this group
were less given to affect storms, which
prior to treatment had often carried them
into impulsive, irrational behavior. Following treatment their use of avoidance
was less prominent, and indeed in several
of the cases heightened conscious anxiety
was seen. Probably the most striking common feature in the changed pattern of
functioning characteristic of this group
was an increased use of ideational activity
to bind anxiety. Insight, reflectiveness,
self-awareness all tended to increase.
Longer, more productive Rorschachs, less
banal and cliché-ridden TAT stories, and
Word Association protocols pointing in
the direction of at least greater awareness
of (if not complete resolution of) conflicts tended to be the rule. Affects and
anxiety became less diffuse and free-floating and were more often seen in an appropriate ideational context. This "focalized"
rather than diffuse quality to affect experience also tended to characterize the alloplasticity which, of course, remained an
important part of the functioning of such
patients despite their movement toward
increasing autoplasticity. The alloplasticity
was, following treatment, often more restricted and controlled.

*II: Increased Anxiety Tolerance with In-
creased Prominence of Alloplasticity*

Six of the 18 patients comprise another
group. While showing increased anxiety
tolerance (as did patients in the group
described above), this is, in the main, a
group of patients who prior to the start
of treatment showed a variety of primarily
autoplastic pathological manifestations.
This group was characterized at the time
of initial study by the extreme prominence
of ideational activity. In some this took
the form of rigid obsessional intellectual-

izing (accompanied by isolation and re-action formation), all of which defensive activity tended to preclude, to a great extent, the experience of spontaneous affect. One of the group was characterized by the presence of severe depression and phobic ideation. Two of the group, at the time of their initial testing, revealed throughout their test protocols gross confabulations, peculiarities of thought and language, and reality distortions indicative of ideational pathology of a psychotic degree. Again, we found a number of common elements which seemed to be associated with increased anxiety tolerance. Principally, there was greater ideational control; these patients were more able to curb the loose, overexpansive thinking that had been so characteristic of them. At the same time, these individuals showed an increased tolerance for affect. Each of the reports alludes to their being "less afraid of the strength of their affects." Constriction of ideational activity (in the sense of curbing its more overexpansive deviant manifestations) was accompanied by a tendency toward freer affect experience and impulse expression. It is a striking clinical characteristic of this group that all but one, shortly after the termination of treatment, made major changes in his life situation: three married, one began career training, another assumed a significantly and appropriately important role in his family's business.

### III: Decreased Anxiety Tolerance with Increased Prominence of Autoplasticity

Next let us look at a group of five patients in whom we saw, following treatment, a decrease in anxiety tolerance and increasing reliance on what proved to be *inadequate* autoplastic ego devices. These are people who to begin with had relatively rigid defenses against self-scrutiny. They most often presented meager constricted and guarded test protocols. It is striking that the initial assessments of each of them mentioned, in one way or another, their chronically being threatened with the possibility of extreme and not readily reversible regression. For this group, change as seen on the tests generally took the form of an increase in ideational fluidity, the appearance of arbitrary misperceptions of reality; in short, decompensation in the direction of thought disorder.

The role of ideation for these patients deserves special consideration. In the Group I patients we described, those in whom an increase in anxiety tolerance was accompanied by greater prominence of autoplastic intrapsychic events, ideation was relatively successful in binding anxiety. In the Group III patients, on the other hand, ideation did not successfully serve this purpose. Instead, intensified ideational activity was not useful to the patient as a means of either binding anxiety or delaying direct motor impulse discharge. Indeed, fantasy, rather than serving as a check to impetuous action, more often served as a spur to it. Anxiety was strikingly disorganizing of the formal thought functioning in this group. In the test protocols of these patients were seen numerous instances of autistic and dereistic thinking, ranging from fleeting borderline psychotic manifestations to fixed somatic delusions. At follow-up we learned that this group of patients fared poorly. Three are dead, two by suicide, the third by neglect of a serious physical illness. One of the group, hospitalized at the time of follow-up study, was in a severely regressed state, with a number of fixed somatic delusions and auditory hallucinations.

### IV: Decreased Anxiety Tolerance with Increased Prominence of Alloplasticity

Our fourth group consists of those patients who at termination showed a decrease in anxiety tolerance coupled with greater utilization of alloplastic tension-relieving devices. This group consists of two patients whose psychological tests, for all of their impressive differences, show a number of interesting similarities. Principally, these two patients are characterized by an increased, almost extreme constriction of ideation. The test reports described their increased reliance on avoidance and denial. Heightened negativism and increased guardedness characterize both of them. Along with increased rigidity of defensive functioning, in both patients, we saw greater emphasis on alloplastic behaviors. Both had prematurely terminated psychotherapy and both psychotherapies were characterized by faulty communication between patient and therapist. In one case psychotherapy was characterized by lengthy silences which could not be successfully dealt with. In the other case, psychotherapy was characterized by the withholding of information on the part of the patient, particularly in regard to homosexual activity. There have been thus far in the project three patients, all of whom have severe disturbances in impulse control, who precipitously interrupted treatment and refused to participate in a psychological test study. Conceivably these patients might also belong in this group.

It should be pointed out that in each of these four groups the striking commonalities would not be visible simply from diagnostic labels or degree of improvement ratings. Nor could such groupings be arrived at on the basis of presence or absence of manifest anxiety. Each of the four categories contains patients seen at termination as less anxious and those seen as more anxious.

Let us at this point attempt to review the logic of this presentation. We have sought to understand as much as we can about changes in our patients viewing them from one restricted standpoint only. We have attempted something analagous to a histological approach looking at one type of tissue in an organism which contains many varieties of cell structure and

tissue. Placing each patient on a microscope slide, as it were, and applying the same stain to each, what structures become visible? We found, however, that our stain was not properly constituted since it "didn't take" on some of the patients. We changed it. We redefined the concept anxiety tolerance to be able to apply it to each patient. Without taking a position on the question of whether there are two variants of anxiety, it became clear in our review of the literature that some people have thought so. We found that for some patients anxiety reflects the danger of the ego's being overwhelmed by instinctual pressures. For others, anxiety rather serves as a signal, not that the internal psychological structure of the ego is breaking down, but that further ego activity is required to meet internal or external danger. To restrict the use of the term anxiety tolerance to the capacity to experience signal anxiety makes it possible to apply the concept to all our patients. We classified patients as to whether change has been in the direction of increased or decreased anxiety tolerance following psychotherapy. We considered the nature of shifts in defensive activity; whether defensive activity moved more in the direction of the tendency to bind anxiety autoplastically, on the one hand, or the tendency to dispel it, or avoid it, alloplastically, on the other hand. Applying these two classification criteria enabled us to discern meaningful commonalities within groups of patients.

The issue of evaluating change in terms of success or failure is relevant here. All those patients we saw as having changed in the direction of diminished anxiety tolerance probably can be thought of as "unimproved" or "less improved." (We do not have available to us an independent criterion of change, at this point, although some of the criteria Luborsky touches upon in his paper can, at a later point, be applied to our groupings.) Not all those patients, however, whose anxiety tolerance increased can be described as therapeutic successes. This is reassuring to us in that it would suggest we are not simply differentiating "the therapeutic good guys" from "the bad guys." Considering patients from the single point of view of anxiety tolerance, as we have, may have brought into focus one important component of therapeutic failure.

Luborsky (1961) suggests, in his contribution to this conference, the hypothesis that, "For the patients who start treatment with at least a moderately high capacity for autonomous functioning, etc., the higher the level of anxiety the greater the change that is likely." This hypothesis is based on his tentative finding that the correlation between amount of change (as reflected by the Health-Sickness Rating) and initial (pretherapy) anxiety level is a function of initial (pretherapy) Health-Sickness Rating. May we suggest that this finding (and the consequent hypothesis arising from it) reflects precisely our point, that the significance of anxiety varies among individuals; that there is pragmatic value in identifying signal anxiety and the individual's capacity (if this is the proper term) for experiencing it.

We hypothesize that to account for and understand changes in patients who have undergone psychotherapy, it is obligatory to consider the extent to which they have developed, increased or decreased, the capacity to experience anxiety as a signal that further ego activity is required. This implies that the presence or absence of anxiety after treatment is not, in itself, sufficient to understand or evaluate the change that has occurred. It is a datum that can only be fully understood in relation to changes in the individual's ways of dealing with anxiety. And it further implies, to us, that close clinical scrutiny of limited aspects of intrapsychic processes and functioning can potentially lead to

conceptual schemata which make it possible to understand more fully, disparate groups of patients. Perhaps now we can better understand what is expressed by many psychotherapists when they consider severe impulse-ridden characters to be just as recalcitrant to psychotherapeutic treatment as regressed psychotics. This truism seems to us clarified when one isolates the relevant intrapsychic variables. We suggest that one relevant variable is the capacity for the experience of signal anxiety or, if you will, anxiety tolerance.

REFERENCES

Ehrenreich, G. A., & Siegal, R. S. Assessing intrapsychic variables with psychological tests in psychotherapy research. (To be published)

Ekstein, R., & Wallerstein, R. S. The teaching and learning of psychotherapy. New York: Basic Books, 1958.

Freud, Anna. The ego and the mechanisms of defense. New York: International Universities Press, 1946.

Freud, S. Inhibitions, symptoms and anxiety. London: Hogarth, 1927.

Greenacre, Phyllis. The predisposition to anxiety: Parts I & II. Psychoanal. Quart., 1941, 10, 66-94; 610-638.

Jones, E. The life and work of Sigmund Freud. Vol. III. New York: Basic Books, 1957.

Luborsky, L. The patient's personality and psychotherapeutic change. (Paper appears elsewhere in this book.)

Rosenberg, Elizabeth. Anxiety and the capacity to bear it. Int. J. Psychoanal., 1949, 30, 1-12.

Sargent, Helen. Intrapsychic change: Methodological problems in psychotherapy research. Psychiatry, 1961, 24, 93-108.

Siegal, R. S., & Ehrenreich, G. A. Inferring repression from psychological tests. Bull. Meninger Clin., 1962, 26, 82-91.

Siegal, R. S., Rosen, I. C., & Ehrenreich, G. A. The natural history of an outcome prediction. J. Proj. Tech., 1962, 26, 112-116.

Wallerstein, R. S., Robbins, L. L., Sargent, Helen D., & Luborsky, L. The Psychotherapy Research Project of The Menninger Foundation: Rationale, method, and sample use. Bull. Menninger Clin., 1956, 20, 221-278.

# Some Aspects of the Psychotherapeutic System[1]

## HENRY L. LENNARD, PH.D.

### What Kind of a Situation is the Psychotherapy Situation?

In considering any social situation, whether it be from the viewpoint of a participant or from the viewpoint of an observer, an explicit or implicit decision is involved as to the character of that situation. Psychoanalysts, for example, tend to view the psychotherapy situation as one which facilitates the recall and exploration of unconscious memories and strivings; or one which deals with the recall and/or re-experiencing of significant events in the patient's infancy or childhood. Doing research within this framework requires the development of concepts and categories by which unconscious ideas and strivings (dependent, aggressive, etc.) might be identified and described, and the creation of categories by which the manifest content of behavior during treatment might be characterized (transference, defense, resistance).

As a result of a previous interest in the present group of researchers at Columbia University and because of the limited number of approaches to the treatment situation derived from the social sciences, it was decided to view the psychotherapy situation in other ways:

1. As an interaction situation, a situation where two people are engaged in an interdependent and reciprocal interaction process. Just as has been observed in other types of interaction systems, it was expected that form and content and com-

munication in psychotherapy would undergo systematic changes over time. It was further believed that it would be possible, just as it had been possible for other social systems, to identify self-regulating processes in the therapy system.

2. In agreement with other investigators, the psychotherapy situation might be considered as a learning situation. But instead of merely considering the learning of particular contents about oneself and others that may occur during treatment, special attention was devoted toward the analysis of the learning of the dimensions of social roles. Psychotherapy was considered a situation wherein as a result of being "socialized" into the therapist-patient system, the patient could learn to identify the relevant dimensions of other role systems in which he participates (deutero-learning).

3. We considered psychotherapy to be an information exchange and information processing situation. We were particularly interested in pinpointing the differential consequences in patients' verbal behavior of varying degrees of specificity in the structure of the therapists' informational behavior.

Adopting one or all of these approaches when studying the psychotherapeutic interaction requires the development of particular sets of categories for analysis of therapeutic process, and affects how much and in what sequence therapeutic data need to be processed. For example, in order to analyze interaction processes through time, it is necessary to classify sequences of communication continuously for a substantial number of sessions. Of course, were an investigator concerned only with the occurrence of a particular

[1] Support for the research reported in this paper under National Institute of Mental Health Research Grants M 1076 and M 2882 is gratefully acknowledged.

This paper is adapted from Lennard and Bernstein (1960).

218

phenomenon in psychotherapy, he might find it possible to restrict his analysis to a less extensive amount of the behavior occurring between the patient and the therapist.

In order to keep within its allotted size, this paper does not review those aspects of the research which were relevant to the conception of psychotherapy as an informational exchange and information processing situation. In covering the work oriented around the study of therapy as an interaction system and as a role-learning situation, I will try to present the conceptual approach and definition of variables fairly completely and be more selective in presentation of findings.

## CONCEPTS RELEVANT TO VIEWING PSYCHOTHERAPY AS AN INTERACTION AND A ROLE-LEARNING SITUATION

While it is not generally denied that the psychotherapy interaction constitutes a genuine interactional relationship (by definition, two or more persons in physical proximity, aware of each other, and exchanging messages constitute an interaction system), the implications of the conception have not been pursued systematically in the study of therapy.

In the study of interaction as a system, a number of concepts have proven useful and we, therefore, decided to introduce them into the study of therapeutic interaction. These concepts were:

### Interdependence

The concept of interdependence between variables rather than a unilateral relationship between variables is central to the concept of system. Interdependence, in the words of Parsons and Shils (1951), "consists in the existence of determinate relationships among the parts or variables as contrasted with randomness of variability. In other words, interdependence is order in the relationship among the components which enter into a system."

### Equilibrium

The order in the interrelationship among the units of the system possesses a "tendency to self-maintenance, which is very generally expressed in the concept of equilibrium. It need not, however, be a static self-maintenance or stable equilibrium. It may be an ordered process of change—a process following a determinate pattern rather than random variability relative to the starting point" (Parsons & Shils, 1951). The sociological restatement of this conception of equilibrium in connection with systems of action would be that "there appears to be something underlying the observed overt behavior, which has a continuity and persistence through time. It seems to act like an accounting system which takes account of deficits and surpluses that appear within given small time spans in such a way as to tend toward restoration of certain balance in quality and distribution of action among members over long time spans" (Bales & Slater, 1954).

### Differentiation

Implicit to a system is a span of time. By its very nature a system consists of an interaction, and this means that a sequential process of action and reaction has to take place before we are able to describe any state of the system or any change of state. Differentiation is defined as a temporal or phase phenomenon in which the behavior of the participants is seen to differ systematically over time. The concept of temporal differentiation implies, for instance, that the distribution of communicative acts of individuals encountering each other for the first time will differ from the distribution of their communicative acts occurring on the tenth encounter.

### Socialization

In order for a therapeutic system to begin to function, it is first necessary for the patient to be inducted into the "patient role," that is, to acquire the set of role expectations which are reciprocal to the therapist. The learning of a social role is referred to by sociologists as: "socialization." Socialization, as defined by Merton et al. (1957), "designates the process by which people selectively acquire the values and attitudes, the interests, skills and knowledge—in short, the culture—current in the groups in which they are, or seek to become a member. Socialization takes place primarily through social interaction with people who are significant for the individuals." In our view, a therapist's task as a socializer is analogous to a parent socializing a child into the family or of a teacher socializing a student into the school situation. Socialization of the patient into the patient role is one of the crucial or necessary tasks in the construction and maintenance of therapeutic systems.

*Deutero-Learning*

This concept, developed by Gregory Bateson, has also been described as "learning how to learn," and refers to the fact that in any given learning situation, one learns not only what one is supposed to learn, but also something about the process of learning itself.

Perhaps two brief illustrations will suffice here. In learning a foreign language, one not only learns the particular language but also about the process of learning a language. Each successive language is more easily mastered. Learning one card game prepares one for the learning of the next because one has not only learned the rules of the particular game, but also that card games involve—among other things—the distribution of cards among players, symbolic meaning of action, patterns of plays, different values of cards, the use of strategy and deception, and so forth.

*Satisfaction*

The concept of satisfaction permits one to assess the reaction of participants of interaction systems. The satisfaction that a participant derives from communication is closely related to his expectations (in the sense of wishes). If the communication fulfills these expectations, he will experience some degree of satisfaction. If the communication does not fulfill his expectations, and he is thereby disappointed, he will experience dissatisfaction.

*Methodology*

The problems inherent in an analysis of communication during psychotherapy are complex. Before a quantitative and systematic attack on these problems could be undertaken, it was first necessary to collect the kind of data which would make such an effort possible. We thus found ourselves faced with the task of assembling a reasonably large body of verbatim psychotherapy data that would constitute a library of facts from which we could draw material to test our hypotheses.

The number of cases that could be recorded and transcribed for the purpose of our study was limited by considerations of time and money. Ultimately, however, it became possible to obtain verbatim recordings of eight therapies over a period of almost a year each. While a sample of eight does not seem large, such a sample consists of well over 500 hours of treatment and contains tens of thousands of scorable communication units.

It would probably be fair to say that we were not engaged primarily in a "fact finding" research but rather in a research designed to develop and test a methodology and to uncover hypotheses. Most of the findings that we report are not sample statistics to be generalized but parameters of our own group of eight therapist-patient pairs. When, for example, we report that a given variable decreases over time, we are not generalizing, but describing what actually happened to that variable within the group of cases we studied.

The study, however, is multidimensional and multilevel, and the confidence that one can place in a generalization from the findings will vary with the dimension or level. Moreover, the number of cases also varies from level to level and category to category. In setting confidence limits, it should be borne in mind that different total numbers are involved in the "sample." There were only 4 *therapists,* but there were 8 *dyads,* 500 *sessions* (over 120 of these were coded), 5,985 exchanges, and 41,513 verbal *propositions* coded along multiple dimensions.

Four psychotherapists agreed to cooperate with the project for the purpose of data collection. Three of the four therapists have been or are currently affiliated with a psychoanalytic institute recognized by the American Psychoanalytic Association. The fourth therapist is a graduate of a program in Clinical Psychology approved by the American Psychological Association and has been in practice for more than ten years.

The patients in our project were referred from psychotherapy clinics in the New York City area. All were informed of the research nature of the project and agreed in advance of their first contact with the therapist to permit the recording of their hours and to fill out questionnaires from time to time.

In addition to the verbatim recordings of the therapy sessions, patients and therapists were interviewed prior to therapy and were given questionnaires to fill out at intervals during treatment. The interviews and the questionnaires sought information on role expectations of therapists and patients; how therapists and patients perceived and evaluated the interaction that had occurred during particular hours (thus similarities and dissimilarities could be compared), and how therapists and patients viewed their interaction in retrospect.

*Units of Quantity*

Our task was to find methods for recording and analyzing the operations be-

tween the patient and the therapist and to find out which of these units of behavior were amenable to management. We could not reasonably expect any single method of examination to give us more than a limited amount of information, and so we were willing to use as many methods as were required for the assignment.

1. *Proposition.* A proposition for the purpose of this study was defined as a verbalization containing a subject and a predicate either expressed or implied. It is the verbal expression of a single idea. Essentially the same definitions and instructions used by Bales, Dollard, Murray, and others were used by our coders to separate the transcripts into propositional units.

In order to determine the reliability of unitization, the same therapy session was coded independently by two different coders. A total of 332 propositions was scored for the session by Coder A and 334 propositions for the session by Coder B, a difference of less than one percent.

2. *Statement.* A statement is an uninterrupted sequence of propositions from either the therapist or patient. While therapist statements rarely consist of more than three propositions, patient statements sometimes contain more than 100 propositions.

3. *Interaction or exchange.* An exchange or interaction is defined as a therapist statement followed by a patient statement, or vice versa. It may consist of several propositions but it represents a complete interaction. The number of exchanges per hour or per transcribed page is the "rate of interaction" and provides a measure of the frequency with which a therapist speaks or interacts.

Each exchange was coded and punched onto a single IBM card. Since an exchange contains both a patient's statement and a therapist's statement, half of each IBM card was devoted to coded information

about the therapist statement and half to
coded information about the patient statement.

*Grammatical Form of Communication*

Each proposition was classified as to its
grammatical form, or mood, as (*a*) declarative, (*b*) imperative, or (*c*) interrogatory. The grammatical form of a
proposition communicates information.
For example, the use of the question form
supplies information as to who is expected
to speak, and thus clarifies communicational expectations. Questions are devices
by which communication processes may
be initiated or set into motion.

*Affective Content of Communication*

The content of each proposition of
either a patient or a therapist was coded
as to (*a*) whether it expressed or referred
to feeling, (*b*) whether it clearly did not
express or refer to feeling, or (*c*) whether
its affective content was not determinable.
Verbal communication about affect is regarded as a basic feature of psychotherapeutic interactions, and therapists frequently seek to get their patients to
verbalize about feelings. Patient affective
propositions refer to their feelings (love,
fear, pleasure, sadness, etc.).

Therapists themselves very rarely discuss their own feelings; hence, when
therapist propositions refer to affect they
take a somewhat different form from those
of patients. Therapist propositions were
categorized as affective when they were
directed toward eliciting patient affect.

*Interaction Process Categories*

Bales has developed a system of classification which permits the scoring of every
interaction in terms of one of 12 categories. As he says, "this classification still
does not catch 'content' in the usual sense
of the term when 'content' is usually taken
to mean the 'subject matter'; that is, the
reference of the symbols used is the interaction, in short 'what' is being talked

about. Our method tries to classify rather
what we might call the 'process significance' of the single interaction; that is, the
'pragmatic' significance of each act in relation to prior acts and acts expected to
come."[2]

We condensed six of the Bales' categories into three, in line with a suggestion
made by Zetterberg (1955). The categories used follow:

1. Descriptive Propositions ask for or
convey information. They give or ask for
orientation, repetition, or clarification.

2. Evaluative Propositions ask for or
convey appraisal or statements of value.
They give or ask for opinions, expression
of feeling, or analysis.

3. Prescriptive Propositions express or
ask for directives. They give or ask for
suggestions.

*Role System*

We are now concerned in a limited
sense with what the proposition refers to,
with what it is about. Our emphasis now
is in classifying communication as referring to the various systems or role relationships in which the patient participates. We are particularly concerned here
with identifying propositions in which
the therapist or the patient discusses their
roles and expectations with regard to
therapy. It was assumed that one of the
ways in which a patient "learns" about his
own and the therapist's roles is through
the references which the therapist makes
to these roles, that is, through role information provided by the therapist. The
subject matter of each proposition was
therefore classified in terms of the following frames of references:

1. *Primary System* (the treatment). Included in this category are patient or
therapist propositions that refer to their
roles during treatment and the process of

----

[2] R. F. Bales, personal communication to
Conrad Arensberg.

therapy, and to the purposes, goals, and accomplishments of therapy. *Examples:*

Therapist: There's no homework, no reference work, it's all done here.

Therapist: Talk about it anyway even though you think it's unimportant.

Therapist: Could you just take a moment to tell me what the specific areas are in which there has been help?

Patient: Isn't a therapist able to tell me a thing like this?

Patient: I want to be cured.

2. *Secondary System.* Included in this category are propositions in which the manifest content refers to therapist and patient in other than their primary roles as patient and therapist. Transference phenomena fall into this category.

3. *Tertiary Systems.*

*a. The family.* Included in this category are propositions that refer directly to the patient's status in the family system.

*b. Other social systems.* Included in this category are propositions that refer to specific social systems other than the family. The actual person or group must be mentioned.

4. *The Self.* Included in this category are references to life experiences past and present that do not refer directly to other reference systems. (Note: In order to save space, illustrations of units and categories employed are omitted, with one exception.)

*Categories Used in Data Analysis*

Units of Quantity:
(1) Proposition
(2) Statement
(3) Exchange

Catogories of Informational Specificity:
(1) Passive encouragement
(2) Active encouragement
(3) Limits to subject matter area
(4) Limits to specific old proposition
(5) Introduces specific new proposition
(6) Interpretation
(7) Limits to specific answer
(8) Excludes discussion

Grammatical Form of Propositions:
(1) Declarative
(2) Imperative
(3) Interrogatory

Affective Content of Propositions:
(1) Expresses or refers to feelings, affective
(2) Does not refer to feelings, nonaffective
(3) Affective content indeterminable

Interaction Process Categories:
(1) Descriptive
(2) Evaluative
(3) Prescriptive

Role System Reference Categories:
(1) Primary System Information
(2) Secondary System
(3) Tertiary System
(4) The Self

## FINDINGS

### Differentiation

Figure 1 shows that therapist behavior characterized as orientation (asking for and giving information, clarification, and confirmation) decreases through the first 50 hours of therapy, while evaluative behavior (asking for and giving opinion, evaluation, analysis, and expression of feeling) increases and then appears to reach a plateau. In general, we found that the pattern of differentiation among the therapists was more nearly analogous to

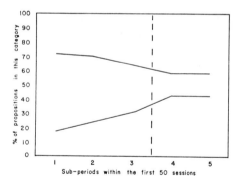

Figure 1. Patterns of temporal differentiation over 50 sessions of therapy: therapist orientation and evaluation propositions. The five subperiods are: (1) Sessions 1-3; (2) Sessions 4-6; (3) Sessions 7-8; (4) Sessions from the third and fourth months of therapy; and (5) Sessions from the fourth to the seventh months of therapy. The vertical broken line is used to call attention to the fact that the later two groups of sessions are not consecutive with the earlier sessions ($n = 101$ sessions or 9,282 therapist propositions and 32,231 patient propositions).

that of the participants in problem-solving groups.

When we examined psychotherapeutic communication from the point of view of system referent, we discovered that there was a very consistent downward trend, over the life of therapy, in the frequency of primary system references (see Figure 2). The decrease was of considerable magnitude, dropping to less than one half of the original amount by the fourth month of treatment. In other words, as therapy progressed, discussion about therapy itself and the reciprocal therapist-patient roles decreased.

The decrease in communication about the primary role system occurs for our study group as a whole and appears as a trend in every one of the eight therapist-patient pairs. It reflects the inevitability of socialization as a consequence of psychotherapy irrespective of the orientation and skill of the therapist and the psychological problem of the patient. To resolve the problem of what a patient may expect and what may be expected of him appears to be an indispensable requisite for maintaining the therapeutic system from one session to the next.

Concomitant with the decrease in discussion about therapist-patient role expectations, both the therapist and the patient

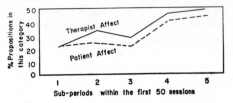

Figure 3. Patterns of temporal differentiation over 50 sessions of therapy: see Figure 1 for specification of subperiods and size of $n$.

tend to increase their communications about affect (see Figure 3). This means that, as therapy proceeded, the therapists increased the frequency with which their propositions inquired into and solicited patient verbalization about feelings, and also that our patients began to verbalize more voluminously about feelings.

## Similarities between Patterning of the Session and of Therapy

A question of particular interest is whether the type of differentiation observed over the longer time periods of therapeutic interaction is similar to that observed during more limited time periods such as the length of one therapeutic session; in other words, insofar as differentiation is concerned, does the single session represent a miniature of therapy as a whole or do variations in the length of the interaction between participants eventuate in variations between the macro- and micropatterns of differentiation?

Most striking among the similarities between movement of communication in the individual session and movement during the first 50 sessions of therapy is the decrease of primary system communications on the part of the therapist and patient within the individual session. In other words, primary role communication is more frequent at the beginning of each hour than toward the end.

It appears as if induction into the patient role is a task which frequently has to be resumed at the beginning of each session. It is only after some discussion of

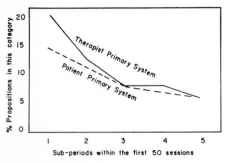

Figure 2. Patterns of temporal differentiation over 50 sessions of therapy: therapist and patient primary system propositions. See Figure 1 for specification of subperiods and size of $n$.

the therapist-patient primary relationship that the patient can once again assume the patient role.

*Interdependence*

We correlated patient and therapist treatment sessions with respect to three dimensions of communicative acts (i.e., primary system references, evaluative and affective references). We found increasing similarity of patient and therapist behavior over time with respect to three dimensions of communication, i.e., primary system communications, evaluative communication, and affective communication (Table 1). We are using the term "similarity" to refer to the increasing correlation over time between specific kinds of patient and therapist communications. For example, while the correlation between percentage of therapist and patient affective propositions is .23 for the first two sessions, this correlation increases to .70 by the third and fourth month of psychotherapy.

This finding raises an interesting question. The data show that during therapy there is a growing similarity in verbal behavior between therapist and patient, i.e., they become more alike in terms of the categories of verbal expression they employ to describe their thoughts, feelings, and action. The theoretical implications the finding raises is whether a grow-

ing similarity in the verbal formulation of experience *also implies* a growing similarity in more lasting and deeper aspects, such as: patient perception of experience and patient value system.

The above relationship is a particularly interesting illustration of *increasing* interdependence between therapist and patient verbal behavior in therapy. However, any kind of regularity in the relationship between given types of therapist/patient communication reflects interdependence rather than random variability. In this sense, all of our findings bear on the conception of therapy as a two-person interaction system. Our work in the informational exchange aspects of therapy which we cannot present in detail here is rich in illustrations of such regularities. For example, therapist statements of low specificity consistently yielded a greater number of patient propositions than high-specificity statements, while therapist high specificity reduced the likelihood that patients would change the topic under discussion. As patient output falls, therapist specificity increases (Lennard & Bernstein, 1960, pp. 131-149).

Since interdependence appears the most obvious attribute of behavior systems (as a matter of fact it is the attribute of such systems which makes possible their systematic study), its discussion can be cut short in order to turn to more controversial aspects of the therapy system.

*Equilibrium*

We believe the concept of equilibrium to be as applicable to psychotherapy as it is to other interaction systems. The tendency of a system to maintain "a steady state" manifests itself in psychotherapy by the presence of limits within which certain system variables fluctuate.

When we examined this hypothesis for a communicational variable such as interaction rate—the pace at which therapist communications and patient communica-

TABLE 1

INCREASE IN SIMILARITY OF THERAPIST AND PATIENT BEHAVIOR OVER TIME

($n = 48$ sessions)

| | Correlations between percent of therapist and patient propositions | | |
|---|---|---|---|
| | Sessions 1 and 2 | Sessions 5 and 6 | Two sessions from 3rd and 4th months |
| Primary system | .72 | .66 | .88 |
| Evaluation | .36 | .45 | .58 |
| Affect | .23 | .43 | .70 |

tions follow upon one another (measured by averaging the number of interactions per transcribed page)—we find very little variation from session to session for any given therapist-patient pair. For example, the interaction rate ranges among different pairs from a high of 10 interactions per transcribed page for one patient-therapist pair to a low of 1.2 interactions per transcribed page for another therapist-patient pair. In contrast, however, the interaction rate for each therapist-patient pair varied very little from session to session. In four of our cases, the standard deviation in interaction rate from session to session was only 1.1. The highest standard deviation was 1.8. The pace of the interaction, therefore, appears to be fairly stable and varies very little over time for any given therapist-patient pair.

Each session as a part of the system of therapy is related to the preceding and succeeding session. We now wanted to ascertain whether disequilibrium or strain occurring within one session affected the structure of communication occurring within the subsequent session. In order to study such sequential compensating processes, it was first necessary to decide how to characterize sessions as to extent of strain present; to develop hypotheses as to what communicative acts could restore equilibrium in subsequent sessions; and then to examine our data.

As one indicator of session strain, we considered the number of silences per session. A large number of silences in a session may reflect a breakdown of communication, or a "resistance." During some silences, productive "internal communication" or reverie takes place, but it seemed likely that sessions containing 10 or 20 extended silences were sessions in which verbalization was impaired (a pause was not counted as a silence unless it was over 10 seconds in length).

We classified 66 sessions (for which

every immediately following session had also been coded) into high-, middle-, and low-silence sessions. We then examined the structure of communication in the session *immediately* following each session which had been classified. We found that the sessions exhibiting most silences were *succeeded* by sessions characterized by a higher percentage of therapist evaluative acts and therapist acts of high informational specificity. In fact, for each pair, the sessions with the most silences were followed by sessions with a higher average percentage of therapist evaluation than those with the least silences. The finding is reported in Table 2.

*Primary System Reference as an Equilibrium Maintaining Mechanism*

Primary system references are propositions in which the therapist and patient discuss problems relating to what therapy is all about. We discuss elsewhere the importance of role learning in psychotherapy. The patient has to learn a new set of expectations appropriate to his function as a patient in the therapeutic relationship. When a patient's initial expectations are not met, he experiences disappointment and/or frustration.

Primary system references center around role discussion. The more primary system references on the part of the patient, the more information the patient is soliciting about his role in treatment. The more primary system references on the part of the therapist, the more the therapist is teaching the patient his role in therapy. Primary system references therefore reduce strain and disequilibrium by clarifying role expectations and reducing the lack of complementarity between the patient's and the therapist's conceptions of therapy.

This role teaching seems to pay off in terms of patient learning. Figure 4 is a graph showing the average number of primary system propositions spoken per

TABLE 2

THERAPIST EVALUATIVE PROPOSITIONS IN SESSIONS
FOLLOWING HIGH AND LOW SILENCE SESSIONS
($n = 64$ sessions)

| | Proportion of therapist evaluative propositions in the next session | | | | | | |
|---|---|---|---|---|---|---|---|
| Number of silences in session | Therapist A Patient 1 | Therapist B Patient 2 | | Therapist C Patient 1 2 | | Therapist D Patient 1 2 | | All therapists |
| High | .19 | .52 | .38 | .24 | .19 | .25 | .34 | .29 |
| Low | .18 | .40 | .28 | .09 | .14 | .12 | .31 | .22 |

session by the two more active therapists[3] (solid line), by the two more passive therapists (dash-dot line), by the patients of the more active therapists (dash line), and by the patients of the more passive therapists (dotted line) through four time periods. The first three sessions comprise the first time period, the next three sessions comprise the second time period, sessions seven and eight comprise the third time period, and the final time period is made up of a sample for each dyad of three sessions taken from the third and fourth months of therapy. There are three important contrasts to be noted in Figure 4. First, we see that the active therapists allot many more propositions during the early sessions to discussion of therapist-patient roles than do the passive therapists. Secondly, while the active therapists produce *more* primary system propositions than do their patients, the passive therapists produce *less* primary system propositions than their patients. This appears to mean that the active therapists take the lead in discussing therapist-patient roles, while passive therapists seem to avoid role discussion even when their patients introduce it. Thirdly, we see that for the dyads

[3] Therapist activity is measured by a series of quantitative and qualitative indicators such as volume and rate of verbalizations, proportion of evaluative and prescriptive communication, etc.

in which there is an active therapist, the amount of role teaching that occurs is initially large but diminishes rapidly, becoming very low in the last time period; while for dyads in which there is a passive therapist, the amount of role discussion remains about the same from the third to the fourth time period.

Of special interest are the curves of the patients. It can be seen in Figure 4 that the amount of role discussion engaged in by the patients of the active therapists is initially much higher than the amount of role discussion engaged in by the patients of the passive therapists. By the fourth month of treatment, however, the situation is reversed. At that time, the patients of the passive therapists are engaged in about twice as much primary role system discussion as the patients of the active therapists.

We suggest that therapy achieves its "role learning goals" to the extent that the patient is able to transfer what he has learned about role patterns in therapy to other significant role relationships. We assume that a decrease in the amount of communication devoted to the therapist-patient relationship, occurring *after* therapy has been underway for some time, implies some resolution of the problems posed by the primary patient-therapist role relationship. It may be a sign that "deutero-role learning" has occurred; that is, that the patient has recognized the similarity and generic relevance of the dimensions of the therapist-patient role to other role relationships.

## The Expectation-Communication System

We suggest, as a minimum, that a social system be conceived of as involving two subsystems, that of communication and that of expectations. Each system can be treated separately from the other and this is what we have done so far. We will now take up some of the interrelations between the systems of expectation and communication. We will try to document the hypothesis that asymmetry in the system of expectations (dissimilarities in

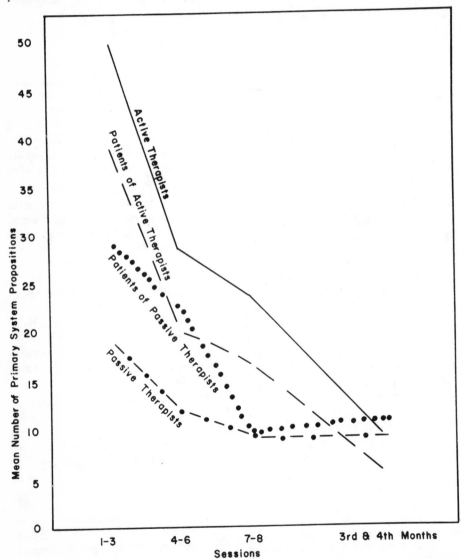

Figure 4. Mean number of primary system propositions per session for active and passive therapists and their patients over time. The designation "3rd and 4th" refers to a sample of three sessions for each dyad from the third and fourth months of therapy ($n = 88$ sessions).

role expectations) is reflected in asymmetry in the system of communication (communicational strain), and we will try to show how efforts are made in the latter system to resolve strain created by the former.

We will now present data regarding the effect upon therapist communication of dissimilarities in one dimension of therapist-patient conceptions—that of "activeness."

An index of dissimilarity in conceptions of activeness was constructed based on five parts of a question asked both of therapist and patient at the beginning of therapy. The value of the index ranges from 0–10, with 0 indicating complete similarity and 10 the highest possible dissimilarity. Table 3 shows the effect of dissimilarities in therapist-patient "activeness" expectations upon the occurrence of therapist primary system (socializing) communications during the first three hours of therapy.

We observe in Table 3 that our hypothesis is strongly documented. Comparing the two patients for each therapist, we find that whenever there is more dissimilarity with respect to activeness expectations, there is a greater number of therapist primary system references. We conceive the emergence of "role" information to be a direct consequence of dissymmetry in expectations. For purposes of dealing with this problem, we regard dissymmetry of expectation as one kind of disequilibrium and communication centered around the primary system as one form of attempted re-equilibrium.

## Satisfaction and the Structure of Communication

Proceeding with our analysis of the interrelationships between expectations and communication, we attempted to discriminate between the communication that occurred in sessions that patients rated as more satisfactory and those that patients rated as less satisfactory.

Satisfaction with communication is related not only to the occurrence of specific content but also to the process of communicating. We hypothesized that strain in communication results not only from lack of consensus on subject matter, but also from disequilibria in the patterning and flow of communication itself.

In this section we shall report on the

TABLE 3

DISSIMILARITIES BETWEEN THERAPIST-PATIENT EXPECTATIONS WITH REGARD TO THERAPIST ACTIVENESS AND THERAPIST PRIMARY SYSTEM REFERENCES
($n = 24$ sessions)

| Therapists | Patient | Index of dissimilarity (ranging from 0–10 High = Dissimilar) | Proportion of therapist primary system references during first three hours of therapy |
|---|---|---|---|
| Therapist A | 1 | 0 | .09 |
|  | 2 | 2 | .27 |
| Therapist B | 1 | 1 | .16 |
|  | 2 | 3 | .49 |
| Therapist C | 1 | 2 | .05 |
|  | 2 | 3 | .20 |
| Therapist D | 1 | 3 | .15 |
|  | 2 | 4 | .19 |

relationship between patient ratings of ease of communication during psychotherapy sessions and some of the actual characteristics of the verbal interchanges in those sessions.

Table 4 summarizes ten variables differentiating the sessions rated as proceeding "more easily" from those rated as proceeding "the same" or "less easily." It should be borne in mind that the ratings of satisfaction obtained from our patients are comparative or relative ratings rather than absolute ratings of patient satisfaction.

We shall now offer some general hypotheses about why the sessions in which therapists were more active, more specific, more concerned with affect, etc. were rated as more satisfactory. These hypotheses relate to two questions: how disappointment was diminished, and how satisfaction was increased.

1. The pattern of communication in the more satisfying sessions is more nearly similar to that of ordinary social relationships, and so is more in line with the patient's previous experience.

2. In the previous professional interactions in which the patients have participated, the professional participant probably has assumed a role more active and reciprocal than that of a therapist. Thera-

## TABLE 4

DIFFERENCES IN COMMUNICATIONAL STRUCTURE AMONG SESSIONS[a]

($n = 23$ sessions)

| Description of variable | For sessions rated as proceeding "more easily" | For sessions rated as proceeding "the same" or "less easily" |
|---|---|---|
| 1. Average number of therapist propositions per session | 90 | 46[b] |
| 2. Average number of patient propositions per session | 305 | 242[c] |
| 3. Average ratio of therapist to patient propositions | .29 | .19 |
| 4. Average number of exchanges per session | 52 | 34 |
| 5. Proportion of therapist propositions that are questions | .30 | .37[b] |
| 6. Proportion of therapist propositions that are highly specific | .37 | .23[b] |
| 7. Proportion of statements in which patient changes the subject | .20 | .28[b] |
| 8. Proportion of therapist propositions that are affective | .40 | .21[b] |
| 9. Proportion of patient propositions that are affective | .27 | .23 |
| 10. Ratio of therapist to patient affective propositions | .41 | .18 |

[a] All the differences reported below hold for each therapist taken separately, except for the case of one therapist with reference to one variable (Items 8 and 9). This internal consistency in the findings is perhaps a more valid test of significance than the formal tests presented below.

[b] Difference significant at .01 level (student's "$t$" distribution, two-tail test).

[c] Difference significant at .05 level (student's "$t$" distribution, two-tail test).

pist behavior thus deviates from what the patient expects of a professional man rendering service.

3. The transference manifestations of therapy prompt the patient to expect the therapist to "give" to the patient. Verbal output on the part of the therapist may be interpreted as a "gift" from the therapist. Therapist passivity and lack of participation is equated with rejection and reacted to with frustration.

4. The patient's substantive problem is that of disorientation with respect to the major role systems in which he participated outside of therapy. Therapist feedback in the form of verbalization, interaction, and informationally specific interventions counters this disorientation and increases a sense of satisfaction.

5. Increase in order and continuity in the flow of communication contributes to a sense of achievement and satisfaction.

6. Increase in affective concern on the part of the therapist gives the patient a sense of being understood. Abreaction and catharsis of feelings contribute to the patient's feeling of satisfaction.

## CONCLUSIONS

There are three types of remarks with which I should like to conclude this partial summary of the psychotherapy research conducted at Columbia University's Bureau of Applied Social Research: (a) First, I will suggest a few of the implications of our research, limited as it is. (b) I will draw attention to the further work which will still have to be done within the same or a similar conceptual framework, i.e., psychotherapy as an action system. (c) I will outline briefly some aspects of the therapeutic relationships (not dealt with in our work) which require intensive study at this time especially with methods of content and process analysis.

a. A Few Implications. We found that

despite major differences in the outlook and the behavior of each therapist and each patient, there are major similarities among therapist-patient pairs in terms of the way the interaction unfolds longitudinally. This finding raises questions for those who tend to stress differences between therapists in their theoretical orientation and who emphasize the importance of the "school" to which a therapist belongs as the determinant for what transpires during therapy.

Within limits, it appears also that the requirements of the system take precedence over expectations and conceptions of therapeutic roles. Much of this occurs outside the awareness of the therapist. Often, the realization that he is departing from a preconceived therapeutic position in the interest of maintaining the system follows upon, rather than precedes, the "system-sensitive" act. We believe that this question of system sensitivity versus theory orientation may have major implications for the training of therapists.

One way of looking at the relationship between our focus on interaction and the analytic exploration of therapy as a situation in which unconscious strivings are manifested may be put in this way: What is latent for the personality system are "unconscious processes," while what is latent for the social system are "system processes." By making the patient conscious of these hitherto unconscious personality processes, the therapist increases the patient's adaptive control and flexibility. The identification of system processes can serve a very similar function for the therapist. By enlarging the therapist's awareness of the processes taking place in the therapeutic systems in which he participates, one may make possible an increased measure of responsiveness and control on his part.

b. Further Research within the Same Conceptual Framework. In the study of psychotherapy reported in this paper, the therapist-patient relationship was viewed as a system, and the concept of homeostasis or dynamic equilibrium was utilized. It turned out to be useful in explaining consistent changes in behavioral patterns of therapist and patient. On the basis of the analysis of the data at our disposal we agree wholeheartedly with the biologist Emerson (1956) who recently said: "At the present time, at least, homeostasis is a remarkably adequate concept for quantitative measurement. Through this concept we can make comparisons between phenomena that, without it, are very difficult to compare, because we don't have a quantitative relationship in quantitative terms that is applicable to different phenomena."

Yet upon further reflection, it has occurred to us that there are further aspects of the concept which could be explored with the type of data we have gathered or similar types of data. Questions of the kind raised by James Miller (1956) with respect to a variety of systems could be meaningfully raised with respect to therapy. Given eight therapist-patient systems (four therapists with two patients each), one might wish to determine which of eight therapeutic systems tends *most* toward homeostasis, which the *least*. A number of criteria proposed to determine the degree of homeostasis in systems in addition to those already explored could be investigated in relation to psychotherapy. For example, Deutsch suggests that a System A is more homeostatic (than System B) if the average deviations from the level to be maintained are smaller. An analogy may illustrate this criterion. If there is too much "play" in the wheel of a car, the task of moving the car straight ahead is more difficult; the correction to be introduced by the driver is larger. In general, the steering mechanism of a system has to work harder when system parameters fluctuate more widely. In the course of our psychotherapy re-

search, we determined a number of parameters of therapist and patient behavior and expectations. With respect to these, we are now in a position to assess which therapist-patient systems show most fluctuation, which least.

A number of other questions to be answered on the basis of our data follow: Are any two systems in which one therapist participates similar with respect to stability or instability? Are some therapeutic systems more stable within smaller time periods; others within longer time periods? If we define homeostasis, as Ashby suggested, as the tendency of systems to maintain their "essential variables within physiological limits,"[4] the question arises as to what are the specific social system's equivalent limits to that, say, of body temperature system. What are the limits within which ratios between fulfilled and unfulfilled expectations or satisfactions and frustrations may vary without damage to the system or its component units?

There exists theoretical controversy about what degree of frustration is within "optimal limits" of the therapeutic and especially the analytic treatment system. Similar controversy, interesting enough, also exists with respect to dimensions of satisfaction and frustration in sociological literature on industrial systems.

Another hypothesis to be explored on the basis of the available psychotherapy study data states that systems become more homeostatic if the oscillations of the system variables around the maintained level decrease in magnitude. Our data suggest that at least with reference to verbal activity variables, such a decrease in the magnitude of oscillations does indeed occur as therapy proceeds. This hypothesis, however, still needs in-

[4] I am indebted to the very provocative comments by Emerson, Deutsch, Grinker, Rapaport, and others reported in Grinker (1956) as well as to Miller's (1956) stimulating review of this book for some of the ideas expressed here.

vestigation with respect to a large number of therapist-patient parameters. If further support for this hypothesis is forthcoming, the question arises as to what accounts for such increase in homeostatic control in systems. One may suggest that increase in homeostasis occurring in therapy as well as in social systems in general may be attributed to "learning." We suspect that the crucial type of learning involved in social systems (and the therapy system is considered such a system) is "role learning" or socialization. Two other general formulations with regard to system homeostasis may be worthy of application and exploration with regard to the therapy system. One states that System A is more homeostatic than System B if the range of loads which will *not* throw it out of gear is larger. The second formulation would attribute more homeostasis to System A than System B if learning in System A proceeds in such a fashion that one range of loads can be dealt with better or that larger loads can be dealt with better.

The relevance of these formulations to biological self-regulating systems in particular is unequivocal. Consider, for example, environmental temperature as constituting a load on the organism. To the extent that one organism can maintain a steady state of body temperature more efficiently than another, despite extremes of environmental temperature, to that extent we are justified in describing the temperature regulating system of that organism as more homeostatic. Learning to deal with loads on the part of biological systems is illustrated by the increase in the body's oxygen carrying red corpuscles in high altitudes, which re-establishes for the organism an equilibrium between oxygen requirements and oxygen availability.

How would one compare therapeutic systems with respect to the criteria outlined and illustrated above? Consider the patient who arrives in the therapeutic

session in great distress; who refuses or is unable to continue with the therapeutic task, who is crying or unwilling to verbalize. In such sessions basic parameters of therapist and patient behavior may oscillate widely around the usual ratios maintained. Though these oscillations in themselves reflect mechanisms of repair, just as fever is a restorative effort on the part of the organism, one would consider systems which show less oscillation under such conditions more homeostatic. The goal of therapeutic systems could be defined as restoration of smoother equilibriating patterns, just as one of the organism's goals can be conceived of as restoration of "normal" temperature variation. One would further assume, but would need to test empirically, that similar distress (load) experienced by the patient during a later phase in therapy would not result in such oscillation.

The same type of "load" (arising from an environmental or intrapsychic source) does not nearly disequilibriate the therapist-patient system as much when it occurs later in therapy. There may be considerable discussions of the issue in therapy now; a great deal of affect may be expressed by the patient about it, but the patient is verbalizing freely and the task of therapy proceeds. The "input" on the patient has now become "grist for the therapeutic mill."

If our assumptions are borne out, then what has happened between Time 1 when homeostasis was threatened and Time 2 when therapy system homeostasis is not threatened nearly as usual? Obviously, the time that the patient has been in therapy has intervened; the patient has participated in the system for a longer span of time. Through this participation he has learned some dimensions of the patient role. And an important component, for example, of this role would be learning of the requirement that whatever happens, the patient is to verbalize his feelings, ideas, reactions, etc. To the extent that the patient has learned this dimension of the role, to that exent the system will now be more homeostatic. Intensifying research on therapy in system terms is expected not only to contribute to the clarification of therapeutic processes but also to add to an understanding of social systems as such.

c. *Suggested Directions for Psychotherapy Research Employing Content Analysis.* With respect to the number of variables involved, the levels at which they can be examined and studied, the range and extent of their interrelatedness, and the changes and movement in the interrelationship, a social relationship such as therapy may indeed present problems of the same order of complexity as posed by the study of the human organism. In David Shakow's (1959) words, "There are perhaps thousands of parallel processes going on during the process of a relatively short time of therapy." Even a preliminary inventory of the types of studies which should be undertaken must be postponed for decades and may involve concepts and methods far different from the ones we are familiar with today.

It may well be that studies of the therapeutic process will in the future be subsumed under studies of personal influence processes per se and that the identification of general principles governing the way in which one individual changes another through communication will precede the identification of the more specific principles governing the therapeutic relationship.

At this point, however, I want to use this opportunity to outline some areas in which current research efforts may be intensified. My remarks will be limited to analyses of data obtained from the study of the therapy situation rather than data obtained through the study of patients or therapists in contexts other than that of therapy:

*Studies of the Flow of Verbalization during Therapy*

Studies of the flow of verbalizations (associations) as they occur, especially in psychoanalysis or psychoanalytically oriented psychotherapy, have been proposed for a great many years, but to my knowledge have not been systematically and comprehensively undertaken. I am not thinking of studies which follow mention of specific topics or persons (father, mother, etc.) over a span of sessions, though these are informative.

I am suggesting the value of studying the changing structure of sequences of verbalizations on the part of the patient as he progresses through therapy. This can be done from many points of view:

*From the point of view of analytic theory:* Menninger (1958), as other psychoanalytic theorists, has offered a general formulation about the types of verbalization sequences which signal a "properly going" analysis. In such an analysis, he writes:

> The patient will usually describe, for example, an aspect of the reality situation which he finds to be unpleasant, and from this go to certain aspects of the analytic situation which he may find either pleasant or unpleasant, but probably pleasant in contrast to the unpleasantness of the reality situation. Under the aegis of this pleasant aspect of the analytic situation his mind reverts to childhood and he recalls something from this area —neither the earliest nor the most recent thing, but something related. From this he soon turns again to the present, to something in the contemporary reality situation and a cycle will have been completed. Formula: Reality—Analysis—Childhood—Reality (p. 151).

Without going into the many questions which this statement raises, it nonetheless affords an opportunity for some kind of assessment of the associational stream. Hypotheses framed on this level permit empirical investigation through currently available content analytic and data processing methods. Thus, sequential arrangement of patient verbalizations referring to childhood, the analysis, and reality could be established.

*Changes in the Proaction Patterns*

Our current research on "psychotherapy as a system" has turned up some tentative suggestions as to the way in which patient verbalization sequences change. For example, when sentences are considered as the consecutive units of verbalizations, there appears a tendency for *patient* sentence sequences occurring later in the sessions to *resemble*—in some respects—*therapist-patient* sentence sequences of early therapy sessions. We have so far investigated this trend only with respect to the descriptive, evaluative affective, and nonaffective characterizations of verbalizations. For an expansion of such research, data processing procedures are required of which we have not yet availed ourselves. Analysis of substantive sequential changes in speech references seems worthwhile for studying the effects of dialogue upon monologue in the sense of "internalization of language interaction patterns."

*Changes in Interaction Sequences*

Research so far has yielded both molar descriptions of therapist-patient relationship over one session or a series of sessions and more atomistic descriptions of therapist-patient behavior on an act-to-act level. The attempt to describe therapy in terms of the way series of therapist-patient acts are strung together in longer sequences still needs to be made.

In describing changes in the patterning of interaction, we also are handicapped by the lack of appropriate conceptual categories of description. While language appropriate to describing the therapist-patient relationship during one session is available from a variety of psychiatric and psychological theories, and while we can borrow from small group theory and research to describe a succession of acts, it appears to me that description of more complex sequences requires the development of a new set of concepts and categories. The descriptive level required might perhaps be pointed to by terms such as "thematic continuity," "affective congruence," etc.

*Concept Learning and Concept Formation*

Changes in the vocabulary of the patient occurring in the course of therapy have often received comments by clinicians. Notice has been taken of the frequency with which certain words are used, changes in the form of sentences (see documentation of this in sections on Interdependence and Equilibrium), etc. Verbalizations express concepts available to the patient to describe and interpret feelings and thoughts, experiences and behavior. The changing structure of verbalization throughout therapy can be studied for "concept formation and learning." How concept learning can be assessed from verbal data obtained in a nonexperimental context represents a challenge yet to be met. If a patient, for example, characterizes as related a number of

behaviors and subsumes them under one descriptive heading (dependent), when he had not done so previously, has he learned the concept of "dependency"? One would wish that psychologists concerned with studying concept formation in the Piaget tradition would take up this challenge.

*The Learning of Role Dimensions*

One focus of the research described in this paper (which I could not outline due to limitations of space) was the consideration of the psychotherapy situation as a deutero-learning situation.[5] Deutero-learning occurs in the psychotherapy situation both in a general and in a specific manner. A patient's generic problem could be conceived of (among other things) as an inability to function adequately within major social role systems (family, occupational, and other systems). In other words, the patient is not properly socialized into his diverse roles and has not acquired sets of expectations and behaviors that would permit social interaction to proceed smoothly. Our hypothesis would be that in therapy the patient not only "learns" a set of expectations appropriate to the therapeutic relationship and how to behave in accordance with such expectations, but in learning this—according to the deutero-learning concepts—he acquires insight into the principles underlying the learning of role expectations in general. These principles are then available for use in learning or relearning other patterns of expectations governing relationships in which he participates. The learning of role expectations becomes a particularly apt focus for analysis of verbatim transcripts since, as a result of the insistence of most therapists for patients to verbalize thoughts and feelings, the manifest content of verbalization is to a considerable extent concerned with the expression of expectations, discrepancies in expectations, and their resolution.

*Communication of Values*

While a great number of papers have been written on whether, how, and which values therapists communicate to patients, there is, with a few interesting exceptions, a dearth of empirical research with regard to this problem.

The research which has been done, however, does not mainly rely on material produced during therapy but, rather, on interviews and questionnaires administered to therapists and patients. The flow of sanctions both positive and

[5] For discussion of concept of deutero-learning, see Lennard and Bernstein (1960), pp. 27-30.

negative from the therapist to the patient, and their effect upon patients' communications in terms of their form, substance, position, etc., requires study. While scientists working within frameworks as diverse as that of the psychologist, Skinner, and that of the sociologist, Parsons, both hypothesize and document the position of the inevitability of therapist "influence," and influence toward those value orientations held in part by the therapist, the precise specification of the mechanisms whereby this is achieved through the process of verbal communication is still unresolved. Therapists' communications classified as sanctions would include: explicit communications stating therapists' position, therapists' permitting the patient to express views usually negatively sanctioned, therapists' expression of verbal attention, etc. For example, with respect to therapists' selective responses (an area which is receiving a great deal of attention from those psychologists who stress the relevance of the "operant conditioning" phenomenon to psychotherapy), one might argue that the range of topical content introduced and referred to by the patient is considerably larger than that introduced and referred to by the therapist explicitly. The therapist can neither comment nor respond to every topic or proposition communicated by the patient. He reacts to a small fraction of these. These reactions range from the Yes's and "hmmnhs" to more specific comments, inquiries, and interpretations.

The study of therapist communications with regard to the value context in which they are elicited would represent a first approximation toward specifying the mechanisms whereby values might be communicated.

*Interrelationship between Levels of Communication: Congruence and Incongruence*

The emphasis so far has been on suggesting studies of verbal communication data. Although the verbal level is only one of many levels on which therapist-patient communication and influence can be studied. Yet I disagree with those workers in the field of psychotherapy who would downgrade the study of therapist-patient transactions which is limited to one communicational level only. As researchers in this field, I am sure all of us have had the experience that when working on the verbal level, we are told that the nonverbal (kinesic, vocal, visceral, etc.) is more significant; or that when focusing on second-to-second changes, we are challenged on the neglect of more global relationships; or when concentrating on interaction process, we are accused of neglecting psychodynamic content. In this paper I ex-

pressed my feeling, shared with many others, of the horrendous complexity of our problem. However, if we are to proceed, then we cannot work at all levels at the same time.

It would, however, be exceedingly valuable to know in a general way about how much we lose in the study of the therapeutic relationship by restricting our attention to a particular level of intercommunication. Two hypotheses come to mind here; one, which asserts that different communications are exchanged at different levels (incongruence), and one which asserts that there is a great deal of congruence in the information conveyed. Studies oriented around this question, however crude, in particular would be very useful. Consider, for example, communications of a depressed patient on the level of lexical content, kinesic (body motion), or vocal. Are we sufficiently advanced in describing lexical, kinesic, or vocal characteristics to make an assessment of congruence or incongruence? Here, then, is another area of research which I feel would bear exploration.

REFERENCES

Bales, R. F., & Slater, E. Role differentiation in small groups. In T. Parsons & R. F. Bales (Eds.), *Family: Socialization and interaction process.* Glencoe, Ill.: Free Press, 1954.
Emerson, A. E. Discussion of paper by Rapaport. In R. R. Grinker (Ed.), *Toward a unified theory of human behavior.* New York: Basic Books, 1956. P. 243.
Grinker, R. R. (Ed.) *Toward a unified theory of human behavior.* New York: Basic Books, 1956.
Lennard, H. L., & Bernstein, A. et al. *The anatomy of psychotherapy: Systems of communication and expectation.* New York: Columbia Univer. Press, 1960.
Menninger, K. *Theory of psychoanalytic technique.* New York: Basic Books, 1958.
Merton, R. K., Reader, G. G., & Kendall, Patricia. *The student physician.* Cambridge: Harvard Univer. Press, 1957.
Miller, J. G. Review of R. R. Grinker (Ed.), *Toward a unified theory of human behavior. Behav. Sci.,* 1956, **1**, 319-326.
Parsons, T., & Shils, E. A. (Eds.) *Toward a general theory of action.* Cambridge: Harvard Univer. Press, 1951.
Shakow, D. Discussion of papers by Leary and Gill, and Rogers. In E. A. Rubinstein & M. B. Parloff (Eds.), *Research in psychotherapy.* Washington, D. C.: American Psychological Association, 1959. Pp. 108-115.
Zetterberg, H. L. Toward an action theory. Unpublished manuscript, 1955.

# Discussion of Papers Relating to Definition of Variables

## DAVID SHAKOW, PH.D.

Drs. Butler, Lennard, and Siegal, and the groups they represent, have made my task difficult and frustrating—though I cannot but admit, enjoyable—by providing us with three individually rich papers that invite much discussion. The task of dealing with them together is additionally difficult because the approaches are so diverse. But it is just this diversity of approach for which we should congratulate ourselves. It merely points up, on the one hand, the complexity and multilevel nature of psychotherapy and, on the other, the general paradigmatic contribution of psychotherapy for all dyadic interactions. Since I have to be selective, I shall limit myself to a few theoretical points in each presentation and leave detailed points relating to results for the general discussion.

Our area of concern in this session is threefold:

1. Which variables in psychotherapy are *significant?*

2. How can they be *defined* rigorously?

3. How can they be *measured* adequately?

To start with, let us set up the proper hierarchy of values. Needless to say, the most important of the three questions is the first—the selection of significant variables. Yet I am afraid that too often psychologists tackle the latter two problems first—particularly the problem of the adequacy of measurement. They concern themselves to such an extent with measurement that they show insufficient regard for the importance or nonimportance of the variable measured.

Before going on to a specific consideration of each of the three papers, I should

like to make some general comparative comments. Although it is not easy to characterize any approach briefly, I think it is approximately correct to say that Lennard provides us with a formal, sociological approach, centered on the notion of system. The Butler approach is behavioral-clinical centered on the notion of interaction, and that of Siegal and Rosen is distinctly clinical, based on inferences from related contemporary data—in this case, psychological test data. The first two, on the contrary, base their conclusions on the therapy material itself.

Lennard samples, from the various stages of therapy, the particular parts used being determined by the specific question asked. He makes a formal analysis of the therapy protocols according to certain descriptive categories. Butler, on the basis of naturalistic observation, develops a classification system, evaluates according to this system, and then orders his material conceptually with the help of factor analysis. For his data he depends on the second and next to last sessions to determine what changes have taken place in the therapy. Siegal uses the inferences from the test data to measure the constructs of anxiety tolerance, and movement along the continuum of auto-/alloplasticity. He examines the patient before and after therapy with a battery of psychological tests, and bases his judgment of the effect of therapy on this outside measure.

The Butler-Lennard approaches seem to have more in common since they deal with more discrete, descriptive characteristics, many of which depend directly on

237

protocol material. In their present reports, they are also the only ones who provide data about interaction effects between patient and therapist.

Now, let me comment specifically on each of the papers. Butler and his group provide us with a careful and thoughtful analysis of the place of naturalistic[1] observation and argue that the psychotherapy process falls into this area. The straightforward acceptance of this point of view is in marked contrast to the efforts of some therapists, particularly some psychoanalysts, to characterize the therapeutic situation as an *experimental* situation (Kris; Ezriel; Reider). This borrowing of status, even if understandable, does not seem to me to serve well the needs of a growing and respectable field of research. Butler's discussion of naturalistic observation as applied to the therapeutic situation is the fullest and most sensible I have seen.

Although I agree with him that in general the function of naturalistic observation is to generate hypotheses, I find it difficult to go along with him completely when he says, "It is not to test hypotheses. The testing of hypotheses is in the province of the experimental method and, in certain situations, of statistical methods. Generally speaking, the use of experimental method depends upon control, and by control is meant the control of *relevant* conditions or variables."

If by his inclusion of "statistical methods" he means the *post hoc* manipulation of the naturalistic data through statistical devices, then perhaps we are in agreement. For it appears likely that it may never be possible to place the hypotheses derived from certain kinds of naturalistic observation, for instance, the therapy situation, under truly experimental conditions. However, the development of increasingly

---

[1] As I have said elsewhere (1960, p. 88), I would prefer to characterize the therapeutic situation as seminaturalistic.

powerful tools of data reduction and analysis can help us to deal with what Warren Weaver (1948) has called "organized complexity," and the psychotherapy situation certainly falls into this category. This very meeting represents a faith that "dis-" is not an appropriate prefix for the first word of Weaver's phrase! These tools can help in ways which might enable us to achieve the control the Butler group speaks of, by partialling out selected variables that occur naturally from the immediate context of the many uncontrolled variables.

What I am saying is that I would extend much further than they are apparently ready to, the limits of naturalistic observation. I am arguing that for certain kinds of phenomena, where experimental attack might perhaps destroy their very nature, the combination of the powerful tools of prediction and computational partialling may provide us with data having equal "dignity"—to paraphrase the Helmholtz school thesis—with the experimental. It is this assumption of differences in dignity of approach to which I was referring earlier in my criticism of certain psychoanalysts. Both John Benjamin's paper "Prediction and Psychopathological Theory" (1959) and Weaver's "Science and Complexity," which I have already mentioned, are worthwhile reading in this context.

I do agree strongly with Butler that the use of naturalistic observation for the development of hypotheses should lead to more refined hypotheses. However, I do not believe it is necessary that the more refined hypotheses be tested in *experimental* situations. I think that our new recording techniques, which provide us with "full" reports of the actual events, make possible this successive refinement of hypotheses *within* the actual therapeutic situation. And of still greater importance, it permits this refinement to take place on *exactly the same data,* since these data, unlike those of the ordinary experimental situation have, for all practical purposes, a "half-life" of infinity!

Butler presents a good rationale for their classification system for the patient and therapist. I am impressed by the psychological sophistication of the system. This seems to me a distinct advance in formal systems. It gets at more subtle differentiations in human, especially psychotherapeutic, interaction. It undoubtedly places considerably greater demand upon the judges for fine discrimination. However, the human instrument has surprising capacities in this direction, when proper controls are provided for training, for continued training, and for checking reliability. I find the Counseling Center's use of "drift" records a worthwhile innovation. This deals with a generally unrecognized—at least undealt with—weakness in all evaluation systems and should go far to help maintain the sharpness of the judges.

I like, too, the way the classification system is built up around a theoretical view—in this case that therapy is "a continuing search for new elements and the forming of creative recombinations of new and old elements," based on the notion that "stimulus hunger" lies behind what is sought for in the therapy process.

Whether we accept exactly this way of putting it, I trust that the Counseling Center group will test their method to the full. The therapist classification system with its reformulation of the impact of the therapist on the patient, even though it sometimes leaves one feeling that there is a built-in bias in favor of the poet as therapist, deserves special testing.

Lennard provides another point of view. I wish to discuss two points from his paper: his general approach and the problem of socialization and deutero-learning.

With regard to his *general position:* I am glad that our Second Conference includes an approach to psychotherapy

which emphasizes the more formal qualities a sociologist is likely to see in an interaction situation. The sociologist cannot, of course, remain a narrowly defined sociologist when dealing with a psychotherapy situation. He must in part become a social, if not a clinical, psychologist! This is reflected in some of the material presented by Lennard. But on the whole he deals with psychotherapy as system. The categories used in his data analysis present in a general way how a person of this persuasion approaches the problem. These categories are valuable for what they contribute; but, as Lennard himself clearly recognizes, they reflect only one facet or level of the psychotherapy situation.

Dr. Lennard touches on one of the most important principles of psychotherapy in his discussion of socialization and deutero-learning. I suppose it is because of my differing orientation that I have some questions to raise about his views in this area. Specifically I raise a question about the socialization process he describes, the analogy he draws between, on the one hand, the therapist socializing the patient and, on the other, the parent socializing the child or the teacher socializing the student. Taken literally, in the sense in which he mainly talks about the patient-therapist relationship, one wonders whether the analogy is accurate. The patient-therapist relationship must be recognized for what it is socially—really a *very* peculiar one. Not only is it of relatively short duration (except perhaps in Boston!), but it is ordinarily unlikely to be repeated during life. It has a distinct artificiality, especially as represented in the extreme of the psychoanalytic situation. In itself—in its formal game quality—it has little potential for deutero-learning. Its very strength may perhaps lie in the fact that the actual situation, because of relatively few common elements, does *not* provide a basis for transfer of training. Is it not rather the technical *trans-*

*ference* aspect of the therapeutic situation which is the essential one for deutero-learning? It is the patient's own role-playing and his projection of roles onto the therapist, followed by the working through of this material, whether conscious or unconscious, which makes possible the real deutero-learning that the therapeutic situation provides.

The concept of deutero-learning in itself is particularly relevant to the therapeutic process. Considering its importance, it is surprising how little attention it has received. Why such an obvious principle was not given its proper place in the psychology of learning until Harlow's paper on "learning sets" (1949) is difficult to understand. It is true that as Bateson points out in his paper on deutero-learning (1942), the principle was touched upon by several previous authors, notably Lawrence Frank and Norman Maier. Still, it was not stressed, except as it was involved in the concept of transfer of training. In the analytic concept of transference, we have a somewhat special case of deutero-learning. Presumably here the therapist becomes the surrogate for important persons in the environment of the patient, and therefore one has in a sense not so much a transfer of a generalized set, but rather a transfer from actual practice in the role-played situation.

Therapy seems therefore to involve at least three kinds of learning: (*a*) the patient-therapist role relationships—learning the rules of this game as of any game—which on the whole have little transferable quality; (*b*) the transference relationships which have a literal transferable quality to others important in the patient's life and which are worked through verbally/affectively during therapy; (*c*) the more pure deutero-learning which carries over from the practice with the first two, and from the rehearsal of other life situations—learning the patient generalizes to his daily life.

The Menninger material reported by Siegal and Rosen provides us with still another approach to the analysis of therapy. This approach does not deal with the interactive effect of therapist and patient. It is deliberately limited to what the patient was like before and after therapy, not, as judged by other participants, through an analysis of the protocol material, but rather through the use of contemporaneous psychological tests. It is important also to emphasize that for Siegal and Rosen it is not the *scores* on tests, but rather the inferences drawn from them by experienced psychodiagnosticians which serve as the basis for the study.

From Drs. Siegal and Rosen's paper I should like to discuss primarily the method they have used and make some comments about the constructs of anxiety tolerance and auto-/alloplasticity.

Drs. Siegal and Rosen are to be congratulated on the forthrightness with which they have taken a point of view and maintained it consistently—even though it might not be popular in some quarters. They argue cogently for the value of taking the clinician's stand and using the clinician's method—inference—as the basis for evaluation.

But must we—and they—not admit that their "clinical" approach is only a "modified" clinical approach. It is one which draws its inferences from psychological test data rather than from therapy material itself. Although it has many resemblances to the kind of material that derives from protocols, this material still has many fundamental differences. The core of the distinction can be found in the rationale for psychodiagnostic procedures, such as those used in clinical psychology. The psychological test devices used by Dr. Siegal provide at least a common basis from which to draw inferences. The free therapeutic situation, on the other hand, provides no such common controlled material across which to compare persons, or even to compare a person with himself from time to time. The point I am making is not at all weakened by their argument with regard to the significance of context in evaluating responses. My feeling is that they protest a little *too* much and have gone overboard—undoubtedly in the effort to make their point—in arguing for nonconstancy in relation to scores and responses. It is a wise clinician who keeps in mind that the same score may not have the same meaning in different contexts, but does not this wise clinician also recognize, with equal flexibility, that the same score *may* sometimes have the same meaning in different contexts? What is important, isn't it, is to maintain objectivity about our subjectivity!

In choosing to concentrate on anxiety tolerance and auto-/alloplasticity, the authors have selected what would seem from general experience to be highly significant variables. The problems arising when anxiety has been used as a criterion of change are well discussed in the paper. They give sound support to their distinction between primary and secondary anxiety, and the decision to use signal anxiety as a criterion. I was impressed with the description of the steps they went through in cleaning up the concepts and their arrival at a fairly rigorous definition of anxiety tolerance. The same holds for the concepts of auto-/alloplasticity.

I was interested in the presentation of the four types into which their patients fell. I was struck by the fact that the first two types—apparently the patients who made the best adjustment—showed a tendency towards the average rather than the extremes, both of which seem particularly pathological. Of importance, too, was that they found it necessary to combine two

parameters in order to distinguish adequately among the groups—which suggests an explanation for the frequent failure of evaluations based on unidimensional aspects.

I have deliberately limited my discussion to a number of general theoretical points in these three papers, each of which in its own way significantly advances research in this field. Consideration of the more detailed aspects of these studies seems to me more suitable for the small group meeting on this topic.

In relation to the Butler paper, I raised several questions about the place and limits of the naturalistic approach in the study of the psychotherapy situation. In the case of Lennard, I considered particularly the problem of deutero-learning and its relationship to the kinds of learning which take place in psychotherapy. And with respect to Siegal and Rosen's paper, I examined further the use of inference in the psychodiagnostic situation.

REFERENCES

Bateson, G. In L. Bryson & L. Finkelstein (Eds.), *Conference on science, philosophy, and religion in their relation to the democratic way of life: Second symposium.* New York: The Conference, 1942. Pp. 81-97.

Benjamin, J. D. Prediction and psychopathological theory. In Lucie Jessner & Eleanor Pavenstedt (Eds.), *Dynamic psychopathology in childhood.* New York: Grune & Stratton, 1959. Pp. 6-77.

Harlow, H. F. The formation of learning sets. *Psychol. Rev.,* 1949, **56**, 51-65.

Shakow, D. The recorded psychoanalytic interview as an objective approach to research in psychoanalysis. *Psychoanal. Quart.,* 1960, **29**, 82-97.

Weaver, W. Science and complexity. *Amer. Scientist,* 1948, **36**, 536-544.

# Definition of Variables

DR. BUTLER: My first reaction is to thank Dr. Shakow for being so merciful to me and my colleagues, and the second is to say that I share misgivings he expressed. I always feel queasy when I say things which implicitly set limits on any endeavor, and I am not at all sure that experimentation as defined by logicians like Reichenbach, the verification of hypotheses through the use of experimental controls, is the only way of really knowing; at the moment it is the official way of really knowing scientifically, and in its own right it possesses, I think, considerable dignity. I do feel some severe reservations about statistical methods. I refer to the discussions in *Science* a few years ago when some scientist said, "People doing ESP work are liars; we might as well face it." You perhaps recall that controversy.

I think it was the physicist, Bridgman, who suggested that we abandon probability as a criterion against which to measure whether events really happened in a nonrandom or orderly way. In other words, if you throw the dice in one distribution and the empirical distribution differs from the theoretical distribution, then you really have ESP. He pointed out that the difference between experimentation as physical science understood it, and this sort of thing, is that in physical science you are pitting sets of events against other sets of events. I think there was something to his argument, and I think that perhaps statistics shouldn't quite have the prestige that they do have for us in evaluating experimental material. On the other hand, how can we get along without them? There I leave the matter.

DR. LENNARD: There are two points which I would like to make. As you know, the deutero-learning idea in the paper submitted to this conference and in the research project upon which it is based was an afterthought and is still in the stage of an hypothesis. What we were able to document is a process of patient's socializations during therapy. Now, what kind of data would one like to have in order to get some bearing on the deutero-learning concept and to see whether or not learning in psychotherapy about the patient role helps in the learning of expectations and how to respond to expectations? The ideal data from our point of view would be to get data on patient-family interaction or patient-tester interaction. Then we could see whether role learning in therapy facilitates role learning in patient-family or patient-psychologist interactions. Now, we don't have data of this kind, even though hopefully we shall one day.

Let me also comment on Dr. Sanford's paper because it has some bearing on the kind of thing which we were trying to do in our study. I am concerned with the interrelationship of long-term outcomes which were discussed previously and short-term outcomes which cumulatively lead to the long-term outcomes. I have some difficulty in distinguishing the treatment variables which refer to short-term processes from patient variables which concern long-term changes in patient adaptation. Now, the problem seems to be that we have some measures of these long-term outcomes or approximation of measures, but we don't have the vocabulary and the tools to come to grips with the

242

short-term outcomes. By short-term outcomes I mean sequences in the therapist-patient interaction where there is a change in the patient or in the therapist. This is one of the areas where the kind of film data which Dr. Shakow has collected and where tape recordings of therapy can be very helpful. Repeated scrutiny of such data can help to identify and locate the points of transition in sequences of communication, both verbal and nonverbal.

The problem is, of course, that it is a long step to relate act by act sequences in therapy to long-term personality changes conceptualized analytically. This is one area I would like your comment on—how to make the transition.

DR. SIEGAL: First, thank you, Dr. Shakow, for your sympathetic discussion of our problems and our methods.

I would like to comment first on the term naturalistic, and here I think both in relation to Dr. Butler's paper and our paper, the questions arise, "What should one be naturalistic about? What is one being naturalistic about?" A generally unrecognized aspect of the Menninger project up to now—I guess we have never stated it explicitly—is that we try to observe naturalistically not only the process of therapy but, in addition, we want to observe current clinical practice as it is carried on in our setting; that is, not only psychotherapy but psychodiagnosis and the concepts that we currently use.

Our patient variables and treatment variables, for example, as Dr. Luborsky pointed out before, were not chosen solely on the basis of theoretical relevance but were chosen also because these are the concepts that the people we work with every day use in trying to assess suitability for psychotherapy, and so on. And what we have done in our paper is to let the use of the concepts speak for themselves. We did not start out to write a paper about anxiety tolerance. We looked over the test reports we had already written about our

project patients and this is what jumped out at us. We could as well have written about something else, but this seemed to be a concept that was important in daily clinical work. In line with Dr. Butler's statements about naturalism, what we hoped for as a result of our examination of the concept was a somewhat more refined definition; not to try to prove anything about anxiety tolerance but just simply to refine the concept a little more.

Dr. Shakow's caution not to "go overboard" on the subjective side is well taken and one with which I am in full agreement. I would only say that since it is also one of our aims to study the way clinicians naturally operate in using psychological tests, the way we naturally operate is to sit down with the tests, go over them and see what we think about them, and write down what we think rather than statistically comparing scores or group means or something more formal like that. I think that is all I would like to comment about. I don't know if Dr. Rosen would like to add something.

DR. ROSEN: I, too, very much appreciated Dr. Shakow's comments and found them very helpful. I agree very strongly with his point about the importance of relevant variables, and in a sense I think our paper is a critique of one of the variables that we had chosen for the project. We started with one notion of anxiety tolerance, examined it through the psychological tests as it showed up in our patients and as change in this variable manifested itself, and found that we then had to redefine the variable itself. In one sense, the whole of our project can be thought of as an attempt to sharpen and clarify our definition of the variables and really to see which ones are useful in assessing personality change.

I agree, too, with the point about scores representing the same thing in different clinical contexts. In addition to studying intensively any one aspect of changed personality functioning, we also look at changes in each of our other variables, in defensive structure, in symptoms, in overall personality organizations, and try to embed our thinking about any one aspect of change in a wider context. I think it would also be fruitful to discuss the point that was raised about the differences that might occur when one takes as the source of one's data psychological tests and when one takes as the source of one's data material directly from the therapy process itself.

In our psychological testing we took an "independent" view of the patient, a cross-sectional view, describing his current personality functioning in a way that is perhaps more difficult to do in the interview situation where one discusses with the patient, for example, certain aspects of his treatment which by their very nature become historical (i.e., "How do you feel as compared with how you felt at Points X and Y back in time?").

DR. HUNT: These papers are open for discussion from the floor. Dr. Snyder.

DR. SNYDER: I wanted to direct a question to Drs. Siegal and Rosen. I think maybe this is an extension of Dr. Shakow's question about the matter of subjectivity versus objectivity. Let me tell you that I am quite sympathetic with subjectivity, but I don't recall your discussing the reliability and validity of the judgments that you reported. As I remember, when you classified the people, you said that something like six people fell in this class, and five people fell in that class. Do you have any way of saying how you can be sure not only that you are right about the numbers (which I think is not very important, and which you weren't trying to say at this point) but even about the validity of the classes that existed? Did you check yourselves against each other in independent judgments, or did you just come to consensual agreement as you spoke about the thing with each other,

and is this not a major problem and one which prevails in a lot of the things done in your research center?

DR. SIEGAL: Yes, what is called for is a good solid reliability study, which we don't have the manpower to do, and which we didn't do. I think if we were able—if we had been able to make these judgments independently—we might have worked out a reliability study which I think would have a strong bearing on validity.

DR. SNYDER: Well, let me say something further that may seem harsh, and I don't want it to. At the last meeting I criticized Dr. Robbins and Dr. Wallerstein for the fact that you people consistently have refused to record therapy interviews, and I said that if you don't do so, you ignore the most essential data of the whole process. Now, I think you are saying to me that you can't check the validity of the measurements you make. Are these not damaging self-criticisms?

DR. SIEGAL: What would you mean by validity in this instance? What did you have in mind?

DR. SNYDER: Well, I mean that to be dealing with a science you must concern yourself with measurable data and you must have a yardstick which has gradations on it which can be related to the gradations of other people's yardsticks.

DR. SIEGAL: Yes. I think what you are asking for is, quite properly, a new reliability study.

DR. LEVINSON: Could you say why you could not do it?

DR. SIEGAL: There are only two of us doing psychological tests for the project. We simply do not have time to double our work by each writing up the patient independently. Our data, you understand, were the reports which we had written. With another person—an independent person—perhaps we could have done it. Let me get to this point—while this is true in our project about psychological tests, it is not true about other aspects of it where we are able, with greater manpower, to have reliability studies and have reported some reliability coefficients.

DR. GORHAM: Might it not still be possible to do something? If you have tests taken at different times, an independent judge could draw his own conclusions from the test data or from reports based on them. He could then decide whether or not he agreed with your findings.

DR. SIEGAL: Certainly.

DR. LUBORSKY: Are you agreeing that with time you hope to be able to get independent judgments on this variable, but it would require another person going over the psychological tests and going through the whole analysis just as you did, which means an equally great job to the one you have already done?

DR. SIEGAL: Yes.

DR. LUBORSKY: And the standard variables in our project have had reliability studies done on them. However, this anxiety tolerance variable in your paper was a new variable you added as a result of your new analyses?

DR. SIEGAL: Or a redefinition of an old one.

DR. SHAKOW: But you had certain criteria for what you call anxiety tolerance?

DR. SIEGAL: Yes, though not explicit, but subjective in a sense.

DR. SHAKOW: If you were asked to make a list of those things, you could put them down; so that it is definable in some way. In discussing your paper, I was very glad to see some people sticking their necks out with regard to this issue: "We say that we used inference, not scores, as a basis for making judgments and evaluations." The reliability issue is quite separate, and relatively simple. You presumably have your criteria you agree on in your group. The problem then is: can two people take the same test data and draw

their conclusions from these test data so as to come out with reasonably high correlations? Unless you tell me—and this would be very interesting—that only the tester can make these kinds of judgments. If that is true, then you really are in a tough spot.

DR. SIEGAL: No, we certainly wouldn't say that.

DR. SHAKOW: So that what Dr. Snyder is calling for is potentially possible?

DR. SIEGAL: Certainly.

DR. ROSEN: I don't think Dr. Siegal or I want to be in a position in which we say (like, "the law is what the Supreme Court says it is"): anxiety tolerance is what Rosen and Siegal say it is. We did, however, use as our primary source of data the test reports which we had written as a regular part of the ongoing research project. In those reports we found that a major focus of our interest centered around changes in anxiety tolerance and in certain defensive constellations and patterns of personality functioning. It was from these data, from the test reports themselves, that we chose to build the paper. And on that level, "reliability" would simply involve agreement or disagreement as to what the test reports said. The question of the reliability of the reports themselves, of the inferences arrived at, is of course another matter, a task we see as still ahead of us.

DR. BLOCH: Why are you backing away from making the inferences? It seems to me you are backing away from the accolade that was given to you.

DR. LEVINSON: I would like to offer an additional argument for doing a reliability study. From a clinical point of view, you would have to go back to the protocols and write new reports.

DR. ROSEN: Sure.

DR. LEVINSON: I see several possible gains in doing this. One is that the criteria would have to be made more explicit. Dr. Shakow has expressed an optimism that the authors could do this readily. We often discover, I think, that making explicit the bases of our clinical inferences is quite difficult, and it would be useful to have this done. It would be a contribution in itself. Second, I am willing to bet that the reliability wouldn't be too hot at first, even with two colleagues who know each other well and use the same words a lot together. One of the most constructive things for clinicians is to try to get reliability in our ratings on things we talk about every day.

The attempt to make explicit our criteria and to teach them to someone else and discover the degree of interrater correlation would first yield great problems and then would lead to redefinition and further advance. You would get good reliability, but also you would have new and more explicit definitions. This is one of the great needs in clinical studies.

At this time we have two extremes: either people use test scores, about which we have great doubts as to validity, or they use clinical ratings without a very explicit definition of criteria, and without adequate reliability. If we could develop rating procedures involving high level inference but write out scoring manuals, and make explicit the criteria, and teach people to use them, I think we would make important gains toward operationalizing our concepts and also just saying what they are.

DR. SHAKOW: I would like to reiterate what Dr. Levinson has just said. I can think of few places where I would rather see this done than at the Menninger Clinic, the place that has had such a long tradition of using psychological tests in this clinical way. I think it is very important for the development of the field because we have generally evaded issues by falling back on the simplest devices,

such as using literal scores. As you point out in your paper the scores can't be taken literally, that is, scores are not really equatable. Your method, as I interpreted it, would go in the direction of doing this and I would encourage its use.

DR. SIEGAL: I couldn't agree more with both of those comments. I do think that those are precisely the things that we need to do.

With at least some tangential bearing on the validity problem, I would like to hear some discussion on the convergence between Luborsky's results and ours, which, although they happen to be on the same patients, were done entirely independently. We didn't know anything of what he was doing and he didn't know what our paper was about.

DR. BUTLER: I have a few thoughts about the Menninger reliability problem. One of them is that many of the reliability failures in clinical work are artifacts. Now, for example, let me mention our own work embodied in the paper we presented here. We used a complex classification system, and we got people to work on the system, who were students interested in the form of therapy we were doing and practicing. They were interested in research, although one was a theological student, and, in particular, were interested in ideas that the principal investigators had. These people were just about as highly motivated as we were, and they had to be in order to work hard enough to put into it what we ourselves were putting into it. Now, if you ask one of your colleagues to evaluate these patients the way you did, this might fall flat on its face because they are not interested in those cases, but if you were training some bright intern in psychology and you have a favorable influence or a special effect upon him, he may turn out to be the kind of person who could be motivated to think the way you do, or maybe he likes your style of thinking, and then the training could be gotten across—I am speaking about Dr. Levinson's point. Under such circumstances, which have hardly ever been attained or even asked for, I suspect we'll get rather good reliability. We have this paradox: clinicians turn out to be subjective and unreliable, but the human organism in general, apart from clinicians, is a sensitive, highly perceptive organism which is the best nonlinear computer that has yet been devised. It seems that the clinicians have been left out. I think with a little imagination this reliability problem can be licked. Reliability has not been approached in a straightforward way. I think the motivational component is an important part of our problem.

Going to another point, I want to bring out a research result of ours which seems to me to have some relevance for psychotherapy research in general. When we factored our data, as Dr. Shakow says, we found a client factor, which we call a success factor, among other things, because this kind of expression on the part of a client was associated with a rising ego strength on the Barron scale, a drop in anxiety as measured by the Taylor scale, success rating and other measures that Dr. Cartwright and Dr. Fiske are using in their project. The failure factor, the third factor listed, a particular kind of expressiveness, tended to be associated with a relatively inexperienced therapist. We have done other studies using $Q$ sort data and test results. Again we did a factor analysis. The experienced therapist had the clients who were in a success category and inexperienced ones got the ones in the failure category. It was an interesting exception that our most experienced therapists had failure clients and vice versa. This is going to be rather traumatic to a lot of therapists who lent themselves to be subjects, but I think that it means something we should face up to: (a) de-

tailed description of what the therapist does, and (b) evaluation for purposes of research of how well he is doing it.

Then, we look at another problem. The good therapist doesn't do well in certain cases, and the inexperienced therapists do very well with certain kinds of cases. Finally there are the kinds of cases in which both inexperienced and experienced therapists do equally well. These are all embodied in our results.

DR. SIEGAL: I think that is quite true, and our study is designed so that the various elements that go to make a therapy psychoanalytic or supportive or expressive or whatever, are separately rated. I think this is what you are asking for. To the extent that the judges do their job well we will have details about psychotherapy process.

DR. COHEN: What Dr. Butler just said inspires me to make a comment. First, I would like to say something specifically about the failure factor in therapy and whether it correlates with our therapist doing a physical examination on a patient or such things. Dr. Butler's tone of voice convinced me that he felt that doing a physical examination on a patient by a therapist would be a large factor in the failure of therapy, and what I would like to say is that this would depend entirely on the cultural complex in which this behavior occurred. For instance, in the Phipps Clinic, or Sheppard-Pratt where I was trained, the residents uniformly do physical examinations on their patients. They are the responsible physicians of the patients as well as their psychotherapists, and I know of many other contexts in which this kind of approach to therapy is neutral, so to speak, in respect to success or failure. There could be other contexts, of course, for instance, in a psychoanalytic institute where it would have enormous failure significance.

On the whole, in our talk about therapy

it seems to me there is a tendency to slide over the question of the relevance of the variables we are studying. One important thing that seems to be neglected is the question of the matching between the therapist and patient. Nobody would assume that the matching factor is insignificant, and yet it has not been focused on very much for study in this particular collection of papers or in others. The concept I refer to is included in the words "we speak the same language" or "we click" or even more primitively, "the therapist likes the patient," or most sophisticatedly, "the therapist does not reach a level of anxiety which is beyond his optimum in dealing with this particular kind of patient," or in a more general sense, "a therapist will succeed with certain kinds of patients regularly and fail with other kinds of patients regularly." It seems to me that this element is so relevant and is of such crucial importance that it ought always to be taken into account as one of the factors in every approach to the study of therapy.

DR. FRANK: These last remarks remind me of what Dr. Butler said should be taken in conjunction with what Dr. Lennard was talking about—what is a failure attitude and what is a success attitude will depend a great deal, as Dr. Cohen just said, on cultural aspects of the institution. The therapist who goes against the expectations of the center and the patient will probably get failure. In another center this very same failure might militate for success.

DR. LENNARD: This is a very complicated matter and I will probably be sorry later that I raised the issue. However, in relation to the point Dr. Shakow has made, I wonder whether therapy is really such a totally different social situation from other problem-solving and interaction situations and how much and in what respects therapists differ from each other. Certainly, we use a different vocabulary to discuss psychotherapy than we do to discuss problem-solving interaction or family socialization processes, but does that necessarily mean that we are really dealing with radically different processes? There are parallels in the kinds of interaction patterns occurring in psychotherapy with those occurring in problem-solving groups. Also, much has been written, especially by the analysts regarding similarity of the family situation to the psychotherapy interaction. But, over and above specific similarities, there are a number of concepts which have applicability to social systems per se, and psychotherapy constitutes one system of this kind.

DR. SHAKOW: I made both statements in my discussion. I talked about the peculiar character of the psychotherapy situation. I think the reason I separated the different kinds of learning that take place in the psychotherapy situation was to counteract a tendency nowadays to equate the psychotherapy situation too much to the social situation. I think we must recognize not only the similarities between psychotherapy situations and other dyadic situations but also the dissimilarities. It has now become popular to talk about the dyadic situation of therapy as if it were an ordinary social relationship between two people who meet in a railroad car or two people—two friends—who meet for an evening. I think one must recognize that although there are similar features, there are also many features that are different. Different forms of therapy have similarities and differences to varying degrees. I think the psychoanalytic situation represents the extreme difference from the social. It is really so different that I doubt the legitimacy of just calling it another kind of social situation. In doing so, too many things get lost if we do. I think we ought to think about what things are common. Again, as I saw it, I would raise a question about deutero-learning application. There is a narrow socialization process in the psychotherapy situation which has to do with each learning his own and the other's role. This is the game aspect of therapy. But aside from this, there are other levels of learnings which go on besides this role learning. These have to do with the quite different symbolic qualities in the relationship which are not as literal and as direct as the role aspects.

DR. LENNARD: Certainly, I don't underestimate the differences, but if I may offer a hypothesis regarding Dr. Butler's comments, it seems that the more experienced therapists have given up the excess ideological baggage, and that they are responding more to the "here" and to the "now" of the therapeutic system. "System sensitivity" may be a function of experience.

DR. MAHL: First I have a question to ask Drs. Luborsky and Rosen. You two keep saying that your studies support each other. I thought your study, Dr. Luborsky, showed that there was a correlation between the initial level of anxiety and the amount of change in the health sickness ratio. I thought your study, Dr. Rosen, showed that you could make inferences as to the change from pretest to posttest anxiety tolerance. I don't understand where your two studies deal with the same thing. Could you give me an answer on that?

DR. SIEGAL: In Dr. Luborsky's study, for those people who scored low to start with, on the health-sickness rating scale, the correlation between level of anxiety and the amount of change or amount of improvement was much lower—I don't remember the exact figure—than for those people who initially scored high; the point being the same point we tried to make in our paper, that anxiety means different things in different people. In a patient who is pretty healthy to start with, I think most people would agree that anxiety may be good motivation. On the

other hand, if a patient is not very healthy to start with, his anxiety has different implications. That is the convergence that we are talking about.

DR. MAHL: I see.

DR. LUBORSKY: So we could use the label "anxiety tolerance" in a sense for one aspect of my data as well, and therefore on that point there is a convergence.

DR. MAHL: Most of the discussion about Drs. Siegal and Rosen's paper focused on the reliability with which the classifications could be made. I agree with everybody else that the determination of this reliability would be highly desirable. Not much was said about the validity of these classifications, which is more important than their reliability. In this connection, I believe there is a logical problem involved. As I understand your definition of the concepts, autoplastic and alloplastic, you are dealing with autoplastic material when you classify projective test responses. You make inferences, however, about both autoplastic and alloplastic processes which, it seems to me, create a high order logical problem. At least I dislike the semantics of your use of the terms *"autoplastic"* and *"alloplastic."* It seems to me quite different from Freud's meaning when he introduced them. In his thinking, *autoplastic* referred to a change inside a person, immediate discharge over internal paths, and was a characteristic of primary process activity. *Alloplastic* referred to behavior detoured through the environment in order to bring about the desired gratification and was of a higher developmental level, characterized by delay and the other features of secondary process activity. I have these meanings in mind when I read your paper and am confused by your concepts.

DR. SIEGAL: We are aware that there is a difference between the way we used it and the way it was originally used. What we were trying to do—again, to use the term "naturalistic"—we were trying to use the terms the way they are generally used in our setting.

DR. LUBORSKY: In other words, you are saying it isn't the definition that Dr. Mahl just gave. It just refers to the patient's tendency to respond by trying to change things outside of himself rather than within himself. Is that it?

DR. SIEGAL: Yes, that is all.

DR. MAHL: I would like to pose some further questions. The anxiety tolerance variable, I think we all agree, is a crucial one in therapy. It would be very helpful to have a discussion, when there is time, as to how anxiety tolerance shows up in therapy hours. So far the referents have been test material. I think that in good studies of psychotherapy we must devise ways of assessing anxiety tolerance during therapy interviews themselves. In this connection, I have wondered if anxiety tolerance is related to Dr. Butler's Factor I. It could be. Your Factor I, Dr. Butler, is a global factor, isn't it—mere expressiveness, without specification of the affect being expressed?

DR. BUTLER: It specifies in a way. It can be specified in terms of the classification system.

DR. MAHL: But your classification doesn't distinguish between an expression of anger or anxiety?

DR. BUTLER: No.

DR. MAHL: I think it would be very important to push your approach further so that anxiety would be one of the things assessed. Also, I have wondered how the appearance of anxiety tolerance in interviews is related to socialization. Have you made any observations on this, Dr. Lennard? Does the capacity to tolerate some anxiety, the capacity to tolerate the material that provokes the anxiety signals, start to become manifest after this socialization process in therapy has taken place to a certain degree? When the patient (or therapist) cannot tolerate anxiety, is

there a reversion to talk about the socialization process? Or is there no relationship between the two? These are some of the things I would like to hear discussed.

DR. LUBORSKY: I would like to express my agreement with the importance of taking this newly defined concept of "anxiety tolerance," which is based on psychological testing, and pointing it directly to the treatment; I believe we will find out some useful things that way. An investigation ought to be set up to see the way in which high levels (as compared to low levels) of anxiety in a particular hour go with the kinds of changes that take place in that therapy hour. The study could be done both for patients with high and low anxiety tolerance. It would be a feasible investigation with the research tools that are already available.

DR. HUNT: You would put some palmar conductance into this?

DR. LUBORSKY: Yes, that is a good idea. But at first one should try to get observers to make these judgments directly, both of anxiety level and tolerance. You could record the material and use Dr. Butler's method for classifying the responses of the patient and therapist, illustrated in his paper.

DR. HUNT: I am going to ring the curtain down on this topic, and give Dr. Bordin and Dr. Sanford a chance to come in.

DR. BORDIN: This dialogue between Dr. Shakow and Dr. Lennard, to my view, fitted in with the whole timely thought. In fact, I was accumulating some naturalistic observations about a number of processes here, and it culminated in a thought that one central issue may be emerging. It might be fruitful to pose this issue to either one group or to all of the groups. I am inclined in the latter direction because I am not sure that our category system for setting up the groups permitted a meaningful choice of group. I see emerging a strategic question, and I think it has more than a strategic implication, namely, "When does simplification acquire certain additional characteristics that lead us to use the prefix *over?*" It seems to me that this is one way of posing one of the recurring questions that surround the whole issue of "What is the best way to proceed?" We were talking about it in connection with Dr. Krasner's paper. That is, what are the criteria that must be satisfied to make simplifications that permit extratherapeutic studies of therapeutic issues acceptable? This is an important question to me because I have been involved in both therapeutic and extratherapeutic studies. I know that Dr. Colby and others are involved in it, and I think that it would be a disservice to stop at the point of simply expressing skepticism. These smaller groups offer the opportunity to get to a deeper level of consideration of the question. What assumptions are we making either in terms of theory or in terms of our personal observations that are leading us to say this particular simplification is "over"? We must begin talking in these terms to each other to get down to the bedrock of either assumption or observation that leads us to reject what each of us in our research has to say to each other. I have a faith that when a group does this, with curiosity being one of the major motivations, that this dialectic can lead to the clarification of what are the kinds of research that can have the maximum to say to each other. The "each other" in this instance are those who are conceptualizing their data, choosing their variables in different terms. During the break Dr. Shakow was talking about the problem he has of reading certain kinds of papers that go outside of his frame of reference. This ought not to be happening. Increasingly, our papers ought to establish contact between frames of reference so we can decide which trip is really necessary.

DR. SANFORD: I had an impulse to speak when Dr. Shakow said, "Yes, of course, there are some similarities between psychoanalysis and other sorts of social interaction." There are some differences, too. And my impulse was to say, well, what are the differences? I am not proposing that he undertake to answer now, but this does seem to me to be just the question that we ought to be asking. You see I am coming back to my scheme introduced earlier, and I have been encouraged by the feeling that I had an ally in Dr. Lennard. I think what we would favor would be a set of terms that would enable us to describe the differences as well as the similarities between one kind of psychotherapy and another, or psychotherapy and other kinds of interpersonal situations that have some impact upon the individual. If we undertake these descriptions, we will find ourselves discussing what kinds of things do influence people and in what ways, or what kinds of activities engaged in by the psychotherapists, or by other professionals who use verbal means for influencing people, affect individuals having different kinds of characteristics. I think it is very instructive, for example, to compare psychoanalysis and brainwashing, as we started to do this morning. Your group ought to discuss this kind of question in the next session, it seems to me. It doesn't make any difference whether the accent is on similarity or on difference. Such discussion will clarify and perhaps highlight some of the interactions that presumably influence the patient in some desired or predictable way.

DR. BUTLER: I have two comments to make. One is with respect to yours, Dr. Sanford. It seems to me there has been some research which shows that there are more similarities between, for example, experienced therapists of different orientations, than between experienced and inexperienced of the same orientations. On the other hand, as I have listened to recordings of Adlerians,

Rogerians, Freudians, and so on, I have noticed that there are really distinctive differences. I think in this area of research we haven't achieved the useful distinction made by the factor analyst between common variance and unique variance—what is common to all of us as therapists and what is unique? Possibly both of those have their own share in producing distinctive patterns of outcome.

The second comment is a delayed reaction to something you said, Dr. Shakow, about the relationship between naturalistic observations and experimentation. I think that one of our problems is that the therapy situation really is a natural situation, like Darwin's island. Therapy can go on and does go on and has gone on without research. As we begin to intervene in this process we intervene in a known and in an unknown way. One way which has not been considered too much is interaction between the tests and the therapy. I think we have difficulties even in getting to semiexperimentation as shown by the difficulty Dr. Snyder had when he had the same therapists trying to do two types of therapy. Therapists do have preferences. If we develop out of our own situation as a research strategy new ideas about therapy from all kinds of observations, naturalistic and otherwise, it seems to me that one research strategy, for example, is to convince yourself that change in your own therapy is desirable. Then one can go back and look for hours which might exemplify this, the things that led you to the new conclusions. Second, one can try them out in isolated hours in therapy. As a matter of fact this is just what we are doing. We have come to some new ideas as a result of our work. We have taken particular hours in therapy and have gone along as usual and then introduced this new behavior thinking it will not have too much effect on the total therapeutic process. We try this thing as an isolated hour in

the therapy and try to observe the changes in the structure of the therapeutic hour at that point. The control against that is the previous therapy and possibly the previous hours so that I think what we are doing is following your maxim which is, as I understand it, "Don't make too much distinction between the experimental and naturalistic methods." I emphasize however, changing ourselves as therapists instead of going to therapists and saying "You must change for the benefit of our research." That is not only threatening, but in a sense it is destructive of the particular situation we are interested in.

DR. STRUPP: I'd like to refer to Dr. Butler's comment about the common and unique variance. I think a great many efforts are being made these days to tease out the "common variance" in different approaches of psychotherapy, brainwashing, child rearing, and so on. Dr. Frank in his recent book,[1] for example, is trying to spell out the common elements in psychotherapy. Perhaps you will agree that one of the things we are trying to do as researchers is to isolate the common as well as the unique elements in the psychotherapeutic enterprise. If we could do this, we would presumably become more effective as psychotherapists. This is what I have tried to say in different places when I distinguished between the personal and the technical contribution of the therapist. It seems to me that psychotherapy will become more effective insofar as we are able to become more specific about the personal as well as the technical aspects. It may well be that technique maximizes the therapist's personal attributes and/or other common underlying elements in the process. I hope that our small group discussions might address themselves to this problem.

DR. BLOCH: It is getting very late and maybe this should be the last time

[1] Frank, J. D. *Persuasion and healing.* Baltimore: Johns Hopkins Press, 1961.

the word "naturalistic" is used this afternoon, but I would like to speak for one kind of relationship to the material which hasn't been mentioned at all. My work is with children, and in doing process-outcome studies there, we have an opportunity to make direct naturalistic observations of the child's functioning, either in the home or in the school, or in his total life situation. Now, all of us would certainly agree that the ultimate test in therapy is a change in the life situation or life functioning in some way, unspecifiable perhaps, of the patient. Yet it is very rare that we ever have direct contact with that. At best we have some assessment of functioning in the therapeutic situation and we generalize from certain variables there—ego strength, insight, and what have you—to the real world. While it is certainly easier to observe children in their natural habitat, it doesn't seem to me impossible to do even with adults.

I want to speak of the necessity to keep in mind the total life of the patient, to turn one's thoughts ultimately back to the issue of his real daily interactions, his hopes, his fears, his joys, just on that level of abstraction.

DR. KRASNER: I hate to bring up naturalistic observations again, but I must balk at the analogy of naturalistic observations of the process of psychotherapy with Darwin's naturalistic observations. I think there is far too strong an implication of psychotherapy as being a "natural" process upon which we work from a respectful distance so as not to distort it. Psychotherapy is not an inherent natural process, but rather a highly artificial, even an experimental, laboratory situation. As just one example of this, the behavior of the therapist is a function of his training. Different training produces different therapist behavior. This is *not* nature's process. Darwin observed a process that took thousands of generations to develop.

The kind of psychotherapy we are talking about is a very recent innovation created and manipulated by man.

Still reacting to the word naturalistic, I would like to call attention to a fascinating and humorous paper which some of my colleagues may have read, by Jay Haley, called "The Art of Psychoanalysis." It is a semiserious interpretation of psychotherapy as an "upmanship" relationship. Both the therapist and the patient try to get "one up" on each other. Somehow these and similar views influence my nonnaturalistic conception of psychotherapy.

DR. LENNARD: My comment also refers to the issue of naturalistic observation. Now, one of the many problems here is deciding on units of behavior to be observed and methods of observation to be employed. What does one do, as an observer, about processes which proceed at a different tempo or move on a different level than we are used to keeping track of? For example, some sequences may occur within seconds, while other characteristic patterns may evolve only over a number of sessions. In the latter instance it may be most difficult, on the basis of on-the-spot observation, to account for complex interrelationships. An analogy may help to clarify this thought. While it is not fully possible to specify the effects of particular drugs, investigators do have some notions about the time intervals within which to look for these effects. In the case of some drugs it is not likely that the organism will process them for more than a day; in the case of others some physical processing may occur for a week or ten days.

But what guidelines do we have in determining the time interval within which to search for the effect of a particular therapist input to the patient? For how long is a comment, an interpretation, a feeling processed by the patient? For how long is it utilized, if at all? I think

Dr. Colby referred to this earlier when he spoke of stochastic processes. But this general concept does not help us to define the intervals involved.

DR. LEVINSON: Dr. Bloch pointed out that we have tended to focus very narrowly on what happens within the therapy situation or inside the patient or the therapist. I hope that this is something the committee discussing personality change will consider. My impression is that we have talked about personality change largely as it is assessed by means of diagnostic tests or therapist's ratings—how the patient looks to him at the end of the treatment as compared with the beginning of treatment. Very often the therapist will say, "The treatment was very successful. The patient and I now have a very good relationship." This may or may not have anything to do with how the patient is living.

I assume that in naming one of the sections, the assessment of personality changes, the planning committee had in mind the study of outcome, that is, what has been the impact of the psychotherapeutic experience on the patient? If we are going to assess this adequately, then we have to go far beyond what is happening between the patient and the therapist. We have to look at how the patient is living. Here we have, I think, a great need for observational studies. We ought to expand the horizon of the researcher, and in the process we might also expand the horizon of the therapist. We usually know very little in a direct way about how the patient lives, and I think that in studying this we would also get to some of the questions that Dr. Bordin has raised—in what sense is therapy like other situations, in what sense is the role of therapist similar to or different from the roles of others in the life of a patient or of other people? Psychotherapy has tended to be a quite provincial kind of professional role, by and large. Psychotherapists have stayed very much within the office for what they could learn about people. If psychotherapists were to know more about how their patients were living just before therapy started and how they are living when therapy is over, they would probably also learn how to be better psychotherapists.

DR. BLOCH: This amplification is very pleasing to me and I would like to carry it one step along. I believe this is the line of thought which ought to generate the variables, and the behavioral patterns we choose to measure them. It helps us with some serious problems: it guards us against triviality, and it guards us against irrelevance. It doesn't make research easier, but I think the ways in which it makes it difficult may be manageable. As Dr. Strupp noted, our energies are really quite limited. I would hope we would rather be wrong than trivial.

DR. HUNT: The chair would like to underline a couple of points in the hopes of producing some Zeigarnik-uncompleted-task effects for tomorrow. I should like to say that I wish someone had picked up Dr. Cohen's point about the problem of the match between the personality of the therapist and the personality of the patient. I like the idea of thinking about the therapeutic relationship as being not unlike the marriage relationship (even though the therapeutic relationship is hopefully much more temporary). In this sense, there are presumably personalities that can enter into a fruitful therapeutic relationship, and there are presumably other kinds of personalities that cannot. While I was studying the caseworker-client relationship at the Institute of Welfare Research in the Community Service Society of New York, I used to say this sort of thing. It was usually taken as heresy. For this reason, I have been very much interested in Dr. Cohen's making this same point. I believe the relationship of personality variables in the client and in the psychotherapist are probably very important for the psychotherapeutic relationship. In our research at the University of Illinois, we have tried to touch upon them, but we have not been very successful.

Secondly, I should like to underline what Dr. Bloch has been saying about the importance of obtaining criteria for the results of psychotherapy from outside the therapeutic hour and from outside the therapeutic situation. Fascinating stories exist about the contrast between the nature of clients and of their interpersonal behavior as gleaned in the psychotherapeutic situation and as observed outside the therapeutic situation. Sometimes the two pictures of clients can be profoundly different. This fact challenges our attribution of complete validity to our observations of clients or patients within the therapeutic situation.

# Summary Report: Therapist's Contribution (A)

### Morris B. Parloff, Ph.D.

Perhaps some of you will remember a study published a few years ago which purported to show that given a choice, people preferred familiar concepts to unfamiliar concepts and familiar ideas to unfamiliar ideas. It occurs to me that at this hour and at this stage of the conference, what I am about to report to you should, on this basis, be all too congenial.

Dr. Snyder and I, in looking over our notes, found that a reasonable way of dividing up the material for these reports was for one of us to take the morning session and the other the afternoon session, as they were, in fact, quite different. I have chosen to report on the morning conference.

In the morning session we appeared to be concerned with building up a model of sufficient complexity and scope to satisfy our group. In retrospect, the morning session may be characterized as the "it's really more complicated than that" approach, while the afternoon appears to have been devoted to assuring ourselves that "it's really simpler than that."

I believe that the morning activities of our group may be viewed as having passed through three stages: (a) seeking to achieve completeness, (b) practical application or reality testing, and (c) data and problem reduction.

During the first stage of the morning session, we were preoccupied with the aim of achieving a general definition of our mission. This took the form of expanding the mission. It was not enough, for example, to limit ourselves to an inquiry into the therapist's influence on the treatment process. Instead, we believed it was necessary that we also discuss the therapist's relationship to outcome. Fortunately, Dr. Levinson was able to provide us with a ready model based on his paper. He suggested seven areas or domains around which we could focus our discussion: (1) the therapist's personality and social characteristics; (2) the patient's personality and social characteristics; (3) the interactions between (1) and (2); (4) the stages of therapy; (5) outcome; (6) the institutional setting; and (7) the patient's social setting.

It was then suggested that even this was not complete enough because the therapist's personality could not be described as a fixed quantum but rather varied in terms of the therapist's interaction with and reaction to his patients. We would have to take into account the fact

[1] Verbatim transcripts of the three panel discussions on the second day of the conference are not included. The day's discussion by each of the three groups makes a huge amount of prose, and we are in the fortunate position of having excellent summaries in the reporters' reviews.

that the patient would evoke different aspects of the therapist's personality and, of course, the therapist would in turn stimulate different aspects of the patient's personality.

Another complication to be considered was the observation that it was not sufficient for our purposes "merely" to describe the therapist's behavior during therapy. What we would really like to have would be a record of the therapist's thoughts and emotions as he was in the actual process of conducting therapy. Currently we have available only his pallid and tidied-up postinterview reconstruction of them.

It was at about this point that we moved into the second stage of the meeting: practical application or reality testing. This transition occurred with a statement by Dr. Bolgar and an all-too-practical question asked by Dr. Cohen. Dr. Bolgar described a study in which attempts had been made to obtain data regarding the therapist's thoughts during the treatment session. Thus not only was the therapist being asked to provide a "free" report and a "structured" report subsequent to each treatment session, but during the course of therapy was required to indicate his feelings as he became aware of them by manipulating a keyboard. Each of the five keys represented an affective experience of the therapist. There was a sincere attempt to get these data, but the point of Dr. Bolgar's report was that it appeared extremely difficult for a therapist to attend to the patient, to the therapeutic intervention, to his own feelings, and to the experimental requirements. It was so difficult, in fact, that finally the therapist gave up the use of the keyboard.

Dr. Cohen then raised the sobering question of how does one go about analyzing a mound of data such as that which has been accumulated at the National Institute of Mental Health. Sound films of some five hundred psychoanalytic

therapy sessions were available to her, but how was she to go about analyzing that amount of data in order to investigate such problems as the therapist's role and the "therapeutic process"? In responding to Dr. Cohen's question, the group moved into the third phase: data, variables, and problem reduction.

One suggestion for dealing with the problem of data reduction was to abandon the idea of analyzing the 500 hours in any detail, but instead to derive hypotheses from these data which could then be tested by simulating various conditions, variables, and responses on a computer. Thus a computer would be programed in such a manner as to test out the hypotheses with rationally derived rather than empirically determined data.

Another suggestion was that one need but code the specific interventions with which he was concerned and then feed those to the computer. This left open the question of how one identifies the subtle and highly inferential states with which the investigator deals. The data on which an inference may be based must first be identified in order that it may be coded and analyzed in a high speed computer. It was agreed that although machines could process data more quickly, machines could not as yet make the necessary inferences for us. In psychotherapy one does not usually deal only with overt behavior which permits ready identification and coding but, instead, we are concerned also with some rather high level inferences. These inferences can be drawn at various levels of abstraction.

The group was reassured by some that perhaps this was not such an insurmountable task as it had been made to sound. There probably are, in fact, only a "small" number of variables which have to be considered. In the further discussion of the term "small," it was found to mean "little" in the same sense that "finite" is small as contrasted to "infinite." Since it was generally agreed that in all likelihood a relatively small number of variables contributed significantly to the variance of any given research problem, it would be wise to identify these variables.

The emphasis then shifted to a consideration of the strategies which might help investigators to identify these relatively few important variables. Two techniques were discussed briefly: one was modeled after the "approximation technique." One could begin his research with rather broad "coarse-grained" variables and by successive approximation attempts to test out predictions. On the basis of the results, one could then refine the variables and improve his next prediction. The other technique appeared to be the opposite of the first in that it required one to adopt a very meticulous microscopic approach to the data in the hope that the investigator might thereby build up a conceptual mass sufficient to enable him to derive significant inferences. The question was raised, however, of whether the fact of restricting the analyses to a given type of data—coarse or fine grained —would restrict the researcher to one or another level of abstraction.

Still another suggestion for identifying important variables was to manipulate the situation in new ways in order that we might increase the chances of seeing new consequences. It was argued that if we persist in following the classical research techniques and continue to ask the same questions, then we must cherish the megalomaniacal hope that somehow we will be luckier or brighter than all of those who have preceded us along these same avenues. The formulation of new questions and the use of new research techniques would probably increase the likelihood of our success.

With the discussion of data reduction techniques came the suggestion that perhaps we could profitably reduce the question with which the group was concerned. It was agreed that it might be wise to focus on something less than the broad issue of the therapist's role in therapy. We might instead select a small question and get down to dealing with some data which would help document and thereby further the discussion. It was decided, therefore, that in the afternoon session attempts would be made to specify a question and bring relevant evidence to bear.

# Summary Report: Therapist's Contribution (B)

## WILLIAM U. SNYDER, PH.D.

I am a bit more uncertain than Dr. Parloff is about the effectiveness of our group meetings. I have had some images about the group. Perhaps because we were meeting on the top floor of the planetarium I tended to see our group as a lot of independent stars moving in unrelated orbits. The stars seemed to be moving in separate orbits, but I think that I, for one, perceived that there were two galaxies, or maybe three. One galaxy was that of the people who were natural observers *par excellence,* and as Dr. Parloff has said, people who tended to want to collect very large masses of data, perhaps from small groups of patients or subjects, and then see what they could do about it. The second galaxy consisted of those people who tended to be more along the line of theoretically oriented observers, who felt that you have to start with a plan in data collection. They seek the origins of a problem, plan the data collection, set up the variables, and measure only certain variables in a carefully defined way. In this second galaxy, or perhaps as a third galaxy, there was one very bright star which traveled in completely independent orbit. I am speaking about Dr. Krasner. He wanted to take the thing out of the life situation entirely and throw it into the lab and study some microproblems about the behavior, and, in fact, maybe to forget about therapy altogether and just study change in behavior, or something of that sort.

Well, we attempted to go ahead with discussing some more specific studies, and I will run through a few of these quickly. First, there were about six attempts to find out what kinds of studies we should talk about, and we finally settled on one:

studies relating to the question of what factors affect the selection of patients in therapy, i.e., what are the patient characteristics which determine selection. Dr. Levinson reported a study his group had carried out, in which residents were allowed to choose their own patients. There were some questions raised as to why residents chose certain patients versus others, and what were the characteristics of those patients who were chosen. An attempt was made to see whether they could be differentiated by means of diagnosis, but this proved unfeasible (and I might note that this only shows what an inadequate thing diagnosis is). Anyway, the things that did seem to differentiate the patients chosen by the residents for treatment were their age (they were younger), their socioeconomic class (they came from a higher socioeconomic level), their tendency toward authoritarianism (it was lower), their conception of the hospital, and their orientation toward treatment. Some scales were made up to test this. The patients who got therapy seemed to be those who wanted it and for whom it was somewhat meaningful. It was observed that the residents were more similar to the patients they selected than they were to the patients that they did not select. Some attempts were made to explore whether this selection is rational or irrational. It was demonstrated that patients who were high on the F scale would not be as accepting of therapy because, Dr. Levinson felt, they were anti-introceptive. However, one member of the group questioned the point and suggested that high F-score patients may actually be good therapy cases in certain types of therapy because they tend to be compliant persons. They are accessible to therapy because of their characteristic compliance.

It was asked, "What is the uniqueness that makes the therapist choose the patient?" These characteristics, as Dr. Levinson has pointed out, are the characteristics that often go with our personal associations in life. Patient and therapist must have something in common. Is selection based on anything that has validity, or is it simply some sort of cultural stereotype? And to what extent do the therapist's attitude and personality influence the kind of treatment the therapist engages in?

At this point we got into a discussion of the question of clinical intuition and the feelings that the clinician has that he can detect, very early in therapy, those cases with which he will be able to work and those with which he will not, and the words "matching" and "clicking" were used. But this idea was challenged. I believe Dr. Colby was one of the stronger advocates of this challenge, but it was challenged by other people, including Dr. Bolgar, who said that she has evidence which clearly demonstrates that therapists can work successfully with patients with whom they do not "click." The point was raised by Dr. Parloff that if in research one follows the idea that one can only work with patients with whom he "clicks," this is a self-fulfilling proposition. The therapist who says "I can't work with this man" and then can't work with him, cannot be subjected to research.

Dr. Bernstein reported a pilot study of an attempt to combine therapist's personality with techniques, and this seems to be a rather important idea that has pervaded the literature frequently of late. He said that, using sound-film recordings, his group was able to predict the content at the end of the interview, whether the patient would stay in therapy, and sometimes perhaps the outcome, but he was a little dubious about that point. He also reported some case material suggesting his concerns about what happens to the patient's chief complaint. It seems to disappear during therapy, and he wondered whether the patient has been talked out of his chief complaint and into something else. This brought up Dr. Frank's idea that if the patient has been given a plausible answer by therapy, this may be sufficient to produce a cure.

Dr. Cohen brought out the important question, "Should we make a distinction between the selection of patients and the succeeding with patients?" These are not synonymous, although they are sometimes treated as synonymous ideas.

Getting back to the "matching" idea, Dr. Krasner described in his paper the Sapolsky[1] study in which it was apparently shown that the most effective matching was based on those cases where there were compatible need-systems of the Schutz type.[2] (Snyder hoped to make a remark, but didn't get a chance, that he had confirming evidence of this finding.) If one talked about need-systems, such as the Edwards (EPPS) system, it may be true, but the opposite is true if one is talking about a different type of need-system, such as altruism versus exploitativeness.

During the second half of the afternoon we turned to a more specific discussion of papers, but we covered only one set of papers—those of Dr. Krasner.

As you know from the previous discussions, Dr. Krasner's interests are in operant conditioning, and he was asked to discuss some of the situations regarding ambiguity, awareness, sensory deprivation, set, and some of the factors which

---

[1] Sapolsky, A. Effect of interpersonal relationships upon verbal conditioning. *J. abnorm. soc. Psychol.*, 1960, **60**, 241-246.

[2] Schutz, W. C. *A three-dimensional theory of interpersonal behavior.* New York: Rinehart, 1958.

may affect operant conditioning. His discussion was of great interest to the group, I thought. He reported one experiment in which the expectancies with regard to the amount of antipathy and the amount of awareness that were demonstrated toward the patient were varied in four different ways in a very carefully described pattern, and the operant conditioning occurred successfully, I believe, in those where there was strong antipathy, with an awareness on the part of the patient of what was going on. He described another interesting pilot study regarding manipulative behavior that intrigued all of us. In this study the schizophrenic patients were made the interviewers or examiners, and college students were made the subjects, and the schizophrenics were taught to reinforce certain behaviors on the part of the college students, and were told how to do this, by reinforcing any self references, but they were not told that they were the reinforcers and the college students didn't know that they were the subjects. Neither was aware of what he was doing, and some of us thought it sounded a little bit like psychotherapy. The students did not know that conditioning took place, as expected, and the schizophrenics did condition the college students quite successfully rather than the reverse, as you might have expected. This was found to be not true in the case of new admissions, but it was true in the case of the patients who had been hospitalized for some months or more.

Dr. Cohen raised the very pregnant question at this point as to whether in these operant conditioning studies it is the "Western Electric phenomenon,"[3] that is, the attention that is being given to the patient or the sense of responsibility that is being given, which causes the conditioning to take place, rather than necessarily the conditioning process.

[3] Roethlisberger, F. J., & Dickson, W. J. *Management and the worker.* Cambridge: Harvard Univer. Press, 1939.

The question was raised by Dr. Strupp as to whether we can create an instructional setup which produces factors that are capable of reinforcing, and whether this is comparable to the concepts of faith, integrity, placebo, etc. Dr. Krasner felt that it was possible, and said that it has been demonstrated that one can produce a warm psychotherapist, and one can also create a hostile atmosphere; that one can do any of these things just as one wants. Dr. Strupp questioned whether you can create an atmosphere just by instruction: how generalizable the operant conditioning phenomena findings are to psychotherapy, and whether it is possible to carry over from the laboratory prototype to therapy. Dr. Saslow proposed that even if it is not very generalizable, this does not affect the problem very much; for example, in the situation of sensory deprivation, the individual has to become immersed in the environment, and to sense a feeling of responsibility. If one were to alter the situation he could use an operant conditioning model to teach the person to control his life in new ways.

Dr. Krasner brought out that the technique which he was describing could be used in role-training situations as well as in psychotherapy situations. He described a study in which college students were told that they would be in an experiment and they were just to go in and talk with patients about sports, weather, and other nonrelevant material. The patients were told to go in and see how well people can count the self-references which other people make, presumably the college students, but that the way to count this was not by saying, "1, 2, 3, 4," but rather just to say "uh hunh" every time a self-reference occurs, and the recording machine would pick it up and count it for them; then they were able to reverse roles. Dr. Krasner was asked what he hoped to achieve by this experiment. He said he felt that it is possible to train the patient in the role of being more responsible, with the hope that this can be expected to generalize to other contexts.

Dr. Saslow brought up, at this point, the important parallel to George Kelly's[4] concept of the "fixed-role psychotherapy." The patient is persuaded to go around for a period of time assuming a certain role. He is told, "You are a person for the next two weeks who loves everybody he meets," or something of this sort. Having to do it only for two weeks makes it a task that he can carry out, and he finds himself eventually functioning in that role with a reasonable degree of success.

Dr. Levinson asked whether this change in behavior in the studies can lead to "deep" personality changes. Here we are back again to the question of the generalizability of operant conditioning studies, and Dr. Krasner defended his idea by raising the large question of the nature of personality. He pointed out that it is possible to change scores of personality and attitude tests, for example, and asked what other things ought to be included as personality.

Dr. Betz brought up the interesting question of whether the difference between her A and B doctors might be due to the fact that her B doctors were perpetuating the situation of the "double bind." That is, they were reinforcing behavior at one level but not managing to reinforce it at the other level, so that the patient was really finding himself am-

bivalent in terms of how to respond to this situation.

I think Dr. Krasner at this point proposed a study not yet done, but one which might test the situation, in which medical students were to be shown examples of certain stories, one story by a very schizophrenic person and one by a college student. The schizophrenic story would be loaded with emotional words. He would then get the students to tell stories and would reinforce them every time they used emotional words. Thus, he would be producing incompatible drives in the students, the one to be more normal and the one to be more schizophrenic in character.

Finally, we got into a discussion of whether the phenomenon that occurs in sensory deprivation is due to the existence of sheer anxiety. It was pointed out by someone that this depends on how much anxiety is created, and I think someone else proposed that the data have shown that the positive expectation of a pleasant response will sometimes produce little anxiety in situations where anxiety would normally be produced, such as walking out into a dark place. Other persons elaborated further evidences of situations of this sort.

It was at about this point that we decided to conclude our deliberations. I personally feel one very valuable contribution came to me in this situation. However pessimistic I might sound about what our group accomplished, I found it extremely valuable to have met and learned to know so many wonderful people, all deeply interested in psychotherapy research. Sometimes I think that is the main point of these conferences.

[4] Kelly, G. A. *The psychology of personal constructs.* New York: W. W. Norton, 1955.

# Therapist's Contribution

DR. HAMBURG: Thank you, Dr. Snyder. The discussion is now open. Dr. Luborsky.

DR. LUBORSKY: I had a comment saved up about Dr. Betz's paper. It is about the principal finding on the Strong test, the discrimination between A and B physicians. We found in the project on the selection of psychiatric residents for training[1] that the Strong test generally did not discriminate competence. However, on the lawyer key it had a significant discrimination (.22 and .23 with the two psychotherapeutic competence criteria). That is one finding which corresponds to yours. It almost leads one to suggest facetiously that we are neglecting an important resource in lawyers for the treatment of schizophrenics!

DR. BETZ: We have considered this point, and at one time discussed the research possibilities in linking up with a law school to see how young lawyers learn to interview their clients, and to observe the way lawyers go about appraising human problems.

DR. PARLOFF: I was wondering if you would suggest lawyers for client-centered therapy!—But I have a more serious question about the A and B therapist groups. I gather the way an A therapist was defined was that he was an individual who, over a period of time, had been successful with three out of four of his schizophrenic patients.

DR. BETZ: A cutoff point of 68% has been arbitrarily used for designating doc-

tors as "A" or "B." This point was selected because, in the first exploratory study of differences between doctors based on the seven most successful and the seven least successful doctors, the success rates of the seven most successful doctors with their schizophrenic patients were found to range between 68% and 100%. Each doctor included in the studies had treated a minimum of four schizophrenic, four depressed, and four neurotic patients.

DR. PARLOFF: This would imply that a long period of time had elapsed between the administration of the Strong Vocational Aptitude Test and the determination of an individual's success as a therapist. What concerns me is that if such good predictions can be made prior to training, what impact, if any, does the training period have on the therapist? That is, your data suggest that an A therapist is an A therapist and a B therapist is a B therapist regardless of his subsequent training. In your experience does the training program transform a B therapist into an A therapist?

DR. BETZ: Some years ago I checked a series of A and B doctors in terms of their success rates with schizophrenic patients in their first, second, and third years of residency. The A doctors achieved 75% improvement in each of the three years; the B doctors remained below 30% in success rates in each of the three years. However, there are undoubtedly doctors in whom A and B characteristics are mixed, and who might be assisted to cultivate their A characteristics with schizophrenic patients if properly informed and motivated.

[1] Holt, R. R., & Luborsky, L. *Personality patterns of psychiatrists.* New York: Basic Books, 1958.

DR. GLAD: Does this suggest that residents in psychiatry are more unmodifiable than patients?

DR. BETZ: I think that our studies raise the question as to whether there is a general good therapeutic personality, or technique which any therapist can cultivate and use effectively for any kind of patient; or whether there are actually a number of aptitudes or skills, cultivatable by some doctors but not by others, and effective for some patients and not for others. There may be differences in the problems that patients have, and in the capacities of physicians to assist in the solutions of these different problems.

DR. HAMBURG: This question Dr. Glad has raised reminds me of a comment that Norman Polansky made at a conference some years ago about an institution he studied. He said the difference between the patients and the staff there was that the patients got better. (Laughter.)

DR. LORR: In general we found just about the opposite of what Dr. Betz found: B type therapists were most successful with neurotic patients. Our criteria for success were various self-report data as well as therapists' judgments of change.

DR. COLBY: I wanted to elaborate a little bit on a point that came up in our group. If you talk to analysts who are resistant to research, some of the things they say are: "The subject is so complex." "There are so many variables." "If you tape record four years of analysis you've got 38 miles of tape and how are you going to handle all of this?" And they throw up their hands. But if you sit down with them and talk to them about a single hour, they will say, "Well, you know there are only one or two themes in this hour." Or if you sit down with them for an hour and talk about a whole analysis, they will boil it down to a few themes characteristic of the patient. Maybe if we look at our data this way, every case might be viewed as comprising only 10 to 50 themes. A

theme represents not a variable but a repeated combination of variables such as words or utterances which make up a paragraph having a point. If we could look at the research situation in this way there is no insurmountable complexity at all. It is no more complex than anything else in life. If we would reduce data to themes and try out different combinations of themes, then we would have a feasible approach to data reduction. I think we are of sufficient age now in psychotherapy research to stop whining about the complexities of the subject matter—first, because complexity is a property of any subject matter, and, secondly, we now have a set of known physical mechanisms, the digital computer, which can handle any degree of complexity that any human being can think up.

DR. SHAKOW: I would go along with you if this is what you want to do. If you want to study the themes over 500 hours of analysis and come up with a dozen themes, you can do that. But if you want to find out how a process of relationship gets established, then you have to examine the details of the process. I don't think that you can ask one question about therapy. You ask different kinds of questions. For some people the epitome of an hour is enough. Others must have not only the full film of the hour, but need also all the associations of the therapist during the course of the time that he is interacting in the situation. I think that we have different kinds of purposes in approaching therapy. There has been a tendency either to overemphasize its complexity or to underemphasize it. Therapy is quite simple when looked at in some ways. My usual answer to analysts who tell me about how complex the process is and how impossible it is to analyze the 38 miles of tape is that I am not interested in analyzing 38 miles of tape. We just want the material available so we can ask different kinds of questions from the tape.

At one time I have one kind of question, at another time I have another question, and the data are there available for me to put the question to.

DR. COLBY: Since people like to complain about the complexity of a subject matter, I wanted to point out that it all depends on the degree of complexity you yourself have chosen to work at. Certainly 300 sentences might all concern what we could agree on to be the same theme, so we have reduced them down now to one phrase or sentence. This is the sort of approach used by people working in computer simulation of cognitive processes. For example, they give problems in symbolic logic to people and ask them to solve the problems out loud. The spoken descriptions are taped, and the simulation theorist listens to these tapes trying to abstract from them how the subjects go about problem-solving. What are their heuristics, what are the themes, how is it being done? He writes a program containing what he guesses to be the essence of a great wealth of observable detail. He then runs this program on a computer and sees if the inferred causal processes contained in the program can generate a trace from the machine that is reasonably similar to the trace generated on the protocol tapes by the subjects. This kind of approach seems promising to me because it is what the computer up here in the head, the wet, soft ware of the psychotherapist, is really doing. The clinician is finding themes and inferring heuristics from thematic data and these are what he is responding to and interpreting in his work.

DR. BOLGAR: I just wanted to say that by and large the people who collect miles of tape are not nearly so overwhelmed by the data as one might think. Somehow, people who get started on collecting exhaustive data have some idea why they want them and they seem to be able to tolerate having the material without necessarily using all of it. Usually it is the people who don't collect data this way who are so concerned about "What are you going to do with all this?" I think it is important to have both kinds of data collection—wasteful and economical.

DR. SASLOW: I wanted to draw to the attention of the group that the ingenuity of some of the things that Dr. Krasner was describing could well be communicated by a particular example. I was going to urge Dr. Krasner to describe those observations of his based upon information that behavior ratings are correlated with affective words and how he used this information experimentally.

DR. KRASNER: First, I want to thank Dr. Snyder for his review of the illustrations of this type of approach. In listening to his review, it sounded as if we have undertaken a relatively simple task. I want to point out that, on the contrary, we are running into a considerable amount of complexity. I do not think they are quite the complexities of the order of the 300 yards of film, but they are related to Dr. Bordin's comments on simplification and oversimplification. I am not sure whether we *are* oversimplifying, but for a simplification our problems are quite complex. Dr. Snyder and others referred to the studies of behavior manipulation as laboratory studies. In one sense this may be true, but I feel that what is too frequently implied is that "laboratory" studies are divorced from reality. Often the so-called laboratory studies are contrasted with the "real-life" psychotherapy situation. I feel that psychotherapy itself can just as well be termed a laboratory situation. The differences between the two types of studies are *not* in terms of one being "real-life" and the other "laboratory," but these differences are in terms of role expectancies, task orientation, instructional set, etc. It is erroneous to imply that one situation is more "real" than the other. Both are laboratory situations which investigate real-life interpersonal situations under various conditions.

The study that Dr. Saslow was referring to was a study using change in group therapy behavior as an outside criterion associated with verbal conditioning. This is part of a series of studies in which we are concerned with outcome criteria. We selected a class of behavior to reinforce which we felt would be relevant to behavior in another situation. We used patients who were in group therapy, and requested that the therapist rate the patient's behavior on a formal rating scale. The patients then were placed in one of three experimental groups. All three groups were requested to perform a story-telling task in four separate sessions over a period of two weeks. In the first group, emotional words were followed by the verbal reinforcer "mm-hmm." In the second group, emotional words were followed by an impersonal "clicker." In the third group, the patients came in and simply told stories without any kind of reinforcement. We predicted that the behavior of the patients receiving positive personal reinforcement would change in a desirable direction in the group because previous studies had shown a direct relationship between the use of emotional words and patient behavior in group therapy. However you look at it, it would make sense, because therapists consider that it is "good" for a patient to talk, to use emotional words. Our results indicated that we could influence the group therapy behavior by the kind of reinforcement we gave in the experimental situation. That is, the group that received the interpersonal reinforcement, the "mm-hmm," significantly improved in their rated behavior at the end of the two-week period, as compared with the other two groups. Of course, the therapist did not know in which procedure his patients would be involved, or even the purpose of the study.

DR. BLOCK: The therapist was the reinforcer?

DR. KRASNER: No, the group therapist was not the reinforcer; he was a completely different examiner.

DR. SASLOW: How many days elapsed between your last experimental reinforcing session and the first group therapy testing session?

DR. KRASNER: The group therapist rated the patient on his behavior in group therapy immediately prior to the experimental sessions. These sessions lasted over a two-week period. Within a day after the end of this two-week period the group therapist then rerated the patient.

DR. SHAKOW: He had additional sessions, didn't he?

DR. KRASNER: Yes.

DR. SHAKOW: He wasn't rating them again?

DR. KRASNER: No. He rated them based on his observations of their behavior in the group therapy session.

DR. SHAKOW: What was the inference? I think this is the crucial thing. What was the inference from that?

DR. KRASNER: The inference was that we changed behavior in one situation with the purpose of influencing behavior change in another situation. I might point out that we have replicated this study on another group. We found the same results as in the first study when we used patients who had been hospitalized three or more months. When we used a group of patients who had been hospitalized for less than three months' duration, we did not get change in behavior in the group therapy situation. We do not contend that we have made any long lasting changes in these patients. However, these studies are presented as an example of a technique to approach this question of outcome. What we are doing is investigating the relationship between systematic behavior change in one situation and consequent change in a criterion situation which is related to the first situation.

DR. SHAKOW: Haven't you contaminated your rater?

DR. KRASNER: Oh, no.

DR. SHAKOW: Of course you have. No, you have not done anything to your patient naturally. You have taught him to say certain kinds of words more frequently—to use warmer words. Secondly, you have introduced an artificial factor into a situation where you ordinarily expect no other particular emphasis during the course of therapy. Ordinarily with the progress of therapy there may be an increase in the number of emotional words, words which presumably carry with them certain kinds of affective values. But here you have introduced another kind of factor which has through an extraneous device increased the number of warm words that you had without the therapist knowing about it, and not related at all to the therapy. The therapist mistakenly judges these warm words before him as being the warm words which have affect related to them. You then have two kinds of warm words, don't you? The point is similar to the one I was making previously with Dr. Saslow. He used the word "affect laden," and I raised the question whether they were "affect *laden*" or just affective words. This is the question I have.

DR. KRASNER: We are not saying that we have increased the amount of emotional words used in group therapy. We do not know specifically what causes the change in group therapy behavior. It may have been the fact that these patients went through a positive personal rewarding experience. This may have influenced their behavior to the extent that they increased their use of emotional words and thus appeared better to the therapist. However, the study is uncontaminated in that all three groups went through the same experience except for one thing, the kind of reward they received.

DR. SASLOW: There is one point I am not clear about. As I understood it

from him, Salzinger was rating words. He had a behavior rating something like Dr. Betz.

DR. SHAKOW: That's right. What I am saying is that there is an assumption in the whole experiment in the way the rating scale was used and the judgments made in evaluating the patient. This was on the basis of the kinds of things that the patient said in the hour. If he said "emotional" *words* — without necessarily having the "expected" emotional connotation—this was the basis for the therapist thinking of the person as being in a better condition.

DR. BLOCK: I do not know enough of the experimental design employed to speak precisely, but I understand Dr. Shakow's point to mean that a given affective word may be mediated or intended in several different ways. It may be genuinely affect laden or it may be simply affect *labeled*. Simply recording the emission of the word does not clarify the kind of emotional significance that word happens to have in the context.

I fully agree with Dr. Krasner's suggestion that psychotherapy is a highly artificial and laboratory situation. Moreover, I think the orthodox psychotherapist would countenance this—at first glance—provocative interpretation. The difference between the operant conditioning situation and the psychotherapy situation is not their comparative artificiality or realness. Rather, the difference relates to the extent of emotional involvement that develops in the one situation as compared to the other. As a second, related point, I would acknowledge the rephrasing that psychotherapy is intended to create behavior change, and that operant conditioning also is intended to create behavior change. But because both procedures are intended to create behavior change does not mean therefore an equivalence relation between psychotherapy and operant conditioning. The way behavior change is mediated in psychotherapy seems to me to be radically different from the way behavior change is mediated in the operant conditioning situation. This is a fundamental difference that I think explains the concern, irritation, and sometimes hostility that operant conditioners who claim they are involved in psychotherapy are receiving from more orthodox psychotherapists. I suppose considerations of threat to the ensconced from the unorthodox are involved here. But the operant people would do well to remember that so far their demonstrations of behavior change have not been demonstrations of changes affecting value systems or underlying behavioral premises or the integrative capacity of the individual. All of these are changes that we have reason to believe successful psychotherapy helps bring about. It is these kinds of changes that operant conditioning must also seek to achieve if it aspires to be viewed as a model of psychotherapy.

DR. HAMBURG: I am going to ask Dr. Krasner to make a brief closing remark for this session.

DR. KRASNER: One of the comments often made is that the subject in conditioning studies is merely trying to please the experimenter. Of course, this comment could also be made about "real" psychotherapy. To some extent I think that this is true. The question would then be, "What are the personality correlates of the individual who tries to please?" This

is a question that is relevant for both kinds of situations, therapy or conditioning, and the operant conditioning studies again give us a technique of investigating this problem. I might add that there has been considerable difficulty in getting clear-cut personality correlates of responsivity to conditioning. As for the reported failure of replications, I found in reviewing the literature that approximately 30% of the verbal conditioning studies reported negative results. Although one may assume that there are further negative studies unreported in the literature, this figure is interesting because of its similarity to reported figures on lack of success in "real" psychotherapy. We now know that there are a number of ways, such as instructional set and atmospheres, which affect the influenceability of the eaxminer. I think we will find that the same kinds of variables which affect effectiveness in operant conditioning also affect effectiveness in psychotherapy. Just as there are psychotherapists who are more "effective" than others, there are also operant conditioners who are more "effective" than others. I think that Dr. Saslow and Dr. Matarazzo are on the right track in their investigation of the relationship between attitude of the examiner toward conditioning and his effectiveness as a conditioner.

DR. SASLOW: We considered it because we were suspicious of it.

DR. KRASNER: Yes.

# Summary Report: Measuring Personality Change (A)

IAN STEVENSON, M.D.

Our group had difficulty in agreeing on its purpose and assignment, and the best way of spending the available time. Half the group seemed to be interested in discussing problems relating to the measurement of particular functions and how this might be accomplished; the other half favored discussing the theory of measurement—what do we aim to measure? In general we thought the assignment was too broad to accomplish these tasks, and I am sorry to say that none of us thought we had succeeded with either. But, in the course of the day, we managed to take up a number of important points.

We spent most of our time—certainly in the morning—discussing the measurement of anxiety. Anxiety was considered as a major variable, which should be measured in any effort to evaluate change. We discussed at some length various available methods for measuring anxiety. We also noted and deplored the fact that often the various measures do not correlate with each other.

Dr. Lorr made an excellent point by reminding us that many measures of anxiety — particularly questionnaires and rating scales—fail to specify the time dimension. Thus a person may have had marked anxiety throughout life, or at different periods of his life, yet he might at the moment experience very little anxiety. Therefore, the current state of anxiety may show little relationship to his earlier history of anxiety.

We proceeded to discuss the possibility that anxiety, as currently experienced, may have little relationship to the outcome of psychotherapy. Examples were given of patients whose anxiety had actually increased rather than abated during the course of what seemed to be successful therapy. Some of these persons had become more adventurous as a consequence of therapy and had exposed themselves to situations which they had formerly avoided. Therefore, an instrument measuring the global level of anxiety—assuming that this could be done before and after therapy—would not always be a reliable guide to the success of the therapy.

It was also pointed out that an experience of anxiety in therapy may be helpful. Some said it may even be essential for successful outcome. This led into a further discussion of the concept of anxiety tolerance. Often patients continue to have considerable anxiety in a wide variety of situations, yet they may respond differently to the anxiety experience. This may signify definite improvement, but it might not be apparent if the patient's level of anxiety alone were regarded as an index of outcome.

Next, we considered that the degree of the patient's discomfort should not be regarded as the only significant variable to be evaluated at the beginning or at the end of therapy, although it of course provides important clues. In the past too much importance has been attached to simple evaluations of the patient's subjective state before and after therapy. We also know that many patients enter therapy not only because of their own discomfort but because of the distress they are inflicting upon others. What these other people think of changes in the patient should be given at least equal weight along with the patient's self-evaluation.

We discussed at some length criteria for improvement and some of the hazards in evaluating criteria. Many of the commonly accepted criteria of mental health are in fact the therapist's projections and are a result of his immersion in our culture. Sometimes the therapist's personal biases influence his evaluations of outcome. Some therapists assume that if a patient has had many hours of therapy, he should show greater improvement than a patient who had fewer hours of therapy.

We spent some time discussing methods of measurement. I am going to mention four points on which our group seemed to agree: (1) The therapist himself is not an adequate judge of treatment outcomes with his patients—we should not place sole reliance upon one rater. It is also asking too much of the patient to be the sole judge of his own improvement; the opinions of others should be sought and considered. (2) We need something more than global ratings of changes in the patient. We should aim at ratings in which changes are specified in some detail. For example, a patient may show symptom improvement but his social adjustment may have deteriorated, or vice versa. Dr. Lorr mentioned an itemized scale of this kind that he has developed. (3) It is difficult to measure change in absolute terms; it may be easier to rate movement within a specified area. (4) Finally, we should develop scales or other measures having wide applicability —if not across the nation, at least in a

variety of treatment centers. These centers might then begin to compare their respective results. Clearly, many efforts are being made to measure personality change, but the methods vary widely. Thus, it would be helpful to achieve a degree of uniformity and comparability.

I have given a more or less chronological account of our discussion, as I remember it. Before closing, however, I wanted to mention a contribution by Dr. Glad, to which I cannot do justice in a few minutes but which was fruitfully discussed at some length by the group. Dr. Glad had made an effort to isolate common factors in the various invited papers and presented these to the group. The two essential ingredients of successful therapy to which Dr. Glad drew our attention are (a) an atmosphere favorable to learning, and (b) some kind of curriculum or system of values toward which the patient is expected to change.

Finally, I should mention that we spent a good deal of time discussing the differences and similarities between education and psychotherapy. Some participants thought of psychotherapy as a species of education, whereas others viewed the two pursuits as completely different. A third group tended to think that they shared common features but, also, that there were extremely important differences.

# Summary Report: Measuring Personality Change (B)

## JACK BLOCK, PH.D.

I anticipate difficulty in avoiding redundancy with the reports of Dr. Haggard and Dr. Bordin, by virtue of common elements in the definitions of our group topics, and I expect that they will deal in their remarks with matters upon which we too had focused. I think perhaps all I can offer is a further emphasis of some points made by Dr. Stevenson and a possibly constructive suggestion. The suggestion is really an affirmation of a possibility which might be rather immediately denied by some, but I will affirm it anyway.

Our group was concerned much with theory versus empiricism, the question being whether measures could be employed or selected without an underlying theoretical basis. All of us are concerned with this issue, of course, but I myself chose for crass empiricism in this particular situation because it seemed to me, as evidenced in the course of our discussion, that the several theories available have proved not to be very different after all in the way they have guided the selection and construction of measures.

Regardless of the theoretical persuasion of the participants in our group, everybody agreed there was such a thing as anxiety and that anxiety was important. Everyone also agreed that there were methods of coping with anxiety—call these methods defenses, ego structure, character style, or what have you—that were theoretically and functionally quite separate from what we call anxiety. Also judged as of decisive significance was reality, the environmental context, society —what is out there.

Here were three classes of variables or categories — anxiety, character structure, and social context—that somehow were

conceptually separate but had to be integrated and related to each other. If I read the group correctly, it is no longer profitable to think in global, undifferentiating terms but instead one has to look at the situation of the individual and compartmentalize it into something akin to this tripartite division: (a) the individual's level of anxiety, (b) the individual's anxiety-dealing mechanisms, and (c) the formal characteristics of the social context in which the individual finds himself. Having made this analytic separation, then hopefully rules of integration can be formulated bringing these elements together again and recreating in a psychologically relevant and incisive way the circumstance of the individual, where he came from, and where he is going to go.

Now, if all the viewpoints advanced agree on or do not find intolerable a conceptual outline such as this, then it would follow, it seems to me, that we should be able to achieve some uniformity in the way these various broad concepts or categories are made operational. I would wish we could have devoted more time to this aspiration in our group. There was a remark made during the course of our discussion to the effect that we already had too many measures, the field being littered with alternative measurement procedures. The implication of this view was that what we really needed now was some theory to orient and organize these measures. My own feeling, however, is that we do not have so very many measures after all, that although there is multiplicity there is also astonishing redundancy. With the data available presently and with some straightforward psychometric analyses, we should be able to discard large numbers of redundant measures. The simple act of throwing out a lot of measures only trivially different from other measures would, I think, help the field enormously. Findings could become cumulative and be seen to dovetail where, presently, seemingly different measures prevent that perception. In the clarified atmosphere following upon the elimination of duplicating measures, we might be able to construct new and genuinely different measures. I do not believe we have yet plumbed the possibilities of constructing measures that indicate more usefully, and more deeply, the processes that go on in psychotherapy and the kinds of changes we are trying to bring about.

And so, by this chain of reasoning or hope, I am led to my suggestion. I wonder whether it might be considered fruitful to form a group that would attempt to survey the literature, and become familiar with the various researches going on that have not yet been reported in the literature. This group would evaluate in depth the measures that have been used, perhaps carry out certain comparisons of its own and then propose a small select set of measures for research in psychotherapy that hopefully would do the job the whole panoply of measures is represented as doing now. Certain measures would be suggested for recording the individual's levels of anxiety over time, other measures would have demonstrated their capacity for reflecting character structure and changes in character structure, still other indices would specify the properties of the social setting of the individual.

A small, cogent battery of measures would not prevent researchers from adding favorite procedures of their own. There would still exist the option of pursuing special hunches and theoretical inclinations. A small, hard standardized core of procedures, however, would bring the possibility of aggregating and interlocking findings where, presently, results have solitary import.

# Measuring Personality Change

DR. HAMBURG: We are again very much indebted to those whose reports have given us a remarkably clear and coherent presentation. Now, for the discussion.

DR. LUBORSKY: I would like to describe further three ideas which came out during our panel discussion on the measurement of change. These are especially worth pursuing in our research centered at The Menninger Foundation.

The suggestion by our panel to make ratings of different types of anxiety, I believe, can fruitfully be investigated even within the present data of our project. In the Menninger Psychotherapy Research Project, Form B, we made a thorough survey of six or seven varieties of each patient's anxiety. In my paper I utilized only one composite form of anxiety—observers' judgment of the *amount of the patient's anxiety* (whether manifest or averted). I can go back now to the Form B descriptions and get separate ratings on these varieties of anxiety and see whether we get different relationships between the form of anxiety and change.

Secondly, I notice that the results of several studies referred to by participants in this conference may dovetail with ours. For example, there were some findings described by Dr. Hunt, from his psychotherapy research studies, on the relationship between anxiety and change. Something comparable may be evident in Dr. Butler's study in the relation of Factor I and change. And Dr. Lorr finds that patients who have greater anxiety stay in treatment. It was mentioned in our panel that there may be some opposite findings in the literature which report a negative relationship between level of anxiety and change.

This brings me to the third point that came out in our discussion. It bears stressing. I would predict that further research studies on this relationship between level of anxiety and change will turn up divergent results. These will be explainable in a way that we should all anticipate. The results will depend upon the subject group being studied. The correlation will differ for patients at the low versus high end of the Health-Sickness Rating Scale. It will pay to be sophisticated about the character structure of the patients in relation to the level of anxiety if we are to get further in understanding any correlations.

DR. STRUPP: I wonder what criteria this small group advocated. In this connection, I was thinking of a recent article by Zax and Klein[1] which delineated three common types of criteria in psychotherapy research: (*a*) intratherapy measures, such as changes in the patient's verbal communications within therapy, (*b*) self-ratings by patients describing their own status, which were rejected by these authors as being for the most part inadequate, although they may still be a source of valuable information, and (*c*) outcome criteria external to the therapeutic relationship. These would include behavioral changes that could be observed by others, but which are still to be developed. These authors strongly favored the third group of behavioral criteria. Everyone is aware of the problem of agreeing on a universal

[1] Zax, M., & Klein, A. Measurement of personality and behavior change following psychotherapy. *Psychol. Bull.,* 1960, **57**, 435-448.

set of criteria. We also know that the interrelationships of criteria are rather variable. I was wondering whether the members of the small group that was just reporting might wish to comment on the problem of selecting criteria, how they might be interrelated, and how we might come to a better approach of what certainly is one of the most important problems in psychotherapy research today.

DR. COHEN: I want to make a comment about the concept of anxiety, because it is so important and yet it has become more and more a catchall for our concepts of what is wrong with people, what causes malfunction in patients, and what is a criterion of improvement, and also what is a sign that therapy is going well. One thing I think I do a great deal, and I think I am catching other people here doing, is to assume that anxiety exists as a kind of entity, sort of like libido used to exist, as a thing which has attributes both of quantity and quality which are open to observation and to measurement. I would like it if this were so, but I doubt it very much. I have spent a great deal of time in the last 20 years in mulling over this question of what anxiety is and what this whole concept means, and have never so far arrived at anything in my own thinking that even approximates an answer to this question.

I am fairly sure that in order to deal with anxiety intelligently you have to consider it to be a process rather than an entity, and that we do not as yet know enough to define this process or measure its changes, either from the theoretical or from the operational point of view. I would just like to throw that skepticism in and see whether anybody else fundamentally differs with me.

DR. STEVENSON: Certainly I think this is where we got stuck, since part of our group felt that the question you have raised, Dr. Cohen, is paramount and that we should not go on until we have dealt

with it in some way. Others, however, did think that you can get some kind of measure of magnitude of discomfort as reported by the patient for his life span. And you can also get some measures of the range of stimuli which can initiate discomfort that he has. So, we are not completely at sea with regard to the possibility of measuring change in relation to the concept of anxiety.

DR. LEVINSON: On the question of the assessment of anxiety, the suggestions that have been made as to how we go about this are still mainly two, as far as I can see. One is what the therapist can judge on the basis of his impression of the patient at the end of treatment. The other is what the psychologist, as diagnostician, can learn through the use of tests, projective or otherwise. I imagine this was another controversial issue in the meeting, and I think it is worth general discussion.

What about other ways of getting at the level and kind of anxiety of the patient? My own preference here is that both the therapist and whatever tests we can develop should be used for this, but in addition we have to widen the base of our experience in assessing anxiety or any other aspect of personality, by some kind of observation of the patient in his everyday life. I personally am not ready to assume any more that either the therapist or psychological tests of any kind give a sufficient basis for saying, "What's going on with regard to anxiety in the patient?" We have to look at what he is—the way he is living in the family or at work or with his friends, not simply for the sake of describing this, not to get involved in other things necessarily, but as a means of learning about the way in which his inner dispositions are activated in various environmental settings and how he is coping with these. Until we get beyond the office —the therapy or the test situation—we are going to be severely limited in the significance of the things we can say about how the patient has changed. Therapists and personality researchers have tended to limit themselves to what they can learn in an office.

DR. SHLIEN: We also said that we should not devote ourselves entirely to tracking down the intricacies of anxiety, but that the other side of the coin—the tolerance, or coping mechanism—might be the essential feature. I hope we'll take up the questions raised by Drs. Strupp and Block, and keep in mind that we must do more than devise measures dealing with pathology at the presenting level. We will also need to devise measures to deal with the tolerance level and coping mechanisms which are the significant things at the *end* of therapy after anxiety is no longer critical.

DR. HAGGARD: I suspect that one of the main difficulties with the variable of anxiety is not that it cannot be estimated or rated meaningfully but rather that it is often defined too generally or globally. If, for example, a single over-all measure of anxiety is used at the beginning and end of therapy to measure change, it is probable that such a variable would have to lump together so many factors that, as a measure, it would lose much of its meaning. From the standpoint of psychoanalytic theory, or even learning theory, we are led to believe that symptoms or other things talked about in therapy generally result from experiences laden with anxiety, and that in order to work them through, the associated anxiety is often reinstated during that phase of the therapy. Consequently, the anxiety related to a particular symptom or area may wax and wane as therapy progresses, so that under certain circumstances an increase in anxiety might be a sign of progress in therapy, and only at a later date would a decrease in anxiety indicate progress. Perhaps, like my earlier comments about the importance of dealing with con-

tent, I am suggesting the need to tie our methods to the particular aspects of what seems to be going on in psychotherapy and, if possible, to use a set of differentiated measures that correspond as closely as possible to the events in the therapeutic process.

DR. LUBORSKY: Several participants have emphasized the necessity of being more precise about the kinds of anxiety, and the difficulties of definition. I would like to add some content to this.

Dr. Helen Sargent[2] made a classification which we use in our project for describing the forms of anxiety of each patient. Anxiety turns out to be, as Dr. Cohen would anticipate, a very complicated kind of concept. It can be sliced in many different ways. First of all, you can classify the intensity of the anxiety. Secondly, you can discuss how the anxiety is evident. Under this there are two main ways it is evident —*manifest* or *averted*. Under each of these headings you can make many subclassifications. For example, manifest anxiety can be free-floating anxiety or it can be attached to specific experiences, and this, I believe, would tie in with the point Dr. Levinson is emphasizing. We specify to what situations, as well as ideas, the anxiety is attached. We do not actually go out of the office and follow the patient in his everyday life, although we do interview his relatives and, where possible, his employer as well. Manifest anxiety also includes "anxiety expressed as tension." We all know dozens of behavioral manifestations of anxiety, autonomically and muscularly, in terms of mannerisms, word blocks, respiratory symptoms, and so on. The catalogue is huge.

Under "averted anxiety" there are also

[2] Wallerstein, R. S., Robbins, L. L., Sargent, Helen, & Luborsky, L. The Psychotherapy Research Project of The Menninger Foundation. *Bull. Menninger Clin.*, 1956, **20**, 221-278; cf. pp. 241-242.

many subclassifications. We mean by "averted anxiety" the way anxiety is kept from awareness by some defensive maneuver. For example, the first subcategory is "How is the anxiety bound?" Is it bound in particular compulsive symptoms, so that you don't see the anxiety, you must infer it, and infer that it is averted by a particular defensive operation. The anxiety may be averted by "episodic discharge," for example, alcoholic binges or promiscuity. Another large classification is the varieties of awareness the patient has of the anxiety.

All of these varieties are included in our assessment of the global "level of anxiety" and in the paper for this conference. It is a curious thing. One can get high reliability among observers even though one cannot specify perfectly clearly the content of a variable. Judgments of "mental health" provide another example of a global term which can be reliably rated.

DR. BETZ: The patient's own attitude toward the anxiety he feels is also an important variable.

DR. HAMBURG: On the question of coping behavior, one factor that has contributed to a certain impoverishment in attempts to deal with these issues has to do with the concept of defense. The concept of defense I think has an arbitrarily restrictive effect upon the analysis of coping behavior, since this concept and its subdivisions are largely preoccupied with minimizing recognition of threatening elements in the individual's life. It does not deal in any penetrating way with a very wide range of problem-solving behavior that would be highly pertinent to changes in therapy. Therefore, I think it would be useful to employ a broader conceptual scheme that would include the usual concept of defense within it as one important class of coping behavior, but would also take into account the wider range of problem-solving functions that I think we would really have to deal with if we are seriously going to consider the whole range of changes in therapy that we ordinarily would designate as improvement. The same kind of consideration applies to the analysis of adaptive behavior in relation to psychological stress which is quite important in psychotherapy.

DR. SASLOW: I have always thought that Norman Cameron's way of dealing with this dilemma was a helpful one. He proposed the term, habitual adjustive techniques, and in that way got away from the more restrictive connotation that one always acted *in defense of* something. I think his concept is a much more natural one from a biologist's point of view in that it is congruent with concepts highly useful in studying all organisms within the evolutionary framework.

DR. COLBY: In certain areas of psychoanalytic theory the definition of defense is becoming increasingly restricted. If you think of the psychic apparatus as having an initial state and an input is made into it, one way the input can be handled is through an integrative mode. It is somehow mapped into the initial state without difficulty. The second way would be an accommodative mode in which the input comes into conflict with the initial state and is adjusted to without distortion. The third is a defensive mode of handling conflict which is pathological. That is, the input of information producing conflict is split off or distorted or deflected so that the resultant state consists of misinformation or even inaccessible information.

DR. BUTLER: This is a somewhat different kind of remark occasioned by something that Dr. Haggard said. He said yesterday that if you are looking at a correlation chart and find low correlations, the data bringing about the low correlations are very often lawful. You find things off the regression line in bunches and clumps, and this leads to new hypotheses about what went on. You find in such cases that there is a basic kind of correlation and something throws it terribly off: the original basic hypotheses weren't wrong but they weren't enough, and that is one of the implications of your remarks. This seems to apply to our discussion of anxiety here. As much as I am discontented with this kind of situation, I am also discontented that we all feel that anxiety is connected with the self-limited and inhibiting mechanisms, and yet it is a complicated topic and central to the psychotherapeutic process. If we looked at all these different ways as opportunities in a sense, most of them have some reality. That is, the Taylor Anxiety Scale, a much-blamed instrument, yields fairly consistent results in many situations. At just the point where it doesn't work out we have a research opportunity. At Wisconsin they found that if you have all sorts of indicators wired, literally speaking, to the patient, and if the therapist is groping for a phrase, the anxiety indicators go way up during the silence. This probably does not correlate with the Taylor scale but obviously it is a momentary fear that the therapist is going to say something damaging to the self-esteem of the patient.

It seems to me that all these different formulations have been fruitful in one way or another, and they show both the complexities of the situation and the valid ways in which we are able to look at this whole complex group of phenomena that we call anxiety. It seems to me that if we follow systematically these different ideas through, as well as pressing for unitary definitions which are satisfactory, we will have the opportunity of running these disjunctures head on into each other. Here is just the point where we have not only a new researchable problem but also the point at which we are likely to get new information and change of ideas rather than decide which definitions of anxiety, for example, are the best. I think this ex-

ample that Dr. Haggard mentioned yesterday could apply to our concepts of anxiety. Most of them seem to me to be pretty good in the sense that relationships with the therapy process, with critical incidents in therapy, etc. have been found with nearly all of these instruments, which very often correlate negatively with each other. Very often we have not even looked at the scatter plots.

DR. HUNT: Apropos of Dr. Butler's remarks, we were very much disappointed at first when the Taylor Manifest Anxiety Scale failed to correlate with such measures of anxiety as palmar sweat measured colorimetrically with impressions on paper impregnated with ferric chloride. In the work of one of my students,[3] scores on the Taylor scale correlated with neither of the palmar sweat levels, nor with the degree to which his subjects showed an increase in palmar sweat between measures made some weeks away from the date of their doctoral examinations or of opening night of a play in which they were acting, and measures taken the day before the doctoral examinations or the afternoon of "opening night." There were methodological problems in the Beam study, however, and only recently have we got the proper kind of situation in which to test the relationship between palmar sweat and such inventory measures of anxiety. Carl Haywood, another of my students, has arranged a standard situation in which he feeds his subjects a message which contains a disconcerting conglomeration of information. When palmar sweat is measured before and immediately after this message, it shows an increase. Moreover, when an instrument very much like the Taylor scale is used, this instrument predicts fairly well the degree of change in palmar sweat that occurs in this situation.

DR. BORDIN: I guess this discussion

---

[3] Beam, J. C. Serial learning and conditioning under real-life stress. *J. abnorm. soc. Psychol.*, 1955, **51**, 543-551.

moves me to propose another category of anxiety, namely, scientific anxiety. I am more than flippant about it; I am serious about it. As we talk we must combine data language (behavior language) with concept language. Collectively, we introduce a wide variety of observations as well as a wide variety of concepts. Inevitably, anyone faced with this kind of a complex cognitive field must respond with some effort to simplify it. In fact, my impression is that the progress in knowledge follows exactly that form. Some of the data language proves peripheral and gets dropped as repetitive. I think this is what Dr. Jack Block was talking to—the redundancy of some concepts. Our concept language proves peripheral as well as redundant. We go through a cycle similar to that with regard to data language, dropping certain kinds of concept language, of recombining and structuring and simplifying it. I have the impression that there is no substitute for this kind of cycle as long as we are clear as to just what the ingredients of the cycle are. We must avoid mixing our data language and our concept language with a resulting confusion that obscures this cycle that scientific enterprise entails and that may lead to something that does not make us even more anxious as scientists.

DR. PARLOFF: I wonder if it would be appropriate now to return to the question that was asked earlier by Dr. Strupp. Do you recall the question, which was about criteria—whether one should use intratherapy criteria, therapist's ratings, or external measures of the outcome of therapy?

DR. STEVENSON: I have been very uncomfortable since Dr. Strupp asked that question. I had not forgotten it and felt that if there was a pause I would try to discuss it. I think we did not reach any firm opinions on the best criteria of measuring change, and a short answer to Dr. Strupp probably would be that all three

of these measures are important and should be used and compared with each other. At the same time we should recognize that the simplest one—to ask the patient how he is before and after treatment—is the least valuable; the most important one—the judgments of other people about the patient's behavior and changes—is the most difficult to attain. So we are probably going to have to try to develop all three of these methods of measuring.

DR. SHLIEN: Sooner or later this job is going to have to be done, and I think there is a common recognition among us that it will be done and the comment on the scientific anxiety is one *recognition of that.

Just let me propose that I think this will be the image of events shortly, so why not put it into action instead of letting it fall upon us. Let there be a committee of astute and honorable men who spend the next five years providing us with one criterion in each of these categories so that we can have comparability amongst all our studies and still allow measurements regarding individual interests of the researcher. Let me just state my bias: I hope you will give us measures which concentrate on the measurement of strength—this is what I have been saying all through the conference. I think it is the essential thing to measure. I really wish Dr. Saslow would comment on some of the remarks he was making to me yesterday regarding concepts of health as more than residual, or the absence of disease. I do not know whether you are going to take that up. If so, I would like to see that thrown in as a line of thought.

DR. SASLOW: I wasn't clear what kind of committee you wanted to set up.

DR. SHLIEN: The kind of committee that is composed of astute and honorable men. I think it will have to be both of those things. I do not know how the committees operate or are selected, but isn't it the obligation of this conference and the responsibility of this kind of conference to move in that direction?

DR. HUNT: Although I recognize that fruitful research on psychotherapy demands organization, that it demands even complex organization, I am troubled by Dr. Shlien's suggestion for a coordinating committee, no matter how astute and honorable the men composing it might be. I am troubled because this looks like an attempt to give away our freedom, our freedom to investigate our own hypotheses. The suggestion reminds me of that play by Archibald MacLeish which is titled, I believe, *The Land of the Free*. In it, he has the line, according to my now dim recollection, "They cannot stand their freedom." My point is this: I believe we cannot force even research development by artificial organization of committee structures. The research we see needed will have to come by a growth process in which each of us will contribute, with our own groups, as we investigate our own hypotheses in our own way. Gradually, there may come a time—if psychotherapy as we now see it continues to be considered important—when a major center is created to investigate the kinds of issues we cannot investigate via small individual enterprise. I suspect that each of us, in his own way, will grow beyond the kind of things that Dr. Bordin has been talking about. Yet I agree thoroughly that we must get outside of our psychotherapeutic offices in the search for criteria of client or patient change. This, however, need not call for a coordinating committee.

DR. BOLGAR: It seems to me that the definition of criteria is closely related to the purpose of therapy and the specific stance a therapist takes concerning his goals and the patient's goals. If psychotherapy is essentially a process of "curing the sick," the criteria would inevitably be selected in terms of reducing illness. If, on the other hand, therapy is viewed as an experience of growth in and through an interpersonal relationship, then we will have to look for criteria of growth, and the changes will have to be measured in entirely different ways. In our own study we are developing two sets of criteria which may overlap at some points. I suspect that both sets measure changes in growth rather than in reduction of illness. One set of criteria deals with the changes in tolerance—for anxiety, for ambiguity, for complexity, for uncertainty. The other set of criteria is based on Erikson's thinking about growth and development. We have tried to construct a $Q$ sort utilizing Erikson's illustrations of the "eight stages of man." We have put concepts like identity, intimacy, integrity, as well as those of the preadolescent conflicts into first person descriptive terms of interpersonal and intrapersonal experiences. While these two sets of criteria may not tap all the possible outcomes of psychotherapy, we find them useful for our long-term psychoanalytic psychotherapy cases. Probably there are no universal criteria which could be applied to all forms of therapeutic experience.

DR. SHAKOW: In line with Dr. Shlien's comments and the remark of Dr. Bordin, it certainly seems within the province of a conference of this kind to take stock of the present status of the field and to make recommendations of any kind that it wants to make. If the group feels at the present time that a committee such as Dr. Shlien suggested or some conference such as Dr. Bordin suggested would be profitable, there are agencies to take care of this. For instance, the Social Science Research Council has committees of various kinds which take responsibility for certain areas. I do not see why psychotherapy should not be one of these areas. A committee of this kind could be set up through the Social Science Research Council. The Council has obtained funds to support summer conferences, small conferences, or short conferences as well. I had hoped that something of this kind would come out as recommendations of a conference of this kind. Perhaps Dr. Saslow was hoping to get into this in his concluding remarks. We could continue with these three-day conferences for many, many years. The question is how much further they advance us. Perhaps we are ready for more rapid advance than we have been making, and this could be accomplished by other devices.

DR. BUTLER: I certainly would want to second this, although I am not sure this is the appropriate point.

For example, it occurs to me that in our studies of psychotherapy, from pretherapy to follow-up periods, of whatever duration they are, we are really short of the mark. We cannot do in 20 years what a man with a program of studies working with animals can do in two or three years. Let me give you an example from my own experience which I think seriously limits our knowledge.

In doing a study some years ago at the Counseling Center, which was reported by Rogers and Dymond, we found that certain of the clients terminated therapy because they moved away. Certain clients terminated therapy because therapy was over, they thought, and the therapist so thought. Certain clients terminated therapy because they thought they were through and the therapist didn't. Because of limitation of time and money we had to consider all of these people as having terminated therapy. However, the results were differential, and it is very clear that if we had taken the people who terminated therapy when the therapist and the client had agreed that therapy was over—we had a large number of such clients, say 25—the results would have been much more clear-cut, much more consistent, and so on. We arbitrarily defined our clients as being in the same stage of the process

when, actually, they were in entirely different stages of the process.

I would suggest seriously that studies of psychotherapy require at least ten-year spans, and that a program should be allowed to run for ten years even for a relatively modest sample. Now, this might be costly. A good strategy might be small yearly grants.

DR. HUNT: While I was at the Institute of Welfare Research of the Community Service Society of New York, we had a sample of 38 cases that we used continually in the development of our Movement Scale.[4] We also followed those cases up. The follow-up interviews were made between five and seven years after the cases were closed. It was an amazing experience. Parenthetically, I should call attention to the fact that in family casework, a case is a family rather than an individual, and that there were 130-some individuals comprising these 38 cases. In our follow-up study, Phyllis Bartelme found the individuals in these 38 cases all over the country. She found some in California, some in New Orleans, some in Virginia, some in Chicago, others in Detroit. We made the effort and succeeded in seeing nearly all the individuals in all of these cases. We demonstrated that it can be done. It certainly takes the investigator outside the office. Moreover, it was very expensive; that study cost in the neighborhood of $60,000.[5]

DR. SASLOW: I would like to speak a little bit to what Dr. Shlien said. It makes a good deal of difference what point of view you take about your goal in dealing with a client or patient. As Dr.

---

[4] Hunt, J. McV., & Kogan, L. S. *Measuring results in social casework: A manual on judging movement.* New York: Family Service Association of America, 1950.

[5] Kogan, L. S., Hunt, J. McV., & Bartelme, Phyllis. *A follow-up study of the effects of social casework.* New York: Family Service Association of America, 1953.

Bolgar has said, I think one works very differently—if you think as the conventionally trained doctor does that his goal is curing the sick or helping the sick—than when the viewpoint is that if a person has come to you for some kind of psychological help, then whatever his presenting symptoms, incapacities, difficulties, complaints, or the stress he causes others, your goal is to discover what kind of person this could be. In the latter case, you often find, as you help him examine his life and help him choose new purposes, that his presenting difficulties are matters *en passant*. For this reason I find most stimulating George Kelly's way of looking at the goals of psychotherapy in his book *The Psychology of Personal Constructs*.[6] He regards psychotherapy not as having to meet the criteria of reducing discomfort, abolishing or minimizing symptoms, etc., but rather as helping the person learn by a variety of methods that he need not be a prisoner either of his biography or of his situation. He considers the goal of psychotherapy to be helping the person learn this. When he thinks a person has learned this, he is not particularly interested in counting the number of persons who apply their emancipation in this way, the number who apply it in some other way, etc. Kelly, like me, has no commitment whatever to what kind of life the patient then chooses. In a sense he regards him as having broken out of a circular fence—once out, he is free. My experience has been that this attitude is far more powerful than the conventional doctor's attitude. Whatever disabilities a patient has brought to me initially, whether they are symptoms in the conventional physiological sense or behavior disabilities, I make the assumption that the likelihood that they will develop zero strength is probably zero, but that the role these disabilities will play,

subsequently, if he has been freed from his past and his situation in Kelly's sense, becomes entirely bearable, acceptable, often very understandable, and very much less preoccupying and determining than before. Thinking of the psychotherapeutic process in this way takes you away from some of the issues we have been talking about, for one thing, and for another allies you in your psychotherapeutic activities with many other people who study the socialization, the education, the growing process of persons not referred to you for consultation. To this way of regarding psychotherapy, Dr. Levinson's approach is most congenial: the psychotherapist looks at the problems of his patient as if he were examining a career. I find to my surprise that although he and I have never talked to each other about our views of psychotherapy, his paper about regarding the patient as having a career has fundamental similarities to the principles I used four years ago in designing a psychiatric ward on which patients live, are studied, work on their problems (with their families if necessary), as if we are concerned chiefly with their careers.

DR. BORDIN: I want to respond to Dr. Saslow's comments about people being caught in traps by referring to the purposes of a conference like this, or a summer conference, or any exchange between research workers. I would see its major purpose being to free us of the traps we are caught in by our own concepts and our own measures of behavioral variables. I think that a conference like this one is too brief to permit this kind of process to take place. We made some starts on it in our small groups. I know that through my interactions with others a start was made at releasing me from the traps I was caught in. For this reason I appeal for a more extended conference, one in which this kind of dialectic can take place and in which there is some opportunity for us to find out how much

[6] Kelly, G. A. *The psychology of personal constructs.* New York: W. W. Norton, 1955.

we must give up of our cherished assumptions in order to escape our traps. This is why I respond very much to Dr. Shakow's suggestion that we need to set in motion some more extended process of exchange, one that endures long enough to permit deeper communication.

DR. SASLOW: I wanted to add in relation to the concept we were just discussing a very interesting set of observations presented at Chicago at the American Psychiatric Association meeting. It concerned the criteria used for studying 50 adult men, labeled 50 normal men, defined as normal because they scored (on various scales) within one standard deviation from the mean on the MMPI (Minnesota Multiphasic Personality Inventory). When these youngsters were boys of nine or so, there was a study at Minnesota, a total sample of school children of a particular grade. A certain number of years later these adults have now been followed up, using some of the original methods of the research group. They followed them into their homes; they talked to their wives and about their occupations, and learned a great deal about them. The observers reached the conclusion that if your initial criterion was that a normal person is one who scored within plus or minus one standard deviation on the MMPI you found that you had in adulthood a complacent group of fellows who were a kind of caricature of American life: very happy, their wives thought they were wonderful, their kids loved to go to school, they had a house, and they had a car, but they were shockingly lacking in imaginativeness and creativeness. Wesley and Epstein, who are conducting a study on what they call normal students at McGill in Canada, have used quite different criteria of normality. In commenting on the American study, they were surprised that anyone would think of the MMPI score as described above as a criterion for normalcy. They clearly included in their own

acknowledgment of what a healthy functioning human being is, someone who has unresolved tensions of various kinds, has unresolved aspirations, or ego enhancing models, and so on, a very different and much more dynamic concept. This struck me as relevant to what I find myself caught up with over and over again in a medical setting. Although there are many ways in which we find the analogy of psychotherapy with medicine very useful, here is one of the traps we may fall into: curing the sick always seems to be closely related to exorcising demons or pathogenic agents, with the hoped-for result that the organism so afflicted with a short-term kind of process will then be ready to revert to the status quo ante illness or disability. I think a great many psychiatric problems cannot be dealt with effectively in terms of that concept. Our problems in general have more to do with the long-term quality of a human life which will have a duration of 80 to 100 years.

DR. SHLIEN: Dr. Bolgar says that there are two therapeutic orientations. Let us test the truth of that. Are there really those primarily interested in curing, and those primarily interested in growth? We do seem to have divided in terms of what we measure—some measure anxiety, present at the beginning of therapy, absent at the end—while others may focus on "self-esteem"—absent at the beginning, present at the end. Would the first group be accurately identified as "curing" and the second as "growth" oriented? Do we really divide on orientations this way?

DR. BLOCH: Much of this discussion points to the desirability of having certain classes of persons as part of this conference group. The philosophical anthropologists, for example, certainly belong here if we can find any such who would be congenial to coming, and those sociologists who speak to the issue of what kind of social phenomena *we* are also ought to be here. *We* need to be in context in addition to having the patient in context, and should recognize the relationship between our purposes and the society's purposes for us. It bears on the kind of research that is generated. Perhaps some disagreement would be resolved if we could understand more clearly our relationship to the social and philosophical context in which we as therapists or researchers operate.

DR. KRASNER: I want to comment on something that Dr. Butler said, but first I want to second with whole-hearted agreement what Dr. Bloch has said. Dr. Butler suggested the need for long-range 10-year studies of psychotherapy. While I agree with the need for such long-range studies, there are a large number of questions that this conference has generated that can be answered in shorter periods of time in so-called laboratory settings. Thus, I would give one additional job to this committee, to ask the kinds of questions that can be answered in laboratory settings and to explore the implications of the so-called laboratory studies for the long-term psychotherapy process.

DR. BUTLER: I would hope that leading from there would be some kind of interaction to find out what grows out of psychotherapy. We have not been in the office as much as we say we have, except as therapists. In fact we have been in the office very little as therapists; as researchers we have not been. Show me more than

a very small handful of satisfactory process therapy studies! Now, if we can well describe the process, we can well theorize about it. We have more realistic opportunity for just the kind of interactions you propose.

DR. HAMBURG: The discussion of the last half hour or so I think reflects a rather widespread concern in the mental health field, particularly among those interested in criteria of mental health in a more positive sense than the absence of gross mental illness. It is reflected in publications in recent years by Erikson, Jahoda, Scott, Hartmann, and others. While I am personally sympathetic to these approaches, I have been very much impressed with the difficulties involved. One of the most formidable difficulties, it seems to me, could be briefly stated, "Whose values?" This raises a question, which may have been discussed in some of the subgroups about the bases for evaluation of change in therapy. Here, as Dr. Bloch has suggested, we get into some of the fundamental questions of the social sciences, and I think it would be very important to consider these problems with the help of anthropologists and other social scientists. One way in which this second psychotherapy conference seems to me to have made a significant advance over the first conference is in its greater recognition of social factors. I believe we could go even further in future meetings.

# Summary Report:
# Definition of Variables (A)

ERNEST A. HAGGARD, PH.D.

Dr. Shakow, our chairman, opened our meeting with the suggestion that we attempt to define the topic or topics we wished to concentrate on in order to limit the scope of our discussion. In looking over my notes, I suspect that, instead, we adopted the working assumption that if we could get enough variables into orbit we could establish our own universe of discourse.

After obtaining a blackboard, we listed a variety of proposed topics, out of which we hoped to select a few for intensive discussion. At this stage we set only one restriction on ourselves—namely, that the topics should have to do with some form of therapist-patient interaction. In order to give you an idea of how this phase of our discussion went, I will list the suggested topics as they were proposed. The list includes:

(1) The dependency of the patient on the therapist and the therapist's commitment to support and nurture the patient in therapy.

(2) The relative congruence of the therapist's and the patient's value systems and, more generally, their view of the nature of man (e.g., a bundle of operant responses or a superstructure built on a fluid unconscious).

(3) The relation of intratherapy interactions and processes to behavior in non-therapy situations (e.g., what does the patient talk about and deal with in therapy and how does he live and act in the outside world).

(4) The extent to which the therapist makes his goals and values known to the patient and their effect on the patient's behavior in and out of therapy.

(5) The effects of different levels of anxiety in the therapist and in the patient, with primary reference to the problem of establishing and maintaining some optimal level of anxiety.

(6) The nature and generality of the working contract between the therapist and the patient, with particular reference to their activity levels during therapy.

(7) The effects of the therapist's varying his own roles and goals on the therapy process (e.g., the therapist's shift from the role of helper to that of investigator).

(8) The degree of communicational efficiency between the therapist and the patient, including both the substantive content and the affective aspects of their communications.

At this point, the blackboard was filled, and I think we were all relieved that it was not a larger one.

Since we had run out of space for any more topics-at-random, Dr. Shakow then suggested that we attempt to work from our first list of suggestions toward a shorter list of topics, again with emphasis on therapist-patient interaction variables. On this go-around, there were four topics or areas suggested. They were:

(1) The degree of structuredness in the therapy situation, that is, the extent to which the situation and all its dimensions are structured or allowed to remain undefined and ambiguous.

(2) The definition of the therapist: his tasks, goals, how he presents himself as a person to the patient and his view of the

patient, and, correspondingly, the patient's view of the therapist and of himself, of the therapeutic task and of his participation in it, and the effect that such factors might have on the therapeutic process.

(3) Variations in anxiety level (especially the patient's) with particular reference to differences between acute and chronic anxiety, such as a temporary anxiety attack as opposed to a chronic obsessional or psychotic state.

(4) The problem of transference and the patient's perception of himself.

Although the reduced list of topics was drawn up to focalize our discussion, it can hardly be said that we were intimidated by the list and, like most any other group, our discussions splashed over from time to time into an assortment of other topics. But I will try to summarize the sense of our discussions by following two threads: one was concerned essentially with clinical content and theory and the other with methodological aspects of the psychotherapy process.

Most of the discussion during the morning session focused around considerations of what we may call the "continuum of ambiguity structuredness." Broadly speaking, this continuum has to do with the extent to which various factors or characteristics of the therapy situation as a whole tend to maximize or minimize the range of the therapist's and the patient's behavior. We discussed at least five aspects of this continuum which can be thought of as variables or dimensions along which there can be degrees of ambiguity or structuredness.

The first dimension has to do with the nature of the therapeutic task. One could, for example, be either quite specific or quite ambiguous about what is to be done, as to free associate or to discuss current life problems, or to give the patient freedom to discuss whatever he likes. The second dimension has to do with the nature of the required or acceptable content to be given by the patient. Although similar to the first, this dimension has to do with the extent to which the patient is free to discuss different types of content, whether it be, for example, past or present sexual and aggressive impulses, interpersonal relationships, feelings, fantasies, or current reality experiences. The third dimension has to do with the therapist-patient relationship. Thus, the therapist could fix and maintain a particular relationship (e.g., seemingly impersonal or personally involved in the patient's problems) or he could allow the relationship to vary over the course of therapy, depending on such factors as variations in the patient's anxiety level, the content being dealt with, or the occurrence of significant external events in the life of the patient. The fourth dimension has to do specifically with anxiety level—especially of the patient, but also of the therapist to some extent. In this case, the therapist might permit or even facilitate variations in the patient's anxiety level or he might try to maintain some fixed or optimal level of anxiety, as defined in terms of various other characteristics of the situation or his goals for the therapy. And, finally, the fifth dimension has to do with the relative activity or passivity of the therapist and/or patient. For example, the therapist might define for himself and the patient a relatively active or passive role in the therapy situation, and in addition might attempt to maintain such a level of activity over the course of therapy or might attempt to vary it during particular phases of the therapy.

There were also, of course, a number of examples which suggested possible effects of variations in the degree of ambiguity or structuredness in the therapy situation. For instance, with increased ambiguity (or decreased structure) the patient is not only freed to behave in a greater variety of ways, but the ambiguity also permits such phenomena as transference to emerge and flourish. As in the use of projective techniques where one presents the subject with an ambiguous (rather than well-defined) stimulus, the subject is both permitted and required to bring structure to it, to add characteristics of himself by "projections" from his own attitudes and experiences. In some types of therapy, such as psychoanalysis, a condition of relatively great ambiguity similarly permits if not requires the patient to fill in important aspects of the situation which are not made explicit by the therapist. And, since to the patient the therapist is perhaps the most important aspect of the therapy situation, and since a large component of therapy has to do with emotional reactions, it is not surprising that the patient's view of the therapist, of his interests, his likes and dislikes, and of what he approves and disapproves will be in large measure a projection or transference based on the patient's own character, experience, and affects. If, on the other hand, the therapy situation is well defined, vis à vis, and the therapist is active and explicit in responding to the patient, one would expect any transference phenomena to be less intense and pervasive.

We also discussed, of course, various types of styles of therapy, and in so doing we made use of the usual oversimplifications of such men as Freud, Rogers, and Sullivan in comparing different degrees and types of therapist-patient interaction and their probable effects on the material presented by the patient. We hypothesized, for example, that if the therapist is vis à vis the patient and is highly responsive to him, the patient will be apt to deal primarily with his "conscious" reactions to his current life experiences and interpersonal relationships. However, under conditions where the therapist is removed from the patient's view, and remains relatively unresponsive, it was suggested that the patient would be more apt to deal with his "unconscious" reactions to previous (e.g., childhood) experiences and interpersonal relationships. In this connection, it appears that Freud proposed that therapy should be conducted under conditions of relative "sensory deprivation," in the sense that active sensory stimuli, whether proprioceptive or visual, should be reduced by having the patient lie quietly on a couch with the therapist removed from his view. And, as in the more recent and radical "sensory deprivation" experiments, the relative removal of sensory stimuli seems also to remove the glue that holds men firmly to a sense of current reality.

Another line of discussion had to do with the extent of the therapist's responsiveness and whether he responds differentially to different types of material, as they might affect what the patient will be inclined to deal with over the course of the therapy. Thus, the more the therapist uses a sort of conditioning technique, or (in terms more acceptable to some therapists) becomes actively involved in the interchange by showing interest in certain types of material, or by making interpretations of the material to the patient, the more he will tend to control and restrict the flexibility and range of what the patient talks about—since the patient will tend to talk about what he thinks will interest the therapist. Or, on the other hand, the more the therapist is noncommittal and responds permissively to all types of material, the more freedom the patient will have to discuss a broad range of topics or experiences, and the more he will tend to do so.

Along with our theorizing, a number of clinical examples were given in support of, or as qualifications to, our discussion of the various topics. For instance, Dr. Will indicated how a therapist might start the treatment under conditions of relatively clear structure and later increase ambiguity as the therapy progresses. In working with a disturbed patient, for example, he initially defined the therapeutic task rather specifically and restricted the patient to a few areas which, he felt, could be dealt with at the time. Later, as the patient's ego strength grew in therapy, he increased the ambiguity to permit the patient greater freedom to deal with a wider range of affects and experiences. The reverse trend also occurs, especially in psychoanalysis, as when the patient becomes too anxious or begins to show signs of pathology during a particular phase of the therapy. Under such conditions, the therapist may ask the patient to sit up until the disrupting anxiety is worked through, and after the patient has regained control will allow him to return to the couch.

In summarizing this aspect of our discussion, we speculated about ways in which the therapist is able to exert control over the therapeutic process, including the productions of the patient, by manipulating the degree of ambiguity or structuredness in terms of, for example, the nature of the therapeutic task, the nature of the therapist-patient relationship, or the nature and range of the acceptable content to be given by the patient. In some instances this could be done by controlling the more specific components of the therapeutic situation, such as the level of activity or anxiety.

I mentioned earlier that there were two main threads that ran through our discussion: clinical content and theory on the one hand and research methodology on the other. From time to time, studies were cited which had to do with one or another aspect of ambiguity or structuredness in therapeutic situations. For example, Dr. Bordin cited studies by two of his students,[1] who found that raters showed a high degree of agreement in judging the

relative ambiguity of the therapist's statements—specifically, the extent to which statements by the therapist were expected to (and in fact did) maximize or minimize the range of responses that the patient could give. Using a sample of protocols from 30 therapy hours, the findings of these investigators held up regardless of whether the ratings were based on specific topical segments in the hour or on the hour as a whole.

In another example, Dr. Lennard reported findings[2] regarding the effects that differing degrees of ambiguity or structuredness tend to have on the nature of the therapist-patient interchange. In rating the therapist's statements, he used an eight-point scale—from most ambiguous, such as "Tell me more" or "Continue" through increased structure such as "Tell me more about . . ." to the most structured, which was, "Let's not talk any more about that right now." He found that with increased ambiguity in the therapist's statements, the patients tended to talk more, to cover a wider variety of topics, and to change the direction of their remarks more often than when the therapist's preceding statement was highly structured. He also found that, after the patient had been silent for a period of 10 seconds or more, the therapist's statements tended to be highly structured, such as "Tell me more about . . . ," rather than, say, "Please continue."

Finally, Dr. Butler reported a study investigating changes in the cognitive structure of patients over the course of therapy, with particular reference to changes in their view of the significant persons in their life. He found at the beginning of therapy that patients frequently protested excessively positive views of themselves and negative views of others, such as "I am good; it is they who are at fault." As

[1] Osburn, H. G. An investigation of the ambiguity dimension of counselor behavior. Unpublished doctoral dissertation, University of Michigan, 1951.
Townsend, A. H. An empirical measure of ambiguity in the context of psychotherapy. *Mich. Acad. Science, Arts & Letters*, 1956, **41**, 349-355.

[2] Lennard, H. L., & Bernstein, A. *The anatomy of psychotherapy: Systems of communication and expectation.* New York: Columbia Univer. Press, 1960. Pp. 131-153.

therapy progressed, their tune often changed to, for example, "Honestly, I am not such a good guy after all—and they have some good points too." And, by the end of therapy, the patients characteristically tended to show more subtle and realistic appreciations of themselves, of the others, and of their interactions with them.

In citing examples of research studies which bear on some of the concomitant effects of relative ambiguity or structuredness in the therapy situation, I have selected examples to illustrate the role of this variable with respect to the therapist's statements, to the therapist-patient interchange, and to changes in the patient during therapy. There were others, of course, but these three will suffice to indicate the nature of our thinking with respect to this variable.

Now, my time is up. In closing, I want to say that in summarizing our discussion, I have taken a few liberties—by occasionally abstracting or generalizing, add-

ing to or taking from what was said explicitly—but I hope that the other members of our group will recognize the content of my report as being at least implicit in our discussion of yesterday morning. I also want to add two brief personal comments, one of which has already been made by Dr. Hamburg. It is that, by the end of the day, we felt we were sufficiently acquainted and ready to settle down to hard work, that we were on the threshold of making progress in grappling with a number of points that we had touched upon earlier in the day. In other words, we ended the day wishing that we could have continued our discussion. The other point has to do with the composition of our group—specifically, the inclusion of clinical and research persons. I was particularly impressed by a sensitivity to the integrity of the clinical situation balanced by an active interest in investigating the nature of the clinical or therapeutic situation. The fact that we were able to maintain this balance was one of the most satisfying aspects of our discussion.

# Summary Report:
## Definition of Variables (B)

### Edward S. Bordin, Ph.D.

I have arranged the rest of our discussion under three topics. One of them was introduced by Dr. Butler under the title of activity level, and I think was incorporated in the first factor of the analysis reported in his paper. This appeared as an expressiveness factor, and as we talked about it, it began to have other characteristics. It seemed to reflect the therapist's interest in the patient, the therapist's caring for the patient. Some of us gave other terms to it, such as the therapist's spontaneity, his effort to understand the patient. As Dr. Butler described it, it had in part the character of the therapist setting himself, by his posture and so on, so that all senses were directed toward the patient. The other element had to do more with the therapist's freedom to express himself. It was captured in the vividness that he imparted to his communication through bodily movement, through gestures, as well as by the choice of his language, the imagery of his language, and so on. Here is a variable that differentiates therapists. In trying to see where it fits into psychotherapy, we discussed such notions as that this characteristic was a basic ingredient in making a communication process effective. Somehow this stimulating characteristic of the therapist (vividness of communication) activated the patient's capacity to receive the therapist's message and to some extent perhaps increased the capacity of the two persons to communicate with each other. Dr. Butler reported some studies—I think they are unpublished studies at Chicago—in which successful cases of experienced therapists were characterized by the thera-

pist working with a patient who was at a lower level of expressiveness to begin with, and where the therapist was at a high level of expressiveness, but as therapy progressed the patient was brought up to a comparable level with the therapist. With the inexperienced therapists, their successful cases were patients who happened to be at the same level of expressiveness as their therapists, and this was at a somewhat higher level. The inexperienced therapists as a whole tended to establish their level of expressiveness at the level at which the patient was, and the unsuccessful cases with the inexperienced therapists were those where the level was low in both participants.

There was some attempt to rationalize the significance of this variable in terms of saying, particularly in neurotic difficulties, that the individual is unable to be expressive as a function of anxiety. The therapist by being so helps the patient to learn to break away from this anxiety, to overcome it, and to become expressive. Dr. Butler told us of experiences in training students to do therapy in which they taught the students how to be more expressive and where this seemed to have an important impact as compared to other ways of training students. They felt they got much better progress toward mastering therapeutic skills. The training involved partly talking about this issue of expressiveness; apparently this was a departure from previous training methods where the main emphasis was more on the prohibitions toward action rather than giving the student a particular conception of some positive way of acting. Recordings were used to illustrate what was meant, and there was also some role playing.

The second topic we took up was the topic of the patient's view of his therapeutic experience. There were a number of statements expressing the feeling that we do not know enough about just how patients do view their therapeutic experience, and comments on the quite extreme differences there will be between the therapist's view of what has gone on in therapy and the patient's view. In the end, our discussion narrowed down to the patient's view of himself, and treated various kinds of studies, some in which the patient's view of himself is compared with either the therapist's view of him, the patient's view of how much was accomplished, or the therapist's view of how much was accomplished. Dr. Hamburg reported a study by Board[1] where patients were followed up and where the therapists gave reports on how successful or unsuccessful they thought therapy had been. Dr. Hamburg was struck by quite a large number of instances where the therapist was quite definite in feeling that therapy was unsuccessful, but where the patient, at some period afterward, offered what he felt represented quite striking reports of something very meaningful having happened—reports of changes in their interpersonal relationships, changes in their life situation that somehow were at variance with the terms in which the therapist had characterized the therapy.

We also heard of a report of a study by Pfeffer,[2] in which the patients were given, what I would call, a very ambiguous task; they were simply asked to tell whatever

thoughts they had about therapy and to talk as much or as little as they wanted. One of the characteristic events that was noted here was the seeming resurgence of transference responses.

There was a lot of emphasis upon the lack of correlation between, for example, the patient's view of himself before and after therapy and the therapist's view of him and independent observer's reports. There had been some remarks on this lack of correlation the day before. Dr. Butler reported on some studies[3] where, when the patient's report on himself was analyzed further into purer more distinct factors, higher relationships were found with reports on the patient by the therapist and by others.

Finally, we discussed the topic of capacity to like the patient. It was proposed that the therapist's capacity to like the patient may possibly be one of the crucial variables in the therapist's ability to be helpful to him. Talking in terms of the therapist liking or disliking the patient, the question was raised whether there was a cultural or, perhaps, subcultural (therapist culture) pressure for the therapist to like or, at least, not to dislike his patient, resulting in a reluctance of therapists to admit dislike. Some of us began to express more confidence in a therapist who could admit to liking and disliking than one who is reluctant. It may be more important for the therapist to be able to experience and to admit to these experi-

---

[1] Board, F. A. Patients' and physicians' judgments of outcome of psychotherapy in the outpatient clinic. *AMA Arch. gen. Psychiat.,* 1959, **1**, 185-196.

[2] Pfeffer, A. Z. A procedure for evaluating the results of psychoanalysis. *J. Amer. Psychoanal. Assoc.,* 1959, **7**, 418-444.

[3] Butler, John M. Self-concept change in psychotherapy. *Counseling Center Discussion Papers,* 1960, **6**, No. 13.

Rice, Laura N., Wagstaff, Alice K., & Butler, J. M. Some relationships between therapists' style of participation and case outcome. *Counseling Center Discussion Papers,* 1961, **7**, No. 5.

Wagstaff, Alice K., Rice, Laura N., & Butler, J. M. Factors of client verbal participation in therapy. *Counseling Center Discussion Papers,* 1960, **6**, No. 9.

ences of disliking as well as liking than it is for him to like the patient. In that connection there was general agreement that feelings of contempt for the patient were more likely to be detrimental to the therapeutic process than either liking or disliking as such. Along with that we moved into the discussion of the equal importance of the therapist's willingness to have the patient grow. I remember that Dr. Will was talking about experiences where it seemed as though the critical issue was the therapist's unwillingness to let the patient grow away from him and from his need for the therapist; in essence, perhaps the therapist needed the patient more, or as much, as the patient needed the therapist. We moved into a related idea that therapists do have needs, and that one of the basic gratifications of therapeutic work are those of participating in the growth of other people, and that perhaps this gratification is intimately related to the process of being grown oneself. This brings us back, of course, to the mutual effect of patient on therapist. And that concludes my part of the report.

I think I would want to underline one of the last points that Dr. Haggard made by expressing my feeling that we could with considerable profit have gone a lot further, particularly at the level of getting down to specific methodological issues that would be involved in following up these kinds of ideas. I propose that a succeeding conference be so arranged that one can move quickly into the development of these ideas within a small group so as to make possible the explication of just what are the methodological issues: under what terms would we be satisfied with efforts to observe the kinds of variable being discussed, and what kinds of experimental or naturalistic studies will test the fruitfulness of the ideas behind the variables? A conference, so organized, should be able to go far toward finding the answers to such questions or, at the very least, outlining in clear detail the obstacles to seeking these answers.

*Group Discussion*
DR. DAVID A. HAMBURG, *presiding*

# Definition of Variables

DR. HAMBURG: Dr. Bordin, thank you. As a member of the group I was very much impressed that Dr. Bordin and Dr. Haggard have given an accurate and informative summary. It is a very difficult task. I would just like to underline a point, made by Dr. Haggard, that I feel about this group. There was a constructive balance involving respect for clinical observation and hypotheses derived from clinical observation, along with a search for methods that would permit dealing with such hypotheses systematically and in some cases quantitatively. We did feel toward the end that we could very well pursue the discussion for another whole day. I think it is something to be considered for future conferences—whether something like one day of plenary sessions and two days for the small group discussions might be profitable. However, this was the experience of only one group.

At this point we do have time for some discussion, so let us open it. Dr. Colby.

DR. COLBY: If the group had continued, I wish they could have come to grips with an interactional variable which seems to me to be very important, perhaps the most important, and that is the problem of the weight of meanings of statements. I realize the term meaning is very nebulous and the weight of meaning may be even more so. But it seems to me that linguists and information theorists and now research psychotherapists avoid the essence of utterances. They shirk the fact that it is not statements themselves; it is the meaning and import of statements that is crucial. It relates to the question of activity and nonactivity in therapy. If a

therapist utters 200 sentences in a single session, we say he is being very active; whereas, if another utters one sentence, he is not being active. But those 200 sentences might have very little import to the patient. They carry no weight; they have no impact. The other therapist might be completely silent for 40 minutes and then utter one sentence of ten words that has a very strong reverberative effect on the patient; yet, I wouldn't want to call him an inactive therapist. It seems to me that he is a very active therapist. He can think of things to say which have a far-reaching impact on the patient. I realize it is perhaps useless to exhort, but I think we, the psychotherapists, have to face up to this hard problem of the meaning of utterances delivered by the therapist.

DR. BORDIN: Would you be willing to call him a verbally inactive therapist?

DR. COLBY: Yes. He is active in the sense of being able to produce activity in a system, whereas the other therapist who may be talking like mad produces no activity in the patient system.

DR. BORDIN: I have the feeling that in our description of behavior we ought to try to get away from incorporating the impact in the description. If our theory requires that certain behavior has a particular impact and we incorporated the impact in the definition, there could be no proper empirical test of the tenability of our theory. So I have some feeling of wanting to retain a description of the therapist's behavior that doesn't in itself incorporate a description of his impact.

DR. COLBY: I would be willing to retain it, but put it secondary to effective-

292

ness which might be a better term than activity.

DR. BORDIN: In effect, one could put what you have been saying as a theoretical proposition to be tested, namely, that the verbal activity of the therapist is uncorrelated with the impact of his communications on the patient. One could test that.

DR. STEVENSON: Not without a good deal of evidence that the impact of the same words under different circumstances can be extraordinarily different. It needs a great deal more study. The experiments on hypnosis bring this up very clearly. You say, "Fire!" The patient has been given a posthypnotic suggestion that when he hears the word "Fire!" he will feel as if the seat of his pants is hot. This has a totally different impact, that one word, than it would on somebody who was not so prepared.

DR. HAGGARD: I would like to make an observation about something that has concerned me during these proceedings—namely, the reluctance to deal with the actual content of psychotherapy material. It is, of course, much easier to deal with the formal aspects than with the content. One reason is that we do not have any system for dealing with content, and in that we are like the linguists, persons studying aphasics, and so on. It is no problem to code and classify what words are used, but it is much harder to appraise how the words are put together, the implications of style—or even "what is being said" by the patient and the therapist. And yet, in our project, we have found that when we did try to determine the meaning of the content, or even levels of meaning, we were able to learn much more of what was going on during the session than when we dealt with only the more formal aspects of the protocols. In other words, I want to emphasize that, in my opinion, we must not be misled into doing only what is easy, that we must also work out methods to study and analyze

the content, and cannot ignore the fact that it is an essential part of psychotherapy material.

DR. STEVENSON: Even content is at a level above what Dr. Colby is talking about.

DR. SHLIEN: Let me second the opinions voiced by Dr. Haggard and by Dr. Colby. It seems to me that Dr. Haggard is saying that we should not concentrate on what is measurable at the cost of what is significant. Education gives us an easier parallel to think about. We tend to measure the obvious and that means the most active displays. If activity were really all we cared about, we would just watch the teacher teaching madly. But what we really care about in education is *learning*, and we now measure that more impressively. But we don't do this in therapy. We focus too much on the parallel of teaching, not enough on learning.

DR. HUNT: Mr. Chairman—apropos of Dr. Shlien's seconding of the point made by both Dr. Colby and Dr. Haggard that our research should not concentrate on what is measurable at the cost of what is significant, and especially apropos of his drawing a parallel between psychotherapy and education, I should like to recall Dr. Betz's semantics of "evoking change." I believe that psychotherapists, like educators, *are* in the business of "evoking change." I like Dr. Betz's semantics better than I like the semantics of reinforcement which Dr. Krasner has brought to the focus of our attention at this conference. I prefer the semantics of "evoking change" because I believe they are descriptively more apt. I believe change occurs in organisms, and by change I mean both epigenesis and growth in the structure of behavior and in the structure of those central processes which mediate behavior. I believe growth in the structure of behavioral processes occurs when the situation or information encountered is so related to the organism's existing structure of behavior or of opinion, on the one hand, that it is relevant and, on the other hand, that it falls within the accommodative capacity of the organism. Although it is very much worth while to look at the psychotherapist as an educator, I suspect the investigations of those social psychologists who are studying attitude change are more relevant to the work of the psychotherapist.

In this work, change in attitudes and beliefs is seen to be a function of the logical relationship between the message to which the subject listens and the attitudes and beliefs which the subject holds on the topic of that message. The terminology of Leon Festinger[1] is particularly apt. According to this terminology, change occurs when the relationship between the input message and the attitudes and beliefs already in the storage is one of *cognitive dissonance*. This is to say that the message is related to those beliefs, but it disagrees with those attitudes and beliefs. But there is more than mere dissonance involved in evoking change. If the message is seen as too dissonant to be accommodated by the subject, he will somehow discredit the message or the source of the message. I have begun to believe that many of the mechanisms of defense that Freud described are actually defenses against dissonance. Thus, the proper relationship between the message and the existing attitude and belief structure in a person provoking change may be described as one in which the message appears to the subject different enough from his already established attitudes and beliefs to be interesting but not enough to arouse his defenses. Some of these studies of attitude change point out that the amount of change obtainable is markedly increased when the degree of dissonance in the message turns out to be greater than the subject was led to expect by the opening phrases of the message.

[1] Festinger, L. *A theory of cognitive dissonance.* Evanston, Ill.: Row, Peterson, 1957.

Shakespeare was well acquainted with this principle. As you recall, he had Mark Anthony employ it in his funeral oration for Julius Caesar. In that oration, Mark Anthony opened with a statement, "I came not to praise Caesar but to bury him." He thereby started his oration with a statement that was very close to what his listeners already believed. As Mark Anthony proceeded to produce the message of his oration, he gradually introduced information which was more and more dissonant with those original attitudes and beliefs of his listeners. Inasmuch as the dissonance was introduced gradually, however, those listeners were led along toward a very big change in their attitudes and beliefs. Mark Anthony's performance, of course, is merely a figment of the Bard's imagination. It is not evidence.

There are, however, a number of studies of attitude change (see especially Ewing and Festinger[2]) which clearly demonstrate this principle that when the recipient of the message is led in the opening phrases to expect information which essentially agrees with his ready-made attitudes, the impact of the dissonant information that comes later makes an especially big change in the subject's attitude; whereas, if he is led by the opening phrases to expect something that disagrees with his own ready-made attitudes, he will defensively discredit the message so that it has no effect on his attitudes and beliefs at all.

I suspect that when nondirective or client-centered psychotherapy is used in the skillful hands of a Rogers, a Butler, or a Shlien, it becomes a mode *par excellence* of introducing messages to clients in which the dissonance is produced in small doses. On the other hand, in the interpretative therapies, I suspect that the disso-

[2] Ewing, T. N. A study of certain factors involved in changes of opinion. *J. soc. Psychol.,* 1942, **16**, 63-88.

See Footnote 1.

nance is often introduced in such larger doses that they provoke a good deal of defensive argument. I suspect we can profitably compare the work of various therapies from this point of view.

Trying to do this will, however, create a technical problem, and this problem concerns the way in which we diagnose what the existing attitudes and beliefs of our clients are at any given time. I suspect that our existing modes of diagnosis such as the Rorschach and the TAT may not be very helpful here. We may well have to be satisfied with the import of what clients say within the therapeutic session. At any rate, I would like to see someone look at psychotherapy from the standpoint of the theory and methods employed by the social psychologists studying attitude and opinion change. I am inclined to believe that insofar as the psychotherapist employs skill in managing the relationship between his messages and the attitudes and beliefs of his client or patient, he is, to use again Dr. Betz's phrase, "evoking change."

DR. FRANK: It seems to me that the only way you can get at the meaning of communication is by the impact on the recipient. Dr. Hunt suggests that you have to know what the sets of the recipient are before you can judge what the meaning of the particular content of the behavior is. This is a nasty methodological problem.

DR. BETZ: The word "attitude" has been used several times. This is a useful word for characterizing patients in our clinical vocabulary.

Dr. Colby was focusing on what is significant as opposed to what is more or less volume. Methods are needed to measure or show what is significant in clinical happenings — the heightened moments and the valleys between. How to recognize them, how to conceptualize about them so that we can communicate meaningfully to other people—this is an im-

portant problem. One obstacle, methodologically, may lie in the fact that we work with secondhand material a great deal, even when recordings or recorded transcripts are used. I would hope that we can begin to have more studies of doctors and patients in actual operational settings where what is happening can be observed while it is happening, as we are able to observe a surgeon when he is operating. There are problems here, but many of them are surely surmountable.

DR. BLOCK: It seems to me that what we are talking about now is the hoary and thorny and usually evaded problem in psychology—what is the stimulus. Dr. Colby suggested that we needed to be concerned with what is significant rather than what is simply easy to count or the frequency of words, and so forth, and I think or hope everybody would agree. I think the way he happened to phrase the problem toward the end of his remarks precipitated the countering reaction of Dr. Bordin. Dr. Colby said we shall know significance by the subsequent effect of the stimulus upon the individual. But this statement develops problems of logical circularity because the nature of science is such that one has to state in advance rather than retrospectively the effects of the stimulus upon the subsequent response or behavior change. Just how to set about to do this is a damnably difficult problem, but one must continually recognize that we cannot define significance in terms of subsequent effect. We cannot look backwards in time and then decide what was significant if we wish to predict behavior.

One admittedly unsatisfactory solution to this problem is to talk of what a stimulus or a therapist intervention should do to an individual—I put *should* in quotes. Afterwards, one looks to see what the therapist intervention did do. By virtue of talking of what should, and what did happen, one can perhaps separate and clarify the notion of therapist intervention and talk about it in advance and independently of the effect of this intervention.

Going back to Dr. Haggard's remarks on the necessity of dealing with content, I would certainly agree. But I think there are formal qualities of content that if recognized would permit the classification and coding of the therapist's activity into incisive categories—categories that respond to the meaning rather than the sheer volume of words. I do not think a systematic approach to therapy has to be reduced necessarily to the formalism of counting words and length of sentences and time gaps.

DR. BUTLER: I want to clap my hands and say "Bravo!" to Dr. Colby on this, because I think that messages, which are embodied in the flow of the sequence of sentences, are very important and have a unity which neither words nor sentences have. And the next thing I would like to say is that in our group I think we considered this in a certain sense which bears on your comment and might be worth bringing out to the conference as a whole. It is in this notion of activity level that we discussed as being different than therapeutic intervention, as being in the dimension of active versus passive, active meaning being expressive. One hypothesis was that it increases meaningfulness for a given formal content and, therefore, in the respondent, whether he is client or therapist; the result would be increased connotations and possibly increased meaningfulness on the part of the respondent's own response, to be contrasted then with the less active type of statement or message which might be formally the same but does not have this stimulus value. I think one specific hypothesis that we discussed along these lines was that for one kind of relationship, for example, in one kind of technique an increased activity level, in the sense of expressiveness on the part of the therapist, might lead to a great increase in richness of messages from the client or patient. In another relationship the increase in connotation might be very anxiety-producing and produce both the impulses to express, and at the same time inhibiting effects of anxiety. What we came out with was something that can be studied, the relationship of activity levels to specific therapeutic strategies within a given hour in interaction. I think this really would be a quite desirable study, if done in a systematic way.

DR. BOLGAR: With respect to Dr. Colby's suggestion, I think we have to differentiate between the emotional impact of the therapist's communication and its meaningfulness. It seems to me that this may have something to do with the therapist's activity level in terms of the quantity of communication. In the case of a classically silent therapist, the mere fact that he is making a comment may have a tremendous emotional impact on the patient. However, I think that this is somewhat different from making a meaningful comment which sets off a chain reaction that may manifest itself much later. There is also an important methodological difference between finding evidence for the impact of a communication on the one hand and its long-range meaningfulness on the other. Usually the patient can and does indicate what made an emotional impact on him, but it is much more difficult to trace back a meaningful comment which may have started some very important internal activity in the patient but may take a long and unpredictable period of time to re-emerge on the surface.

DR. LENNARD: If you compare different therapist-patient pairs, then the counting of the absolute volume of a therapist's activity is probably not very useful. But think of therapists who are operating within different orientations, who have different base lines for how often they talk, or how much they will say, then the volume of comments may be related to impact. If a therapist is only going to talk if he has something very important to say, then if you compare hours for the therapist who is operating on a particular base line (sessions in which he talks more versus sessions in which he talks less) you can find some interesting things, as we did. For example, the patients were more satisfied with sessions in which the analytic therapist talked a little more. Now, you may point out the psychodynamics underlying this finding and say that the patient is interpreting the therapist's talk as a gift from the therapist. Yet interestingly, if you also ask the therapists, you will find that the therapists were more satisfied with hours where they talked somewhat more. All I am pointing out is that the variable of activity level in a formal sense, while certainly only a very small part of the total problem for analyzing the impact and the meaning of the therapists' statement, does nevertheless have some very useful implications for understanding differences in the vicissitudes of a particular therapist-patient pair.

DR. BLOCH: In the final analysis we establish meaning only by the careful explication in advance of what our goals for the patient may be. Clinicians are loath to do this, yet I cannot see any other way of handling this problem than to be able, in the beginning of therapy, to say in detail and on as many levels as possible precisely what the therapeutic goals are and how one hopes to achieve them.

DR. COLBY: In response to Dr. Bloch, the clinical analyst has some rough and ready criteria by which he judges what should happen ahead of time. For example, when he offers an interpretation, let us say in the form of a causal correlation in which he asserts to the patient, "You do X because of Y," he expects, if the various empirical rules about timing, dosage, and tact have been followed, that the patient will then take up this correlation, elaborate it, extend it, qualify it, or

reject it. At least he will process it as a piece of information in some way with a terminus that is roughly defined. If left alone, theoretically he should be able to go for minutes and maybe hours on it. Usually some external or internal contingency changes the associational flow. So one sort of response that we think ideally should occur after an adequate interpretation is that the patient should process it. When he doesn't, and often he doesn't when we have touched him at a sensitive spot, then we observe an avoidance of the message. He will not process it. He moves away from it or he falls completely silent. Now this is a measure of immediate response to input which I think the clinician uses. He feels that he says something that has meaning, import, and usefulness to the patient if the patient is able to information-process it.

DR. LEVINSON: I would like to comment on the title of the working group and their theme, the derivation of variables. The discussion earlier focused mainly on variables that people can think of. Presumably the research would start with variables that people have in mind and would try to see what significance they have, what else they are correlated with, what their consequences are, and so on. I think there is another kind of study that ought to be mentioned, the kind in which the *aim* of the study is the derivation of variables. One would spend time looking at what happens and then decide at the end of the study on a small number of variables that seem to be worth pursuing.

This certainly is not a new idea. I imagine that we all agree that it is one useful kind of thing to do. It is often the aim in process studies to examine in a microscopic way what is going on in therapy with the aim of deriving variables for further study. Actually, we rarely do this. I think it would be worth including in our report—what sorts of ideas there are in this group about this kind of research. One reason we don't do it, I think, is that it is very hard to get it published. It just does not fit the model of the usual journal article. You are supposed to end up with conclusions about the way in which a variable operates rather than simply saying on the basis of a lot of qualitative observations, "I propose that this is an important variable; it is as far as I have gotten so far in my research, but it is still worth publishing on the basis of findings to date."

DR. LUBORSKY: I am impressed that several participants in this conference went through that strenuous process of following hunches about variables and gradually came to a formulation of promising ones. Dr. Levinson did this. Dr. Butler, at the beginning of his paper, describes the kinds of mental processes one must go through in listening to one's data to hear useful variables to measure. And the same is true of Drs. Siegal and Rosen's paper. Don't you agree?

DR. LEVINSON. Yes.

DR. ROSEN: And Dr. Luborsky's.

# Final Summary

GEORGE SASLOW, M.D.

It is hard to add meaningful comments to what you have already experienced and heard, but I have accepted the charge of the committee and will do my best.

I shall present some reflections at levels a little different from what would be appropriate to the other reports and the general discussions. To begin with, since I was at the previous conference in 1958 as well as this one, I should like to add my impressions to those of other participants in both conferences—that there is a very striking difference between the two with regard to the much greater ease of all participants and openness to one another during the research conference. There was a much greater wariness in 1958, a feeling of being on guard, even to difficulty in hearing each other's rather different language, than I noticed at the present conference. This seems to me a great advance and perhaps gives us a suggestion as to the utility of devices of this kind in the future.

I comment next on a number of issues which came up at this conference. With regard to the discussions we had about the variables significant for personality change, I was struck by the continued pertinence of the eloquent statement by Gordon Allport (1955), in his little book *Becoming,* of his dissatisfaction with our not having found in psychology and psychiatry suitable units for personality description, units of a kind which would represent adequately what we might call central rather than peripheral features of personality, features which deal with what gives us the feeling of a personality being well tied together rather than of a bundle of separate traits, responses, dispositions, or attitudes. This problem, it seems to me, is still just about as far from being solved in 1961 as in 1955. The search for suitable units of personality study is still in process. From this point of view, I thought that Dr. Shlien's attempt to deal directly with much more general ways of describing personality, by use of variables at high levels of abstraction, was an exciting approach to this kind of problem. There may be many other such novel attempts. This one may not prove to be useful. Whether you think of the variable of self-esteem he was experimenting with in a nonverbal way as one of high abstraction, or high generality, or high centrality, or as belonging to what Allport called the proprium or the propriate system, the real I, makes no difference. I think none of us will be satisfied until we have units for personality study that are of this order or kind, the rest of psychology up to that time having to be considered as still being in an elementary state, even though a tremendous amount of effort has been necessary to take us to that state.

Content as a variable relevant to personality appraisal was not discussed thoroughly at this particular meeting. Others have commented on it, and this has some significance. I want to mention also a point which Dr. Colby brought up, that we have paid relatively little attention to the meaning of statements which are made. When we have a patient in action it is hard for us to study this matter. It is hard for us to design methods to estimate the impact of therapists' statements upon patients. In connection with this last point we have the interesting hint from Dr. Hunt that the students of attitude change can perhaps give us a notion of procedures which might be helpful. I believe that these procedures are used implicitly by skilful therapists, but that they have never been made the object of adequate study. Essentially, the procedures as Dr. Hunt described them seemed to me to amount to what, in psychotherapist language, is "knowing where the patient is," making very sure, by using his language and even his inflections and his tempo (as the more sensitive therapists that I have watched always know how to do), that you know exactly when you stand on common ground with such a patient. You then produce those dissonances which lead him to change his attitude along with you. Sometimes the first dissonance is simply a questioning inflection, joined to a statement which is an exact repetition in IQ 85 language of what the patient has said (if that is his IQ).

One other comment about variables relevant for estimating personality change. The group which dealt with that topic pointed out to us again that single variables are not likely to prove particularly predictive, even one we think of being so central as anxiety or subjective discomfort or relief of same. By and large this group came up with the notion that more than one informant was needed if you were to form some reliable estimate of what had happened to a person as a result of psychotherapy, and that this kind of description (of the extratherapist patient interactions) was most predictive of the outcome which in the long run is the pay-off of psychotherapy. There seemed more agreement than I have noted in previous years regarding the desirability of study of the outcome of psychotherapy as not being something limited to the therapist-patient interactions, but as requiring data from an ongoing natural or viable life situation.

As study of outcome of psychotherapy was being discussed, another topic came up which was left completely unresolved because it sets before us two very broad pathways, either of which one could take, and both of which have been taken. These have to do with the criteria of success in psychotherapeutic efforts. Shall the criterion be reduction of illness? Shall the criterion have to do with growth of personality? Although there is some obvious overlapping between these two concepts, psychotherapists will lean much more one way than the other, and will work in conspicuously different ways with their patients depending upon which way they lean. This topic was only mentioned and left.

Dr. Levinson drew some important matters to our attention. As he tried to wrestle with the topic (therapist characteristics) in the group he was assigned to, he found it impossible to deal with that topic within the framework for discussion which our conference steering committee had arranged. Dr. Levinson rejected the scheme the committee had set up with its tripartite division of topics, and came up with a very interesting idea. He found he could not think separately of therapist variables and patient variables, variables useful for handling the therapist-patient interaction. He made an analogy between the career of a person who presents himself as a possible client or patient (from the time of presentation until he is discharged from care) and other kinds of career: the career of a student, or the career of a professional person. In short, his analogy was with other kinds of socialization processes. He regarded such a career as socialization process in terms of a number of domains, some seven of them; variables characteristic of the therapist could be important in any one of these seven domains right from the start, when a person appears before the therapist asking for therapy and being either accepted or rejected, until the termination of care when the person is discharged to the outer world. One can consider therapist variables in any one of the seven domains: acceptance–rejection, therapist-patient interaction (properly called psychotherapy), the institutional setting, family setting, and so on. One can also consider the relation of therapist variables in one of these domains, for example, at the point of the applicant's appearance, to therapist variables in another domain, for instance, in the therapist-patient interaction called psychotherapy.

Levinson's portrayal of a patient's progress, like Pilgrim's Progress, in terms of a career makes it more difficult to omit any of the essential elements which one has to consider if he wishes to evaluate either variables pertinent to personality change or significant about the therapist, or related to the outcome of therapy. Levinson's concept of a patient career also helped me to see more clearly where each of the very diverse approaches to the study of psychotherapy represented in this conference probably has its place. One could see that it was possible, by use of his scheme, to ask quite diverse questions about the patient's progress, in relation to his career at any point, and in terms of various levels such as Dr. Shakow was talking about. Some of the studies represented in the conference concentrate almost exclusively upon the therapist-

patient interaction as such, in greater or lesser detail. In material presented by Dr. Hedda Bolgar, emphasis was upon a very fine detail, a single act, the significance of which is examined during a single hour and also throughout a three-year process of therapist-patient interaction. Some such approaches, whether they concentrate on the therapist-patient interaction as such in fine detail or over a long period of time, nevertheless omit from regard what Levinson portrays as the beginning of those therapist-patient interactions: the antecedent domain of acceptance–rejection, etc. Other investigators who concentrate upon the therapist-patient interaction as such pay little or no attention to the subsequent domain: what follows the therapist-patient interaction.

Levinson's scheme appears to be an instrument of considerable utility. In addition, its obvious face validity suggests the likelihood that if research on psychotherapy continues to be too preoccupied with the therapist-patient interaction as such, we shall probably discover that such limiting of our concern to a part of the patient's career will turn out to have been limiting us unnecessarily in our theories of personality, society, and society-personality relationships. We will tend to start with a particular personality theory, to study the therapist-patient interaction within that framework and not be very hospitable to alternative personality theories which we would actually otherwise be more prone to consider were we looking at larger segments of the patient's career, including his impact on the outer world, his sociocultural situation, the effect of his class membership upon the initial portions of his career, and so on. I have the general impression that excessive concern with the therapist-patient interaction as such as an object of research will tend to tie us to existing personality theory more rather than less, and to tie us to our pre-existing definitions of variables relevant to personality change more rather than less.

In connection with Levinson's notion of a patient's career, one must consider the possibility that those characteristics of a dyadic interaction system which Lennard has described for the therapist-patient interaction, as such, will turn out to have relevance for the interactions of the patient in the other systems of which he is a part during his career: the economic system to which he goes on conclusion of the therapist-patient interaction, or the institutional system if hospitalization has been a part of his career, his family, and so forth. In short, we are likely to want to find out whether the system characteristics Lennard thought relevant may be useful to us in other sustained interactions of the patient during his career.

Some comments on Dr. Strupp's dissatisfaction with the results of studies of the therapist-patient interaction as such are next in order. You remember he felt that our approach had been characterized by being oversegmental and prematurely experimental. He had the impression that investigators have been prematurely concerned with experimental design, rigorousness of design, statistical analysis, controls, and similar matters. He has been sufficiently dissatisfied with the results to date, as are many of us, that he thought one had to return to closer observation of the therapist-patient interaction or psychotherapy process just as it occurs in the hope of discovering new leads for investigation. For such a procedure, he and others here used the term "naturalistic." I say, in agreement with Dr. Krasner, that I don't see anything more "naturalistic" on the face of it about one kind of psychotherapy than another: Rogerian psychotherapy to me is as naturalistic or artificial as Freudian psychotherapy, or Adlerian, or other varieties. I think rather what one means is to study a particular therapeutic process

as it would be going on anyway if we were not subjecting it to deliberate experimental design or other manipulation. We want to look in on it and see if we can get any hints about aspects we could subsequently define more explicitly and perhaps make hypotheses about to verify in post hoc fashion, as Chapin (1955) did in his sociological studies, without having to limit or distort the situation or manipulate it in advance. Studies can be conducted in the way Dr. Strupp proposes, but I think the term "naturalistic" need not be used in the way it was, as if it signifies some special virtue.

Dr. Butler presented to the conference some observations of the client-centered therapy process as it occurs, in line so to speak with the kind of suggestion made by Dr. Strupp. As he examined afresh the kind of material long familiar to him, he made observations which, it seems to me, must modify the generally held conception of the therapist's behavior in client-centered therapy. (Such leads, I take it, are Dr. Strupp's objective.) You remember Dr. Butler found that successfully treated clients more often had worked with a client-centered therapist who was more expressive and more active in a complex way defined in his paper. These therapists had been doing more than reflecting and clarifying what a client said. Dr. Butler was saying that as I look at this process, which I have been familiar with for quite a number of years, with a fresh eye, I find that the more the therapist is active in certain ways, the more his behavior shows aspects outside his conceptual framework, the more responsive patients are in a way which the same therapist calls successful treatment. He used such words as "expressiveness" and "activity" to characterize this rather noticeable departure from the orthodox conception of client-centered behavior.

Dr. Butler's observations at once raise such questions as, why couldn't one train therapists to put on expressive and active behavior experimentally? If experimental observation shows that such behavior is systematically predictive of more successfully treated cases, why can't it become part of a therapist's armamentarium of therapeutic skills which his teachers help him learn?

But increased therapist expressiveness and activity are not always useful. You remember Dr. Haggard's report, in connection with his group's discussion about ambiguity, that under conditions of low expressiveness, low activity, low specificity and high ambiguity of therapist's behavior, certain patients definitely talk more, show more variation in their talk, and shift more from topic to topic. In other words, there are patients for whom —contrary to the observations Dr. Butler made in client-centered therapy—the more the therapist is in the background and not explicitly definable, the more the patients come out of themselves. I put these two observations together and say it is impossible to maintain that therapeutic effectiveness can be reduced to any one formula for therapist behavior. Will one have to become sensitively aware, possibly by emitting one's own behavior as signals, that the patient belongs to the class with whom the therapist had better be "low specific and high ambiguous," or to the class with whom the therapist had better be "high expressive and Butler active"? Clearly this means highly individualized therapist procedure, but again I point out that this is quite sensible to therapists not committed to any existing allegedly correct framework. Furthermore, such individualizing of therapy can be studied experimentally, it can be taught systematically, and it can be learned.

It is natural to relate the material of Drs. Butler and Haggard to Dr. Krasner's review of operant conditioning procedures. The discussion of these procedures aroused more feeling than any other topic during the conference. These procedures will probably continue to arouse strong feelings for a variety of reasons. Dr. Krasner will probably continue to be deliberately provocative (if we could get him to admit it) as he was by describing the therapist in the title of his paper as a social reinforcement machine. All he has to do is to use the word "machine" in that context and his hearers will respond strongly. One could start out with a standard question: if the therapist is a reinforcement machine, is a reinforcement machine a therapist? If one starts off with that, one generates at once a wonderfully hot discussion on fundamental viewpoints about the nature of men and of machines. To return to Dr. Krasner's presentation— what is being done now with operant conditioning is evidently covering an increasingly broad spectrum of behaviors in animals and man. The behavior being studied by this method is becoming increasingly complex. The possibility that, to an unknown extent, man's operant conditioning behavior may be a response to personal or social expectation—a placebo effect—does not reduce the importance of the procedure. The work of H. K. Beecher (1955) on "the powerful placebo" leads to the conclusion that we shall have to take such placebo effects into account far more explicitly than heretofore, whether we be dealing with them in pharmacotherapy, in surgical therapy, or in psychotherapy (including subdivision operant conditioning). There is much about operant conditioning along these lines which we have yet to understand. We should not be unaware of the ingenuity which can be applied to some of the procedures; probably we are about to see new developments of them rather rapidly.

The limits of behavior change by operant conditioning techniques are of course not known. To what extent behavior which is altered by operant conditioning (and for whatever reason—including the placebo type of reason) is followed by appropriately integrated physiological states, such as symptom loss —or altered feelings, altered thinking, or altered attitudes—remains to be learned. One cannot exclude the fact that such accompanying alterations may occur, since over and over again it can be observed that if a person can carry out a new, more effective response, a new, more effective visible behavior in a formerly self-defeating situation and does it with reward, does it X times (whatever X is for him), he then develops new thoughts about himself, thoughts which are integrated with his new behavior, and new attitudes, new feelings, and different physiological states. If he has the idea—I am now a more self-confident person—and has begun to act more self-confidently, he soon has also a different feeling about himself, and his physiological state is different. In other words, it is not at all an unimportant question to wonder whether one can alter behavior by operant conditioning methods, even if the alteration is brief. One must not minimize in advance the possibilities here by saying, "Well, it's only overt behavior that is changing," or "It's only verbal behavior," because in the long run, if you watch people and if you watch children, it is behavior that is learned first. They then develop thought systems which explain to themselves what their behavior is like. It is very difficult to say to a person, "Stop having thoughts A and B," "stop having feelings C and D," "stop having hyperactive stomach or hyperactive bowel." It is easier to say, "Talk, do." What one can observe happening, if one can make the right guesses as to what new behavior could occur and be reinforced, is that in association with successful new behavior one sees a new integrate of new successful behavior, attitude, feeling, and physiological function. This is the possibility suggested by operant conditioning, even if it is effective, by itself, only briefly. There may result new appropriately inte-

grated states at all levels. How such new states generalize to other interpersonal situations remains to be learned, as well as how long they will endure.

Dr. Krasner has already begun to experiment with procedures which deal with these questions. He has been able to design operant conditioning settings in which schizophrenic patients take more responsibility, pay more attention, receive more attention, take initiative—in short become involved at multiple levels of interpersonal activity. For the nonparticipating schizophrenic patient, such involvement is potentially of major significance. If one can achieve it by operant conditioning methods and it is sufficiently rewarding to endure for even a short time, and to generalize to new situations, the possibility arises of unfreezing certain self-defeating patterns in patients by methods like this which may have nothing to do with the conventionally defined psychotherapy process as such. It may next be possible to find intermediate steps from such an unfreezing by a briefly enduring, feebly generalizing operant conditioning procedure to having the patient learn to so use his own symbolic processes as to set up self-perpetuating rewarding ways of behavior of high generality and long persistence. The next step beyond that will be to help the patient find for himself in the world outside the therapist-patient interaction those self-perpetuating interpersonal situations which he has come to know how to define so as to include the reinforcers which he needs for his new behavior. One cannot say how much of a place operant conditioning will find in such a sequence of therapeutic events, or of a patient's career.

Dr. Krasner mentioned some interesting experiments which indicated that operant conditioning need not have first place in such a sequence: after sensory deprivation, under certain circumstances, operant conditioning is quicker. Imagine the fascinating possibilities of starting with sensory deprivation to produce an organism sensitized to operant conditioning procedures, having already found out a little bit about the patient's self-defeating patterns in a few interviews, and then trying particular operant conditioning procedures. If the specifically chosen operant conditioning procedures are effective, perhaps the patient can break out of his mold quickly. But how can one make such effects endure? How can one make them generalize? How can one extend them into his thinking, his self-regulating mechanisms and (outside the therapist-patient interaction) into the necessary interpersonal self-perpetuating regulating mechanisms? The possibilities I have mentioned are based upon a resolute rejection of the premise that we can expect the therapist-patient interaction by itself to produce a permanent result independent of external physical and interpersonal conditions. They are based also upon an acceptance of the notion that the integrity and stability of a person's functioning depends upon the continued integrity of the web of external circumstance in which he is immersed (as all the work on sensory deprivation demonstrates).

From the point of view I have been presenting, whether one is making "naturalistic" observations of the psychotherapy process or is doing experimentation becomes an unimportant question. When I say unimportant, I do not mean that naturalistic observation isn't useful, but I don't see that the distinction means anything. I cannot tell you which kind of knowledge we will find more useful and at which points, but I see no point in looking at these two approaches to the study of alteration of personality or of behavior as if they must be mutually exclusive.

If operant conditioning techniques increase in diversity and complexity, if they stand up as useful, we shall have to give careful attention to the implications for the control of patients' behavior which such methods involve. If these methods continue to show promise, no matter for what reason, psychotherapists at that point will not be able to escape dealing with the same ethical dilemmas that our colleagues in all other agencies which have social control as part of their function have to face, whether these be political agencies, educational agencies, or military agencies. We shall no longer be able to take the position that in psychotherapy permissiveness is all, that love is all, that we never control, that we have only the noblest interests of the patient at heart, etc. You will find that just such language is used by the agents of Chinese thought reform—a far from permissive procedure —as quoted by Lifton (1961) in his book on Chinese totalism. Even more—the persons who have gone through the (totalistic) processes of having their behavior so thoroughly controlled come out with the same statements about themselves as our graduates of psychotherapy—"I had a most extraordinary beneficial experience; I express myself more freely; I am closer to others; I am a nobler human being." At certain levels there seems little to distinguish the statements of the graduates of thought reform, who are thoroughly controlled in the way Americans say they despise, from the statements of the patient-graduates of psychotherapy in our society. The differences many of us believe to exist between these two procedures will become even less clear if the implications I have been sketching, of our present operant conditioning procedures, become explicitly defined and used practices.

Perhaps the dilemmas instigated by our awareness that there may be more control of a patient in psychotherapy than we like to think and the kinds of safeguards we could think about in our society are worth another conference. I should like to draw to your attention that as far as I know only B. F. Skinner (1953) faced this issue clearly and openly, years ago. He labeled psychotherapy one of the agencies of social control and tried to examine it as such. Those of you who read his extraordinary book, *Walden Two* (Skinner, 1955), have experienced appropriate shudders, and those of you who have not read it will find it germane to this conference.

A number of things which came up during the three days are worth stating for the record of the conference. Each of the three working groups indicated that they felt a lack of closure about the time that they had spent together. They all got to points beyond which they wished to continue. That is a fine way for a conference to go. These are, as Dr. Hunt reminded us two days ago, typical Zeigarnik effects. I have the idea that it may be because of such lack of closure in the 1958 conference that we started off this time in such a very different way and continued our functioning in a far more open way with a minimum of defensiveness. A number of suggestions were made with regard to this general state of lack of closure. There is, of course, an obvious one—another conference like this. But when? Robert Harris, who wrote the review on psychotherapy in the Annual Review of Psychology several years ago, commented on how little difference there was in the literature he surveyed in that year from what I had surveyed a few years before. He thought the tempo of development of the topic was such as to warrant a review every five years. This is three years after the preceding conference. Our committee might be thinking about a suitable time interval if another conference is thought to be useful. A summer conference was suggested by Dr. Bordin for a smaller group working more closely on a more limited number of topics for perhaps a longer number of days. A suggestion was made by Dr. Butler for cooperative research ventures involving

some of the conference participants. This was also made at the last conference, as I remember; this is like the cooperative clinical studies in any field concerned with chronic intermittent disease problems. Examples are the world-wide cooperative clinical study of rheumatic fever, cortisone and aspirin; and the Veterans Administration hospital studies on psychotic reactions and tranquilizers. The suggestion was made that ideas for the evaluation of therapy could be gathered and pooled; perhaps that a variety of evaluation techniques in use could be examined by a group and important redundancies could be found. These redundancies could be pruned, and a scale which survived could be used by more investigators. This has its own hazard of the least common denominator phenomenon. You remember that Dr. Butler objected that perhaps at the present time it is wise to allow what look like redundant instruments, variables, and approaches to exist but to keep on talking to each other about where the perturbations are. That is how the new planets were discovered, he keeps telling us, and I think we have to remember there are very important virtues in such an approach.

I had the impression that dissatisfaction was general, even with such a central concept as "anxiety," although many people felt it had some usefulness. We have difficulty in defining it or its parameters, despite the excellent things written about it by people like Professor John Reid (1956) and various students of drive in psychology who have tried to anchor it operationally to antecedent and consequent circumstances. The question was raised whether, as a construct, it is definable, useful, or even necessary.

A question of great interest was raised by Dr. Bloch about the necessity of our looking upon our own function (as students of psychotherapy) in a social context. Dr. Levinson had drawn to our attention that problems of patients could be looked at in terms of the career of the patient by analogy with other careers. Medicine everywhere has a social function and reflects its society. We, too, must be part of a social context, Bloch was saying. What is the context of psychotherapy in our society? We have a society which has more psychotherapy than any other society. We differ in various other ways from apparently similar societies. Are there meaningful relations between such statements?

On this note I shall conclude, Mr. Chairman, and say that I have left many questions for the rest of the conference to answer.

## REFERENCES

Allport, G. W. *Becoming: Basic considerations for a psychology of personality.* New Haven: Yale Univer. Press, 1955.

Beecher, H. K. The powerful placebo. *J. Amer. med. Assoc.,* 1955, **159**, 1062-1606.

Chapin, F. S. *Experimental designs in sociological research.* New York: Harper, 1955.

Lifton, R. J. *Thought reform and the psychology of totalism.* New York: W. W. Norton, 1961.

Skinner, B. F. *Science and human behavior.* New York: Macmillan, 1953.

Skinner, B. F. *Walden Two.* New York: Macmillan, 1955.

Reid, J. The concept of unconscious anxiety and its use in psychotherapy. *Amer. J. Psychoanal.,* 1956, **16**, 42-53.

# Research Problems in Psychotherapy: A Three-Year Follow-Up

LESTER LUBORSKY, PH.D. AND HANS H. STRUPP, PH.D.

No matter how the field of psychotherapy research is segmented for the sake of a conference, it makes little difference in a free discussion; whatever the designated topic, people soon discuss the same basic issues. This was true of the first as well as the second conference. Therefore, the organization of headings in the final chapter of the last conference book— *Research Goals, Research Methods,* and *Selection of Variables*—works as well for our chapter and, in addition, facilitates comparisons between the two conferences. These headings are not arbitrary; they are the actual topics around which the discussion clustered.

The Parloff-Rubinstein chapter is an incisive summary of that conference and of the issues of psychotherapy research in 1958. We will use it as a point of reference to follow up on what has remained the same or changed in the three-year interval. In this chapter we shall highlight the issues that emerged in the course of the present conference and consider how well its aims were reached. By pointing out the growing edge of work in this area, we hope to offer useful leads to investigators.[1]

The planners of the second conference tried to give it greater focus than the first conference. While the first was designed to give a broad overview of current research efforts in the field, the present meeting centered upon (*a*) factors associated with change in psychotherapy; (*b*) the role of the therapist; and (*c*) problems in the selection of relevant variables. Additional objectives included: considerations of recent research contributions and significant new developments; review and follow-up of several projects which were in the formative stages at the time of the first meeting; and exchange of information among investigators. The planners hoped to provide continuity of contact among investigators which might guide and stimulate further research. Finally, the hope was to place research in psychotherapy more squarely within psychological research concerned with the understanding of interpersonal processes.

## RESEARCH GOALS

Everyone contributing to the conference seemed to be going his own way, but not so blithely as was the case three years ago.

---

[1] For our source material for this chapter we will draw on:

(*a*) The papers submitted to the conference

(*b*) The prepared discussions of each topic by Drs. Kenneth Mark Colby, Nevitt Sanford, and David Shakow

(*c*) The summary reports of the panel discussions by Drs. Morris Parloff, William U. Snyder, Jack Block, Ian Stevenson, Edward S. Bordin, and Ernest A. Haggard

(*d*) The final summary by Dr. George Saslow

(*e*) The recorded comments of each participant (for Days 1 and 3)

(*f*) The postconference questionnaire of each participant containing reflections upon the conference.

The editors drew heavily upon the above ten discussants for the content of this final chapter. We owe them a special debt.

Several helpful readers contributed opinions and suggestions: Drs. Aaron T. Beck, Albert Stunkard, Albert E. Scheflen, Eli Rubinstein, Lloyd Silverman, John M. Butler, Cyril Sofer, and Morris Parloff. We also wish to acknowledge the intensive critical reading by Dr. Martin Wallach and the editorial consultation of Mrs. Ruth Samson Luborsky.

Some of the diversity in the conference was limited by the Planning Committee's invitation of papers in only three areas. These were, however, broad areas, and the papers were intended to be a representative sample of current projects.

Since our subject, psychotherapy, is so complex, one response at the conference was that we should congratulate ourselves on our diversity. At this stage of psychotherapy research, it was thought, we need to make many diverse beginnings to try out methods and concepts. Then we should distill the better approaches, throwing out the poorer ones.

The goal of most of the research contributions was to identify one or two interactions among or within the main sets of variables: patient, therapist, treatment, or life situation. The accent nowadays falls upon interactions among these variables, for example, "the relationship of treatment frequency to patient change," or "the interaction of therapist personality and patient change," etc. Another large group of papers aim at methodological clarification and better definition of variables; these have high priority at the present stage of psychotherapy research.

*Outcome vs. Process Studies*

These alternatives as incentives for debate have been outmoded and put away in the closet. A review requires taking them out, brushing them off, and trying them on to see what was in vogue. Studies of outcome were those that asked the question: *what* changes took place in treatment. These studies typically used patient or observer ratings of improvement or psychological tests before and after treatment. The process studies asked the question *how* change came about and typically used microscopic analysis of the records of the treatment.

In the last psychotherapy conference the editors devoted a considerable section of their final chapter to the reasons why

outcome studies have been scorned by psychologists. Most of the critical attitude toward outcome studies originally came from their association with applied research and their reliance upon unsophisticated improvement ratings. Apparently the last conference worked through this prejudice against outcome studies, and the improvement has been maintained at the present conference. Very little heat could be generated by this issue; the conferees seemed done with it as an issue, although it was referred to by some people in the postconference questionnaire. The tenor of the comments reveals acceptance of outcome studies because of the greater sophistication of recent work. The feeling was that there are many passable roads and that both the outcome and the process roads are respectable.

*Process Scoring Systems*

For many years researchers in this area have hoped that generally applicable scoring systems for the process of psychotherapy could be developed. Although this hope has not been fully realized, technical improvements have constantly been incorporated in the newer process scoring systems. Many of these have come from the field of communications analysis, which has made great strides in the past two decades. Several annual reviews of psychotherapy research have referred to process scoring systems as getting better from year to year as more new systems are developed. In the last psychotherapy conference two new systems were described (the Rogers' content analysis system for the dimensions of experiencing and the promising but overcomplex psychoanalytic process scoring system by Leary and Gill). At the present conference at least three process systems were represented (Butler, Lennard, and Strupp).

Despite this profusion of instruments, most researchers have felt the need for manufacturing their own brand. As a result, there is no generally accepted or

thoroughly investigated system. Furthermore, one cannot detect sustained interest,
either by the originator or others, in any
one system—systems like the Discomfort-
Relief Quotient or Raimy's PNAvQ
which were popular a decade ago are
rarely used now. The reasons for this state
of affairs are complex. In addition to
technical difficulties of quantification,
systems are usually anchored to particular
theoretical orientations; consequently they
are limited in scope and not very useful
for comparisons across theoretical boundaries; and finally, for the testing of specific hypotheses, specific systems are
needed. The Bales system of interaction-
process analysis, designed as a general-
purpose system, seems to have greater via-
bility than most, although it may be too
general for many research purposes in
psychotherapy.

One of the scoring systems taken up by
the conference (Butler) was discussed in
terms of its psychological sophistication
which entails a high demand for fine judgments. This is a persistent requirement of
many systems and one that creates resistance to its application by other researchers. However, the trained human
instrument when kept in bounds by controls on reliability is well equipped to
make many complex discriminations. In
the conference there was considerable emphasis on the need to define larger psychologically meaningful units or themes that
are related to psychotherapy process and
outcome (possibly, e.g., shifts in major
transference pattern). However, the resistance to scoring complexity is not
deeply seated; it probably arose in this
conference from two precipitating events:
the overcomplexity of several recent systems and the contemplation of the analysis
of miles of tape and film of psychotherapy.

*Personality Theory*

Most psychotherapy researchers hope to
contribute ultimately to basic personality

theory. They share the common faith that
a good theory of personality will emerge
from a good theory of treatment (and vice
versa).

In the conference the specific bodies of
theories which were most often discussed
were: (a) learning theory, (b) theory of
social processes, and (c) psychoanalytic
theory. The part of learning theory most
frequently referred to was the theory of
verbal or operant conditioning. A number
of participants were also fascinated by the
application of the concept of "deutero-
learning" to psychotherapy. Their feeling
was that much of the learning that takes
place in psychotherapy is in the nature of
learning how to learn. One not only learns
to work out specific conflicts, but learns
the general principles of working out conflicts for oneself.

An amorphous issue, the extent to
which psychotherapy is a socialization
process, came up for discussion. It certainly seemed questionable to most participants to speak of psychotherapy as
though it were *only* another version of a
parent-child relationship, even to the
many participants who thought primarily
in terms of psychoanalytic theory.

Despite the fact that psychoanalytic
theory in both its clinical and metapsycho-
logical aspects is increasingly being regarded as the most comprehensive attempt
to account for psychic processes, it cannot
be said that the theory has led commensurately to controlled psychotherapy research investigations. The methodological
obstacles in the theory have been dealt
with exhaustively by Rapaport (1960).
By this time one would expect to have
seen research focused on such central concepts as transference, resistance, the ego's
defensive and adaptive operations, interpretations (to name but a few). Nor was
a great deal of discussion devoted to these
topics at the conference.

## METHOD

Problems of method, especially in the choice of variables, were a *leitmotiv* throughout the conference. In fact, method tended to be more enthusiastically discussed than research findings. There were several possible reasons for this: (1) Researchers in this field have been deeply concerned with problems of method, for they are convinced that one of the greatest impediments to progress is the lack of powerful yet practical methods. (2) When there is diversity of interest in a group of discussants it is sometimes more comfortable to stick to topics which everyone has thought about and everyone has in common.

As was true at the last conference, the most natural division of participants, according to preference for method, was between *experimenters* and *naturalists*. The distinction may not have been quite so clear as it was at the first psychotherapy conference, but it was still there. There were probably more participants at the second conference representing the advanced view that both approaches can be useful and might be tried even by the same person. This issue was not so sharply drawn as it was in the last conference, but possibly because this was a more placid meeting. Even pronouncements like the following seemed to produce more of a peaceful consensus than they posed a threat to the experimentalists: The crisis in our field comes from the fact that the honored methods of physical science and mathematics have not helped the psychological sciences as much as they have the physical sciences; we may have to be more ingenious in using these methods, or make new ones of our own.

### Naturalistic Observation vs. Experimentation

The contributions at this conference showed growing recognition of the special suitability of naturalistic observation for psychotherapy research. Next to the topic of operant conditioning, this one provoked the most sustained discussion.

A curious satiation effect developed around the constant use of the term "naturalistic observation." It seemed to be the same kind of satiation effect that one gets from repeating any term over and over—a gradual disintegration of meaning. People began apologizing for the term "naturalistic." One participant finished off the term "naturalistic" by saying, "Well, 'observation' expresses it well enough. The word 'naturalistic' before 'observation' is superfluous. I don't know what an 'unnaturalistic observation' would be." It was as though the term "naturalistic observation" had run its life course in the three-day period of the conference among some of the participants. The naturalists, however, seemed to remain certain of the value and the vitality and capacity of the idea to rise from the dust.

The editors of the first conference report gave a lengthy account of the sets of attitudes going along with a belief in naturalistic observation vs. a belief in experimentation. We shall not attempt to reiterate their points, but only to highlight that part of the controversy which was most prominently reproduced at the present conference. There seemed to be three core themes in the discussion: (*a*) the capacity of each approach to get at the complexity of the phenomena; (*b*) the capacity of each approach to be generative of new hypotheses; and (*c*) the relative status of the two approaches in terms of scientific prestige.

To some participants, the naturalistic observation approach seemed ideal for getting at the complexity of a phenomenon. On the other side, experimentalists were willing to run the risk of missing some things in order to gain the chance of isolating and manipulating one aspect

of a phenomenon. In terms of generativity, some participants asserted that
when experiments go wrong they do not
lead to discovery, whereas observations
can always lead to new experiments. The
reply of the experimentalists was that one
can miss things too in the observational
method, because of the complexity of the
phenomena.

Some conferees expressed annoyance at
the naive assumption that verification of
hypotheses through experiment can be the
only way of testing knowledge, and at the
uninformed contemporary overevaluation
of statistics and complex research design.
Hypotheses can obviously be examined
from the recorded data of psychotherapy;
therefore, the testing of hypotheses is not
a function solely of formal experiment.

*Experimental Analogues of Psychotherapy*

This section takes up the relative merits
of "the real thing" (psychotherapy itself)
vs. quasi-therapeutic or therapeutic analogies as media for psychotherapy research.
A simpler way to put the topic is: "Which
questions can be answered in the laboratory and which cannot?" Two main examples of experimental situations were
discussed in this conference: (*a*) filmed
sequences of psychotherapy to which
therapists respond (Strupp); (*b*) verbal
and operant conditioning or reinforcement experiments (Krasner). The discussion centered predominantly about the
operant conditioning experiments and
relatively less on the film techniques. The
latter seemed to most people the more
acceptable and justifiable experimental
analogue, since actual therapy (or acted
therapy) was the stimulus to which the
judges responded.

Even though the participants had serious objections to the operant conditioning experiments and the experimenters'
theories, some of them were intrigued
almost against their better judgment by
the ingeniousness and possibilities of the

approach. The discussion on this topic was
quite lively, with people feeling strongly
pro and con—mostly con—but the net
effect of the discussion was a heightened
interest in the area. Many participants,
however, remained bothered by (*a*) ethical
questions raised by the operant conditioning techniques, and (*b*) serious differences between the conditioning situation
and the psychotherapy situation that made
any inferences tenuous or even impossible.

The tenor of the comments concerning
the ethical implications was that these
conditioning experiments promoted the
wrong idea about the degree to which
people are predictable and controllable.
They imply that the therapist is a machine. Many participants, especially those
who were primarily clinicians and therapists, objected to the words "control" or
"influence," and preferred instead to think
of the patient's own wish to change. The
therapist wants to *evoke* change, not force
change.

Seven types of differences were suggested between operant conditioning experiments and psychotherapy. These led
many participants to decide that one cannot directly apply results from conditioning techniques to psychotherapy:

1. The role expectancies in operant
conditioning and in psychotherapy are
quite different. Patients in psychotherapy
are ordinarily voluntary participants who
want to change in certain areas. Subjects
in an operant conditioning experiment do
not experience themselves as being in a
helping relationship; they participate for
a variety of (often unrelated and unclari-
fied) reasons.

2. The change that can be effected
through operant conditioning may not be
very deep, lasting, or extensive.

3. The extent of the emotional involvement in operant conditioning experiments
is considerably less than in psychotherapy.

4. Change in psychotherapy is mediated
quite differently.

5. Individuals who do change via operant conditioning experiments are those who want to please. This is not necessarily true in psychotherapy.

6. The definition of reinforcement is too general in the operant conditioning experiments. It is unclear what is being reinforced.

7. The nature of that which is influenced in psychotherapy is much more complex than that which is influenced in operant conditioning; for example, in operant conditioning it is "plural nouns" or some such specific response.

Some participants thought that these differences were not serious; for example, even if the responses in operant conditioning are in the nature of a placebo effect, the conditioning technique may still have a lot to teach us about similar kinds of effects in psychotherapy. The criticism about the artificiality of operant conditioning experiments was answered by the counter-charge that the operant conditioning studies are no more unreal and divorced from reality than the psychotherapy situation which can also be considered to be artificial. The person who changes in the operant conditioning situation may be the one who wants to please and there may be other personality correlates; nevertheless, it would be valuable to explore these correlates and find out whether they are the same for people who change through psychotherapy. The same can be said for the types of experimenters and therapists who can influence patients or subjects to change.

One historically minded participant reminded the conferees of the naive assumption—perhaps related to American positivist thinking—that human behavior is easily changed or "conditioned." This may be true as far as the emission of plural nouns, pronouns, and the like is concerned. However, the history of modern psychotherapy has taught us the hard truth that deeply ingrained (neurotic)

patterns of human behavior are exceedingly resistant to change. Freud found it necessary to postulate the repetition compulsion to account for this phenomenon, and a large part of the job in psychoanalytic therapy is devoted to breaking down the patient's unconscious resistances to change. Learning to change is easy in those areas in which the patient's ego has little need to defend itself; the difficulties, on the other hand, are great when change threatens important defensive functions.

*Values and Snares of Clinical Inference*

Everybody thinks clinical inference is important, but pedantic emphasis on method divorced from problems has discouraged research on the inference process. This may explain why research plans usually try to steer as clear of it as they can. Many participants hoped to be able to devise ways, for example, of finding the main themes in a vast collection of psychotherapy data. Of course, this would necessitate the use of clinical inference, since machine reduction could not do it.

What people mainly worry about with clinical inference is the reliability problem. Reliability studies would tell us not only whether independent observers could make the same judgments, but they would advance research by fostering greater explicitness of the criteria of judgment, leading to the redefinition of the variables. However, perfectly good variables and concepts can be ruined by poor judges. One needs judges who are highly trained and highly motivated in order to get a fair test of the reliability of clinical inferences.

The problems of clinical inference are encountered in the analysis of all data from psychotherapeutic (and diagnostic) interviews. The problems are especially evident in two tasks of psychotherapy research: (*a*) the construction of content-analysis systems, and (*b*) the assessments of patients leading to predictions of course and outcome of treatment. Relatively little systematic research has been devoted to the process of clinical inference, although one of the projects represented at the conference has such a study under way (Menninger Project).

## Use of Electronic Computers for Data Reduction

The machine age for psychotherapy research was visible on the horizon—although some thought it a mirage. What computers can and cannot do for psychotherapy research was broached; there was no such talk at the preceding conference. The discussion, however, was temperate—the largest computer on earth could not find the themes of a treatment, whereas the "soft grey computer" (the brain) is well designed for this. Although machines are not apt at finding themes, they are often useful for handling large masses of data. The suggestion was made to try to simulate the mental operations of the therapist's mind by a machine as a way of trying to understand better the therapist's mental operations. In this way, one might also explore the question of whether the therapist could be assisted in reaching the patient by the type of "spoken inputs" which the machine has evolved through its digestion of the information of the treatment. A possible advantage of the machine is its explicitness and the readiness with which its conclusions can be put to experimental test.

### SELECTION OF VARIABLES

Issues concerned with the selection of variables were omnipresent. Not only was this topic one of the three major ones at the panel, but it was the unofficial topic as well in the panel on the therapist and the panel on change. And several of the papers explicitly dealt with problems pertaining to the selection of variables. The best way to deal with such a large topic is to apply the techniques of data reduc-

tion and organize the material into the major themes around which discussion centered. By way of introduction, two topics will be considered: (a) problems of data reduction and the size of units, and (b) neglect of content variables. The body of the section will be broken up into the usual major areas: "techniques of therapy," "the therapist," "the patient," plus a new one, "the match between patient and therapist."

Finding the right concepts and the right units is one of the basic problems of science; it is crucial for psychology, and in particular for psychotherapy research. It is even more important than the measurement of variables. When chemistry stopped looking at "odor" and "hardness," etc. and shifted to such units as "the reactivity of the substance with hydrogen and oxygen," a big advance was made in chemistry. With our shift of focus to interactional variables—variables which comprise not only the patient singly or the therapist singly, but the interaction between them—we, too, seem to be moving to the stage of functional units. A separate topic heading, Match between Patient and Therapist, will therefore be included. However, even the variables listed under the single headings, e.g., Therapist, are also conceived of in interactional terms.

By careful listening for major themes, it is possible to reduce the types of general issues that were brought into the discussion of any variable to nine: (1) possible definitions and difficulties of these definitions, (2) reliability of measures, (3) range of stimuli that influence the variable, (4) relationship of the variable to mental health and to the outcome of psychotherapy, (5) correlates and interrelations with other variables, (6) varieties of the variable as these show up within psychotherapy and within psychological tests, (7) degree of awareness of the variable that is achieved by the patient, (8) meaning or significance of the variable to the patient, (9) "generativity" of the concept that gave rise to the variable—the extent to which it opens up new knowledge and stimulates further research.

## Problems of Data Reduction and Size of Unit

There was much interest, but some uncertainty, in how to go about managing the mountainous mass of data usual in psychotherapy research. The natural response of the naturalist when confronted by a complex behavior sequence is to observe and listen quietly in order to get in tune, and then to classify the main concepts. Several participants advocated this approach to research.

The task of data reduction from miles of tape or film is formidable; many discussants suggested the reduction of the data to what is relevant to specific questions. Many observed that this problem is no different in other fields. Every phenomenon is complex and there is always a question of data reduction.

Why not, for example, simply reduce all the data to the main themes? There was considerable sympathy for this solution, provided there was a sure way of identifying "main themes." There was a dissatisfaction with the kinds of segments that had been used in many process scoring systems; for example, systems in which the sentence is used as the unit. Such units are not only arbitrary, but also not large enough. We need to define for ourselves *meaningful molecular* units which are related to treatment process and outcome (cf. the discussion under Process Scoring Systems and Clinical Inference).

## Neglect of Content Variables

It was striking to observe that *all* the variables suggested were formal. One discussant tried to analyze this neglect as a *"resistance to content"* on the group's part. Possibly a resistance was also shown in the rarity with which specific patients were mentioned at the psychotherapy con-

ference. At the last conference there was a similar lack, although one of the proposed scoring systems (Leary and Gill) contained some content variables. However, the present conference was probably the more "clinical" of the two. (This was partially a function of the planning in that a deliberate effort had been made to invite more "pure" clinicians to the second conference, since researchers and clinicians too often have proceeded in "splendid isolation," both feeling that they have little to contribute to each other.)

The discussion came closest to consideration of content with the issue of the definition of "activity of the therapist" and what determines the impact and meaningfulness of a communication to the patient. Some resolution of the issue was attempted by the conclusion that the therapist says something meaningful when the patient is not too disturbed by it so that he is able to "process" it.

### Treatment

Four topics caught the attention of the contributors and discussants: (*a*) the nature of therapeutic influence upon the patient, (*b*) the effects of activity-inactivity upon the patient, (*c*) the classification of different treatments along the dimension of ambiguity-structuredness, and (*d*) the spacing of therapy sessions.

Interest in treatment techniques increased as compared to the preceding conference, possibly because researchers in psychotherapy have become more experienced in practicing psychotherapy and as they have made it an important focus of clinical activity. The proper spacing of therapy sessions is a topic of immediate practical concern to clinicians. While the clinical literature has much to say about it, only recently have controlled studies been attempted—the project represented at this conference is the most comprehensive of these (Lorr).

In the area of treatment techniques, as

well as in each of the others, the lack of a standard set of terms or variables was felt. These could help compare different kinds of psychotherapy with each other and with different interpersonal situations. (Some attempts to list treatment variables are available; e.g., Bibring (1954) and Luborsky et al. (1958).)

*The Nature of Therapeutic Influence: Manipulation vs. Growth Facilitation*

Certain words used in the conference to describe therapeutic action were highly loaded. Therapists do not like to think of themselves as manipulators or "controllers"; they do not enjoy being compared with "brainwashers" or faith healers. The immediate stimulus for discussing the nature of therapeutic influence came from the injection of such words by proponents of the operant conditioning techniques.

This issue has been with us for centuries. Physicians have had two schools of thought corresponding to the same opposed concepts: one school of medicine conceiving of the physician's function as merely facilitating natural reparative functions, the other school believing that the physician actually cures and that he is the agent of cure. Some of the onus attached to "influence" and "manipulation" may derive from the bad repute in which suggestion and advice-giving as therapeutic techniques are held in some quarters. A decade ago there was a lively controversy about Franz Alexander's recommendations for "manipulation" or "regulation" of the transference. Alexander felt that time could be saved if the transference were only "allowed" to develop as much as needed for the treatment, in contrast to the classical position whose prime aim is to analyze the transference, not to "manipulate" it. More recently, the issue was debated by Carl R. Rogers and B. F. Skinner at one of the best attended symposia held at the American Psychological Association meetings. Rogers took the view that in psychotherapy the individual

realizes himself by a positive striving toward growth and creativity. Skinner maintained that in treatment one is manipulated.

Most of the participants in our conference felt strongly that the language of conditioning, manipulation, and control was out of place in psychotherapy. They preferred to think instead of assisting healing potentialities, allowing a person to choose for himself, and to help him find new purposes by releasing him from the bonds of his biography.

Many participants could accept partial resolution of the problem expressed in the following terms: the therapist wants to influence the patients toward using his own faculties and growing in the best possible directions. It is recognized that the ways in which therapists implement this influence differs in different forms of therapy.

*Therapist Activity vs. Inactivity as a Technique of Change*

Discussion of this issue was stimulated from at least two sources: (a) the observation reported from one project that expressiveness of the therapists, especially in the form of posture and vividness of communication, could be used consciously to show an interest in the patient and hence facilitate change (Butler), and (b) the use in another project (Lennard) of the amount of speaking on the part of the therapist as an index of activity.

Considerable interest was shown in the suggestion that activity in the form of expressiveness that reveals interest could facilitate change in the course of treatment. A number of participants took this idea away as one to be thought over, tried out, and retested.

The tendency of information theorists and others to treat statements solely quantitatively was questioned. The view was neatly expressed by Gilbert: "The meaning doesn't matter if it's only idle chatter of the transcendental kind." Most discussants were convinced that without the meaning, words spoken have no relationship to activity-inactivity. The number of words uttered by the therapist is a secondary variable and the meaningfulness of what he says, the impact upon the patient, becomes the primary variable. (Recent studies have included aspects of the therapist's messages beside the number of words or the type of message, e.g., "interpretation," and "reflection of feeling." This is a typical example of an increment of sophistication among researchers over the past decade or two.)

## Ambiguity vs. Structure of the Treatment

The participants were intrigued with this concept; it seemed one that had been insufficiently exploited. One of the panels was stimulated to a definition of the variable as well as a listing of the main qualities of the treatment that contribute to it. They defined it as "The qualities of the treatment situation which maximize or minimize the variability of patient behavior." They listed the following nine influences upon this variable: (1) type of task, (2) type of procedure, (3) patient-therapist relationship, (4) type of content expected, (5) anxiety level of the patient, (6) activity-passivity of the therapist, (7) restriction by the therapist of the variety of the statements, (8) definition of the therapist's tasks and goals, and (9) definition of the therapist in the eyes of the patient.

Like most variables, ambiguity-structure has been in the literature for some time (e.g., Ekstein, 1952). Clinicians have believed for a long time that the more structure, the less transference development, and the less structure, the more transference potential of the treatment. There was general recognition that just as there is no one formula for effective therapist behavior, so there are some patients who need ambiguity and a nonexpressive

therapist, while others need the opposite qualities of the dimension.

## Therapist

At the first conference, interest was expressed in a fuller description of the therapist. At this conference he was elevated to the status of a formal position on the program. Still, he proved to be a hard one to get to know.

A review of the brief history of the modern era of psychotherapy reveals that Freud in his contributions at first paid little attention to the therapist. Then, in 1910 he introduced the concept of the countertransference which for several decades was the focus of interest in the therapist's personality. In this conception, the therapist's personality was viewed as a possible source of interference with the progress of psychotherapy, and the goal was to minimize such interferences. The royal road to this objective was the personal analysis of the therapist, which was intended to make him a standard instrument, maximally objective and sensitive to the patient's and his own transference maneuvers. It was implied—but never made explicit (except in tangential references)—that the therapist was a mature, dedicated person who could serve the patient as a model for healthy identification. Thus, the therapist's technical contribution (primarily his interpretive skill) came to occupy a position of foremost importance for the outcome of psychotherapy.

During the last decade or two, the human relationship aspects of psychotherapy have come in for more explicit stress in the literature. In fact, some writers propose that the therapist's personality is more important than any technique he might use. Some go so far as to question whether technique is important at all; they suggest that it only matters whether the "right" patient encounters the "right" therapist at the "right" time. The congruence and mutual impact of the patient and therapist on each other received special attention during the conference. Much of the panel on the Therapist was devoted to thinking of variables of an interactional sort involving both therapist and patient—for example, "dependency of the patient on the therapist," "comparative value systems of the therapist and patient," "comparative level of anxiety of therapist and patient," "therapist's capacity to like the patient," "therapist's willingness to allow the patient to grow," etc.

### The Basic Question: How Does the Therapist Influence the Patient?

The basic question was central to many issues, even when the focus was not specifically upon the therapist. (See the discussion earlier on "the nature of treatment influence.") The issue has sometimes been put in terms of what the therapist *does* vs. what he *is*. Of prime importance, of course, is how *the patient* interprets the therapist, both cognitively and emotionally. For example, at different times and in different combinations, the therapist may be experienced as a reasonable father, a loving mother, a religious figure, a serious therapist, an inspired healer, a charismatic leader, or as a reinforcement machine that has been programed to emit certain responses. Can the therapist's activities be reduced to operations and roles which he shares with other members of the culture (for example, parents, teachers, religious leaders, or brainwashers)? These were some of the questions which arose in many guises at the conference. At least in the context of psychotherapy research, such questions have rarely been squarely faced.

### Personal Qualities of the Therapist

As might be expected, research is more plentiful on those personality characteristics which can be studied quantitatively by available research techniques. Since there is often an inverse relationship be-

tween the importance of a variable and its amenability to objective research, it is not surprising that more superficial characteristics have been more extensively studied than more important ones. For example, it is easier to count the therapist's use of interpretations vs. "reflections of feeling," and the number of each used in a given hour, than it is to judge the quality of a particular verbal intervention, the therapist's attitude in making it, and its impact upon the patient. However, there is progress to point to. Fairly extensive data have been reported in the literature on differences between more and less experienced therapists, and between therapists adhering to various theoretical orientations. We have also learned more about the effects of the therapist's warmth, personal conflicts, and anxiety level on the therapist's judgments of the patient-therapist interaction.

There was considerable interest in differences among therapists who were more vs. less successful in treating schizophrenic patients. (The topic was stimulated by the paper submitted by Dr. Barbara Betz.) Apparently the better therapists succeeded in fostering a trusting relationship with their patients. A natural question came next: Why has it been so hard to establish equally identifiable qualities for therapists who treat neurotic patients? Symposium participants suggested as possible explanations: (a) the criterion for change for schizophrenic patients who recover is quite gross, and therefore easier to establish than it is for neurotic patients, and (b) the anxiety stirred up in some therapists by empathizing with schizophrenics is very great, and some therapists find this anxiety almost intolerable. Astonishment was expressed about the great difficulty of retraining the less effective therapists to become more effective therapists (with schizophrenics).

Such characteristics as the therapist's dedication, faith, integrity, honesty, and firm belief in the efficacy of his procedures were mentioned as crucial for therapeutic progress, but have so far been resistant to investigation. The therapist's system of values and his degree of authoritarianism are important variables which have recently been included in research projects. The therapist's personality is presumably intertwined also with his theoretical orientation, his therapeutic goals, his techniques, and the kinds of patients he prefers. Recently, such variables as social class, religion, age, sex, and ethnic group membership have come in for research attention which has pointed up their relevance in a striking fashion (e.g., Hollingshead & Redlich, 1958).

### Therapist's "Resonance" to the Patient's Personality

The therapist's response to the qualities of the patient (including sociocultural characteristics) might further or impede the therapy. Diagnostic and prognostic judgments are influenced by the therapist's attitudes toward the patient. In extreme cases, the therapist's diagnoses or negative attitudes toward the patient act as a self-fulfilling prophecy, resulting in therapeutic failure.

The therapist must be capable of communication which is profoundly meaningful to the patient, and his expressiveness must create a responsive resonance in him. Patient and therapist must meet each other's expectations at least in part if change is to occur. As one participant put it, "the patient's capacity for improvement may lie in his ability to be emotionally aroused in certain ways by the treatment he receives." Freud (1935) in describing the dynamics of the transference neurosis, made a similar point: "The outcome in this struggle (between the repressive and expressive forces in the patient) is not decided by his intellectual insight—it is neither strong enough nor free enough to accomplish such a thing—but *solely by his relationship to the physician*" (p. 387; our italics).

The therapist communicates both intellectually and affectively with the patient, and the patient responds to the messages both cognitively and affectively. The cognitive component serves to restructure the patient's affective responses in a new framework. The learning is mediated mainly by linguistic communication: the more the consensus reached between patient and therapist, the more the possibility of a successful outcome to the treatment. (See also the section below, The Match between Patient and Therapist.)

### Mental Processes of the Therapist

Long before the present-day type of research scientist in psychotherapy came along, the therapist was faced with the job of ordering the data emerging from his interaction with the patient. He had to be able to listen attentively or with "free floating attention," to draw inferences and incorporate these in his communications to the patient. It was partly through this process that theories of psychotherapy have evolved.

The scientist is keenly interested in how the clinician's mental processes work in arriving at his communications to the patient. This topic has been repeatedly suggested as a potentially significant frontier for psychotherapy research, but, with few exceptions, very little research has been done so far. (David Shakow suggested a method years ago as did Franz Alexander in his current psychotherapy research project.) The relentless researcher who wishes to ask such potentially embarrassing questions as whether independent observers can make identical observations and draw similar inferences has therefore thus far been frustrated. However, some research studies are getting under way in this area.

### Patient

The problems of establishing criteria for change captured the attention and interest of the participants more than any other topic in this area. Only a few specific variables about the patient were discussed at length.

Although the role of the therapist was stressed in this conference, there was no implication that this was meant to depreciate the importance of the patient and his personality. At the last conference, one investigator stated that practically all the variance in outcome level was a function of variance within the patient at the beginning of the treatment. At the present conference, one contribution was thought to have a somewhat similar implication. The initial level of rated health-sickness was reported to correlate highly with the termination level of health-sickness obtained. This, of course, says nothing about the role of the therapist, but it does emphasize the patient's initial state as a significant factor in outcome.

A perennial question came up about which therapists at times feel overoptimistic or overpessimistic: How drastically can treatment change an individual? This question gained meaning in the context of discussion of potential dangers in therapeutic influence as an instrument for manipulation of people.

### Criteria for Change

*a. Lack of Correlation among Criteria from Therapist, Patient, and Other Sources.* Here is an opportunity for research. The lack of correlation among criterion measures has thwarted researchers for some time. Rogers was probably one of the first to make this observation on the basis of his study at the Counseling Center, University of Chicago. The lack of correlation among criteria was brought up in the present conference, but no satisfactory discussion nor cogent explanations developed. (One participant observed, however, on the basis of a study he had recently completed, that observer, therapist, and diagnostician actually agreed in their judgments if one correlated the self factors.)

*b. Necessity for More than Single (Specific or Global) Measures of Change.* In view of the complexity of the concept of mental health and the lack of correlation among criteria, the sophisticated solution to get a rounded picture of change is to use more than one rater and take into account the view of several observers. Among the criteria which have to be considered are those listed by Zax and Klein (1960): (*a*) intratherapy measures (the verbal productions of the patient), (*b*) therapist ratings, and (*c*) behavioral criteria outside the treatment relationship. At the present conference, several participants stressed the worthwhileness of the last of these criteria, which too often have been neglected.

No single measure of change, even when repeated on the patient over time, is sufficient, since any change may involve altered interactions with other areas of the personality and with the environment (Luborsky & Schimek, 1962.) Several specific criteria were utilized in the Phipps Clinic project reported at the last conference; for example, "discomfort" and "social ineffectiveness" (and Lorr is developing scales for separate criteria).

Global measures of change have been widely used, such as ratings of "improvement," "mental health," and "success" in treatment. They have a rule-of-thumb value in broad surveys of psychotherapy results, but should never be used singly. This recommendation was contained in a number of contributions at the conference; for example, the global Health-Sickness Rating Scale of the Menninger Foundation Project is more complete when used together with the ratings of the seven specific criteria which compose it.

*c. Need for Better Measures of Outcome.* Scales or measures which could be used both nationally and across projects were recommended by several conferees. Also tools are needed for measuring *short-term* outcome or changes. Measures of outcome should be of all three types suggested by Zax and Klein (1960). One conferee expressed the sentiment, which was shared by others, that we need measures of strength as well as measures of illness.

The most consistently voiced suggestion for implementing the recommendations was to hold future meetings (preferably of smaller working groups) to examine the variety of evaluation techniques. One participant believed that the development of these measures would probably come about by natural growth. Another school of thought, probably the largest one, held that there are too many measures already and that we need now a theory to organize the measures and to apply statistical techniques designed to reduce redundancy. One way would consist in running correlations between these measures and discarding overlapping ones. Areas could be found in which there are no measures, and these gaps could be filled. One participant objected, however, that it may not be wise at this stage to throw out any measures; rather we should allow for redundancy of instruments, variables, and approaches. The conciliatory point was made that criteria depend on the purpose of the treatment; as the aims vary, so might the criteria one would select.

*d. The Best Level of Abstraction for Criteria.* This question held a fascination for several participants. Impetus to discuss it came from the interesting data presented by one of the contributors (Shlien). These data showed that an individual responds in approximately the same way in terms of his own self-ideal ratio whether he is presented with specific items in the form of verbal questionnaire items or with an over-all question about his self and ideal self, put to him via a little gadget that he simply adjusts to demon-

strate the relative positions of his self and ideal self concept. An intense discussion followed on the definition of abstract-concrete and how the designation "abstract" applied to the visual demonstration. The definition of abstract was given by the contributor as the capacity of a variable to be conceptualized and raised above specific content. After the fascination came questions. One participant wondered whether the criterion really becomes *less* important and *less* meaningful as it becomes more abstract. Another participant concluded that different levels of abstraction are fitting for differing research purposes.

*The Nature of Change: Reduction of Illness or Growth of Personality?*

The discussion on this issue was quite similar to the one on the nature of therapeutic influence—is the influence upon a patient a product of the therapist's manipulation or the result of conditions which facilitate the patient's own growth potentialities? There was considerable consensus about the conclusion that with reduction of illness there is usually resumption of growth.

Logically and inevitably this topic veered into the always-near-the-surface issue of the nature of mental health. It is difficult to list the criteria for mental health, although this has been attempted increasingly in recent years with some success by Erikson, Jahoda, Hartmann, and others.

*Principal Patient Variables Discussed at the Conference*

The value of diagnostic variables was considered briefly. Finding such categories has been a perennial goal and a perennial dissatisfaction. Clinicians tend to feel that current diagnostic concepts are not very good but are much better than nothing. Whitehead said, in a different context, "Nature doesn't come as clean as we can think it." Clinicians and others are naggingly aware that our concepts are too "clean," and would be more satisfied with "unwashed" ones corresponding more closely to nature. Much of the discussion on diagnosis centered on the label "schizophrenia." It was pointed out that certain themes uniformly go along with each diagnosis. It was also commented that over the years, with the lessening of the stigma attached to the term, more patients are classified in the category "schizophrenia."

The following variables were mentioned: Self/Self-Ideal Ratio, Anxiety, Anxiety Tolerance, Patient's Participation, Perception of the Therapeutic Field, Transference Pattern, Perception of Self, and Patient's and Therapist's View of Treatment Results. Since only the first three came in for more than cursory attention, they will be reviewed here principally as examples of the types of problems that come up in discussions about specific variables.

*Self/Self-Ideal Ratio.* The concept of self/self-ideal ratio was brought into the discussion as an example of the best level of abstraction for a criterion. Concern was expressed about the composition of the self/self-ideal ratio. One discussant considered that since self-ideal descriptions are similar, the variance must come from the self description. Concerning the correlates of the self/self-ideal ratio, anxiety was suggested as a likely possibility. One participant who had done considerable work with self/self-ideal ratios, listed several correlates. His findings suggested that people who are extreme in their self/self-ideal correlation are among the ones who are the difficult cases in treatment. Patients with high self/self-ideal ratios include among them the more maladjusted. After a variety of questions had been raised about the self/self-ideal ratio, one proponent of the variable replied that these questions raised were good ones but were general and applied equally to any other criterion of change, and not uniquely to self/self-ideal ratios.

*Anxiety and Anxiety Tolerance.* Despite considerable research on "anxiety," the term still resists simple definition. One of the difficulties with the definition of many variables, and particularly this one, attends the attempt to mix "data language" (behavioral language) and "concept language." A participant who had spent years trying to analyze the concept, concluded that anxiety has to be considered as a process rather than an entity open to observation and measurement. Despite difficulties in definition, other participants argued that one could get useful global reports of magnitude of "anxiety" from the patient.

Several investigators reported instances in which anxiety measures failed to correlate with each other. Much of the difficulty was attributed to inadequate specification of the time period for which the person is supposed to make a judgment about his anxiety level. Since anxiety varies considerably over time, the question to the self-rater must include an explicit time specification, otherwise considerable unreliability can be reaped. The topic or activity engendering anxiety should also be specified. It was recognized that anxiety scales may not work in one situation but work in another. This implies that no one definition is best; different ones must be tried in different situations. For instance, the example was given of the Taylor Anxiety Scale which correlates with *change* in palmar sweat but not with *level* of palmar sweat.

The same variety of vantage points which we described as applying to judgments of any criterion of treatment outcome and treatment can also be applied to judgments of anxiety: judgments can be made by the patient, the therapist, or by an observer on the basis of psychological tests, process recordings of treatment, observations of the patient in family life and at work.

One contributor (Luborsky) reported a positive correlation between measures of initial anxiety level and of change in the course of psychotherapy. However, this correlation may not always be positive. Two reasons for this variation were put forward: (1) Following therapy, the patient often deliberately exposes himself to anxiety-provoking situations which previously he may have avoided. (2) Patients whose mental health is rated high tend to show a higher correlation between level of anxiety and amount of change than patients whose initial rating of mental health is low. Ratings of the patient's anxiety level should not be considered by themselves; rather, they must be judged along with measures of anxiety tolerance or "the capacity to *use* anxiety as a danger signal"—as opposed to being overwhelmed by it—(Siegal and Rosen). Because of these considerations future studies of anxiety in relation to outcome will probably produce varying results, since the population samples themselves will differ in terms of anxiety tolerance.

Anxiety is central to treatment; the conferees were almost unanimous on this point. Therefore, it is important to achieve better definitions and more knowledge of how judgments can be made of anxiety and its form varieties as they appear during treatment. (The old "Discomfort-Relief quotient" was getting at one aspect of anxiety level in the course of psychotherapy.) So far, in the reports in this conference, it was judged mainly from evaluation interviews and psychological tests. In addition to these problems, the patient's awareness of his own anxiety and its meaning to him must be taken into consideration.

### Match between Patient and Therapist

Matching is crucial in marriage; so may be the match between patient and therapist in therapy. So far we know more about the first than the second. We know less about those characteristics of the therapist promoting a beneficial relationship than we know about the characteristics of the patient which make him a good candidate for psychotherapy.

There has been an increasing amount of research on this problem. One study (Counseling Center, University of Chicago) has separated three kinds of patients: those with whom both experienced and inexperienced therapists have equally fair success; those with whom experienced therapists do well; and those with whom inexperienced therapists do poorly. These patients are characterized by different styles of expression. In the operant conditioning literature, a study found that compatible need systems underlie the most effective matching (Sapolsky, 1960). One participant reported a situation in which residents, when given the opportunity to choose their own patients, tended to select patients who were young adults, who had higher socioeconomic status than other patients, who had lower scores on the F scale, who wanted treatment more than other patients did, and who were less anti-intraceptive.

The problem of patient-therapist compatibility is described in a review of psychotherapy (Strupp, 1962) as an area in which more work is currently being done. Among the patients who are considered good prognostic risks are those who are very much like the preferred patients chosen by the residents: they are "young, attractive, well-educated, members of the upper-middle class, possessing a high degree of ego strength, some anxiety which impels them to seek help, no seriously disabling neurotic symptoms, relative absence of deep characterological distortions and strong secondary gains, willingness to talk about their difficulties, ability to communicate well, some skill in the social vocational area, and a value system relatively congruent with that of the therapist; such patients also tend to remain in therapy, profit from it, and evoke the therapist's best efforts." These characteristics may actually contribute to a better outcome of psychotherapy, but further research needs to be done to establish them.

### Life Situation
### (Extra-Treatment Environment)

The consensus was that this conference gave greater recognition to social factors than the last one. The last conference report, in fact, included no major heading for this category. As a mark of its newer status, it now rates a heading of its own.

Psychotherapy researchers were admonished by their fellows: they stay in the office too much; they should get out and see how the patient lives. So far, their knowledge about patients has come either directly from the treatment or from diagnostic tests. Yet the ultimate test of the outcome of treatment is the manner in which the patient actually changes his way of living outside the treatment.

### EPILOGUE

We shall comment on two main topics: the rate of development in psychotherapy research, and new areas showing promise of growth.

### Rate of Advance in Psychotherapy
### Research

What we cannot reach flying we must reach limping—
The book tells us it is no sin to limp.

—Freud quoting Rückert's
translation of *al-Hariri*

"Slow" is the adjective used most commonly by reviewers of psychotherapy research in the *Annual Review of Psychology* for describing the rate of advance. Reviewers usually recommend a five-year interval between reviews as being more suitable than the current annual interval.

We will now take up some of the obstacles to progress[2]; by identifying the obstacles, we believe it should be easier to cope with them.

### Problem of Building on Other's Work

Psychological research generally has tended to be insufficiently additive. Research people often find it hard to keep informed of related work done on the same site and elsewhere, and therefore do not build upon each other's foundations. (There are notable contemporary efforts to counteract this trend: the Mental Health Research Institute at the University of Michigan, the National Institute of Mental Health in Bethesda, and the Research Center for Mental Health at New York University.) The problem is compounded in those psychological fields in which definitive research studies are hardest to perform. Naturally, when another project seems so shaky, why build on it? Psychotherapy research unfortunately is an example of such a field.

The Second Conference on Research in Psychotherapy and this book were aimed at repairing this defect by providing interchange and reviewing a representative sample of current work. Almost every participant responding to the postconference questionnaire wrote in that "knowledge of others' work" and "increased acquaintance with people who were doing work in the same area" were the outstanding gains of the conference. Still, many participants were concerned about the problem of insufficient additiveness. Some urged conferences focused around even more specific topics and working over a much longer time period.

---

[2] The listing covers outstanding obstacles to advance in psychotherapy research; it is not intended to be exhaustive. Obviously advance in this area is also limited by the obstacles to development of psychology. Both therapeutic and practical obstacles have been listed by Rapaport (1960, pp. 137-144).

## Problem of Maintaining Historical Perspective

Psychotherapy research cannot look back on a long history. Freud began scientific studies in this area about 65 years ago with his new observations, theory, and technique. The quantitative and experimental approach is only about 20 years old (Frank, 1961). Its initiation points spark off from the well-known follow-up studies in Berlin, London, Chicago, and Topeka; and from the prodigious and continuing work of Rogers and his students. We can anticipate much growth, but growth will take time.

## Problem of Discouragement

It took temerity to hope for a second conference matching the enthusiasm and contributions of the first. Each of us had psychological obstacles against coming with the proper spirit: the hesitation at disruption of work schedules by another conference; the discordance of opening our minds to other points of view; the unregenerate wish for the new and remarkable to happen (just as we sometimes wish for improbable change in our patients)—for the discovery jumping us forward qualitatively. Clearly, the participants had to call upon their reality testing to rein in these feelings. A recommended attitude for psychotherapy researchers (attributed to Zen) is: "Work as though everything depended upon it, but don't care about the result."

It is too much to expect emergent advances resulting from one or two conferences. A conference can simply fulfill its stated aim of facilitation of interchange and therefore be satisfying. It can pull together a set of original papers representative of work in the field. It can even, as this one also did, lead to the planning of new research projects by people who almost certainly would not have thought of collaborating. One participant expressed his gains: "It gave me the opportunity to meet others in the field and to learn: (a) that differences in professional terminology need not block communication; (b) that some supposed differences between analysts, psychologists, etc. are more mythological than otherwise (even though unfortunately they may be self-perpetuating); and (c) that serious working contact with others can renew and widen my own interests."

All three working groups emerged at day's end frustrated at not being able to digest the assigned topics more adequately. The topics had been too big to assimilate in the allotted time. These feelings, they suggested, might have been diminished by setting up smaller working groups, by building more homogeneity of interest into each group, by providing even better leadership and more focused topics; but they could not have been eliminated. The field grows hard and difficult problems are hard to avoid and harder to face.

## Problem of Commitment of Researchers

If it takes courage to think of handling the problems in psychotherapy research, it takes tenacity to commit a major portion of one's productive energies to the field and stick with it. But involvement in investigation is often fueled by deeper motives than the prospect of easy progress. This can be a blessing, as the history of science shows. Nevertheless, a disconcerting discrepancy exists between the large number of psychologists who say they are interested in psychotherapy as a clinical and research activity and the small group who invests significant efforts in psychotherapy research. (According to the Directory of The American Psychological Association, interest in psychotherapy research is listed by approximately 25% of all members.) An even smaller group remains firmly committed to a research career in psychotherapy; shifts in commitment have occurred even within the group which participated in the last psychotherapy conference.

The commitment problem is further burdened by the time it typically takes to carry through a project—one participant estimated that ten years of dogged work was about par for working out even a small research question in the area. Length of commitment is also in part a function of opportunity. Such research takes money, and lots of it, over a long time period.

## Problem of Background and Training

Investigators must be well trained in psychotherapy and quantitative methods. As Rapaport (1960) pointed out, we cannot rely solely on knowledge of quantitative method; we also need sophistication in psychology. We cannot use simple quantifications from our data without understanding the processes determining them. One prime example is using quantitative measures, such as single scores from psychological tests or $Q$ sorts without appreciating the processes producing them.

Participants attending both conferences remarked that the second was less tense; the spirit seemed less defensive and more accepting. Much of this change may have followed from the fact that there were more people who knew each other and had been at the first conference. Some of this change may have been caused by participants' greater sophistication about the variety of therapeutic techniques and their own greater immersion in them. The greater interest of this conference in treatment techniques may have had the same root.

## Problems of Method

Researchers have been consistently concerned with problems of method: Brenman et al. (1947), Bronner et al. (1949), Ezriel (1951), Edwards and Cronbach (1952), Butler (1953), Rodnick (1953), Bordin et al. (1954), Rosenzweig (1954), Watterson (1954), Schafer (1955), Leary and Harvey (1956), Strupp (1960), and Sargent (1961). The section under Method repeats some of the issues in these publications. Together they make clear that we do not yet have the conceptual tools and the standardized measures to carry us forward faster: for the present we must persevere with what tools we have.

## Growing Edges of Psychotherapy Research

The diversity and complexity of the researches in the field of psychotherapy make it easy to miss the growing patches in the terrain, or to mistake undergrowth for new growth. Our listing of such new or continuing growth spots derives from participants' expressions of opinion in the conference and in the postconference questionnaire. There cannot be unanimity about the worth of new ideas; we have included those which, at least some of the participants believed, promised significant advance. All change is not progress, but in a field at an early developmental stage, many beginnings are a good sign.

1. *Quasi-therapeutic Analogues and Experiments Reproducing Ingredients of Psychotherapy.* The verbal (operant) conditioning or social reinforcement studies attracted considerable conference attention. These studies suggested some interesting research questions: Can we identify the kinds of patients who respond well to social reinforcement in an experimental situation? Are they different, or how are they different from those who respond well in the psychotherapy situation? Why do some experimenters seem better able to get positive results than others? How can we identify the effective qualities of these experimenters?

It seems surprising at first that so much interest was stirred up in this area of research which was not unknown to the conferees before their coming to the conference. Possibly the introduction into a discussion of a controversial and provocative idea attracts much pro and con discussion regardless of the idea's merit. Some of the interest may be seen as a flight from tolerance of ambiguity; much of it may be the scientific mind's usual search for reduction of complexity.

New film techniques for standardized presentation of therapeutic situations have yielded interesting results and promise more to come.

Considerable productive work has recently been done in comparing placebo effects with effects of psychotherapy.

*2. Studies of Therapists' Mental Operations.* Examining the therapist's working mental operations—his hypotheses and feelings as he listens to the patient—has been suggested before; it now appears that workable ways will be developed for studying this problem systematically.

*3. Analysis of Factors Influencing Free Associations.* Several researchers are beginning intensive studies of free associations. Although the free association technique has a central place in psychoanalytic treatment, researchers, even psychotherapy researchers, have neglected it. (An exception is Colby, 1960.) It is astonishing how little research has been conducted upon and with this technique which is such a rich source for the study of intra- and interpersonal dynamics. At most American universities, Janis (1958) observed, "psychoanalytically oriented" has come to mean merely some knowledge of the "theoretical superstructure" without experience with the "empirical foundations," especially the free-association interview, since training in the free-association technique as a research tool is hard to come by. The recent beginnings of research are inspired by increased interest in psychoanalytic theory and an effort to comprehend the clinical phenomena

confronted by the therapist in his daily work.

*4. Improved Studies of Outcome and Outcome Criteria.* Recurrent complaints about the paucity of adequate studies of psychotherapy results obscure the fact that significant developments have occurred. In the past ten years, several systematic and closely controlled studies of the outcome of psychotherapy have been completed or are under way (cf. the work of Rogers, Snyder, Phipps Clinic, VA Mental Hygiene clinics, and Menninger Foundation). These studies have given us (or promise to give us) much more than the studies of the past, based upon global ratings of "improvement," which Eysenck singled out for attack.

We still need better criteria of outcome —this was one of the most persistent suggestions at the conference. Many urged the formation of a committee charged with working out this problem.

*5. The Match between Patient and Therapist.* New evidence has recently been obtained on the characteristics of the patient and the therapist which may be responsible for their getting together and working together productively. The well-known work of Hollingshead and Redlich (1958) is one of the nearest things to a breakthrough in recent years; it showed that social class membership of patient and therapist play a part in the establishing and prospering of the patient-therapist match.

Therapists have many other expectations about the attributes which will make a patient a "good" patient as we described above. New work is getting under way on the "career" of the patient. In it, the kinds of factors determining the patient's acceptance into treatment by the institution as well as by the therapist are being scrutinized (Levinson).

*6. Expressive Behavior of the Therapist.* One aspect of expressive behavior which received most attention at the conference was the therapist's attention and interest in the patient. A number of investigators considered that posture and other expressive behavior which are interpreted by the patient as conveying interest in him, improve the results of treatment (e.g., the University of Chicago group). Research developments in the area of expressive behavior in psychotherapy (kinesics) are increasing (e.g., Pittenger, Dittmann, Scheflen, and Birdwistell) but were not adequately represented at the conference.

7. *The Role of the Computer in Psychotherapy Research.* More individuals are trying out computers, not only for more complicated data reduction but for attempts to simulate mental processes. However, enthusiasm is being tempered by the recognition that computers are dull at making clinical inferences and are no substitute for the scientist's or the clinician's thinking.

8. *The Role of Qualities of Affect and the Experiencing of Affect in Relation to Change.* Both at the last conference and at the present one, this area was considered both basic and promising. This belief was based on the old but widely and firmly held hypothesis that in order to change, the patient must learn to experience and be able to tolerate the appropriate affect.

9. *New Scoring Systems for Psychotherapy Process.* We are still in a necessary "do-it-yourself" stage, where everyone constructs his own system. Development of new process scoring schemes individually tailored to the researcher's theory and problem has been constant. Many of them work well for their specific purposes. So far, none of these have been used widely. Many investigators advocate the application of scoring systems across therapies and different types of patients.

10. *New Sound Film Records of Psychotherapy and Psychoanalysis.* In the past five to ten years technical problems of obtaining sound film records have been largely solved. Several such records are being made (e.g., by Shakow et al., Haggard, Alexander, and others). The next phase to be faced is the solution of the technical problems of analyzing these data. Cohen and Cohen (1961) give a first-hand account of a venture into the analysis of samples of the first hours of a long-term filmed psychotherapy.

11. *Conceptual Analyses of the "Domains" of Psychotherapy.* Recently, a number of contributions have appeared whose major focus was upon deciding which concepts are best to work with and then dividing up the territory to be covered (e.g., Levinson; Wallerstein et al., 1956). It remains for these writers and their colleagues to make good on these promissory notes. This kind of survey can be important in providing guides for future crucial research.

These are eleven spots in which to look for growth. Psychotherapy is a young discipline, although it has had a long tradition as an unformulated clinical art. The quantitative (and experimental) approach to research in psychotherapy is even newer. We believe it has a great *potential* contribution to make to clinical knowledge. Increasingly, researchers in this area represent a combined sophistication in both clinical and quantitative approaches. These individuals are the ones most likely to succeed in fulfilling the potential. As the two research conferences have demonstrated, the new researcher is already playing a notable role in the development of the field.

## REFERENCES

Bibring, E. Psychoanalysis and the dynamic psychotherapies. *J. Amer. Psychoanal. Ass.,* 1954, **2**, 745-770.

Bordin, E. S., Cutler, R. L., Dittmann, A. T., Harway, N. I., Raush, H. L., & Rigler, D. Measurement problems in process research in psychotherapy. *J. consult. Psychol.,* 1954, **18**, 79-82.

Brenman, M. (Chmn.: papers by Kubie, L. S., Rogers, C. R., & Gill, M. M.). Research in psychotherapy, round table, 1947. *Amer. J. Orthopsychiat.*, 1948, **18**, 92-118.

Bronner, F. (Chmn.), Kubie, L. S., Hendrick, I., Kris, E., Shakow, D., Brosin, H. W., Bergman, P., & Bibring, E. The objective evaluation of psychotherapy. *Amer. J. Orthopsychiat.*, 1949, **19**, 463-492.

Butler, J. M. Measuring the effectiveness of counseling and psychotherapy. *Personnel Guid. J.*, 1953, **32**, 88-92.

Cohen, R. A., & Cohen, Mabel B. Research in psychotherapy: A preliminary report. *Psychiatry*, 1961, **24**, 46-61.

Colby, K. M. Experiment on the effects of an observer's presence on the imago system during psychoanalytic free-association. *Behav. Sci.*, 1960, **5**, 216-232.

Edwards, A. L., & Cronbach, L. J. Experimental design for research in psychotherapy. *J. clin. Psychol.*, 1952, **8**, 51-59.

Ekstein, R. Structural aspects of psychotherapy. *Psychoanal. Rev.*, 1952, **39**, 222-229.

Ezriel, H. The scientific testing of psychoanalytic findings and theory: II. The psychoanalytic session as an experimental situation. *Brit. J. Med. Psychol.*, 1951, **24**, 30-34.

Frank, G. H. On the history of the objective investigation of the process of psychotherapy. *J. Psychol.*, 1961, **51**, 89-95.

Freud, S. *A general introduction to psychoanalysis.* New York: Liveright, 1935.

Hollingshead, A. B., & Redlich, F. C. *Social class and mental illness.* New York: John Wiley, 1958.

Janis, I. The psychoanalytic interview as an observational method. In G. Lindsey (Ed.), *Assessment of human motives.* New York: Rinehart, 1958. Pp. 149-182.

Leary, T., & Harvey, J. S. A methodology for measurement of personality changes in psychotherapy. *J. clin. Psychol.*, 1956, **12**, 123-132.

Luborsky, L., Fabian, Michalina, Hall, B., Ticho, E., & Ticho, Gertrude. Treatment variables. *Bull. Menninger Clin.*, 1958, **22**, 126-147.

Luborsky, L., & Schimek, J. Psychoanalytic theories of therapeutic and developmental change: Implications for assessment. In P. Worchel, & D. Byrne (Eds.), *Personality change.* New York: Wiley, 1962.

Rapaport, D. The structure of psychoanalytic theory: A systematizing attempt. *Psychol. Issues*, 1960, **2**, 1-158.

Rodnick, E. H. Some problems of research in clinical psychology. *Amer. J. Orthopsychiat.*, 1953, **23**, 307-314.

Rosenzweig, S. A transvaluation of psychotherapy: A reply to Hans Eysenck. *J. abnorm. soc. Psychol.*, 1954, **49**, 298-304.

Sargent, Helen. Intra-psychic change: Methodological problems in psychotherapy research. *Psychiatry*, 1961, **24**, 93-108.

Schafer, R. Psychological test evaluation of personality change during intensive psychotherapy. *Psychiatry*, 1955, **18**, 175-192.

Strupp, H. H. Some comments on the future of research in psychotherapy. *Behav. Sci.*, 1960, **5**, 60-71.

Strupp, H. H. Psychotherapy. *Annu. Rev. Psychol.*, 1962, **13**, 445-478.

Wallerstein, R., Robbins, L. L., Sargent, Helen D., Luborsky, L. The Psychotherapy Research Project of the Menninger Foundation: Rationale, method and sample use. *Bull. Menninger Clin.*, 1956, **20**, 221-280.

Watterson, D. J. Problems in the evaluation of psychotherapy. *Bull. Menninger Clin.*, 1954, **18**, 232-241.

Zax, M., & Klein, A. Measurement of personality and behavior changes following psychotherapy. *Psychol. Bull.*, 1960, **57**, 435-448.

Zubin, J. Evaluation of therapeutic outcome in mental disorders. *J. nerv. ment. Dis.*, 1953, **117**, 95-111.

# Index of Names

# Index of Subjects